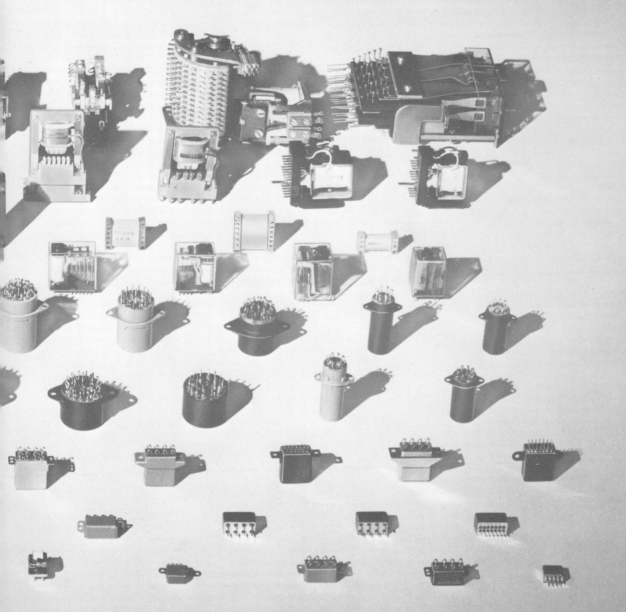

Engineers' Relay Handbook

Engineers' Relay Handbook

REVISED SECOND EDITION

sponsored by

The National Association of Relay Manufacturers

HAYDEN BOOK COMPANY, INC., NEW YORK

Preface to the
Second Edition

The aim of the Second Edition remains that of bringing together information that simplifies and clarifies the specifying and obtaining of correct relays. From the Preface of the First Edition:

> It is important to recognize that the information contained in this handbook is not intended to be of direct aid to the designers and manufacturers of relays. It is aimed, rather, at those individuals responsible for specifying the correct type of relays for a given application.

Engineers' Relay Handbook is a working handbook not an encyclopedia. That premise dictates the desirability of standardization where none exists, deliberately leaving out nonpreferred or proprietary information, or voluminous data peculiar to a single industry.

Most of the information contained in the First Edition is retained, with the addition of advancements in the state of the art associated with relay applications, corrections, and changes to make the handbook even more useful. New sections on reed and mercury wetted relays and on electro-mechanical relays and solid state devices increase the scope of the handbook, making it a valuable reference book for the engineer's library, as well as a source for application engineering information.

For specific and specialized interests outside the scope of the handbook, the reader is encouraged to refer to the Bibliography for publications directly concerned with specific areas of application.

Preface to the
First Edition

DEFINITION OF A RELAY: *An electrically controlled device that opens and closes an electrical contact to effect the operation of other devices in the same or another electrical circuit (see USASI, Definitions of Electric Terms, C42.25).*

To a large number of product and system design engineers, technicians, and servicemen, the relay — its construction and behavior — has been something of a mystery. To a great extent, their uncertainty has been the result of the limited amount of technical information heretofore available on the subject in printed form.

It is true that a large number of articles have appeared in various technical publications, but no complete roundup of objective relay information has been at hand. To remedy this situation, the National Association of Relay Manufacturers has prepared this handbook in the hope of providing a complete source of information on the operating principles, properties, performance characteristics, application requirements, specifications, and testing of relays.

It is important to recognize that the information contained in this handbook is not intended to be of direct aid to the designers and manufacturers of relays. It is aimed, rather, at those individuals responsible for specifying the correct type of relays for a given application. Consequently, it deals primarily with performance factors, the specification of these factors, and application considerations. To the manufacturer, relay specifications are governing design parameters. The way in which he meets them is not the concern of this book. In writing performance specifications and testing for conformance to them, however, there should be an agreement between user and manufacturer first about terminology and second about procedures. Surprisingly, there has been more disagreement on performance terminology for relays than for almost any other electromechanical device. This handbook will attempt to clear up misunderstandings by citing all "call outs" while still emphasizing the preferred terminology. The only design information included is that which will help the user recognize design limitations and thus keep him from overspecifying. The manufacturer should be free to meet the specifications within the limits of his own design philosophy.

Summing up, special effort has been made by the editors to cover specification parameters in sufficient detail to provide systems and product design engineers with all the information they need to obtain the correct types of relays for their applications.

Acknowledgments

First Edition

The National Association of Relay Manufacturers is deeply indebted to each of its member companies for the outstanding support given by them in the publication of this handbook. All of the member companies recognized the need for an impartial treatise, and it can safely be said that this publication is truly an industry-wide effort. Without question, anything less than such an effort would have greatly reduced the value of the work.

The Association is particularly indebted and grateful to the dedicated individuals listed below, each of whom served as a member of the Board of Editors and as a contributing author, giving selflessly of his valuable time, ability, and knowledge of relays in order to make this handbook a true contribution to all industry.

H. D. Steinback, *Magnecraft Electric Co. Chairman*

R. M. Brumfield, *Potter & Brumfield Div., American Machine & Foundry Company*

L. DeLalio, *Filtors, Inc.*

V. A. Hedlund, *RBM Controls Div., Essex Wire Corp.*

Waldo Holcombe, *Sigma Instruments Inc.*

V. E. James, *Automatic Electric Company*

J. L. Pfeffer, *Struthers-Dunn, Inc.*

C. Schneider, *Bell Telephone Laboratories*

T. L. Sipp, *C. P. Clare & Co.*

The Board of Editors also wishes to acknowledge with gratitude the assistance of the technical representatives of the National Association of Relay Manufacturers member companies for their valuable contributions to those sections in which each is a recognized authority. Many individuals assisted the editors in varying degrees out of their consuming interest in relays and the relay switching art. Without their help, the publication of such a complete handbook would not have been possible.

The Association also acknowledges its indebtedness to the C83 Committee of the United States of America Standards Institute on relay testing procedures for their valuable assistance in co-ordinating their efforts with the Board of Editors.

The Board of Editors and the National Association of Relay Manufacturers express their appreciation to Frank J. Oliver for his immeasurable contribution as technical writer for this publication. Mr. Oliver reviewed and rewrote, where necessary, all sections of the book to assure continuity of style, grammar, and technical content. It was his work that made this publication a finished product.

H. D. Steinback
Chairman, Board of Editors

Second Edition

The Publications Board of the National Association of Relay Manufacturers thanks each of the following individuals for their contribution to this revision of the handbook. Without their helpful criticisms and suggestions, plus the new material they contributed, this corrected and expanded issue would not have been possible.

C. C. Applegate, *Wheelock Signals, Inc.*

R. M. Atkins, *WABCO, Aerospace Div.*

J. W. Ayers, *Automatic Electric Co.*

Ralston Bates, *Teledyne Relays*

Thomas E. Beling, *Sigma Instruments, Inc.*

R. Belsan, *Cornell-Dubilier Electronics*

B. S. Bengtsson, *C. P. Clare & Co.*

R. W. Bowman, *Hi-G, Inc.*

Wayne Brumfield, *Potter & Brumfield, Inc.*

Frank Burridge, *Sigma Instruments, Inc.*

E. Floyd Bryant, *Babcock Electronics Corp.*

R. W. Cobean, *G-V Controls Inc.*

J. E. Davies, *Cutler-Hammer, Inc.*

E. J. Dooley, *Deutsch Relay Div.*

C. H. Fluder, *Vapor Corp.*

Thomas Fox, *C•P. Clare & Co.*

S. Freedman, *Hi-G, Inc.*

J. A. Garratt, *Babcock Electronics Corp.*

H. I. Hamilton, *Price Electric Corp.*

E. Hartzler, *Giannini-Voltex*

L. A. Hemp, *Price Electric Corp.*

J. S. Jordan, *Struthers-Dunn, Inc.*

K. Kiefer, *Price Electric Corp.*

T. M. Krizman, *The Adams & Westlake Co.*

S. T. Kubicz, *Automatic Electric Co.*

J. J. Lacker, *Automatic Electric Co.*

D. R. Morrison, *ITT Jennings*

M. G. Nelsen, *Leach Relay Div., Leach Corp.*

G. Pahud, *Sigma Instruments, Inc.*

William Pierson, *Electronic Specialty Co.*

W. J. Richert, *Potter & Brumfield, Inc.*

E. L. Roback, *Oak Electro/Netics Corp.*

Spencer Schantz, *Deltrol Controls Corp.*

Charles Schneider, *Western Electric Co. (Bell Tel. Labs.)*

George Schulze, *Guardian Electric Mfg. Co.*

H. D. Steinback, *Magnecraft Electric Co.*

M. S. Steinback, *Magnecraft Electric Co.*

P. C. Talmadge, *Essex International, Inc.*

Edward U. Thomas, *SAE, A2R Committee*

Edward G. Tutle, *G.E. Co., Specialty Div.*

J. J. Vitola, *Wheelock Signals, Inc.*

Hugh O. Wells, *Potter & Brumfield, Inc.*

Charles Williams, *Potter & Brumfield, Inc.*

Warren Wright, *Guardian Electric Mfg. Co.*

V. E. James
Automatic Electric Co.
Chairman, NARM Publications Board

NARM Publications Board Members
O. H. Groteluechen, *Essex International, Inc.*   J. W. Scannell, *C. P. Clare & Co.*
Carl B. Knox, *Babcock Electronics Corp.*

NARM Member Companies
In addition to the companies listed on page x, the Publications Board wishes to thank the following member companies:

Branson Corp.   Wheelock Signals, Inc.

About the National Association
of Relay Manufacturers

The National Association of Relay Manufacturers (NARM) was founded in May of 1947 by a dozen farsighted relay manufacturers of that day. Within a few years, the Association was composed of twenty-five member companies and was acting as a clearing house for information about Government Directives concerning the relay industry as well as for promoting the establishment of industry standards. The framework of this organization provided a forum for the exchange of ideas and a meeting ground for the solution of common problems of a technological nature. The early founders of NARM set down the purposes and aims of the organization as follows:

> *To encourage the advancement of the art and science of making and using those switching devices generally known as relays; to promote and further the interest of the relay manufacturers consistent with the best interests of the relay users; to create a spirit of mutual esteem, respect, and recognition among members, and between the members and their customers and suppliers. The NARM shall promote the most widespread use of relays and shall collect relay information and disseminate it to NARM members and the public, as well as to those related in the industry.*

The National Association of Relay Manufacturers, in the spirit of these purposes and aims, has built a comprehensive portfolio of technical publications providing a direct service to the NARM membership and to the electrical/electronics industry at large. As part of this program, the Association offers the *Engineers' Relay Handbook* to industry in general and the relay user in particular.

The National Association of Relay Manufacturers is dedicated to the advancement of the switching art through technological effort. Its members have not only recognized and accepted their responsibility to industry and government, they have also wholly committed their talents and capabilities to the fulfillment of these obligations.

Member Companies of the
National Association of Relay Manufacturers

The Adams & Westlake Co.
Allied Control Company, Inc.
Automatic Electric Co.
Babcock Relays Division, Babcock Electronics Corp.
Bourns, Inc.
C. P. Clare & Co.
Comar Electric Co.
Cook Electric Co.
Cornell-Dubilier Electronics
Couch Ordnance, Inc.
Cutler-Hammer, Inc.
Deltrol Controls Corp.
Deutsch-Filtors Relay Div.
Electronic Controls, Inc.
Electronics Specialty Co.
Electro-Tec Corp.
Essex International, Inc., Controls Div.
General Electric Co.
Giannini-Voltex
Guardian Electric Manufacturing Co.
G-V Controls Inc.
Hart-Advance Relay Div., Oak Electro/Netics Corp.
Hi-G, Inc.
ITT Jennings
Leach Corp.
Magnecraft Electric Co.
Potter & Brumfield, Div. of American Machine & Foundry Co.
Price Electric Corp.
Sigma Instruments, Inc.
Struthers-Dunn, Inc.
Teledyne Relays
Vapor Corp.
Ward Leonard Electric Co.
Western Electric Co., Inc.
Westinghouse Air Brake Co., Aero Space Dept., a subsidiary of
American Standard

Contents

1
Relay Terminology

Introduction

1.1 The problem of standardization

The industries using relays are many and varied. They are also somewhat isolated from one another with respect to having a common relay language. There has been a tendency over the years, by usage and practice peculiar to each company's own operations, to establish differing designations for the identical, or similar, relay item. The desirability for a standardization of relay terms, definitions, and symbols is thus apparent, but it appears impractical to bring about such a standardization at this time.

A beginning in the direction of standardization has been made in this book, however, by listing terms that seem by weight of usage to be preferable (P) along with the corresponding nonpreferable (NP) terms. The work of the C83.16 committee of the U.S.A. Standards Institute has been extensively drawn upon in compiling this list.

The sheer volume of material in current usage has prevented making similar recommendations for standardization of circuit practices or symbols. Each industry's symbols and circuit techniques are thus shown nonpreferentially.

1.2 Scope of this section

This section covers classifications, definitions, terminology, and symbols of relays for general switching purposes, military applications, electronic circuits, and airborne and space-age equipment. Certain specialized forms of relays have their own set of standards and may be designated by other terms (for example, the contactor[1]).

For a discussion of relays associated with electric power apparatus see *Relays Associated Electric Power Apparatus,* C37.1-1950, of the U.S.A. Standards Institute. Also, see NEMA *Standard for Industrial Control,* ICI-1954, as revised to May, 1958, or later.

1.3 Classification of relays

Relays classified by electrical input requirements:
1. Direct-current relays
   (a) Neutral
   (b) Polarized
2. Alternating-current relays (for a specified frequency range)

Relays classified by contact load requirements:
1. Direct-current relays
2. Power or heavy-duty relays
3. Alternating-current relays
   (a) Commercial power frequencies
   (b) Radio frequencies
   (c) Higher frequencies (coaxial connector)

Relays classified by duty. Classification of relays by duty should be given by a precisely quantitative statement of the contact capability of the relay, the number of contacts, their rating, and the number of operations in their useful life. Such a statement is preferable to general descriptive terms like light, medium, and heavy duty.

By custom and usage relays are also broadly defined as commercial, industrial, military, and the like. The term "general purpose" is often

---

[1]See *Definitions of Electrical Terms,* C-42.25, of the U.S.A. Standards Institute.

1

incorrectly used to define a type of relay. This work defines a general-purpose relay as any relay of any type that is not a special-purpose or a definite-purpose relay.

Relays classified by performance:
(1) General-purpose, special-purpose, or definite-purpose relays
(2) Marginal relays
(3) Fast relays
(4) Slow relays
(5) Sensitive relays
(6) Timing relays
(7) Latching relays
(8) Sequential relays
(9) Frequency sensitive relays
(10) Thermal relays
(11) Other relays

Relays classified by environment:
(1) Relays for standard conditions (that is, normal room conditions)
(2) Relays for special conditions (for example, a tropical environment)

Relays classified by industrial application. Relays are occasionally classified in terms of the industry in which they are used. Such classifications commonly reflect the necessity for a balance between performance desired and purchase price and for this reason are discouraged. However, specific terminologies that relate to the system function of relays used in various industrial applications — such as in electric power transmission, telephony, telegraphy, and certain forms of industrial control (relays used for the control of machine tools, for example) — are acceptable.

1.4   Defining relay performance

There is a sequence of events in relay pickup (operate) and dropout (release) with respect to current rise and decay. These events are defined in terms of duration of coil current, armature motion, and contact actuation. Figures 1-1 and 1-2 show contact performance — as a series of oscillograms — for a relay with a normally open contact, a normally closed contact, and a transfer (break-make) contact. In Table 1-1, preferred and nonpreferred terms relating to relay performance are summarized. These terms are fully defined in Paragraph 1.9 in alphabetical sequence. Figure 1-3 is a graphical presentation of relay performance related to definitions. Figure 1-4 depicts basic relay parts.

Pickup (Fig. 1-1).   Upon coil energization, current begins to rise at a decreasing rate, but no armature movement occurs until the power developed is sufficient to operate the contact spring load. This period is sometimes referred to as *waiting time.* Contact actuation occurs during the armature movement. The final actuation time exceeds the initial actuation time by the amount of the contact bounce. For normally closed contacts, operate time and initial operate time are identical. On break-make contacts the time interval between initial opening of the normally closed contact and closure of the normally open contact is called *transfer time.*

Dropout (Fig.1-2).   On de-energization of the coil, the magnetic flux does not die out immediately. How long it persists depends upon the release characteristics of the coil (fast to release, slow to release, and the like). The sequence of events described under pickup is essentially reversed under dropout. It will be seen that a normally open contact may be momentarily reclosed as a result of armature rebound off the backstop. This effect, which is not always present, depends on many factors, such as contact spacing, contact spring load, backstop design, and the like.

Relay Designations, Symbols, And Diagrams

1.5   Contact assembly designations

The contact spring combinations available on a relay are defined in terms of number of poles, number of throws (single or double), normal position (open or closed contacts), and the sequence of make and break. The various combinations have been given form letter symbols in Fig. 1-5 to simplify over-all identification. Abbreviations used to define the exact nature of the contact are as follows:

SP — Single pole	DP — Double pole
ST — Single throw	DT — Double throw
NO — Normally open	NC — Normally closed
B — Break	DB — Double break
M — Make	DM — Double make

Number of poles.   The term single pole (SP) contact denotes that all contacts in the arrangement connect in one position or another to a common contact. A double pole (DP) contact consists of a two-pole contact.

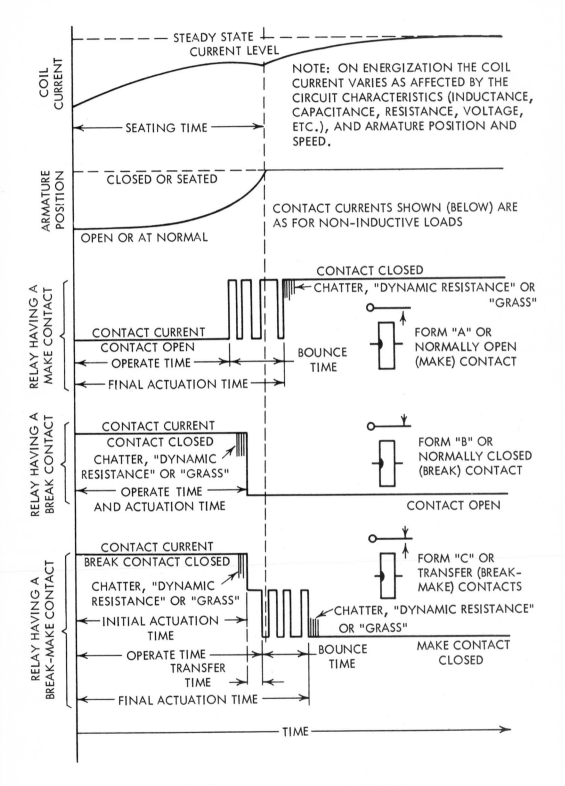

Fɪɢ. 1-1. Tɪᴍᴇ ᴛʀᴀᴄᴇs ᴛʏᴘɪᴄᴀʟ ᴏғ ʀᴇʟᴀʏ ᴘɪᴄᴋᴜᴘ

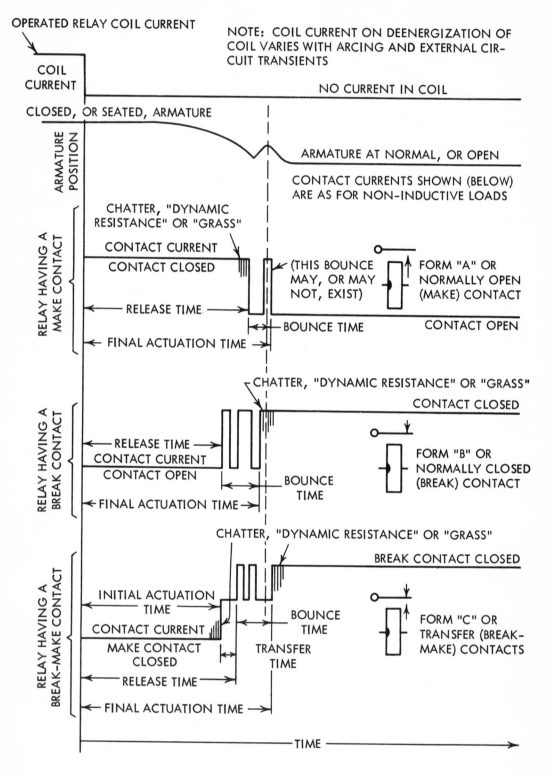

Fig. 1-2. Time traces typical of relay dropout

Table 1-1. Most Commonly Used Terms Relating to Relay Performance

Preferred	Not Preferred
Hold, measured	Nondropout, measured Nonrelease, measured
Hold, specified	Maximum dropout Nondropout, specified Nonrelease, specified
Nonpickup, measured	Nonoperate, measured
Nonpickup, specified	Minimum pickup
Pickup, measured	Operate, measured Pull-in (or pull-on) value, measured Operate value, just
Pickup, specified	Operate, specified Pull-in (or pull-on) value, specified Operate value, must Maximum pickup
Operate time	Pickup (or pull-in) time
Dropout, measured	Release, measured
Dropout, specified	Release, specified Minimum dropout
Release time	Dropout (or drop away) time
Transfer time	

Number of throws. Single throw (ST) contact combinations have a pair of contacts open in one relay position and closed in the other. Double throw (DT) contact sets have three contacts. The middle one is in contact with the second, but not with the third, in one position of the relay, and reverses this connection in the other relay position. The basic double throw contact combination is the *break-make* (Form C).

Normal position of contacts. The combination in which the contacts are open in the normal or unoperated position of the relay is designated *normally open* (NO). The combination in which the contacts are closed in the normal or unoperated position is designated *normally closed* (NC).

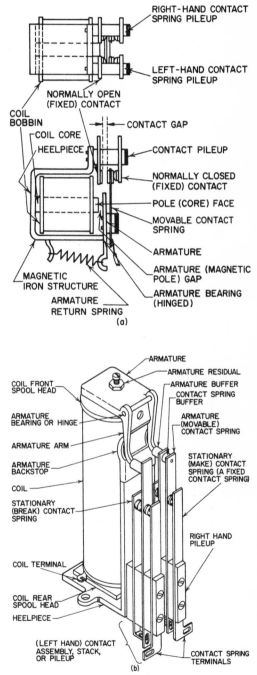

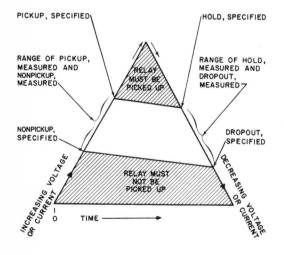

FIG. 1-3. RELATIONSHIP OF RELAY PERFORMANCE TO DEFINITIONS

FIG. 1-4. TWO TYPICAL RELAY FORMS WITH BASIC PARTS IDENTIFIED

Form	Description	USASI Symbol		Form	Description	USASI Symbol
A	Make or SPSTNO			L	Break, Make, Make, or SPDT (B-M-M)	
B	Break or SPSTNC			M	Single pole, Double throw, Closed Neutral. SP DT NC (This is peculiar to MIL-SPECS.)	
C	Break, Make, or SPDT (B-M), or Transfer			U	Double make, Contact on Arm. SP ST NO DM	
D	Make, Break or Make-Before-Break, or SPDT (M-B), or "Continuity transfer"			V	Double break, Contact on Arm. SP ST NC DB	
E	Break, Make, Break, or Break-Make-Before-Break, or SPDT (B-M-B)			W	Double break, Double make, Contact on Arm. ST DT NC-NO (DB-DM)	
F	Make, Make SPST (M-M)			X*	Double make or SP ST NO DM	
G	Break, Break or SPST (B-B)			Y**	Double break or SP ST NC DB	
H	Break, Break, Make, or SPDT (B-B-M)			Z	Double break, Double make SP DT NC-NO (DB-DM)	
I	Make, Break, Make, or SPDT (M-B-M)					
J	Make, Make, Break, or SPDT (M-M-B)			Special A	Timed close	
K	Single pole, Double throw Center off, or SPDTNO			Special B	Timed open	

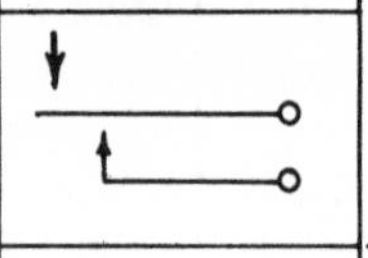

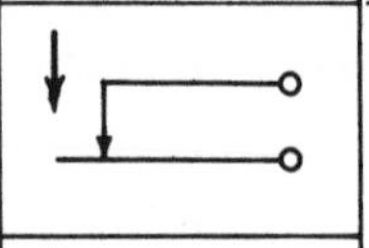

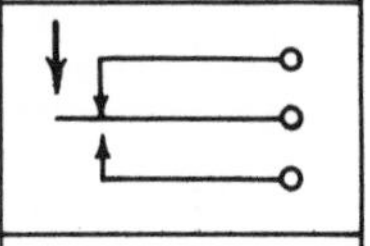

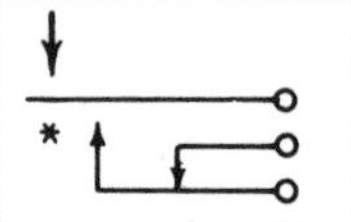

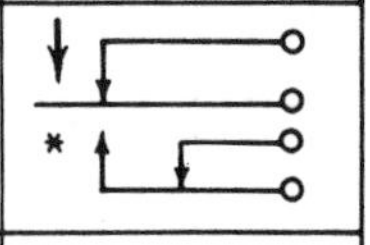

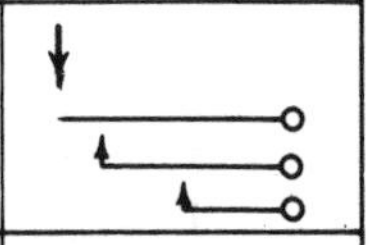

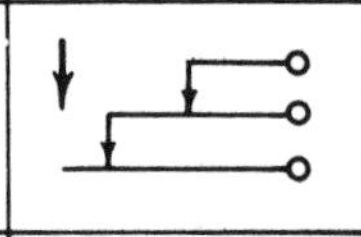

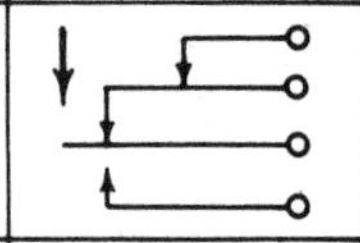

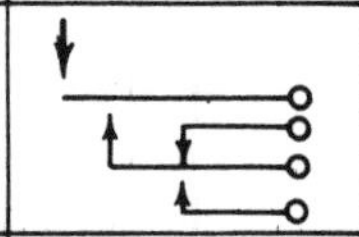

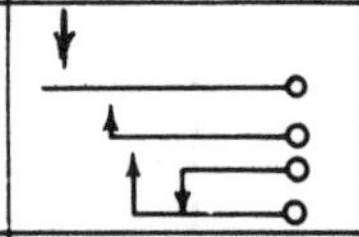

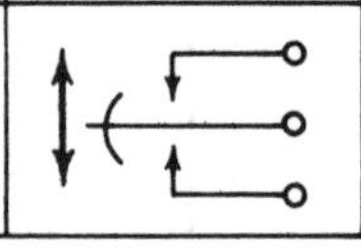

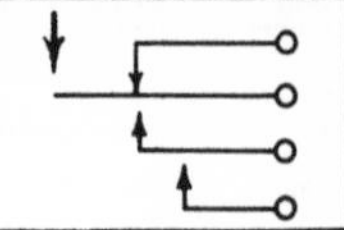

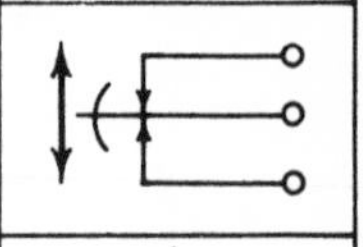

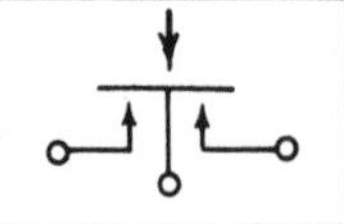

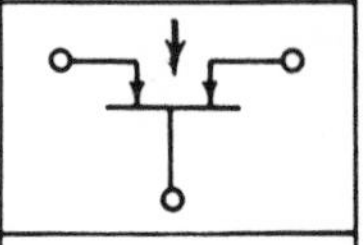

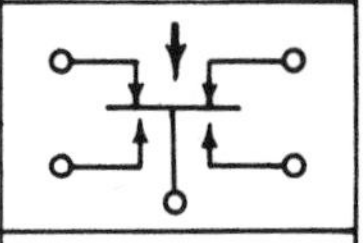

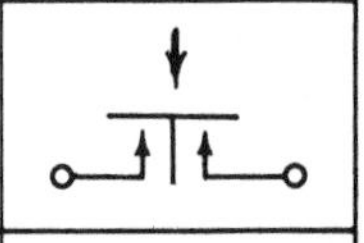

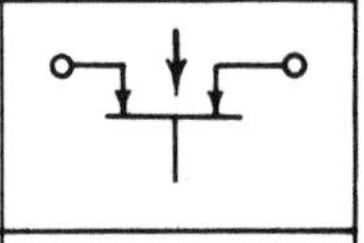

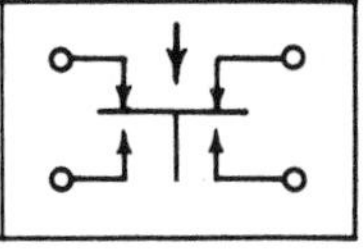

* Not to be confused with preliminary ("X") make
** Not to be confused with a late ("Y") break

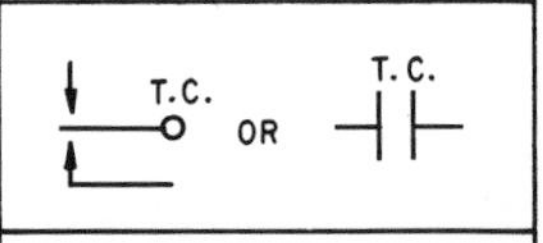

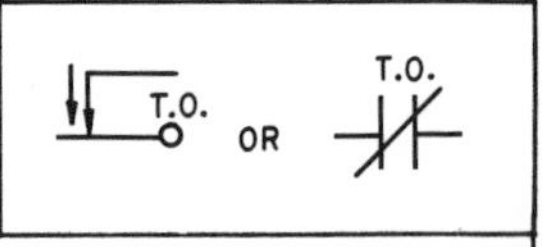

Multi-point selector switch — or —

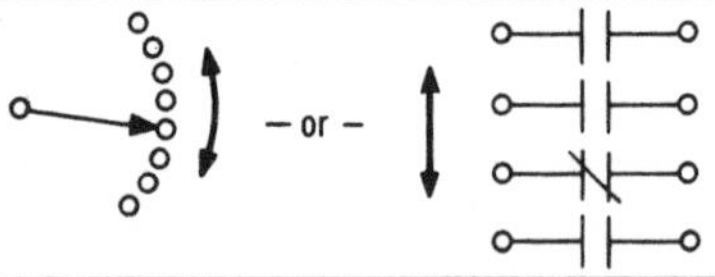

FIG. 1-5A. SYMBOLS FOR RELAY CONTACT COMBINATIONS ESTABLISHED BY UNITED STATES OF AMERICA STANDARDS INSTITUTE (USASI)

The heavy arrow indicates the direction of operation. Armature contact spring (indicated by the long spring in each example) move downward. In forms D and E some electrical discontinuity may be caused by contact chatter. Symbols taken from USASI C83.16-1959, Y32.2-1962, and Y32.2a-1964.

Double make and double break. These contact combinations have two independent contacts both connected to a third contact in one position of the relay. They are designated *double make* (DM) when normally open and *double break* (DB) when normally closed.

Sequence of abbreviations. When abbreviations are used to designate a contact assembly, the following order is used: (1) Poles, (2) throws, (3) normal position, (4) double make or break (if applicable).

Example: SPST NO DM refers to single pole, single throw, normally open, double make contacts.

1.6 Preferred order of contact arrangement

It is significant in the symbolic presentation of contact combinations in Fig. 1-5 that although Form A comes before Form B alphabetically, in a normal relay contact assembly the closed contacts are closer to the armature than the open contacts (see Fig. 1-6). This prevents any armature spring tension from going to waste by keeping the back contacts closed with as much pressure as possible. Thus, an order calling for a relay having 1A, 2B, 1C contact combinations will usually be arranged in the order of 2B, 1C, 1A, unless otherwise specified by the purchaser, and for a good reason. If an "early make" is required, it must be specified (as in Fig. 1-11, where the "X" associated with a make combination indicates that the circuit requires one A combination to be preliminary).

It is notable that the 2B, 1C, 1A contact assembly designation referred to above appears to be simpler and less likely of being misunderstood than the equivalent "one DPSTNC, one SPDT, and one SPSTNO."

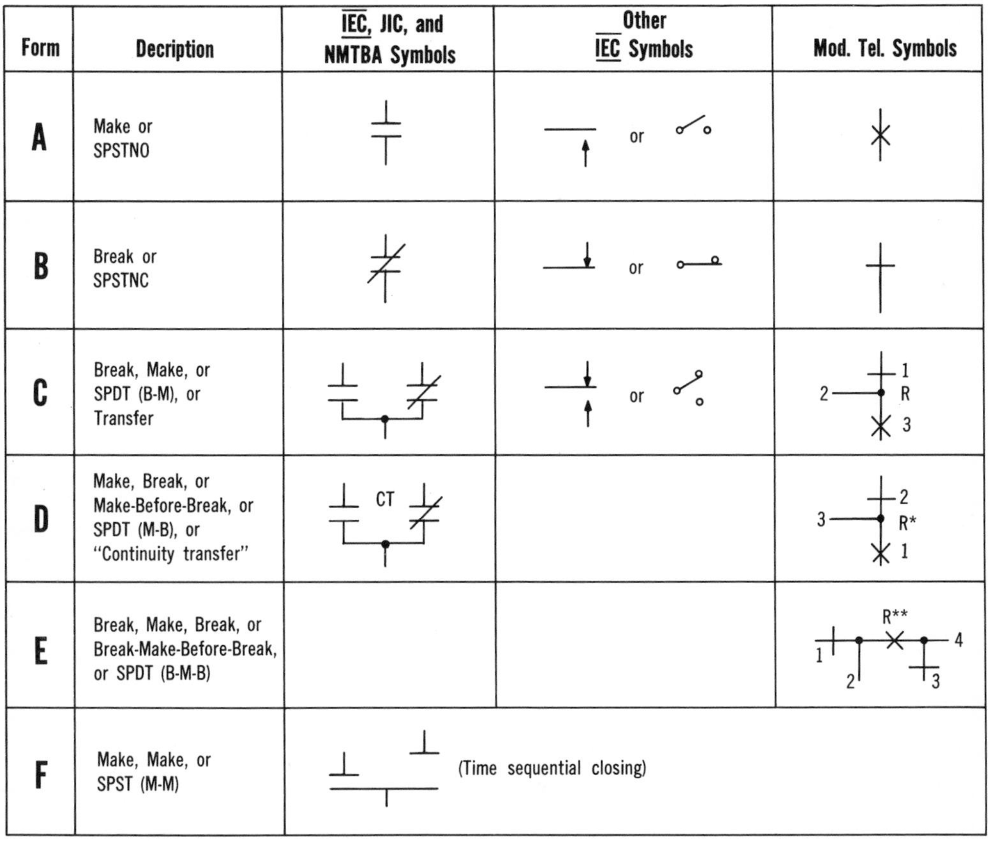

Form	Decription	IEC, JIC, and NMTBA Symbols	Other IEC Symbols	Mod. Tel. Symbols
A	Make or SPSTNO			
B	Break or SPSTNC			
C	Break, Make, or SPDT (B-M), or Transfer			
D	Make, Break, or Make-Before-Break, or SPDT (M-B), or "Continuity transfer"			
E	Break, Make, Break, or Break-Make-Before-Break, or SPDT (B-M-B)			
F	Make, Make, or SPST (M-M)	(Time sequential closing)		

* Denotes Make-Before-Break ** Denotes Break-Make-Before-Break,

FIG. 1-5B. ALTERNATIVE SYMBOLS FOR RELAY CONTACT COMBINATIONS

Source of symbols: IEC — International Electrotechnical Commission; JIC — Joint Industry Conference, Electrical Standards for Industrial Equipment; NMTBA — National Machine Tool Builders Association, Electrical Standards; Mod. Tel. — Modern telephone practice. Note: "CT" indicates continuity transfer, one asterisk denotes Make-Before-Break, and two asterisks denote Break-Make-Before-Break.

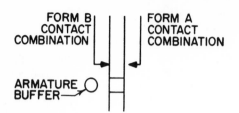

FIG. 1-6. PREFERRED CONTACT ARRANGEMENT IN A RELAY PILEUP

1.7   Relay letter symbols

In accordance with American Standard Y32.2-1962, the following letter symbols may be used with any relay symbols to show the special features a relay possesses. Symbols commonly used in telephone practice are also shown (marked "Tel.").

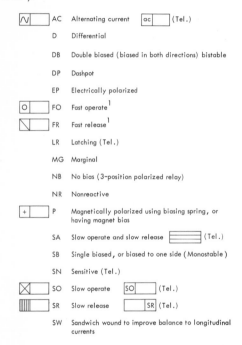

The terms "slow" and "fast" are relative, and the degree of rapidity is not to be implied by the repetition of the symbol on a relay. Relays that are d-c operated are not marked.

The proper poling for a polarized relay is shown by the use of plus (+) and minus (−) designations applied to the winding leads. The current in the direction indicated is to be interpreted to move, or tend to move, the armature toward the contact shown nearest the coil on the diagram. If the relay is equipped with numbered terminals, proper numbers should be shown.

---

[1]Used where unusually fast operation or releasing is essential to good circuit performance.

The following relay abbreviations are to be used on elementary wiring diagrams drawn to the Joint Industry Conference Standard for Industrial Equipment (JIC):

Type of Relay	Designation
General use	CR (1CR, 2CR, etc.)
Master	CRM
Automatic	CRA
Electronically energized	CRE (1CRE, 2CRE)
Manual (pushbutton)	CRH
Latch	CRL (1CRL, 2CRL)
Unlatch	CRU (1CRU, 2CRU)
Time delay	TR (1TR, 2TR)
Overload relay	OL (1OL, 2OL)
Motor starter	M (1M, 2M)

1.8   Relay coil and contact symbols

Commonly used symbols for relays of various kinds and for various applications are illustrated in Figs. 1-7 through 1-18.

TYPICAL POLARIZED RELAY COILS

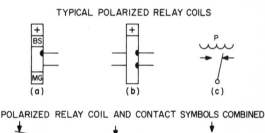

POLARIZED RELAY COIL AND CONTACT SYMBOLS COMBINED

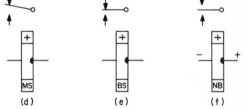

FIG. 1-7. SYMBOLS FOR TYPICAL POLARIZED RELAY COILS AND FOR COILS AND CONTACTS COMBINED

(a) Coil with double bias (DB) and margined (MG); (b) coil with two windings (up to four windings is common practice); (c) polar relays sometimes in this form; (d) single biased (SB), single side stable, two position permanent magnet relay (electromagnetically biased relays of this type are labeled "EP" and usually have two windings, one permanently energized); (e) double biased, bistable, two position relay, sometimes called a magnetic latch; (f) no bias (NB), center stable, three position relay that assumes center, or neutral, position when no power is applied. Note: See appendix for additional information.

COMMON, FAST-ACTING, NEUTRAL TYPES

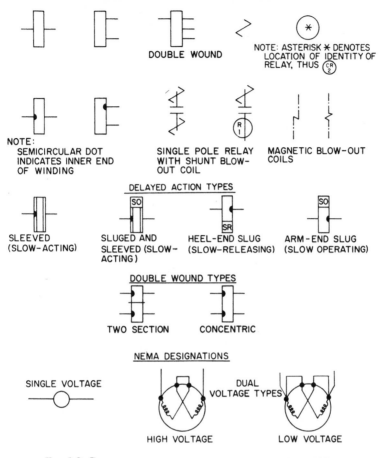

DOUBLE WOUND

NOTE: ASTERISK ✳ DENOTES
LOCATION OF IDENTITY OF
RELAY, THUS

NOTE:
SEMICIRCULAR DOT
INDICATES INNER END
OF WINDING

SINGLE POLE RELAY
WITH SHUNT BLOW-
OUT COIL

MAGNETIC BLOW-OUT
COILS

DELAYED ACTION TYPES

SLEEVED
(SLOW-ACTING)

SLUGED AND
SLEEVED (SLOW-
ACTING)

HEEL-END SLUG
(SLOW-RELEASING)

ARM-END SLUG
(SLOW OPERATING)

DOUBLE WOUND TYPES

TWO SECTION   CONCENTRIC

NEMA DESIGNATIONS

SINGLE VOLTAGE

DUAL
VOLTAGE TYPES

HIGH VOLTAGE   LOW VOLTAGE

FIG. 1-8. COMMONLY USED SYMBOLS FOR RELAY COIL FORMS

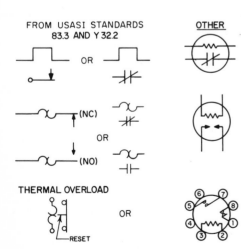

FROM USASI STANDARDS
83.3 AND Y 32.2

OR

OR

(NC)

OR

(NO)

OTHER

THERMAL OVERLOAD

OR

RESET

FIG. 1-9. SYMBOLS FOR THERMAL RELAYS

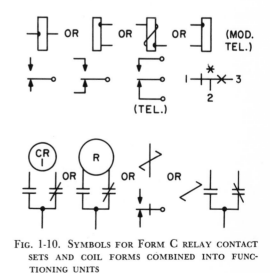

OR   OR   OR   (MOD.
TEL.)

(TEL.)

CR
1   R   OR   OR

FIG. 1-10. SYMBOLS FOR FORM C RELAY CONTACT
SETS AND COIL FORMS COMBINED INTO FUNC-
TIONING UNITS

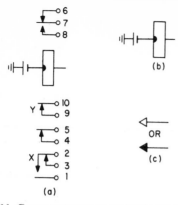

FIG. 1-11. COMMON SYMBOLS USED FOR RELAY COILS AND CONTACTS IN COMMUNICATIONS AND GENERAL SYSTEMS

(a) Contacts are drawn in vertical alignment with the coil symbol. Movable, armature, or lever contacts are drawn as if attracted to the coil on energization. The contacts are numbered in sequence from the mounting surface outward; No. 1 is closest to the mounting and No. 10 the farthest away. X contacts are preliminary and operate first. Y contacts are Break contacts and operate last. As Make contacts normally operate last, they are not so identified. (b) Battery and ground symbols are shown connected to the coil (negative battery to inside terminal, positive battery grounded) to minimize electrolysis in permanent installations. Switching ground is telephone practice at 48 V.D.C. nom. This is not permitted above 50 V.D.C. by National Electrical Code. (c) A nonpreferred symbol for negative battery.

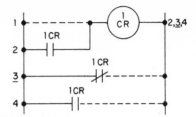

FIG. 1-12. LOCATION OF CONTACT SYMBOLS WITH RESPECT TO COIL ON JIC/NMTBA SIMPLIFIED DIAGRAM

Sequence of numbers at right of coil symbol locate associated contacts in lines numbered in left column. An underscored number signifies a normally closed contact.

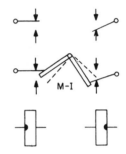

FIG. 1-13. SYMBOLS FOR MECHANICAL INTERLOCK RELAY

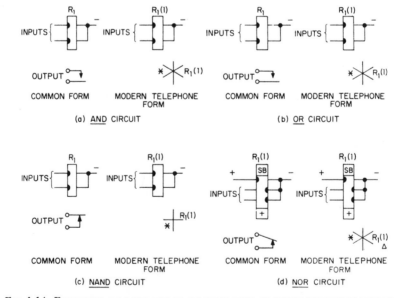

FIG. 1-14. EXAMPLES OF BASIC RELAY SYMBOLS USED IN LOGIC CIRCUIT DIAGRAMS

In an AND circuit (a), both windings must be energized to operate (close) contacts. In an OR circuit (b), either winding produces enough flux to operate (close) contacts. In a NAND circuit (c), both windings ("inputs") must be energized to operate (open) contacts. In a NOR circuit (d), either winding produces enough flux to operate (open) contacts; if both wind-

ings are energized, the contacts will reclose. Note: Asterisks are not a part of the symbol but denote a "detached contact" that is placed in the drawing at a convenient location. The number in parenthesis indicates the quantity of contacts on the relay so marked. The Greek letter delta indicates a form A contact that is normally closed.

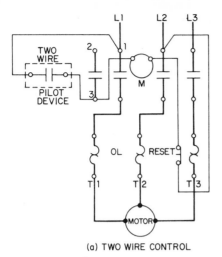

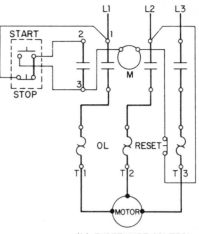

(a) TWO WIRE CONTROL   (b) THREE WIRE CONTROL

FIG. 1-15. SYMBOLS USED IN MOTOR CONTROL RELAY CIRCUITS (JIC-NMTBA)

(a) Two wire control is generally thought of in relation to a pilot device such as a thermostat, pressure switch, etc., or to a simple maintained SPDT toggle or pushbutton switch. As the term implies, these devices require the use of only two wires between the control unit and the starter. The device is connected in series with the main contactor coil of the starter and the opening or closing of the pilot device directly controls the de-energizing or energizing of the starter. The major feature of a two wire control system is low voltage release. The starter drops in the event of a power failure but operates automatically

when the power is restored. (b) In three wire control systems the main contactor coil of the starter is wired in series with its own NO auxiliary contacts. The "Start-Stop" pushbutton station, which requires the use of three wires between the control and the starter, is connected in parallel with the coil. In the event of a power failure, the starter will drop out and remain de-energized until the "Start" button is depressed. Since the starter drops out when there is a power failure and will not operate again until the start button is depressed, this control system provides low voltage protection.

Relay Terms and Definitions

1.9 Glossary

The following definitions do not include terms peculiar to mathematical formulae, statistical analysis, relay reliability studies, and the like. Such terms are defined in the sections where they are used, as in Section 6.

Preferred terms are marked " (P) "; nonpreferred terms are marked "(NP)." A preferred term is one that in the judgment of the editors of this handbook best describes the item being defined or has the best chance of being accepted as a standard.

For a more extensive description of the various types of relays, see Section 3.

A

Actuating card — See Armature card.

Actuation time — See Time, actuation.

Actuator — The part of the relay system that converts electrical energy into mechanical work.

Add-and-subtract relay (NP) *— See* Bidirectional relay (P).

Adjustment — The modification of any or all of the elements of tension, shape, or position of relay parts — for example, armature gap, restoring spring, contact gaps and pressures — to affect one or more of the operating characteristics.

Air gap — See Gap, air.

Alternating current (a-c) — A current which reverses its direction in a periodic manner, rising from zero to maximum and back to zero, and then going through similar variations in strength in the opposite direction.

Alternating current (a-c) relay — A relay designed for operation from an alternating-current source.

Ambient temperature — The temperature of the medium (usually air) surrounding the relay and into which the heat from electrical and magnetic losses in the relay is dissipated.

Ampere turn(s) — The product of the number of turns in an electromagnetic coil and the current in amperes passing through the coil.

On a-c the rms current value is used in the product of current and turns and is referred to as rms ampere turns.

Annunciator relay — A relay that indicates the present or former state of a circuit or circuits.

Antenna switching relay — A relay designed to switch radio-frequency antenna circuits with a minimum of losses. *(See also Sec. 3.)*

Antifreeze pin (NP) — *See* Residual screw (P), pin (P), plate (P), or stud (P).

Arc, contact — The electrical (current) discharge that occurs between mating contacts when the circuit is being disestablished.

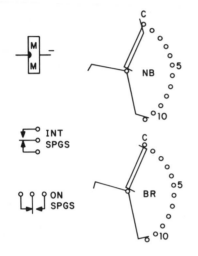

(a) INDIRECT DRIVE (SPRING DRIVEN OR BACK ACTING)

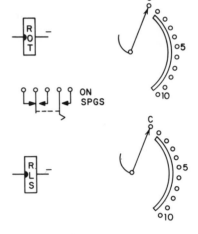

(b) DIRECT DRIVE (FRONT ACTING)

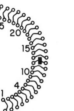

(c) NORMALLY CLOSED LEVEL

(d) 22-POINT ROTARY

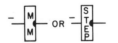

(e) COILS FOR INDIRECT DRIVE

(f) COILS FOR DIRECT DRIVE

FIG. 1-16. SYMBOLS FOR COIL FORMS AND CONTACT BANKS OF ROTARY STEPPING SWITCHES

(a) Also called single coil selector. (b) Also called a minor switch or two coil selector. Wipers are advanced one contact at a time on direct energization of the rotary (or "step") coil. Release takes place from any point all the way to "home" on one energization of the release (RLS) coil. (c) Sometimes called a shorting switch. Contact 12 is shown held open by insulated rotor. (d) Another way to draw switch bank and wipers. (e) Coils may be shown either way. (f) At left, a step coil with noninductive surge suppression winding. At right, a rotor release winding with surge suppression winding differently drawn. Key: MM — motor magnet coil; ROT — rotary coil; RLS — release coil; NB — nonbridging wiper (no trailing tips); BR — bridging wiper (trailing tips); INT SPGS — Interrupter contacts; ON SPGS — off normal contacts; C — common wiper, or feed through brush spring terminals to wiper.

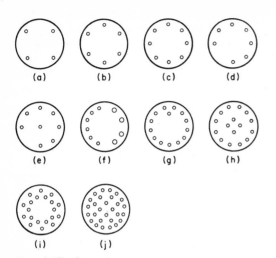

FIG. 1-17. SYMBOLS FOR HERMETIC ENCLOSURE HEADERS

Any number of pins from one to 28 can be placed in a single header. Headers (d), (e), (f), and (g) have pins arranged for polarization. Headers can be rotated on the enclosure for additional polarization.

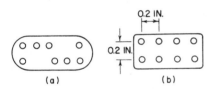

FIG. 1-18. TYPICAL TERMINAL ARRANGEMENTS ON HEADERS FOR CRYSTAL CAN RELAYS

(a) "S" terminal header for crystal can relays (not used for new military design); (b) 0.2-in. rectangular grid header.

Armature — The moving magnetic member of an electromagnetic relay structure that converts electrical energy into mechanical work *(see Fig. 1-4.)*

Armature, balanced — A relay armature that rotates about its center of mass and is therefore approximately in equilibrium with respect to both gravitational (static) and acceleration (dynamic) forces.

Armature, balanced rotary — A relay armature having two or more pole faces equidistant from the center of mass about which it rotates.

Armature, end-on — A relay armature whose principal motion is parallel to the longitudinal axis of a core having a pole piece at one end.

Armature, fully operated — The position of the armature and all its members when securely held again the coil core, excluding inertia overthrow.

Armature, long-lever — An armature with its contact-actuating arm greater in length than the distance from the armature hinge, bearing, or fulcrum to the portion of the armature opposite the pole face.

Armature, plunger (P), or *solenoid* (NP) — A relay armature that moves within a tubular core in a direction parallel to its longitudinal axis.

Armature, short-lever — An armature with its contact-actuating arm lesser in length than the distance from the armature hinge, bearing, or fulcrum to the portion of the armature opposite the pole face.

Armature, side (P), or *Armature, flat* (NP) — A relay armature whose principal motion is perpendicular to the longitudinal axis of a core having a pole face at one side.

Armature arm — The protrusion or lever on one type of armature employed to actuate the associated contact spring pileup *(see Fig. 1-4.)*

Armature bearing — The point at which the armature bears against the heelpiece (fulcrum) or the member securing the armature to the relay. *(See also* Hinge, armature.)

Armature bushing (NP) — *See* Buffer, armature (P). *(See also Fig. 1-4.)*

Armature card — An insulating member used to link a movable contact spring to the armature on some forms of relay.

Armature chatter — *See* Chatter, armature.

Armature contact — *See* Contact, movable.

Armature dropout overthrow — The distance the armature moves beyond its fully released position during dropout, but *before* coming to rest, as a result of inertia overthrow.

Armature dropout overtravel — The portion of the armature travel that occurs between closure of the normally closed contact(s) and the fully released static position of the armature.

Armature gap — *See* Gap, armature.

Armature hinge — *See* Hinge, armature.

Armature lever ratio — The distance through which the armature buffer moves divided by the armature travel *(see* Armature travel). Also, the ratio of the distance from the armature bearing pin (or fulcrum) to the armature buffer in relation to the distance from the bearing pin (or fulcrum) to the point on the armature that strikes the coil core.

Armature pickup overthrow — The distance the armature moves beyond its fully operated static position during operation, but *before* coming to rest due to inertia overthrow.

Armature pickup overtravel — The portion of the available stroke occurring between closure of the normally open contact(s) and the fully operated static position of the armature.

Armature rebound — (1) The return motion or bounce-back toward the unoperated position after the armature strikes the core on forward motion during pickup, referred to as *armature pickup rebound*. (2) The forward motion or bounce in the direction of the operated position when the armature strikes its backstop on dropout, referred to as *armature dropout rebound*.

Armature relay — A relay operated by an electromagnet, which, when energized, causes an armature to be attracted to a fixed pole, or poles, for the purpose of operating contacts. *(See also Sec. 3).*

Armature residual — The protrusion from the armature that provides the residual gap *(see Residual screw, pin, plate, or stud).*

Armature residual gap — *See* Residual gap.

Armature spring — The movable contact spring of a combination. This member is also sometimes referred to as the *swinger spring (see Fig. 1-4).*

Armature stop, nonmagnetic (P), or *core cap* (NP) — A nonmagnetic member separating the pole face(s) of a core(s) and armature when in the operated position. Used to reduce and stabilize the pull from residual magnetism. *(See also Residual screw, pin, plate, or stud.)*

Armature stroke — The distance in air, with the armature fully restored to its unoperated position, between the coil core face and the armature residual. It is equal to the armature gap minus the thickness of the armature residual.

Armature stud (NP) — *See* Buffer, armature (P).

Armature travel — The distance that the armature moves in going from its unoperated to its operated position (usually measured at the center of the associated pole piece), or from one specified operated position to another.

ASCII — *American Standard Code for Information Interchange* — A seven-level coded character set and recording format approved by the United States of America Standards Institute (USASI) for handling data in data processing and communication systems.

Automatic homing relay — A stepping relay that returns to its home or starting position when it reaches a predetermined contact position or when a pulsing circuit fails to provide an energizing pulse within a given time. The relay may either pulse itself forward or be restored to its starting position by a spring.

Automatic-reset relay — (1) An automatic homing relay, or (2) an overload relay that functions to restore a circuit as soon as an overload situation is corrected.

Auxiliary contacts — Contacts used to operate a visual or audible signal to indicate the position of the main contacts, establish interlocking circuits, or hold a relay operated when the original operating circuit is opened.

Auxiliary relay — A relay that operates in response to the opening and closing of its operating circuit in order to assist another relay or device in the performance of a function. Sometimes used for a relay, actuated by a master relay, that controls secondary circuit functions such as signals, lights, or other devices. A slave relay.

B

Back contact (NP) — *See* Contact, normally closed (P).

Backstop, armature — That part of the relay which limits the movement of the armature away from the pole face or core. In some relays a normally closed contact may serve as backstop. Not to be confused with Armature stop.

Bank — One or more contact levels of a stepping switch.

Bar relay — A relay so designed that a bar actuates several contacts simultaneously. Not to be confused with a relay having bar-shaped contacts.

Baud — (1) Unit of signaling speed in telegraphy or data transmission (after Jean Maurice Emile Baudot for whom the Baudot code was named), now used interchangeably with "bits per second." (2) Originally used to express the capabilities of a telegraph transmission facility in terms of "modulation rate per unit of time."

Baud rate — The maximum number of teleprinter impulses that can be transmitted in one second.

Baudot code — A five-level or bit permutation code in which all code elements are of the same length and which has been used internationally by the telegraph industry for about 100 years. Note: There are about 15 types of Baudot codes. *(See also* ASCII.)

Bearing — The fulcrum of an armature.

Bearing pin, armature — The pin of an armature hinge *(see* Fig. 1-4).

Bias, electrical — An electrically produced force tending to move the armature towards a given position.

Bias, magnetic — A steady magnetic field applied to the magnetic circuit of a relay.

Bias, mechanical — A mechanical force tending to move the armature towards a given position.

Bidirectional relay (P) or *Add and subtract relay* (NP) — A stepping relay in which the rotating wiper contacts may move in either direction.

Bifilar winding — Two or more windings with the wire of each winding alongside the other, matching turn for turn; may be either inductive or noninductive. *(See also* Coil, parallel wound.)

Bifurcated contact(s) — *See* Contact(s), bifurcated.

Bimetal relay — A form of thermal relay using a bimetallic element to activate contacts when heated electrically. *(See also* Sec. 3.)

Bimetallic element — An actuating element consisting of two strips of metal with different coefficients of thermal expansion bound together in such a way that the differential internal strains caused by temperature changes deflect the compound strip.

Binary — A system of numerical notation that utilizes the base 2 (rather than the base 10 as in the common decimal system).

Binary number — A single digit or group of characters or symbols representing the total amount of units utilizing the base 2; usually only the digits "0" and "1" are used to express quantity.

Bit — A single electrical impulse or unit of information represented by a mark or space. The smallest unit of any binary digital code. The smallest particle of electrical information that can be transmitted or processed.

Bi-stable contacts — See Contacts, bi-stable.

Blade (NP) — *See* Spring, contact (P).

Blowout coil — An electromagnetic device that establishes a magnetic field in the space where an electrical circuit is broken and helps to extinguish the arc by displacing it.

Blowout magnet — A permanent magnet or an electromagnet located in such a position as to place a magnetic field in the space where d-c electric circuit is to be broken. This field causes the arc to be displaced, thus lengthening it and helping to extinguish it more rapidly.

Bobbin — A spool upon which a coil is wound.

Bounce, armature — *See* Armature rebound.

Bounce, contact — *See* Contact bounce.

Break — The opening of closed contacts to interrupt an electrical circuit.

Break-before-make contacts — Contacts that interrupt one circuit before establishing another. A "C" combination *(see* Fig. 1-5).

Break contacts — *See* Contacts, normally closed. A "B" combination *(see* Fig. 1-5).

Bridging — (1) *Normal bridging:* The normal make-before-break action of a make-break or "D" contact combination *(see* Fig. 1-5). In a stepping switch or relay, the commoning together momentarily of two adjacent contacts, by a wiper shaped for that purpose, in the process of moving from one contact to the next. (2) *Abnormal bridging:* The undesired closing of open contacts, resulting from contact bounce or caused by a metallic bridge or protrusion developed by arcing.

Bridging contact — A contact combination designed to provide bridging.

Bridging time — *See* Time, bridging.

Brush spring — The spring in a rotary stepping switch bank that contacts the associated wiper.

Buffer, armature (P), or *Bushing, armature* (NP), or *Lifter, armature* (NP), or *Plug, armature* (NP), or *Pusher* (NP), or *Stud, armature* (NP) — An insulating member attached to the armature that transmits the motion of the armature to an adjacent contact member *(see* Fig. 1-4).

Buffer, spring (P), or *Buffer, contact spring* (also P), or *Bushing, spring* (NP), or *Stud, spring* (NP) — An insulating member that transmits the motion of the armature from one movable contact spring to another in the same pileup *(see* Fig. 1-4).

Buffer gap — *See* Gap, air.

Buffer spring — An auxiliary spring used to damp spring vibration. Sometimes called *snubber spring* or *damping spring*. *(See also* Spring, balance.)

Bunching time — *See* Time, bunching.

Bushing, armature (NP) — *See* Buffer, armature (P) and Fig. 1-4.

C

Calibration test — A test made to verify the operating characteristics of a relay.

Card, armature — See Armature card.

Characteristic, operate time — The relation between the operate time of an electromagnetic relay and the operate power.

Characteristic, slow release time — The relation between the release time of an electromagnetic relay and the conductance of the winding circuit or of the conductor (sleeve or slug) used to delay release. The conductance in this definition is the quantity N^2/R, in which N is the number of turns and R is the resistance of the closed winding circuit. (For a sleeve or slug, $N = 1$.)

Characteristic, static — The static force/displacement characteristic of the spring system or of the actuating system.

Chassis ground — The metal framework of apparatus used as a common return to the power source of electrical circuits. Not necessarily a connection to earth ground.

Chatter, armature — The undesired vibration of the armature due to inadequate a-c performance or external shock and vibration.

Chatter, contact — The undesired vibration of mating contacts during which there may or may not be actual physical contact opening. If there is no actual opening but only a change in resistance, it is referred to as *dynamic resistance* and appears on the screen of an oscilloscope having adequate sensitivity and resolution as *grass (see* Figs. 1-1 and 1-2). Chatter may result from contact impingement during normal relay operation and release, uncompensated a-c operation, or from external shock and vibration.

Chopper — A special form of pulsing relay having contacts arranged to rapidly interrupt, or alternately reverse, the d-c polarity input to an associated circuit.

Circuit breaker — A device designed to open and close a circuit by nonautomatic means, and to open the circuit automatically on a predetermined overload of current, without injury to itself, when properly applied within its rating.

Clapper — An armature that is hinged or pivoted. *(See* Armature.)

Clapper-type relay — A very large and varied family of relays using clapper-type armatures. *(See also* Sec. 3.)

Close-differential relay — A relay having its dropout value specified close to its pickup value.

Coaxial relay — A relay that opens and closes an electrical contact switching high-frequency current as required to maintain minimum losses.

Coil — An assembly consisting of one or more magnet wire windings, usually wound over an insulated iron core on a bobbin or spool, or self-supporting, with terminals, and any other required parts such as a sleeve or slug *(see* Fig. 1-4).

Coil, concentrically wound — A coil with two or more insulated windings, wound one over the other.

Coil, parallel wound — A coil having two windings wound simultaneously with the turns of each winding being contiguous *(see* Bifilar winding). Despite good balance and close coupling of windings, it is seldom used for voice-current battery feed in telephone communication equipment as magnet wire with heavy insulation and low space factor is required to withstand continuous battery potential.

Coil, sandwich wound — A coil usually used for voice-current battery feed over wired communications lines to provide good balance and close coupling of windings without going to a parallel wound coil. It is normally wound as three concentric windings. Primary turns are 40 to 50 percent of secondary turns, and tertiary turns are 50 to 60 percent of secondary turns. Primary and tertiary are connected in series, with total turns and resistance equal to secondary turns and resistance, giving excellent line balance if properly proportioned.

Coil, tandem wound — A coil having two or more windings, one behind the other, along the longitudinal axis. Also referred to as a *two-, three-, or four-section coil.*

Coil covering — A protective layer of insulating material over the outermost (surface) turns of wire.

Coil serving — A covering, such as thread or tape, to protect the winding from mechanical damage.

Coil terminal — A device, such as a solder lug, tab, binding post, or similar fitting, on which the coil winding lead is terminated and to which the coil power supply is connected.

Coil thermal equilibrium — The condition of an energized coil when the heat generated is equal to that dissipated and there is no additional temperature rise.

Coil tube — An insulated tube on which a coil

is wound.

Coil winding — An electrically continuous length of insulated wire wound on a bobbin, spool, or form.

Coil (winding) mean temperature — The average temperature of an energized coil winding as determined by a measurement of its d-c resistance. *(See* Sec. 10 for the method.)

Coil (winding) final mean temperature — The average temperature of a coil winding at thermal equilibrium, as determined from a measurement of d-c resistance. *(See* Sec. 10 for the method.)

Coil (winding) power dissipation — The electrical power (watts) consumed by the energized winding or windings of a coil. For most practical purposes this is calculated from I^2R or $EI \cos \theta$ of the specific case.

Coil (winding) final power dissipation — The electrical power consumed by a winding or windings when thermal equilibrium is reached.

Coil (winding) initial power dissipation — The electrical power consumed by a winding or windings when the current reaches steady state shortly after application of voltage.

Coil (winding) intermediate power dissipation — The electrical power consumed by a winding or windings at some specified time before thermal equilibrium is reached.

Coil (winding) resistance — The total terminal-to-terminal resistance of a coil at a specified temperature. A tolerance of measured value from a nominal specified resistance is usually allowed.

Comb — An insulating member used to position a group of contact springs, as on wire-spring relays.

Compliant (contact) spring — A contact spring that can, and is intended to, move appreciably when contacted by a mating contact spring.

Contacts — The surfaces of current-carrying members at which electrical circuits are opened or closed.

Contacts, armature — (1) A contact mounted directly on the armature. (2) Sometimes used for a movable contact.

Contacts, auxiliary — *See* Auxiliary contacts.

Contacts, back (NP) — *See* Contacts, normally closed (P).

Contacts, Bifurcated — A forked, or branched, contacting member so formed or arranged as to provide some degree of independent dual contacting.

Contacts, bistable — A contact arrangement in which the movable contact remains in the last operated position on de-energization of the operating winding. The stabilizing force may be either mechanical, electrical, or both.

Contacts, break — *See* Contacts, normally closed.

Contacts, break-make — A contact combination in which one contact opens its connection to another contact and then closes its connection to a third contact. Same as transfer contacts. *(See* "C" contact combination in Fig. 1-5.)

Contacts, bridging — *See* Bridging contact.

Contacts, continuity transfer — Sometimes used for bridging contacts. Note: Although there is mechanical continuity, electrical discontinuity may occur as a result of bounce. *(See* form "D" in Fig. 1-5.)

Contacts, double break — A contact combination in which contacts on a single spring simultaneously open electrical circuits connected to the contacts of two independent springs. In the case of power type relays having noncompliant contacts, double break refers to stationary contacts shorted by a bridging bar. *(See* "Y" contact combination in Fig. 1-5.)

Contacts, double make — A contact combination in which contacts on a single spring simultaneously close electrical circuits connected to the contact of two independent springs. In the case of power type relays having noncompliant contacts, double make refers to stationary contacts shorted by a bridging bar. *(See* "X" contact combination in Fig. 1-5.)

Contacts, double break-make — A contact combination employing the shorting bar principle, but combining both into a double make and a double break. *(See* "Z" contact combination in Fig. 1-5.)

Contacts, double throw — A contact combination having two positions, as in break-make, make-break, and the like *(see* Fig. 1-5).

Contacts, dry — Hermetically sealed contacts without mercury wetting. *(See* Dry reed relay.)

Contacts, dry circuit — (1) Contacts that neither break nor make current. (2) Erroneously used for low level contacts.

Contacts, dry reed — A glass-enclosed magnetically closed contact using reeds as the contacting members.

Contacts, early — A contact combination that is adjusted to open or close before other contact combinations when the relay operates.

Contacts, fixed (NP) — *See* Contact, stationary (P).

Contacts, front (NP) — *See* Contacts, normally open (P).

Contacts, interrupter — On a stepping relay or switch, a set of contacts, operated directly by the armature, that opens and closes the winding circuit, permitting the relay to step itself.

Contacts, late — A contact combination that is adjusted to open or close after other contact combinations when the relay operates *(see* Fig. 1-11).

Contacts, low capacitance — A type of contact construction providing low intercontact capacitance.

Contacts, low level — Contacts that control only the flow of relatively small currents in relatively low-voltage circuits, for example, alternating currents and voltages encountered in voice or tone circuits, direct currents in the order of microamperes, and voltages below the softening voltages of record for various contact materials (that is, 0.080 volts for gold, 0.25 volts for platinum, and the like). Also defined as the range of contact electrical loading where there can be no electrical (arc transfer) or thermal effects and where only mechanical forces can change the conditions of the contact interface. *(See also* Minimum current.)

Contacts, make — *See* Contacts, normally open.

Contacts, make-break — *See* Bridging contact. A "D" contact combination *(see* Fig. 1-5).

Contacts, movable — The member of a contact pair that is moved directly by the actuating system. This member is also referred to as the *armature (contact) spring,* or *swinger spring.* In reed contacts, motion is caused magnetically.

Contacts, multiple break — Contacts that open a circuit in two or more places.

Contacts, nonbridging — A contact arrangement in which the opening contact opens before the closing contact closes.

Contacts, normally closed (P), or *Contacts, back* (NP) — A contact pair which is closed when the armature is in its unoperated position. A "B" contact combination *(see* Figs. 1-5 and 1-6).

Contacts, normally open (P), or *Contacts, front* (NP) — A contact pair that is open when the armature is in its unoperated position. An "A" contact combination *(see* Fig. 1-5).

Contacts, off-normal — Contacts on a relay or switch that are in one condition when the relay or switch is in its normal position and in the reverse condition for any other position of the relay or switch.

Contacts, preliminary — A contact combination that opens, closes, or transfers in advance of other contact combinations when the relay operates. *(See also* Auxiliary contacts and Contacts, early.)

Contacts, reed — *See* Reed relay.

Contacts, sealed — A contact assembly that is sealed in a compartment separate from the rest of the relay.

Contacts, snap action — A contact assembly having two or more equilibrium positions, in one of which the contacts remain with substantially constant contact pressure during the initial motion of the actuating member until a condition is reached at which stored energy snaps the contacts to a new position of equilibrium.

Contacts, stationary (P), or *Contacts, fixed* (NP) — The member of a contact pair that is not moved directly by the actuating system *(see* Fig. 1-4).

Contacts, transfer — *See* Contacts, break-make. A "C" contact combination. *(See also* Fig. 1-5.)

Contact arrangement — The number and types of contact combinations of a relay.

Contact bounce — The intermittent and undesired opening of closed contacts, or closing of open contacts, of a relay, due to the following causes: (1) *Internally caused contact chatter* — (a) from impingement of mating contacts *(see* Figs. 1-1 and 1-2); (b) from impact of the armature against the coil core on pickup, or against the backstop on dropout; (c) from momentary hesitation, or reversal, of the armature motion during the pickup or dropout stroke. (2) *Externally caused contact chatter* — (a) from shock impact experienced by the relay or the apparatus of which it is a part; (b) from vibration or shock outside the relay but transmitted to it through its mounting.

Contact bounce time—*See* Time, contact bounce.

Contact bridging — *See* Bridging.

Contact bunching — The undesired simultaneous closure of make-and-break contacts during vibration, shock, or acceleration tests.

Contact chatter — *See* Chatter, contact.

Contact combination (P), or *Contact set* (NP), or *Contact form* (NP) — A single-pole or basic contact assembly *(see* Fig. 1-5).

Contact compliance — The reciprocal of contact stiffness.

Contact follow — For compliant contacts this is

the distance two contacts travel together after just touching. Also called *contact overtravel*. In the case of noncompliant contacts this is the distance the relay armature travels after the contacts touch one another.

Contact follow stiffness — The rate of change of contact force per unit contact follow.

Contact force — The pressure exerted by a movable contact against a fixed contact when the contacts are closed. Also referred to as *contact pressure*.

Contact form (NP) — *See* Contact combination (P).

Contact gap — The distance between a pair of mating relay contacts when the contacts are open; same as *contact separation*.

Contact load — The electrical power demands encountered by a contact set in any particular application. *(See also* Rated contact current.)

Contact-making meter — A term for instrument relay.

Contact miss — Failure of a contact mating pair to establish the intended circuit electrically. This may be a circuit resistance in excess of a specified maximum value.

Contact overtravel — *See* Contact follow.

Contact pileup — The total assembly of contacts in one stack on a relay *(see* Fig. 1-6).

Contact pressure — *See* Contact force.

Contact rating — The electrical power handling capability of relay contacts under specified environmental conditions and for a prescribed number of operations as defined by the manufacturer. The AIA[1] defines contact rating as "The maximum current for a given type of load (i.e., voltage, frequency and nature of impedance) which the relay (contacts) will make, carry, and break (unless otherwise specified) for its rated life."

Contact resistance — The electrical resistance of operated contacts as measured at their associated contact spring terminals.

Contact separation — See Contact gap.

Contact(ing) sequence — The order in which contacts open and close in relation to other contacts and armature motion.

Contact set (NP) — *See* Contact combination (P).

Contact spring — A current-carrying spring to which the contacts are fastened.

Contact stack — All of the contact springs in one assembly. A contact pileup.

Contact stagger time—*See* Time, contact stagger.

[1]The Aerospace Industries Association of America, Inc.

Contact (spring) tension — The contact pressure developed, usually resulting from the specified adjustment of movable contacts against mating stationary springs, when the relay is unenergized.

Contact transfer time — The interval between opening of the closed contact and closing of the open contact of a contact combination.

Contact weld — (1) The point of attachment of a contact to its support when accomplished by resistance welding. (2) A contacting failure due to fusing of contacting surfaces under load conditions to the extent that the contacts fail to separate when expected to do so.

Contact wipe — The scrubbing action between mating contacts resulting from contact overtravel or follow.

Contactor — A term for a power type relay with heavy-duty contacts. *(See also* Power type relay.)

Continuity-transfer contacts — See Contacts, continuity transfer.

Continuous-duty relay — A relay that may be energized with maximum rated power indefinitely without exceeding specified temperature limitations.

Core cap (NP) — *See* Armature stop, nonmagnetic (P).

Core, coil — The portion of the magnetic structure of a relay about which the coil is usually wound.

Critical voltage (current) — That voltage (current) which will just maintain thermal relay contacts in operation.

Crossbar switch — A switching technique employing multirelay elements in a matrix or grid arrangement to connect selected cross points electrically. *(See also* Sec. 3.)

Crosstalk — The electrical coupling between a closed contact circuit and other open or closed contacts on the same relay or switch, expressed in decibels down from the signal level.

Crystal can relay — A term used to identify a microminiature relay housed in a hermetically sealed enclosure that was originally used to enclose a frequency control type of quartz crystal. The most common size of crystal can relay housing is approximately 0.4 x 0.8 x 0.97 in. *(See also* Sec. 3.)

Current rating — See Rated coil current and Rated contact current.

Current (sensing) relay — A current (sensing)

relay is one that functions at a predetermined value of current. It may be an overcurrent relay, an undercurrent relay, or a combination of both. *(See also* Sec. 3.)

Current-balance relay — A current-balance relay is one that operates when the magnitude of one current exceeds the magnitude of a similar current by a predetermined degree.

Cycle timer — A controlling mechanism that opens or closes contacts according to a preset cycle.

D

Damping ring, mechanical — A loose member mounted on a contact spring to reduce contact chatter.

Dashpot — A device that employs either a gas or liquid to absorb energy and retard the movement of the moving parts of a circuit breaker or other electric device to produce an operate time delay.

Dashpot relay — A relay employing the dashpot principle to develop a time delay. *(See also* Sec. 3.)

De-energization — The removal of power from a relay coil or heater. Also commonly used to indicate a change in coil or heater applied power adequate to produce dropout.

Definite purpose relay — A readily available relay having some electrical or mechanical feature that distinguishes it from a general purpose relay. Types of definite purpose relays are interlock, selector, stepping sequence, latch-in, and time-delay.

Delay relay — A relay having an assured time interval between energization and pickup or between de-energization and dropout. Often referred to as a time delay relay. *(See also* Sec. 3.)

Dielectric constant — The ratio of unit capacitance (C) of a material to that of dry air, which is unity.

Differential relay — A relay with multiple windings that functions when the voltage, current, or power difference between the windings reaches a predetermined value. The power difference may result from the algebraic addition of multiple inputs.

Direct current — A unidirectional flow of electricity.

Direct current (d-c) relay — A relay designed for operation from a direct current source.

Double arm relay — A relay with two pileups, each actuated by a separate armature arm.

Double-break contacts — *See* Relay contact as-

sembly designations (Paragraph 1.5).

Double-make contacts — *See* Relay contact assembly designations (Paragraph 1.5).

Double-throw contacts — *See* Relay contact assembly designations (Paragraph 1.5).

Double-wound coil — A coil or winding consisting of two parts wound on the same core.

Dropout, measured (P), or *Release, measured* (NP) — The maximum current or voltage at which the relay restores to its unoperated position. *(See also* Fig. 1-3.)

Dropout, specified (P), or *Release, specified* (NP) — The specified maximum current or voltage at which the relay must restore to its unoperated position. Sometimes referred to as *minimum dropout.* *(See also* Fig. 1-3.)

Dropout (or *drop away*) *time* (NP) — *See* Time, release (P).

Dry circuit — A mechanically closed circuit with no appreciable applied voltage.

Dry circuit contacts — *See* Contacts, dry circuit.

Dry contacts — *See* Contacts, dry.

Dual coil relays — Relays designed to take advantage of the dual-coil operating principle. *(See also* Sec. 3.)

Dry reed relay — A reed relay with dry (non-mercury-wetted) contacts. *(See also* Reed relays and Sec. 3).

Duty cycle — A statement of energized and de-energized time in repetitious operation, for example, 2 seconds on, 6 seconds off, and the like.

Dynamic contact resistance — A change in contact electrical resistance due to a variation in contact pressure on contacts mechanically closed *(see* Figs. 1-1 and 1-2).

E

Electric reset — A qualifying term applied to a relay, indicating that its contacts must be reset electrically to their original positions following an operation.

Electrical interlock relay — *See* Interlock relay.

Electrical reset relay — A relay that may be restored electrically to its unoperated position.

Electromagnetic relay — A relay whose operation depends upon the electromagnetic effects of current flowing in an energizing winding.

Electromagnetic time delay relay — A relay in which the actuation of the contacts is delayed by the mutual inductance effect of a conducting sleeve or slug (usually nonmagnetic) or a short-circuited winding over the core.

Electrostatic relay — A relay in which operation depends upon motion of two or more insulated conductors caused by electrostatic effects. *(See also Sec. 3.)*

Electrostatic shield — A metallic shield or foil, usually grounded, used between reed switches, between a reed switch and coil, or between adjacent relays to minimize crosstalk effects.

Electrostatic spring shield(s) — Grounded metallic shield(s) between two relay springs to minimize crosstalk.

Electrostrictive relay — A relay in which operation depends upon the dimensional changes of an electrostrictive dielectric. *(See also Sec. 3.)*

Electrothermal expansion element — An actuating element in the form of a wire strip or other shape having a high coefficient of thermal expansion.

Enclosed relay — A relay having the contacts or coil, or both, contained in an unsealed cover as protection from the surrounding medium.

Energization — The application of power to a coil or heater winding of a relay. With respect to an operating coil winding, or heater, use of the word commonly assumes enough power to operate the relay fully, unless otherwise stated. (Examples of the latter are *partially energized, half energized,* and the like.)

F

Fast-operate relay — A high-speed relay specifically designed for short operate time but not necessarily short release time.

Fast-operate, fast-release relay — A high-speed relay specifically designed for both short operate and short release time.

Fast-operate, slow-release relay — A relay specifically designed for long release time but not necessarily short operate time.

Ferreed relay — Coined name for a special form of bistable or latching dry reed switch.

Final actuation time — The time interval from coil energization to the complete functioning of the last contact combination to be operated on pickup, or the last combination to be restored to normal on dropout *(see* Figs. 1-1 and 1-2).

Fixed contacts — The stationary contacts of a relay, disengaged by moving contacts to make or break circuits *(see* Fig. 1-4).

Flasher relay — A self-interrupting relay, usually of the thermal type.

Flip-flop — A circuit or relay with two stable states, as used for storing one binary bit of information.

Follow, contact — See Contact follow.

Follow stiffness, contact — See Contact follow stiffness.

Form, contact (NP) — See Contact combination (P).

Frame — The main supporting portion of a relay, which may include parts of the magnetic structure.

Freezing, magnetic — Sticking of the relay armature to the core or a magnetic backstop as a result of residual magnetism.

Frequency, operating — The rated a-c frequency of the supply voltage at which the relay is designed to operate.

Frequency sensitive relay — A relay that operates when energized electrically at a particular frequency or within specific frequency bands; a resonant reed relay. *(See also* Sec. 3.)

Fritting — Contact erosion in which the electrical discharge makes a hole through the film and produces molten matter that is drawn into the hole by electrostatic forces and solidifies there to form a conducting bridge.

Front contact (NP) — See Normally open contacts (P).

Fulcrum (armature) — See Armature bearing.

Fully operated armature — See Armature, fully operated.

G

Gap, air — Used to describe air space both in the magnetic circuit and between contacts, thus: (1) *Gap, armature (air)* — The distance in air separating the magnetic portion of the armature, when fully restored to its unoperated position, and the coil core face. It is equal to the armature stroke plus the thickness of the armature residual. (2) *Gap, buffer* — The space separating the armature buffer and the armature (movable) spring, or between the armature springs with the armature in its unoperated position. (3) *Gap, contact (air)* — See Contact gap. (4) *Gap, magnetic (air)* — Nonmagnetic portion of a magnetic circuit. (5) *Gap, residual* — See Residual gap. (6) *Gap stud* — See Gap, buffer.

Gasket sealed relay — A relay contained within an enclosure sealed with a gasket.

Gauging, relay contact — The setting of relay contact spacing by means of the use of thickness gauges inserted between coil core and armature residual so as to determine the point in the armature's stroke at which specified contacts are to function.

General purpose relay — A relay that is adaptable to a variety of applications, as opposed to a definite purpose relay or a special purpose relay.

Ground, chassis — *See* Chassis ground (Gnd.).

H

Half-crystal can relay — *See* Crystal can relay.

Hand-reset — A qualifying term applied to a relay indicating that following an operation the contacts must be reset manually to their original positions.

HCL: high, common, low — A type of relay control used in such devices as thermostats and in relays operated by them, in which a momentary contact between the common lead and another lead operates the relay, which then remains operated until a momentary contact between the common lead and a third lead causes the relay to return to its original position.

Header — The subassembly that supports and insulates the leads passing through the walls of a sealed relay.

Heater — A resistor that converts electrical energy into heat for operating a thermal relay.

Heel piece — The portion of a magnetic circuit of a relay that is attached to the end of the core remote from the armature.

Hermetically sealed relay — A relay contained within an enclosure that is sealed by fusion or other comparable means to insure a low rate of gas leakage over a long period of time.

Hertz — A term for cycles per second, hertz is abbreviated Hz.

Hesitation, armature — Delay or momentary reversal of armature motion in either the pickup or dropout stroke *(see* Figs. 1-1 and 1-2).

High-speed relay — A relay specifically designed for short operate time, short release time, or both.

High-voltage relay — (1) A relay adjusted to sense and function in a circuit or system at a specific maximum voltage. (2) A relay designed to handle elevated voltages on its contacts, coil, or both. *(See also* Sec. 3.)

Hinge, armature — A pivot provided by a joint, spring, or reed that secures the armature to the remainder of the relay frame or heelpiece.

Hinge pin — When the armature bearing is of the hinge-type, the pin is called a hinge pin.

History, magnetic — Magnetic status resulting from prior energization or de-energization.

Hold, measured (P), or *Nondropout, measured* (NP), or *Nonrelease, measured* (NP) — The minimum current or voltage at which the armature does not move perceptibly from its fully operated position after having been energized electrically. *(See also* Fig. 1-3.)

Hold, specified (P), or *Nondropout, specified* (NP), or *Nonrelease, specified* (NP) — The current or voltage at or above which the armature is required not to move perceptibly from its fully operated position, after having been energized electrically. *(See also* Fig. 1-3.)

Home — The normal or starting position for a stepping switch or relay.

Homing — A qualifying term applied to a stepping switch where the wipers, upon completion of an operational cycle, are stepped around or back to the start position.

Homing relay — A stepping relay that returns to a specified starting position prior to each operating cycle.

Hot-wire relay (NP) — A form of thermal relay (P). *(See also* Thermal relay and Sec. 3.)

Housing — An enclosure or cover for one or more relays, with or without accessories, usually providing access to the terminals.

Hum — The sound caused by mechanical (lamination) vibration resulting from alternating current flowing in the coil, or in some cases by unfiltered rectified current.

Hybrid relay — A combination of electronic component(s) with electromechanical componet(s) to provide a device for commutating and/or amplifying current or power.

Hysteresis — The characteristic of a magnetic material wherein the value of magnetism lags the changing magnetic force producing ti. This is demonstrated by the corresponding values of flux created when an inductive coil is energized first in one direction, to some maximum value, and then reversed. At zero current the residual magnetism is a demonstration of the effects of hysteresis. If carried through a complete cycle, the result is a loss of energy appearing as heat.

I

Impedance — The apparent resistance, or opposition, to the flow of alternating current through a relay coil. It consists of two components, reactance and the true resistance, added vectorially. *(See* Appendix table C-1.)

Impregnated coils — Coils that have been permeated with a phenolic varnish or other protective material to protect them from mechanical vibration, handling, fungus, and moisture.

Impregnated pileup — Contact spring assemblies treated with a protective material intended to reduce damage from prolonged exposure to moisture or fungus.

Impulse relay — (1) A relay that follows and repeats current pulses, as from a telephone dial. (2) A relay that operates on stored energy of a short pulse after the pulse ends. (3) A relay that discriminates between length and strength of pulses, operating on long or strong pulses and not operating on short or weak ones. (4) A relay that alternately assumes one of two positions as pulsed, as described in Sec. 3. (5) Erroneously used to describe an integrating relay.

Impulse transmitting relay — A relay that briefly actuates contacts during pickup or dropout.

Inductance — The property of an electric circuit whereby it resists any change of current during the building up or decaying of a self-induced magnetic field, and hence introduces a delay in current change with resulting operational delay. For convenience and standardization, rather than any technical significance, winding inductance is measured at a stated frequency, usually 1000 cycles (cps), with the armature held in its operated position unless otherwise specified. True inductance at any instant is very much affected by the degree of magnetic saturation, the presence of any steady current component, the armature position at instant of consideration, and the like.

Inductive winding — A coil having an inductance, as contrasted with a noninductive winding. A coil in which all turns are wound in the same direction, or in which the turns wound in one direction are more effective than those wound in the opposite direction so that there is a net inductance.

Inertia relay — A relay with added weights or other modifications that increase the moment of inertia of its moving parts in order either to slow its operation or to cause it to continue in motion after the energizing force ends.

Instrument relay — A sensitive relay in which the principle of operation is similar to that of instruments such as the electrodynamom-

eter, iron vane, D'Arsonval galvanometer, and moving magnet. This type of relay has a high ratio of nonpickup to pickup current or dropout to pickup current and therefore responds to small increases or decreases in the energizing source.

Insulation resistance (of a device) — Resistance of insulation measured (in ohms) at a specified d-c voltage and under ambient conditions, after current becomes constant. The resistance to leakage current of an intended insulator.

Integrating relay — A relay that operates on the energy stored from a long pulse or a series of pulses of the same or varying magnitude, for example, a thermal relay.

Interlock relay — A relay with two or more armatures, each with an associated contact spring pileup, or pileups, the positioning of which is according to the following: (1) *Mechanical interlock relay* — An interlock relay having a mechanical linkage whereby the position of one armature permits, prevents, or causes motion of another armature. (2) *Electrical interlock relay* — An interlock relay having an electrical interconnection such that the position of one armature permits, prevents, or causes operation of the other armature. (3) *Combination interlock relay* — An interlock relay having both mechanical linkage and electrical interconnection such that the position of one armature permits, prevents, or causes operation of the other armature. Note: If the position of one armature prevents operation of another, the relay is sometimes called a *lockout relay.*

Intermediate current, or *Intermediate switching area — See* Minimum current.

Intermittent-duty relay — A relay which must be de-energized at intervals to avoid excessive temperature, or a relay that is energized at regular or irregular intervals, as in pulsing.

Interrupter contacts — See Contacts, interrupter.

Inverse time — A qualifying term applied to a relay indicating that its time of operation decreases as the magnitude of the operating quantity increases.

L

Latch-in relay — A relay that maintains its contacts in the last position assumed without the need of maintaining coil energization.

Latching relay, magnetic — See Magnetic latching relay.

Latching relay, mechanical — See Mechanical

latching relay.

Lead, finish — The outer termination of the coil winding.

Lead, inside — *See* Lead, start.

Lead, outside — *See* Lead, finish.

Lead, start — The inner termination of the coil winding.

Leakage flux — That portion of the magnetic flux that does not cross the armature to pole-face gap.

Left-hand contact spring pileup — The opposite of right-hand spring pileup. (*See* Fig. 1-4.)

Level — A series of contacts served by one wiper of a stepping switch.

Lever contact (NP) — A term for movable contact spring (P).

Lifter, armature (NP) — *See* Buffer, armature (P).

Linear expansion relay — A relay having contacts actuated by the linear expansion of a solid due to various causes (*see* Sec. 3).

Load curves — The static force/displacement characteristic of the total contact spring load of the relay.

Locking relay — (1) A term for latching relay. (2) A term for lock-up relay.

Lock-up relay — (1) A relay that locks in the fully operated position even though the energizing pulse has been terminated, either by means of remanent magnetic bias (requiring a reverse pulse for releasing) or by means of a set of auxiliary contacts that keep its coils energized electrically until the circuit is interrupted. (2) Sometimes used for latching relay.

Low-capacitance contacts — A type of contact construction providing low intercontact capacitance.

Low level contacts — *See* Contacts, low level.

Low level relay — A term used to designate a relay with contacts capable of functioning in a low level circuit. (*See* Sec. 3.)

Low level test — *See* Miss test.

Long lever armature — *See* Armature, long lever.

Low voltage relay — A relay adjusted to sense and function in a circuit or system at a specific minimum voltage. Also a term used to designate a relay whose coil or contacts are designed to handle only ordinarily encountered voltages.

M

Magnet wire — *See* Wire, magnet.

Magnetic air gap — The nonmagnetic portion of a magnetic circuit.

Magnetic assist — Determination of direction of armature movement, or position, by means of magnetic flux produced by an auxiliary magnet or coil. Usually applies to a monostable polarized relay where a magnet holds the armature de-energized but aids operation when power is applied.

Magnetic contact relay — A relay in which the contact springs are magnetic and are actuated by magnetic attraction when the coil is energized. (For one example, *see* Reed relay.)

Magnetic field — A condition in the vicinity of a remanent magnet or an electrically energized coil of wire which manifests itself as a force on magnetic objects within that space. In a relay the magnetic field energizes the armature and causes its operation.

Magnetic flux — The total magnetic induction or lines of force through a given cross section of the magnetic field.

Magnetic freezing — The sticking of a relay armature to the core, after de-energization, due to the residual magnetism of the core.

Magnetic latching relay — (1) A relay that remains operated from remanent magnetism until reset electrically. (2) A bistable polarized (magnetically latched) relay. (*See also* Sec. 3.)

Magnetic line(s) of force — Theoretical line(s) used to evaluate the size, shape, and effect of a magnetic field.

Magnetic pole — The end of a magnet where the attraction force is the greatest.

Magnetic reed — *See* Reed relay.

Magnetomotive force — The force that establishes the magnetic flux in the magnetic circuit. Mathematically, it is the magnetic flux multiplied by the reluctance. It is directly proportional to ampere turns. The measurement unit is the gilbert.

Magnetostrictive relay — A relay in which operation depends upon dimensional changes of a magnetic material in a magnetic field. (*See also* Sec. 3.)

Make — The closure of open contacts to complete an electrical circuit.

Make-before-break contacts — Double-throw contacts so arranged that the moving contact establishes a new circuit before disrupting the old one. (*See* "D" contact combination in Fig. 1-5.)

Make contact — A normally open contact (*see* Fig. 1-5).

Make delay (NP) — *See* Slow operate (P).

Manual reset relay — A relay that may be restored manually to its unoperated position.

Margined relay — A relay that functions in response to predetermined changes in the value of coil current or voltage. Margining is frequently employed during relay adjustment to establish the desired amount of normally closed contact pressure when the relay is in the de-energized position.

Mark — (1) An impulse in a neutral circuit that causes the loop to be closed. (2) In a polar circuit, an impulse that causes the loop current to flow in a direction opposite that for a space impulse.

Marking contact — A prescribed contacting position of a polarized telegraph relay, opposite the spacing contact position.

Mechanical interlock(ing) relay — *See* Interlock relay.

Mechanical latching relay — A relay in which the armature or contacts may be latched mechanically in the operated or unoperated position until reset manually or electrically. *(See also* Sec. 3.)

Mechanical time delay relay — A relay in which operate or release action is delayed by a clockwork, escapement, bellows, or dashpot. *(See also* Sec. 3)

Memory relay — (1) A relay having two or more coils, each of which may operate independent sets of contacts, and another set of contacts that remain in a position determined by the coil last energized. (2) Sometimes used for a magnetically latched relay of the remanent magnetism type.

Mercury relay — A relay in which the movement of mercury opens and closes contacts. *(See also* Sec. 3.)

Mercury contact relays — (1) *Mercury plunger relay* — A relay in which the magnetic attraction of a floating plunger by a field surrounding a sealed capsule displaces mercury in a pool to effect contacting between fixed electrodes. (2) *Mercury wetted contact relay* — A form of reed relay in which the reeds and contacts are glass enclosed and are wetted by a film of mercury obtained by capillary action from a mercury pool in the base of a glass capsule vertically mounted. (3) *"Mercury contact relay"* — A relay mechanism in which mercury establishes contact between electrodes in a sealed capsule as a result of the capsule's being tilted by an electromagnetically actuated armature, either on pickup or dropout or both.

Meter relay — *See* Instrument relay and Sec. 3.

Minimum (reliable) current — As applied to relay contacts, the range of current at which there is insufficient energy under arcing conditions at the mating contact surfaces to insure good contacting for the kind of contact material, shape, and forces employed. *(See also* Sec. 4.) A test for minimum current is specified in some military specifications.

Miss, contact — *See* Contact miss.

Miss test — A test made to detect a contact miss.

Motor-driven relay — A relay in which contact actuation is controlled through an electric motor, cams, and systems of gears. An electromagnetic clutch may be used to engage and disengage the gear system. *(See* Sec. 3.)

Motor-driven stepper — A nonratcheting type of stepper. *(See* Sec. 3.)

Mounting plane — The plane to which the relay mounting surface is fastened.

Movable contact — *See* Contact, movable.

Moving coil relay — A special form of relay discussed in Sec. 3.

Multiple-break contacts — Contacts so arranged that, when they open, the circuit is interrupted in two or more places.

Multiple pileup — An arrangement of contact springs that has two or more separate pileups, as used on a double arm relay.

Multiple stack — Same as multiple pileup (for an example, see Fig. 1-4).

Multi-position relay — A relay that has more than one operate or nonoperate position, for example, a stepping relay.

Mutual induction — The condition by which a changing current in one circuit or coil winding causes a voltage to be induced in an adjacent circuit or coil winding.

N

Neutral relay — A relay whose operation is primarily independent of the direction of the coil current, in contrast to a polarized relay.

Nominal voltage — A single value of voltage (or a narrow voltage range) falling within the allowable operating voltage range of the relay. *See also* Rated coil voltage.

Nonbridging — A term used to describe a contact transfer in which the movable contact leaves one contact before touching the next.

Noncompliant (contact) spring — A contact spring that cannot, and is not intended to, move appreciably when contacted by a mating contact spring.

Nondropout, measured (NP) — *See* Hold, measured (P).

Nondropout, specified (NP) — *See* Hold, specified (P).

Nonfreeze pin (NP) — *See* Armature stop, nonmagnetic.

Nonhoming — A qualifying term applied to a stepping relay or switch indicating that wipers, upon completion of an operational cycle, do not return to the home position but remain at rest on the last used set of contacts.

Noninductive winding — A coil so wound, or with windings so terminated, that the total magnetic effects cancel in direction and magnitude.

Nonmagnetic shim — A nonmagnetic material used to prevent iron-to-iron contact.

Nonpickup, measured (P), or *Nonoperate* (NP) The maximum current or voltage at which a relay does not operate any contacts, or only certain specified contacts. The ruling specification may or may not permit armature movement.

Nonpickup, specified (P), or *Nonoperate, specified* (NP) — The current or voltage at or below which a relay is required to not operate any contacts, or only certain specified contacts. The ruling specification may, or may not, allow for some armature movement.

Nonreclosure — A term used with dry reed relays to indicate a value of dropout ampere turns that will not bring about false pickup or reclosure.

Nonrelease, measured (NP) — *See* Hold, measured (P).

Nonrelease, specified (P) — *See* Hold, specified (P).

Normal condition — The de-energized condition of the relay.

Normal position — The usual de-energized position of contacts, open or closed, due to spring tension, gravity, or magnetic polarity. The term is also used for the home position of a stepping switch.

Normal sequence of operation — The intended operation sequence built into a relay unaffected by wear or dimensional change. *See* Gauging, relay contact.

Normally closed contacts — *See* Contacts, normally closed.

Normally open contacts — *See* Contacts, normally open.

O

Off-normal contacts — Contacts of a rotary stepping switch or relay that assume a different position when the wiper assembly is in the home position than when it is in any other position. Usually used for wiper position indication or in homing the switch.

Open relay — An unenclosed relay.

Operate, armature rebound — *See* Armature rebound.

Operate, measured (NP) — *See* Pickup, measured (P).

Operate overthrow — See Armature operate overthrow.

Operate, specified (NP) — *See* Pickup, specified (P).

Operate time — *See* Time, operate.

Operate value, just (NP) — *See* Pickup, measured (P).

Operate value, must (NP) — *See* Pickup, specified (P).

Operating characteristics — Pickup, nonpickup, hold and dropout, voltage or current, and the operate and release time(s) of the relay.

Operating frequency — The rated a-c frequency of the supply voltage at which the relay coil is designed to operate.

Overcurrent relay — An alarm or protective relay that operates an alarm or removes power from a circuit when the current through its coil reaches a predetermined or unsafe value. [*See also* Current (sensing) relay.]

Overdrive — A term used to indicate use of greater than normal coil current (applied voltage), and usually employed in obtaining abnormally fast operate time or pulse response. (*See* "High speed relays" in Sec. 3.)

Overload relay — An alarm or protective relay that is specifically designed to operate when its coil current reaches a predetermined or unsafe value above normal. Time delay may be introduced as a requirement of overload.

Overthrow — *See* Armature (dropout or pickup) overthrow.

Overtravel — *See* Armature (dropout or pickup) overtravel and Contact follow.

Overvoltage relay — An alarm or protective relay that is specifically designed to operate when its coil voltage reaches a predetermined or unsafe value above normal.

P

Parallel wound — *See* coil, parallel wound.

Percent break — The portion of an electrical impulse during which no current flows, expressed as a percentage of the total impulse time.

Percent make — The portion of an electrical impulse during which current flows, expressed as a percentage of the total impulse time. Sometimes referred to as *dwell*.

Permissive make contact — A term applied to a contact combination in which the movable contact spring is pretensioned so that it will move from its normal, or unoperated, position as a result of its own force when the relay is energized. In the de-energized position, it is restrained by a member acted upon by the armature return spring. *(See also* "Wire spring relays" in Sec. 3.)

Pick pulse — The initial closure of power to a relay coil insufficient in time or ampere turns, or both, for full operation, but adequate to operate a preliminary (early) make. Closure of the preliminary make is employed to insure full operation.

Pickup, measured (P), or *Operate, measured* (NP), or *Pull-in (or pull-on) value, measured* (NP), or *Operate value, just* (NP) — The minimum current or voltage at which the armature actually seats against the coil core by assuming its fully operated position, or to a specified position.

Pickup, specified (P), or *Operate, specified* (NP), or *Pull-in (or pull-on) value, specified* (NP), or *Operate value, must* (NP) — The current or voltage at or below which the armature is required to seat against the coil core by assuming its fully operated position, or to a specified position.

Pickup (or pull-in) time (NP) — *See* Time, operate (P).

Pileup — An assembly of contact springs or combinations fastened one on top of the other with insulation between them *(see* Fig. 1-4).

Plug, armature (NP) — *See* Buffer, armature (P).

Plunger relay — A relay operated by a movable core or plunger through solenoid action. *(See also* Sec. 3.)

Pneumatic bellows — Gas-filled bellows, sometimes used with plunger type relays to obtain time delay.

Polarized relay — A relay, the operation of which is primarily dependent upon the direction (polarity) of the energizing current(s) and the resultant magnetic flux. The opposite of neutral relay. Also called *polar relay*.

Polarized relays can be further defined as (1) *Monostable* (P), or Single side stable, or Single biased (NP) — for two position relays held in a specific position when de-energized; (2) *Bistable* (P), or Double biased (NP) — for two position relays held in last operated position when de-energized; or (3) *Center-off, Three-position, No Bias* (NB) — when the relay always assumes a neutral position on de-energization. For additional discussion of variations of each class see the Appendix.

Pole — A combination of mating contacts: normally open, normally closed, or both. *(See* Paragraph 1.5.)

Pole, multi — A term applied to a contact arrangement to denote that it includes two or more separate contact combinations, that is, two or more single-pole contact assemblies. *(See* Paragraph 1.5.)

Pole, single — A term applied to a contact arrangement to denote that all contacts in the arrangement connect in one position or another to a common contact. *(See* Paragraph 1.5.)

Pole face — The part of the magnetic structure on the end of the core nearest the armature.

Pole gap (NP) — *See* Gap, armature (P).

Pole piece — The end of an electromagnet, sometimes separable from the main section, and usually shaped so as to distribute the magnetic field in a pattern best suited to the application.

Power dissipation, coil winding — *See* Coil (winding) power dissipation.

Power type relay — A term for a relay designed to have heavy-duty contacts usually rated 15 amperes or higher. Sometimes called a *contactor*.[1] *(See also* Sec. 3.)

Pull curves — The force-displacement characteristics of the actuating system of the relay.

Pull-in time (NP) — *See* Time, operate (P).

Pull-in (or pull-on) value, measured (NP) — *See* Pickup, measured (P).

Pull-in (or pull-on) value, specified (NP) — *See* Pickup, specified (P).

Pulse repeating relay — *See* Impulse relay.

Pusher (NP) — *See* Buffer, armature (P).

R

R.F. switching relay — A relay designed to switch frequencies that are higher than commercial power frequencies with low loss. *(See* Sec. 3.)

Radiation resistant relay — A relay on which a

technique for "hardening" against the detrimental effects of high-energy radiation has been employed. *(See* Sec. 3.)

Ratchet relay — A stepping relay actuated by an armature driven ratchet. *(See also* Stepping relay.)

Rated coil current — The steady-state coil current on which the relay is intended to operate for the prescribed duty cycle.

Rated coil voltage — The coil voltage on which the relay is intended to operate for the prescribed duty cycle.

Rated contact current — The current which the contacts are designed to handle for their rated life. *See also* Contact rating.

Rating — The designated capability of a relay's coil and/or contacts under definite conditions. (1) The coil is usually rated for maximum voltage and/or current that can be tolerated for a specified time. *(See* Rated coil current *and* Rated coil voltage.) (2) The contacts are usually rated according to the type of maximum load to be handled. At maximum power requirements, the nature of the load as well as the voltage and current values to be handled must be specified. These include Resistive, Inductive, Capacitive, Motor and Lamp loads, and the characteristics of each, such as inrush current, steady state, or running current, degree of inductance, power factor, frequency, etc. Other requirements to be considered may include *Dry Circuit, Low Level,* and *Intermediate* or *Minimum Current* capabilities.

Rating, short-time — The highest value of current or voltage that the relay can stand without injury for specified short-time intervals. (For a-c circuits, the rms total value, including the d-c component, should be used.) The rating recognizes the limitations imposed by both thermal and electromagnetic effects.

Reactance — The out-of-phase component of impedance that results from inductance or capacitance or both. *(See* Sec. 10, Table 10-14.)

Reed contacts — The contacts of a reed relay.

Reed relay — A relay using glass-enclosed, magnetically closed reeds as the contact members. Some forms are mercury-wetted.

Relay — Most simply defined as an electrically controlled device that opens and closes electrical contacts to effect the operation of other devices in the same or another electrical circuit. Also defined as an electrically controlled device that converts electrical energy into mechanical energy through electromagnetic, electrostatic, electrostrictive, magnetostrictive, or thermal effects, and by means of mechanical linkages actuates electrical conductors (contacts) that control electrical circuits. For definitions of the various relay types, refer to entries headed by the following qualifying adjectives *(see also* Sec. 3): Alternating current (a-c); annunciator; antenna switching; armature; automatic homing; auxiliary; bar; bidirectional; bimetal; clapper; close differential; coaxial; continuous-duty; crystal can; current (sensing); current-balance; direct current (d-c); definite-purpose; delay; differential; double arm; dry reed; electrical reset; electromagnetic; electromagnetic time delay; electrostatic; electrostrictive; enclosed; fast-operate; fast-operate, fast-release; fast-operate, slow-release; ferreed; flasher; frequency sensitive; gasket sealed; general purpose; hermetically sealed; high-speed; high-voltage; homing; hot wire; impulse; impulse transmitting; inertia; instrument; integrating; interlock; intermittent-duty; linear expansion; lock-up; low level; low-voltage; magnetic contact; magnetic latching; magnetostrictive; manual reset; margined; mechanical latching; mechanical time delay; memory; mercury; motor-driven; multi-position; neutral; open; overcurrent; overload; overvoltage; plunger; polarized or polar; power type; R.F.; ratchet; reed; resonant reed; rotary; rotary solenoid; sealed; sealed coil; sealed contact; sensing, current; sensitive; sequential; slave; special purpose; stepping; telephone type; thermal, undercurrent; undervoltage; vibrating reed; voltage (sensing); wire spring.

Relay contact gauging — *See* Gauging, relay contact.

Release, measured (NP) — *See* Dropout, measured (P).

Release, overthrow — *See* Armature dropout overthrow.

Release, overtravel — *See* Armature dropout overtravel.

Release, specified (NP) — *See* Dropout, specified (P).

Release time (P), or *Dropout (or drop away) time* (NP) — *See* Time, release.

Reliability — See Sec. 6, "Relay Reliability," for definitions peculiar to relay reliability.

---

[1]See *Definitions of Electrical Terms,* C42-25, United States of America Standards Institute.

Reluctance — The resistance offered by a magnetic material to the establishment of a magnetic field. Numerically equal to the magnetomotive force divided by the magnetic flux.

Repeating timer — A timing device that upon completion of one operating cycle continues to repeat automatically until excitation is removed.

Reset — The return of contacts or a mechanism to the normal state.

Reset, automatic — (1) A stepping relay that returns to its home position either when it reaches a predetermined contact position or when a pulsing circuit fails to energize the driving coil within a given time. May either pulse forward or be spring reset to the home position. (2) An overload relay that restores the circuit as soon as an overcurrent situation is corrected.

Reset, electrical — A qualifying term applied to a relay to indicate that it may be reset electrically after an operation.

Reset, manual — A qualifying term applied to a relay to indicate that it may be reset manually after an operation.

Residual gap — The length of the magnetic air gap provided by the armature residual between the pole face center and the nearest point on the armature when the armature is in the energized position. Also called *armature residual gap.*

Residual screw, pin, plate, or stud — Nonmagnetic screw(s), pin(s), plate(s), or stud(s) attached to either the armature or the core(s) of a relay to prevent the armature from directly contacting the magnetic core(s). *(See Fig. 1-4).*

Residual setting — The value of the residual gap obtained by the use of an adjustable armature stop of any kind that prevents iron-to-iron contact between armature and coil core.

Residual shim — *See* Nonmagnetic shim.

Resonant reed relay — *See* Vibrating reed relay.

Restoring spring (NP) — *See* Return spring (P).

Retractile spring — A restoring spring.

Return spring (P) — A spring that moves or tends to move the armature to the released (normal) position. Also called restoring spring (NP).

Right-hand contact spring pileup — The right-hand pileup of a multi-pileup relay, unless specifically indicated otherwise, is arbitrarily defined as follows: Visualize the relay positioned with the contact springs in front, contacts up (at or near the top). The contact stack on the facing right-hand side constitutes the right-hand pileup *(see* Fig. 1-4).

Rotary relay — (1) A relay whose armature is rotated to close the gap between two or more pole faces (usually having a balanced armature). (2) Incorrectly used for stepping relay. *(See also* Sec. 3.)

Rotary solenoid relay — A relay in which the linear component of motion of the plunger or armature is converted mechanically into rotary motion.

Rotary stepping relay — *See* Stepping relay.

Rotary stepping switch — *See* Stepping switch.

S

Sandwich wound coil — See Coil, sandwich wound.

Saturation — The condition attained in a magnetic material when an increase in field intensity produces no further increase in flux density. A degree of saturation (soak) may be specified as a reference point when a relay is being adjusted by current flow methods.

Sealing — *See* Seating.

Sealed coil relay — A relay in which the coil is isolated and hermetically sealed.

Sealed contact relay — A relay in which the contact is isolated and hermetically sealed.

Sealed relay — A relay that has both coil and contacts enclosed in an airtight cover. Not to be confused with hermetically sealed relay.

Seating — The magnetic positioning of an armature in its final desired location.

Selector relay (NP) — *See* Stepping switch (P).

Sensing relay — A relay responding to a condition of overcurrent, overvoltage, undercurrent, undervoltage, and the like. *See also* Current (sensing) relay, Thermal relay, Overcurrent relay, Overvoltage relay, Overload relay, and the like.

Sensitive relay — A relay that operates on comparatively low input power, commonly defined as 100 milliwatts or less.

Sensitivity — Pickup, specified, expressed in milliwatts.

Separation, contact — *See* Contact gap.

Sequence control — The automatic control of a series of operations in a predetermined sequence.

Sequence (contact) gauging — The positioning of

contacts during relay adjustment whereby like contacts (usually the break contacts) do not operate simultaneously but function successively in the armature's forward movement. Employed in some relay designs to insure independence of back contacting. Sometimes called *staggered gauging*.

Sequential relay — A relay that controls two or more contact combinations in a predetermined sequence.

Series relay — *See* Current relay.

Set, contact (NP) — *See* Contact combination (P).

Shading coil — *See* Shading ring.

Shading ring — A shorted turn surrounding a portion of the pole of an alternating-current electromagnet, producing by mutual inductance a delay of the change of the magnetic field in that part, thereby tending to prevent chatter and reduce hum.

Shields, electrostatic spring — Grounded conducting members located between two relay contact springs to minimize electrostatic coupling.

Shim, nonmagnetic — *See* Armature stop, non magnetic.

Short lever armature — *See* Armature, short lever.

Simultaneous (contact) gauging — The positioning of contacts during relay adjustment whereby like contacts are caused to operate at the same point in the armature's forward stroke.

Single side stable — *See* Polarized relay.

Slave relay — Same as Auxiliary relay.

Sleeve — A conducting tube placed around the full length of the coil core as a short-circuited winding to retard the establishment or decay of flux within the magnetic path.

Slow-operate relay — A slugged relay that has been specifically designed for long operate time but not for long release time. *(Caution:* The usual slow-operate relay has a copper slug close to the armature, making it also at least partially slow to release.)

Slow-operate, fast-release relay — A relay specifically designed for long operate time and short release time. Usually accomplished by having the relay open a front-end short-circuited winding through its own contact.

Slow-operate, slow-release relay — A slugged relay specifically designed for both long operate time and long release time.

Slow-release relay — A relay specifically designed for long release time but not for long operate time.

Slug — A conducting tube placed around a portion of the core to retard the establishment or decay of flux within the magnetic path.

Soak — The conditioning of a relay by approximately saturating its core magnetically.

Soak value — The voltage, current, or power applied to the relay coil to insure a condition approximating magnetic saturation.

Solenoid relay — *See* Plunger relay.

Space — An impulse that in a neutral circuit causes the loop to open and that in a polar circuit causes the loop current to flow in a direction opposite to that for a mark impulse.

Spacing contact — A prescribed contacting position of a polarized relay, opposite to the marking contact position.

Spark, contact — The electrical (current) discharge that occurs between mating contacts when a circuit is being established.

Special-purpose relay — A relay with an application that requires special features which are not characteristic of the conventional general-purpose or definite-purpose relay.

Spring-actuated stepping relay — A form of stepping relay.

Spring, balance — A member used in card-actuated relays to provide restoring force. Sometimes called *buffer spring.*

Spring, bracer — A supporting member used in conjunction with a contact spring. *(See also* Stop, spring.)

Spring, buffer — *See* Buffer spring.

Spring, contact — (1) A current-carrying spring, usually a flat leaf type member, to which the contacts are fastened. Contact springs bearing contacts are assembled between insulators in the contact assembly, or pileup, to form contact combinations *(See* Fig. 1-4). (2) A noncurrent-carrying spring that positions or tensions a contact-carrying member.

Spring, damper — On some relay designs, an auxiliary spring added to prevent unwanted movement of some relay member in the presence of vibration or shock. Damper springs are used against armatures, armature bearing pins, and contact members.

Spring, driving — The spring that drives the wipers of a stepping relay or stepping switch.

Spring, restoring — *See* Return spring.

Spring, retractile — *See* Spring, restoring.

Spring, return — *See* Return spring.

Spring buffer — On some relay designs, an insulating member permanently attached to the movable contact springs and used to transmit armature motion to the spring (see Fig. 1-4).

Spring load curves — A plot of contact spring force on the armature versus armature travel for a specific relay.

Spring terminals, contact — The portion of contact springs to which the current-carrying conductors are attached (see Fig. 1-4).

Stack — See Pileup.

Stagger time, contact—See Time, contact stagger.

Stationary contact — See Contact, stationary.

Stepping relay — A relay having many rotary positions, ratchet actuated, moving from one step to the next in successive operations, and usually operating its contacts by means of cams. There are two forms: (1) "Directly driven," where the forward motion occurs on energization, and (2) "Indirectly (spring) driven," where a spring produces the forward motion on pulse cessation. The term is also incorrectly used for stepping switch. (See also Sec. 3.)

Stepping switch — A class of electromagnetically operated, multiposition switching devices. Wipers, or groups of wipers, are mounted on a rotatable shaft, which is rotated in steps so that contact is successively made between the wiper tips and contacts that are separated electrically from each other and mounted in a circular arc called a bank. The wiper positioning is done electromechanically on successive pulses to the actuating coil. (See also Sec. 3.) There are two general kinds in common usage, rotary stepping switches and the Strowger two-motion switch: (1) *Direct-acting (two-coil) rotary stepping switch* — A directly driven rotary stepping switch (see also Sec. 3) is a two-coil switch in which one electromagnet (called a *rotary magnet, motor magnet,* or *step coil*) and its associated armature provide forward stepping immediately on energization, by ratchet action, advancing the wipers, one step for each pulse received, to the desired contacting position. It remains in this position without further coil energization. The rotor is spring restored to normal, or home, position, returning in reverse to the route over which it advanced under control of a second electromagnet (called a *release magnet* or *release coil*) from a single pulse. (2) *Indirect drive, or spring-driven, (one-coil) rotary stepping switch* — The indirectly driven rotary stepping switch (see also Sec.

3) advances the wipers on the return action, or release of the armature, following each pulse to the motor magnet (coil). The rotation is unidirectional, one step for each pulse, on pulse cessation. The switch is returned to the normal, or home position, by being stepped forward to the home position either from externally produced pulses or by being self-interrupted. (3) *Bi-directional (two-coil) rotary stepping switch* — A rotary stepping switch of the ratcheting direct acting type (see also Sec. 3), having two coils and associated stepping mechanisms and capable of rotation either clockwise or counterclockwise. (4) *Strowger two-motion switch* — A large capacity switch having 100 discrete positions and used principally in telephone switching (see also Sec. 3).

Stop, nonmagnetic armature — See Armature stop, nonmagnetic.

Stop, spring — A member that controls the position of a pretensioned spring. (See also Spring, bracer).

Stroke — See Gap, armature.

Stud, armature (NP) — See Buffer, armature (P).

Stud, residual — See Residual screw, pin, plate, or stud.

Stud, spring (NP) — See Buffer, spring (P).

Stud gap — See Gap, air.

Switch, crossbar — See Crossbar switch.

Switch, stepping — See Stepping switch.

Switch, X-Y — See X-Y switch.

T

Tandem-wound coil — See Coil, tandem-wound.

Telephone-type relay — A term most often applied to an armature relay with an end-mounted coil, an "L" shaped heelpiece, and contact springs mounted parallel to the long axis of the relay coil. Originally used mainly in telephone systems.

Temperature, ambient — See Ambient temperature.

Temperature correction — The factor used to convert a measured value of coil resistance at a known temperature (such as 20°C) to a calculated resistance value at some other temperature. (See Sec. 8 for formula and method.)

Tension, contact — See Contact tension.

Terminals, contact spring — See Spring terminals, contact.

Test, calibration — See Calibration test.

Test, miss — See Miss test.

Thermal relay — A relay actuated by the heating effects of an electric current. *(See also* Sec. 3.) Definitions peculiar to thermal relays are

Critical voltage — The critical voltage of a thermal relay is the least energizing voltage that will operate the relay when applied to the heater.

Hold-in voltage, minimum — The value to which the heater voltage of a thermal relay may be permanently reduced without relasing the contacts.

Operate time, normal — The normal operate time of a thermal relay is the time interval between applying power at rated voltage and the operation of the contacts (essentially the same interval as for the electromagnetic relay).

Operate voltage, minimum — The value of voltage at which the thermal relay will operate in not more than four times its normal operate time and will remain operated.

Recovery time, instantaneous — The time interval that must elapse after the thermal relay power is cut off at the operating point and before it has recovered its ability to repeat at least a given percentage of its set operating interval (same as recovery time).

Recovery time, saturated — The sum of the saturated release time of a thermal relay plus instantaneous recovery time.

Release time, instantaneous — The time interval that elapses after the heater of a thermal relay is cut off at operating point and before the relay releases its contacts (same as release time).

Release time, saturated — The time interval required after the cut off of heater power, when a thermal relay has reached its saturated temperature and before it has cooled enough to release its contacts.

Saturation — Saturation occurs when the heater of a thermal relay has been energized until all elements of the relay have reached a substantially stable temperature.

Time, basic — That setting of a particular relay structure at which the operate time and saturate release time are approximately equal.

Time, instantaneous recovery — Recovery time of a thermal relay measured when the heater is de-energized at the instant of contact operation.

Time, instantaneous reoperate — Reoperate time of a thermal relay measured when the heater is de-energized at the instant of contact operation.

Time, recovery — The cooling time required from heater de-energization to subsequent re-energization that will result in a new operate time equal to 85 per cent of that exhibited from a cold start.

Time, reoperate — Release time.

Time, saturated recovery — Recovery time of a thermal relay measured after temperature saturation has been reached.

Time, saturated reoperate — Time measured when the relay is de-energized after temperature saturation (equilibrium) has been reached.

Three-position relay — *See* Polarized relay.

Throat cutting — An industry term used to describe a circuit where a relay's contact disconnects a coil winding prior to complete operation. *Caution:* Improperly used relay may "doorbell."

Throw, double — A term applied to a contact arrangement to denote that contacting is effected in both the operated and nonoperated position, for example, a contact form such as a break-make or transfer. *(See also* Paragraph 1.5.)

Throw, single — A term applied to a contact arrangement to denote that contacting is effected in only one position and not the other, for example, a normally closed or a normally open contact. *(See also* Paragraph 1.5.)

Time, actuation — The time at which a specified contact functions, as follows: (1) *Time, contact actuation* — The time required for any specified contact on the relay to function, subdivided as: (1) *Time, final actuation* — The sum of the initial actuation time and the contact bounce intervals following such actuation *(see* Figs 1-1 and 1-2). (3) *Time, initial actuation* — The time of the first opening of a normally closed contact on pickup or the opening of a normally open contact on dropout *(see* Figs. 1-1 and 1-2). The same as operate time on pickup or release time on dropout.

Time, bridging — The time that contacts in

transit are electrically connected during pickup and dropout.

Time, bunching — The time during which all three contacts of a bridging contact combination are electrically connected during the armature stroke. One form of bridging time.

Time, contact bounce — The time interval from initial actuation of a contact to the end of bounce brought about during pickup or dropout or from external causes (*see* Figs. 1-1 and 1-2).

Time, contact stagger — The time interval between the actuation of any two contact combinations on the same relay (for example, the time difference between the opening of two normally closed contacts on pickup).

Time, instantaneous recovery — *See* Thermal relay.

Time, instantaneous reoperate — *See* Thermal relay.

Time, operate — The time interval from coil energization to the functioning time of the last contact to function. Where not otherwise stated, the functioning time of the contact in question is taken as its initial functioning time (that is, it does not include contact bounce time). (*See also* Fig. 1-1.)

Time, recovery — *See* Thermal relay.

Time, release — The time interval from coil de-energization to the functioning time of the last contact to function. Where not otherwise stated, the functioning time of the contact in question is taken as its initial functioning time (that is, it does not include contact bounce time). (*See also* Fig. 1-2.)

Time, reoperate — *See* Thermal relay.

Time, saturated recovery — *See* Thermal relay.

Time, saturated reoperate — *See* Thermal relay.

Time, seating — The elapsed time from coil energization to the seating of the relay armature.

Time, transfer — The time interval between opening the closed contact and closing the open contact (and vice versa) of a break-make contact combination (*see* Fig. 1-2).

Time delay relay — *See* Delay relay.

Travel, armature — The distance traveled during operation by a specified point on the armature.

U

Undercurrent relay — An alarm or protective relay specifically designed to function when its energizing current falls below a predeter-

mined safe value. [*See also* Current (sensing) relay.]

Undervoltage relay — An alarm or protective relay specifically designed to function when its energizing voltage falls below a predetermined safe value. [*See also* Voltage (sensing) relay.]

Unenclosed relay — A relay that does not have its contacts or coil protected from the surrounding medium by a cover, an open relay.

V

Vane-type relay — type of alternating current relay in which a light metal disc or vane moves in response to a change of the current in the controlling circuit.

Vibrating reed relay — A relay in which the application of an alternating or a self-interrupted voltage to the driving coil produces an alternating or pulsating magnetic field that causes a reed to vibrate and operate contacts. (*See also* Sec. 3.)

Voltage (sensing) relay — (1) A term correctly used to designate a special purpose voltage-rated relay that is adjusted by means of a voltmeter across its terminals in order to secure pickup at a specified critical voltage without regard to coil or heater resistance and resulting energizing current at that voltage. (2) A term erroneously used to describe a general purpose relay for which operational requirements are expressed in voltage. (Note: The operation and release of electromagnetic relays depends upon the flux — or heat in thermal relays — developed by the current in the energizing winding — or thermal relay heater. References that seem to suggest that there may be basic differences which cause some relays to operate on applied voltage and others on current are misleading. Terms such as *current relay* or *voltage relay* are best used to describe a circuit function, rather than to suggest a principle of operation.)

Voltage standing wave ratio (VSWR) — In a relay, the contacts of which handle radio frequency (r-f), the power loss due to the mismatch introduced into the line by the coaxial relay contacts, expressed as a ratio of the highest voltage to the lowest voltage found in the r-f line.

W

Winding — *See* Coil.

Winding, bias — An auxiliary winding used to produce an electrical bias.

Wipe, contact — The sliding or tangential motion between two mating contact surfaces when they are coming to rest. This is developed from pivoting about noncommon centers.

Wiper — The moving contact on a rotary stepping switch or relay.

Wire, magnet — Any coated conductor used to wind an electromagnetic coil in order to develop and maintain a magnetic field under prescribed conditions. (*See also* Appendix A.)

Wire spring relay — A relay design in which the contacts are attached to round wire springs instead of the conventional flat, or leaf, spring. (*See also* Sec. 3.)

X

X-Y switch — A kind of stepping switch used in telephony. (*See also* Sec. 3.)

Multicell battery with 3 taps

  USASI

Multicell battery with adjustable tap

  USASI

Ground

A direct conducting connection to earth or a conducting connection to a structure that serves a similar function, as in an air, space, or land vehicle not conductively connected to the earth.

  <u>IEC</u>

Chassis or frame connection

A conducting connection to a chassis or frame, which may be at substantial potential with respect to earth, or the structure mounting the chassis or frame.

  <u>IEC</u>

1.10 Standard circuit symbols

FUNDAMENTALS

Main circuit   ▬▬▬▬▬

Branch circuit   ————————

Battery

The long line is always positive, but polarity may be indicated in addition.
Example:

  OR   USASI and <u>IEC</u>

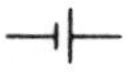

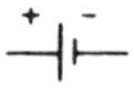

The above are also used to denote a generalized d-c source. Other battery symbols are:

One cell   —|��—   USASI and <u>IEC</u>

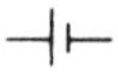

Multicell   —|||—   USASI and <u>IEC</u>

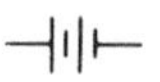

AMPLIFIER

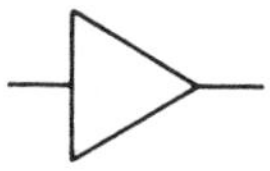

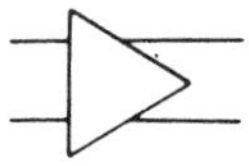

See note 1

Amplifier with two inputs

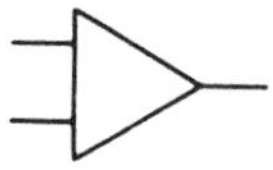

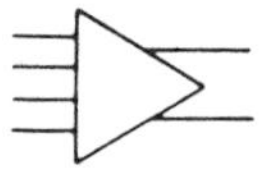

See note 1

Amplifier with two outputs

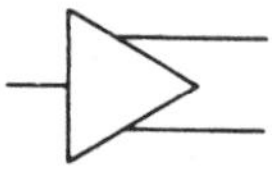

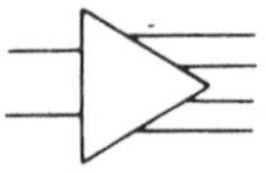

General

The triangle is pointed in the direction of transmission.

Note—Single-line (one-line) symbols appear at the left, complete symbols at the right, and symbols suitable for both purposes are centered in each column.

The symbol represents any method of amplification (electron tube, solid state device, magnetic device, etc.).

Note 1 —If identification, electrical values, location data and similar information must be noted within a symbol the size or aspect ratio of the original symbol may be altered providing its distinctive shape is retained.

Amplifier use may be indicated in the triangle by words, standard abbreviations, or a letter combination from the following list.

BDG	Bridging	MON	Monitoring
BST	Booster	PGM	Program
CMP	Compression	PRE	Preliminary
DC	Direct Current	PWR	Power
EXP	Expansion	TRQ	Torque
LIM	Limiting		

AUDIBLE SIGNALING DEVICE

Bell, electrical; ringer, telephone
   Note —If specific identification is required, the abbreviation AC or DC may be added within the square.

IEC

Buzzer

IEC

Horn, electrical; loudspeaker; siren; underwater sound projector or transceiver

General

Sounder, telegraph

CAPACITOR

General
   If it is necessary to identify the capacitor electrodes, the curved element shall represent the outside electrode in fixed paper-dielectric and ceramic-dielectric capacitors, the moving element in adjustable and variable capacitors, and the low-potential element in feed-through capacitors.

      IEC

Polarized capacitor

Application : shielded capacitor

Application : adjustable or variable capacitor
   If it is necessary to identify trimmer capacitors, the letter T should appear adjacent to the symbol.

See note 2

Application : adjustable or variable capacitors with mechanical linkage of units

See note 2

Note 2—The shaft of the arrow is drawn at approximately 45 deg across the body of the symbol to denote that the device represented is adjustable or continuously variable (IEC).

Continuously adjustable or variable differential capacitor
   The capacitance of one part increases as the capacitance of the other part decreases.

See note 2

Phase-shifter capacitor

Split-stator capacitor
   The capacitances of both parts increase simultaneously.

See note 2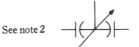

Note—Single-line (one-line) symbols appear at the left, complete symbols at the right, and symbols suitable for both purposes are centered in each column.

Shunt capacitor

Coupling capacitor (for power line carrier)

*See note 3

Note 3   —The asterisk is not part of the symbol. If specific identification is desired, the asterisk is to be replaced by one of the following letter combinations.

COM	Carrier communication
LC	Carrier load control
REL	Carrier relaying
SUP	Carrier supervisory
TLM	Carrier telemetering
TT	Carrier transferred trip

Feed-through capacitor (with terminals shown on feed-through element for clarity)

Commonly used for bypassing high-frequency currents to chassis.

CIRCUIT ELEMENT

An enclosure of any form or shape in common acceptance can be used to represent a circuit element. The accepted USASI abbbreviations that may be employed for further identification are listed in USASI Std. Z-32.13 as follows:

CB	Circuit breaker
DIAL	Telephone dial
EQ	Equalizer
FAX	Facsimile set
FL	Filter
FL-BE	Filter, band elimination
FL-BP	Filter, band pass
FL-HP	Filter, high pass
FL-LP	Filter, low pass
NET	Network
PS	Power supply
RG	Recording unit
RU	Reproducing unit
TEL	Telephone station
TPR	Teleprinter
TTY	Teletypewriter

Additional letter combinations as follows may be employed, but the use of specific graphic symbols included elsewhere in this standard is preferred.

AR	Amplifier
AT	Attenuator

C	Capacitor
HS	Handset
I	Indicating or switchboard lamp
L	Inductor
J	Jack
LS	Loudspeaker
MIC	Microphone
OSC	Oscillator
PAD	Pad
P	Plug
HT	Receiver, headset
K	Relay
R	Resistor
S	Switch or key switch
T	Transformer
WR	Wall receptacle

CONDUCTOR

Conductive path or conductor; wire

———   IEC

Two conductors or conductive paths

IEC   IEC

Three conductors or conductive paths

IEC   IEC

"n" conductors or conductive paths

"n" conductors

Crossing of paths or conductors not connected The crossing is not necessarily at a 90-degree angle.

IEC

Junction of paths or conductors

Junction (if desired)

● IEC

Application: junction of paths, conductor, or cable. If desired indicate path type, or size

———●———   IEC

Application: splice (if desired) of same size cables. Junction of conductors of same size or different size cables. If desired indicate sizes of conductors

SPLICE

———●———   IEC

Note—Single-line (one-line) symbols appear at the left, complete symbols at the right, and symbols suitable for both purposes are centered in each column.

Junction of connected paths, conductors, or wires

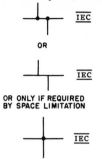

Associated conductors

Pair (twisted unless otherwise specified)

Triple (twisted unless otherwise specified)

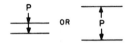

Quad

Assembled conductors; cable
Commonly used in communication diagrams.

Shielded single conductor

Coaxial cable, recognition symbol
Coaxial transmission path
Cable, radio frequency   (Coaxial)

Coaxial symbol

2-conductor cable

Shielded 2-conductor cable with shield grounded

5-conductor cable

Shielded 5-conductor cable

Shielded 5-conductor cable with conductors separated on the diagram for convenience

Cable underground or in conduit (*long dashes*)

— — — — —

Grouping of leads
Normally, bend of line indicates direction of conductor joining cable.

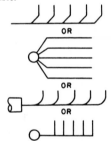

Alternate or conditional wiring
Not commonly used on power diagrams.
The arrowheads in this case shall be solid.
        A note shall explain the connections.

Application: 3 alternate paths

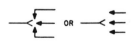

CONNECTOR
DISCONNECTING DEVICE
The connector symbol is not an arrowhead. It is larger, and the lines of the head make a 90-deg angle.

Female contact

IEC —<

Note—Single-line (one-line) symbols appear at the left, complete symbols at the right, and symbols suitable for both purposes are centered in each column.

Male contact

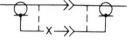

Connector assembly, movable or stationary portion; jack, plug, or receptacle

$$\text{IEC}$$

See note 4

Commonly used for a jack or receptacle (usually stationary)

IEC   See note 4   OR

Commonly used for a plug (usually movable)

IEC   See note 4   OR

Separable connectors (engaged)

IEC   See note 4   OR

Note 4   —Use appropriate number of contact symbols. IEC

Application: engaged 4-conductor connectors; the plug has 1 male and 3 female contacts

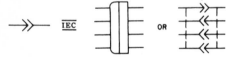

Application: engaged 4-conductor connectors, the plug has 1 male and 3 female contacts with individual contact designations shown in the complete-symbol column

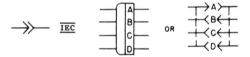

Coaxial connectors

Engaged coaxial and waveguide connectors
  Coaxial recognition sign may be added if necessary.

→》—   IEC

Coaxial with the outside conductor shown carried through

Coaxial with outside conductor shown carried through; with outside conductor terminated on chassis

Coaxial with center conductor shown carried through; outside conductor not carried through

Communication switchboard-type connector

2-conductor (jack)

2-conductor (plug)

3-conductor (jack) with 2 break contacts (normals) and 1 auxiliary make contact

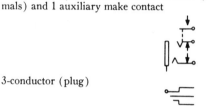

3-conductor (plug)

Communication switchboard-type connector with circuit normalled through jacks as follows:

"Normalled" indicates that a through circuit may be interrupted by an inserted connector. As shown here, the inserted connector opens the through circuit and connects to the circuit towards the left.

Items A through D show 2-conductor jacks. The "normal" symbol is applicable to other types of connectors.

→←

Jacks with circuit normalled through one way

←   Item A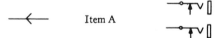

Jacks with circuit normalled through both ways

←→   Item B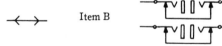

Jacks in multiple, one set with circuit normalled through both ways

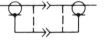   Item C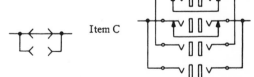

Note—Single-line (one-line) symbols appear at the left, complete symbols at the right, and symbols suitable for both purposes are centered in each column.

Jacks with auxiliary contacts, with circuit normalled through both ways

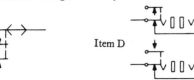

Item D

Connectors of the type commonly used for power-supply purposes (convenience outlets and mating connectors)

Female contact

Male contact

2-conductor nonpolarized connector with female contacts

2-conductor nonpolarized connector with male contacts

2-conductor polarized connector with female contacts

2-conductor polarized connector with male contacts

3-conductor polarized connector with female contacts

3-conductor polarized connector with male contacts

4-conductor polarized connector with female contacts

4-conductor polarized connector with male contacts

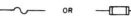

FUSE

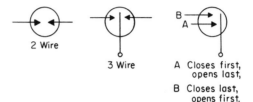 OR

INSTRUMENT CONTACTS

2 Wire

3 Wire

A Closes first,
  opens last,

B Closes last,
  opens first.

INDICATOR (DIAL) LIGHTS (NEMA)

Switchboard type

OR ✳ OR jeweled

*To avoid confusion with other circular symbols, the following letters (for which the asterisk merely substitutes) may be inserted in the circles or placed adjacent:

A Amber
B Blue
C Clear
G Green
NE Neon
O Orange
OP Opalescent
P Purple
R Red
W White
Y Yellow

MOTOR (OR GENERATOR)

M
Motor

G
Generator

✳

Motor or
generator with
separate field

*Put appropriate
designation in circle.

Note—Single-line (one-line) symbols appear at the left, complete symbols at the right, and symbols suitable for both purposes are centered in each column.

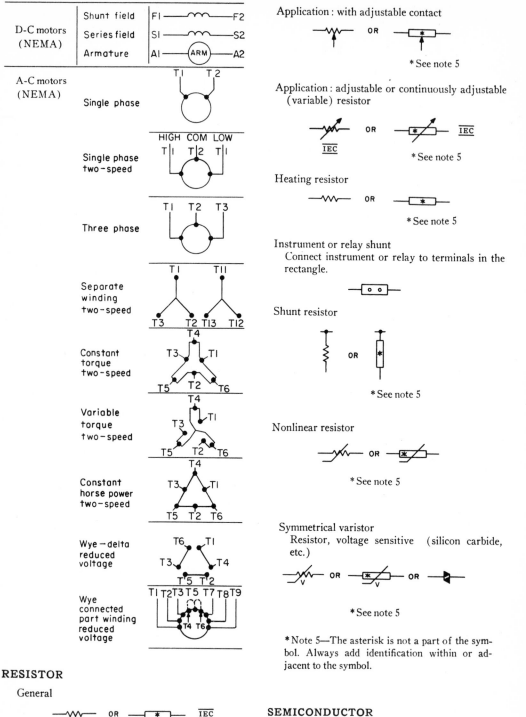

D-C motors (NEMA)	Shunt field	F1 —⌇⌇⌇— F2
	Series field	S1 —⌇⌇⌇— S2
	Armature	A1 —(ARM)— A2

A-C motors (NEMA)

Single phase

Single phase two-speed

Three phase

Separate winding two-speed

Constant torque two-speed

Variable torque two-speed

Constant horse power two-speed

Wye–delta reduced voltage

Wye connected part winding reduced voltage

Application : with adjustable contact

OR

*See note 5

Application : adjustable or continuously adjustable (variable) resistor

IEC   OR   IEC

*See note 5

Heating resistor

OR

*See note 5

Instrument or relay shunt
    Connect instrument or relay to terminals in the rectangle.

Shunt resistor

OR

*See note 5

Nonlinear resistor

OR

*See note 5

Symmetrical varistor
    Resistor, voltage sensitive (silicon carbide, etc.)

OR   OR

*See note 5

*Note 5—The asterisk is not a part of the symbol. Always add identification within or adjacent to the symbol.

RESISTOR

General

IEC   OR   IEC

*See note 5

Tapped resistor

OR

*See note 5

SEMICONDUCTOR

Semiconductor diode
Semiconductor rectifier diode

OR

Note—Single-line (one-line) symbols appear at the left, complete symbols at the right, and symbols suitable for both purposes are centered in each column.

PNP Transistor (example of a 3 element device)

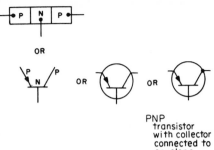

OR

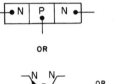

OR OR

PNP
transistor
with collector
connected to
envelope

NPN transistor

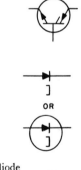

OR

Semiconductor triode, PNPN-type switch

Semiconductor triode, NPNP-type switch

Tunnel diode

OR

Temperature dependent diode

OR

Photodiode

OR

Varistor

OR

SOLENOID

(JIC)

SWITCHES

Single throw, general

$\overline{\text{IEC}}$

Double throw, general

Application: 2-pole double-throw switch with terminals shown

Knife switch, general

Sector switch

$\overline{\text{IEC}}$

10-point selector switch with fixed segment

3-position 1-pole: circuit closing (make), off, momentary circuit closing (make)

OFF

3-position 2-pole: circuit closing (make), off, momentary circuit closing (make)

OFF

Switch, key-type, applications

2-position with locking transfer and break contacts

Note—Single-line (one-line) symbols appear at the left, complete symbols at the right, and symbols suitable for both purposes are centered in each column.

3-position with nonlocking transfer and locking break contacts

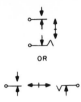

OR

Selector or multiposition switch
The position in which the switch is shown may be indicated by a note or designation of switch position.

General (for power and control diagrams)
Any number of transmission paths may be shown.

Break-before-make, nonshorting (nonbridging) during contact transfer

Make-before-break, shorting (bridging) during contact transfer

Br

Segmental contact

Disconnect switch

Circuit interrupter switch

Circuit breaker switch

Limit switches, spring return (JIC)

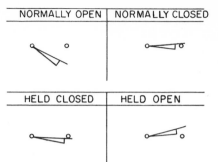

NORMALLY OPEN	NORMALLY CLOSED

HELD CLOSED	HELD OPEN

LIQUID LEVEL		VACUUM & PRESSURE	
NORMALLY OPEN	NORMALLY CLOSED	NORMALLY OPEN	NORMALLY CLOSED

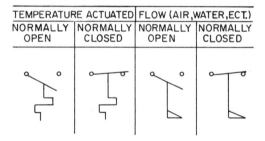

TEMPERATURE ACTUATED		FLOW (AIR,WATER,ECT.)	
NORMALLY OPEN	NORMALLY CLOSED	NORMALLY OPEN	NORMALLY CLOSED

Limit switches, non-spring return (JIC)

MAINTAINED POSITION

SPEED (PLUGGING)		ANTI-PLUG

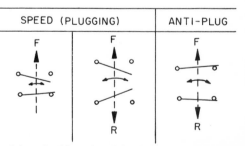

Note—Single-line (one-line) symbols appear at the left, complete symbols at the right, and symbols suitable for both purposes are centered in each column.

Push button switches (JIC)

SINGLE CIRCUIT		DOUBLE CIRCUIT
NORMALLY OPEN	NORMALLY CLOSED	
		○ | ○
○ | ○	○ ⎵ ○	○ ○

TIMER CONTACTS
CONTACT ACTION RETARDED WHEN COIL IS:

ENERGIZED		DE-ENERGIZED	
NORMALLY OPEN	NORMALLY CLOSED	NORMALLY OPEN	NORMALLY CLOSED

TELEPHONE DIAL

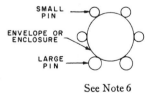

(With auxiliary contact springs)

TERMINALS (FOR ELECTRON TUBES, SEMI-CONDUCTOR DEVICES, ETC.)

Primarily used in application-data terminal diagrams for electron tubes, semiconductor devices, and other devices having terminations of similar type. See also CONNECTOR

Note 6   —Explanatory words and arrows are not a part of the symbol.

Base pin terminals (electron tubes, etc.) ; pin terminals (semiconductor devices, etc.)

See Note 6

The following letter combinations, if shown adjacent to terminal symbols requiring special at-

tention, shall signify the following:

S—Connection to an external shield integral with a device (including metal tube shell, base sleeve or shell; external conductive coating or casing). Not to be used if the external conductive coating serves as one side of a capacitor (as in cathode-ray tubes) and is not designed to function as an electrostatic shield.

IC—Terminal not intended to be used for circuit connection.

IS—Internal shield not depicted in terminal diagram.

Envelope terminals

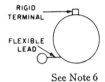

See Note 6

The rigid-terminal symbol is used to indicate customary rigid terminals (caps, rods, rings, etc.) as well as to indicate:

(a) Any metallic envelope or external conductive coating or casing that has a contact area (as in cathode-ray tubes, disc-seal tubes, pencil tubes, etc.)

(b) Mounting flange or stud when it serves as a terminal.

Terminal group orientation

Device with base orientation key

See Note 6

Devices with reference point (such as a boss, colored dot, index pin, index tab, or bayonet pin).

Terminals connected to metallic envelope or enclosure

Two-terminal device with one flexible lead and one rigid terminal connected to a metallic envelope (typical semiconductor diode shown).

Typical octal plug mounted relay

Electronic tube or similar device with 8-terminal keyed (such as octal) base, rigid envelope terminal, and metallic envelope connected to base terminal (typical triode-heptode shown).

Two-terminal device with rigid terminals and reference point located at one of the terminals (typical semiconductor diode shown).

Electronic tube or similar device with keyed (such as octal) base having design capability of 8 pins but with 2 pins omitted, and with 3 rigid envelope terminals (typical disc-seal triode shown).

Three-terminal device with circular arrangement of pin terminals with base orientation determined by gap in pin spacing (typical transistor shown).

Three-terminal device with rigid terminals, one connected to the metallic enclosure, and index pin (typical transistor shown).

Electronic tube or similar device with 9-terminal (such as noval) base utilizing gap in pin spacing to establish base orientation (typical twin triode shown).

Four-terminal device with in-line pin terminals, one connected to metallic envelope, and reference point (typical transistor shown).

Additional notes:

Note A —If the device terminals are in a circular arrangement, the actual angular spacing between the terminals should be approximated on the terminal diagram.

OR

Note B —If the terminals are in an essentially linear arrangement the terminal diagram may show the terminals in either a linear array along one side of the elongated envelope symbol (preferable), or within a maximum angle of 150° around the circular envelope symbol.

Note C —If pins are omitted in an otherwise standard terminal arrangement, do not respace the remaining pins.

Note D —A terminal at the center of the terminal arrangement shall be identified as the CENTER terminal lead or pin.

Five-terminal device with in-line terminal leads, one connected to metallic enclosure and reference point (typical relay shown).

Note E —The typical examples show pin numbering in accordance with standard industry practice, i.e., with the terminals viewed from outside the terminal face of the device.

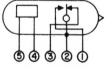

Note—Single-line (one-line) symbols appear at the left, complete symbols at the right, and symbols suitable for both purposes are centered in each column.

THERMAL ELEMENT

(Thermomechanical transducer)

Actuating device

May be either self or externally heated.

Note—Use appropriate number of single-line diagram symbols (see Circuit breaker, for example).

OR

Thermal cutout; flasher

OR

Thermostat

Ambient-temperature-operated device.
Operates on rising temperature.

With break contact

OR

With make contact

OR

With integral heater and transfer contacts

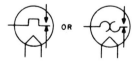

OR

THERMISTOR
RESISTOR, THERMAL

"T" indicates that the primary characteristic of the element within the circle is a function of temperature.

General

With independent integral heater

THERMOCOUPLE

Dissimilar-metals device

Temperature-measuring thermocouple

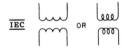

IEC

TRANSFORMER

General

Either winding symbol may be used. Additional windings may be shown or indicated by a note.

IEC   OR

Control transformers

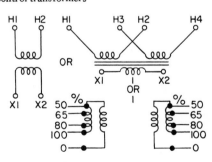

Note—Single-line (one-line) symbols appear at the left, complete symbols at the right, and symbols suitable for both purposes are centered in each column.

2
Classes of Service

Introduction

Relay applications are almost unlimited wherever switching functions are needed in a circuit, system, or product. As a result, relay requirements are highly varied. To meet these diversified requirements, a great variety of styles, types, and sizes of relays have been developed over the years, many of them still identified by the initial class of application. These types are more fully discussed in Sec. 3.

In this section, we have classified broad areas of application in which there are somewhat similar operating and environmental conditions. The description of each application is brief and most rudimentary. It is intended for a user of relays who has had but little experience.

The areas covered are (1) commercial and industrial applications, and (2) military and aerospace applications. As a first step in selecting a relay for an existing or proposed application, an examination of these service classifications should suggest a general type of relay with a history of successful application under given conditions. Further study of Sections 3, 5, and 7 should then provide more specific information leading to the relay best suited to one's needs.

The classifications presented here are discussed in terms of the functional requirements and environments normally encountered.

Commercial and Industrial Applications

2.1 Commercial aircraft

Small private airplanes, medium-size executive aircraft, and the larger planes used by the airlines for commercial passenger and freight service are included in this category.

Relays are used for varied power control and supervisory purposes. Control relays generally are of the contactor or heavy contact load type. They are used as master power switches, motor control switches, or for other heavy-current load switching functions that are remotely controlled by low-current toggle switches located on the instrument panels. Other relay functions are switching of generator or alternator power supplies and their regulation.

Supervisory relays are used to actuate warning lights or audible devices to indicate abnormal conditions, such as power supply failure.

Although not directly related to the airframe, communication and navigation equipment also employ relays. They perform diverse switching functions when actuated manually by the panel function switches. Examples are actuation of the radio transmitter by the "push-to-talk" switch, antenna changeover, and channel selection.

Environmental requirements are quite well understood and defined, largely as the result of the development of military aircraft and their exacting specifications. Such requirements include resistance to ambient temperature variations, pressure variations due to altitude changes, corrosion, shock, and vibration. The extent of these requirements will partially depend on the type of aircraft. Pressures down to 1.3 in. of mercury, equivalent to 70,000 feet of altitude, would adequately cover most commercial jet aircraft, whereas 50,000 feet of altitude will cover commercial piston aircraft. Maximum temperature limits of −65°C and +125°C are realistic for jets, whereas +71°C as an upper limit would serve for piston aircraft. Piston aircraft experience sinusoidal vibration levels of 10 g acceleration over a frequency range of 10 to 55 cycles. Turbo prop or jet aircraft, however, generate higher vibration frequencies. Acceleration levels up to 20 g are encountered near the engines, with an upper frequency limit of 2000 cps. In areas of the plane remote from the engines, 10 g levels at 2000 cps are more realistic. Shock pulses of 15 to 50 g peak and a duration of 11 milliseconds are commonly accepted as required shock resistance capabilities.

Apart from the rather severe environmental requirements of aircraft, it is necessary to consider the reliability of relays consistent with the dependability of all other aircraft equipment and devices. Generous factors of safety should apply in addition to a rugged and simple design. These conditions must be achieved while keeping size and weight at a minimum.

2.2 Air conditioning and heating equipment

The primary use of relays is in the control of compressor motors, fan motors, coolant pump motors, and associated pilot duty functions. Compressor motors generally fall in the range of 1 to 10 hp. Fan and cooling motors vary between $\frac{1}{2}$ and 2 hp. Motor voltages range as high as 480 volts, even for single-phase fan motors as a result of the improvement and cost reduction of the capacitors used to start them. The higher voltages are desirable in industrial and commercial applications since transformer size and cost are reduced.

There are some unique factors to be considered in applying starting relays to hermetic compressor motors. First, the motor ratings may be quite unlike standard NEMA open-frame ratings because of the dependence on a refrigerant for motor cooling. For example, a 4.0-hp compressor motor may have characteristics similar to a normal NEMA 5.0-hp motor. Furthermore, there are wide variations in mechanical classification of refrigeration systems that cause electrical ratings to vary. For three different $1\frac{1}{2}$-ton systems, for example, three different values for the full-load running and locked-rotor currents of the 240-volt compressor motor could be found.

Another important variable is the longer time required for a compressor motor to reach full speed. Relays must be capable of withstanding starting-current conditions for these extended periods. As a general rule, for capacitor-start single-phase motors, potential motor starting relays are used in preference to the current-type starters, although voltage-responsive, current-responsive or shunt and series starters may be substituted. Simply stated, potential type relays pick up at a critical voltage reached at full speed during the starting period. At that point, a set of normally closed contacts open and remove the capacitor from the starting winding. The relay becomes de-energized at a voltage far below its pickup voltage. Current-type starter relays become actuated on inrush current through the main motor winding that is somewhat below the locked-rotor current. A set of normally open contacts connects the starting capacitor to its winding. Release of the relay is on a coil current slightly above full-load running current. These relays are used on compressor units from $\frac{1}{2}$- to $7\frac{1}{2}$-ton capacities.

Standards that apply for air conditioning and heating equipment are under the cognizance of the Underwriters Laboratories or Canadian Standards Association and are covered under Industrial Control Equipment and Temperature Indicating and Regulating Equipment.

Environmental requirements to be met include ambient temperatures as high as 65°C, high relative humidity in many applications, and salty atmospheres in coastal installations.

Ruggedness of relay design is called for since weight and size are not important factors. High volume relay usage allows well controlled mass production principles to be used.

2.3 Household electrical appliances

The broad applications here include clothes washers, dryers, dehumidifiers, freezers, ranges, and a host of similar electrical appliances found in the home or small commercial establishments.

The range of relay contact loads generally varies from 240-volt, 6000-watt heater loads or 1.0-hp motors down to the minimal loads of actuator solenoids, other relay coils, and pilot lamps.

Life expectancy in the range of 5 to 10 years is accepted. In the average application, with low-duty cycle, this could represent 200,000 operations under rated load conditions.

Most appliance manufacturers will desire Underwriters Laboratory approval of relays and other components, and possibly that of the Canadian Standards Association as well. To meet such qualifications will require adherence to the recognized standards of insulation, creepage paths, and flame-proof materials.

Ambient temperatures can be expected to be as high as 65°C. High relative humidity is also common.

2.4 Automobiles and trucks

A most important and expanding use of relays is the automotive industry. As more electrically operated components are made available in its products, the need for control relays increases. A few of the well-known relays are the starting relay to actuate the cranking motor, the horn relay, alternator or generator "cut-out" relays, charging voltage and current regulator relays, turn-signal flasher relays, automatic light-dimming control relays, and air conditioning control relays.

Power supply in automobiles is now well established at 12 volts d-c, and this will usually be the voltage for which relay coils must be designed. Life expectancy in terms of relay operations is variable. Some devices, such as headlight relays, demand a life expectancy of 500,000 operations whereas 50,000 to 100,000 operations would be satisfactory for other automotive applications. Voltage regulator relays operating many times per second would have life requirements measured in millions of operations.

Environmental requirements are quite severe and in some respects not too different from those for commercial aircraft. Ambient temperatures can vary from −30°C to +100°C. Within the engine compartment the relays can be exposed to dust, sand, water, salt, and oil. Vibration and shock can definitely be expected. The magnitudes and frequency ranges should be about as severe as those found in piston-propelled aircraft.

2.5 Business machines

A wide assortment of accounting machines and special machines for various business functions are making extensive use of relays. Normal control functions of routing, sequencing, memory, selection, and computing are handled in conjunction with electromechanical devices like typewriters, card readers, and tape and card punchers.

Relay requirements call for miniaturized, multicontact, fast-operate, long-lived characteristics. Some capabilities of controlled time delay are needed. Life expectancies of 50 to 100 million operations (minimum contact load) apply. Operating reliability is a definite requirement since errors in functioning could be costly. Maintenance downtime should be kept at a minimum.

Office environments are not severe. Permanent installations call for essentially no vibration or shock resistant capabilities. Ambient temperature range is quite nominal, in fact, no greater than 0°C to +55°C. Some installations in humid parts of the country would require additional protective finishes on relays and coil impregnation.

2.6 Coin-operated machines

Vending machines, juke boxes, and pinball types of coin-operated amusement devices represent a large and novel use of relays. Some pieces of equipment are relatively simple, with relays performing straightforward control functions. Others involve quite complex programming and sequencing operations. Record playing equipment, for example, generally includes selection circuits with memory circuits capable of selecting from as many as 100 records.

Environmental requirements are not severe since most installations are within heated public rooms. Vending equipment may be semiexposed to weather, as on subway platforms. Entertainment equipment does receive considerable handling and frequent moving by proprietors who place the devices in premises not owned by them. This handling, and in some cases abuse by patrons, of the equipment does call for shockproof designs and assembly.

Since the pinball machine industry is highly competitive, equipment must be manufactured at minimum cost. Strong emphasis has been placed in turn on minimum-cost relays. It thus has been a problem to provide full relay reliability and optimum life expectancy. Maintenance of equipment is quite a cost factor for the operators.

2.7 Telephone systems

The telephone industry is without question the fountainhead of relay development and usage. From this initial relay application field, extending back more than 70 years, has come the widespread usage seen today in a host of varied industries. This is a natural evolution since practically all the basic control functions are found within a telephone switching system.

The basic relay developed to handle these functions is comprised of an elongated coil mounted on an L-shaped magnetic member called a bracket or heelpiece. At the heelpiece end opposite the coil mounting, an armature is pivoted. An extension of the armature actuates a group of leaf-type springs carrying precious-metal contacts assembled in a pileup on the long arm of the heelpiece. Movement of the armature closes or opens the contacts. This basic design is popularly known as a "telephone type" relay. Its use in the telephone field is based on 40 to 50 years of satisfactory service, and it is being widely applied elsewhere. Stamina, complete versatility of operating characteristics, a large choice of contact arrangements, and good built-in reliability have led to its general acceptance.

Besides the basic relay, special stepping switch type relays are employed for line selection purposes. One is a unidirectional stepping relay with wiper-type contacts traversing a semicircular row of contacts. Another general type of stepping switch as used in a Strowger step-by-step system is comprised of two-motion switches with wipers moving in two directions — either in and across on a flat plane or up and around in a circular pattern. More complete descriptions of these special relays and stepping switches will be found in Secs. 3 and 4.

Other systems, such as the panel and rotary systems, are also in use. The variations in their relays and selection switches will not be discussed here, but the basic principles and functions are similar.

Environmental requirements for telephone switching equipment are not at all critical. Most of this equipment operates in temperature controlled rooms with efforts made to achieve dust-free conditions. There is some minor vibration introduced through operation of the switches on the mounting racks.

New telephone systems now being introduced represent quite a departure from accepted relay systems. These new systems are generally considered to be electronic because of the great reduction in the number of electromechanical relays used.

Solid state devices perform those memory and routing functions that must be accomplished in minimum time. These include the acceptance of a call, storage of the command, scanning for available lines, directing and releasing the call from storage, and final switching instructions. But actual switching of voice circuits is still accomplished by " hard" contacts and not by transistors.

Reed relays are made in special packages to provide the best fit in a switching matrix. Their switching speeds are about one order of magnitude greater than those for telephone type relays. Contacts that are enclosed in glass capsules in a controlled atmosphere help maintain the required reliability objectives in this high-speed system.

2.8   Telegraph systems

Many requirements of telegraph switching systems are not too dissimilar from those of telephone line switching. They are simplified somewhat because the number of lines to be switched is far less, and the full capabilities of a telephone system are not needed.

Relays used are the "telephone type" as well as unidirectional stepping switches. There is one common relay type found in all telegraph systems that is not seen to any great extent in telephony. This is the polarized line-pulse repeating relay, which is quite sensitive, has little or no contact bounce, and provides high speed of operation. The application requires that the relay faithfully follow current reversals or pulses of direct current in a transmission line corresponding to "mark" and "space" portions of a multi-bit code. Operating rates can be well over 100 pulses per second, calling for relay pickup and dropout times of about one millisecond. The line current pulses driving the relays are generally values several times "just pickup" values. This overdrive produces the stable and fast operate times necessary to avoid distortion or loss in reproducing the line pulses. Relay power operating sensitivities are in the order of 10 milliwatts or less.

The relays are normally adjusted as bistable devices. This is to say that the contacts, usually of a single, Form C contact combination or transfer arrangement, will remain in the position to which they were last actuated when the relay windings were de-energized. Multi-windings of the coil are common. Two equal windings are sometimes used, with one winding for actuation of the contacts in one direction and the other winding for reverse contact actuation. Sometimes a special winding is used to provide an electrical bias that causes the contacts to remain in one position (single side stable) as a normal condition. Proper polarity current through another signal winding then produces contact actuation similar to the standard relay type operation.

These pulse-repeating relays experience a high duty cycle of operation and hence must have life expectancies measured in hundreds of millions of operations.

2.9   Radio and microwave systems

Communication systems employing conventional radio or microwaves as transmission media are broad in scope and can vary from very simple systems to the most complex ones. An example of a simple radio system is the small mobile system used by police and fire departments and taxi cabs. Here the relays are usually only those actuated by the push-to-talk switch. Their function is to mute the receiver, energize the transmitter, and switch the antenna from "receive" to "send."

Complex microwave systems may handle complete voice transmission with telemetry capabilities for a widespread pipeline network. The switching of channels entails needs not unlike telephone line switching.

Environmental requirements are a factor in many of these systems. Mobile equipment must take into consideration wide ambient temperature ranges, vibration, shock, and protection against weather in much the same way as has been discussed for automotive equipment. Microwave transmission installations may include unattended relaying stations or switching points that do not afford the same control of ambient conditions as that found in central offices.

2.10   Computer input-output devices

Basic computation and storage of data in digital computers can best be handled by solid-state switching devices like transistors. The ever-increasing speed requirements (now measured in billionths of a second) cannot be met by electromagnetic relays. Relays, however, are used to good advantages in the input and output accessories. They are employed not only because of less critical time restrictions, but also because they can handle the higher work loads of readout devices more effectively.

Due to the heavy duty cycle, a maximum life expectancy and utmost reliability are needed. Speed of operation is important, if not critical. Relays must have power sensitivities in the area of 100 milliwatts so that their over-all power consumption will not be excessive and they will be capable of being driven by transistors.

2.11   Electric power control

Although relays are used in the control of low and high voltage power circuits, their predominant and most important application is in supervisory equipment. The status of line breakers and other switches at remote, unattended substations is observed by means of coded pulse signals transmitted over telephone lines. Relays are used as pulse generators, coders, encoders, and in the output functions of energizing actuating coils and supervisory lamps.

The coded pulse function requires relays that can be adjusted to given time delays for both pickup and dropout. Furthermore, there should be little change in these characteristics over the life span. Although duty cycles vary widely, an average life expectancy of 50 to 100 million operations is desirable. Certain relays must be capable of continuous energization for long periods of time throughout equipment life.

Environmental requirements need not receive special consideration other than the ambient temperature of the control cabinet, which is in the order of 40 to 55°C.

2.12   Electronic data processing

Almost any form of process control falls within this vast field of application. Generally such control consists of the gathering or collection of input data from transducers or sensors, followed by a reduction of the electrical data to a usable form, such as visual displays, charts, or printed records. With this data at hand, decisions can be made and control operations performed. In some respects process control represents a loop that continually functions in amassing data, making analyses, and issuing instructions. This is particularly true of systems using process control computers. In terms of their descriptive functions, system devices include scanners, analog-to-digital converters, add-and-subtract counters, selection units, shift registers, storage units, and a host of logic units.

Relays are appropriately used in these areas and can usually overcome any unusual switching problems. Contact loads are highly variable. The data gathered may be in the form of very low level signals like those generated by thermocouple sensing elements or strain gages. Such applications require relays that do not develop thermal or noise voltages. Consistency of contact resistance is a requirement. At the other extreme, contact loads can be sizeable if control or corrective functions require that significant work be performed by power contactors or solenoid actuators.

Speed of operation is important. Input scanning or sampling rates are high to provide ready feedback information before processes get out of control. Life expectancy is also a sizeable figure, with 100 to 200 million fault-free operations being typical. A reasonable degree of sensitivity is always a factor to keep power supply costs down.

Environment may or may not be an important factor in relay selection. Some process controls are installed in atmospheres that are definitely detrimental to open relay contacts, such as in steel mills and cement plants or any area containing fine industrial dust or powder, explosive or not.

2.13 Laboratory test instruments

As test instruments develop into more sophisticated devices, they present a growing field for switching devices such as relays. Examples are oscilloscopes, digital-type voltmeters, ohmmeters, ammeters, and recorders of various types. Digital voltmeters may use stepping switches, reed relays, and mercury-wetted contact reed relays, as well as solid-state devices, for switching and countings. Inexpensive industrial type voltmeters also use stepping switches to good advantage.

Reliability and consistency of characteristics are the predominate requirements for instrument applications. Suppression of audible relay or switch noise during operation is another consideration. Environmental considerations are of no consequence.

2.14 Lighting controls

The major relay application in the lighting field is the photoelectric control of mercury-vapor street lamps. A sensitive relay (50 to 200 milliwatts) is operated in series with a light transducer that offers a changing series resistance dependent on light intensity. Relays usually have a pair of normally closed contacts that open the lamp circuit in the presence of daylight.

The contact load is up to 15 amperes (1800 va) with surges as high as 20 (or more) times rated current. Power factor of the lamps with the ballast is assumed to be 50 per cent. Life expectancy based on one operation per day and 15 years life is up to 6000 operations.

Environmental conditions include a moderate 120-cps vibration, ambient temperature range from −40 to +65°C, and relative humidity from 0 to 100 per cent.

Special precautions must be taken to protect the relays and other circuit equipment from switching transients, lightning strokes, and lightning-induced voltage surges.

2.15 Machine tool control

Basic control functions in machine tools make use of general purpose a-c relays. Such relays usually are actuated by push button or limit switches. Their contacts may handle solenoid-operated valves, heavier motor starting relays, and signal lights. The source voltage is generally 115 volts a-c taken from taps on a control trans-

former operating from a 220- or 440-volt power source. Such relays usually have to meet Underwriters Laboratories' 300-volt or 600-volt standards.

Numerical control is a blossoming field for relays. Contour milling or hole-positioning operations are programmed from data carried on punched tape. Signals from the tape reader feed into machine directors, memory units, and other logic elements to provide the necessary two- to five-axis control of the positioning servo motors. Drilling machines, milling machines, turret lathes, and engine lathes are readily controlled by this automated means, as well as automatic contour inspection machines.

Ability to handle low-level signals, average sensitivity, high speed of operation, and high switching reliability are the relay requirements in numerical control systems.

Consideration must be given to the environments associated with machine tools. Some vibration is generally transmitted to the control cabinet from the operating machines and nearby equipment. There is also the problem of the tool coolant fluids' being sprayed about as well as of the presence of dry or oil-soaked metallic chips. Normally, the equipment manufacturer provides the necessary protection for control components, but environmental conditions remain a factor in relay selection and design.

2.16 Production test equipment

Adoption of automatic test equipment is a growing field, keeping pace with automated manufacturing. Such equipment includes component testers, cable testers, and complete, complex circuit testing equipment.

Testing of electrical/electronic components usually consists of a sequential checking of parameters to pre-set limits. The readout may be simply on an accept-reject basis. Digital instruments may also be employed, and readout can be on punched cards, thereby providing an individual record.

Cable testers and circuit testers are sequential devices that primarily check continuity, insulation resistance, and dielectric withstanding voltages.

Relay requirements for production test equipment are rigid. Basically the tester must have extreme reliability and accuracy if it is to make quality parameter checks on other units. Attention must be given to the consistency of operating characteristics and stability throughout the expected life of the relay. Required properties of insulation resistance and dielectric withstanding voltage are above normal. Contact resistance, in many cases, must be low and constant. As with most production tools, the over-all design of test equipment, including its relays, must possess stamina and insure operation with a minimum of maintenance.

2.17 Street traffic control

Consistent users of relays have been the manufacturers of street and highway traffic control equipment, which must be capable of handling a wide variety of traffic problems. Installations may be the simple flashing light at an isolated intersection or a complex system that handles heavy pedestrian and automobile traffic and perhaps rail traffic as well. Signals for all three types of traffic must be interrelated to provide optimum traffic flow and safety.

Relays that switch the signal lights and other displays operate directly or indirectly from pulses generated by special electromechanical timers. Contact loads are coils of other relays, stepping switch solenoids, or signal lamps. The latter are generally about 70-watt incandescent types. Speed of operation is not a factor, nor are there any special power sensitivity requirements. The basic need is a relay design possessing rugged contacts, heavy duty armature bearings, and other features yielding trouble-free long life.

There are no particularly rigorous environmental conditions involved except temperature. The gasketed enclosures offer quite adequate protection against the elements. Ambient temperatures encountered range from −30°C to +65°C. Vibration and shock problems are minor.

Military Applications

Many military applications are similar to those listed for commercial and industrial applications. However, military equipment must be designed to meet more stringent environmental conditions with the result that relays have to be modified to provide added environmental protection. Requirements are always well defined and specified in government specifications. See Sec. 9 for more information on military relay specifications.

Modified commercial relays will not satisfy all military requirements. There are certain space and missile applications that require special relay designs used only by the military.

2.18 Military aircraft

The light and heavy duty control relays associated with the military airframe are the responsibility of the aircraft manufacturer. Requirements for the relays are covered to a great extent by MIL-R-6106.

Modern military aircraft require the utmost in shock and vibration resistance. Vibration frequency and levels of acceleration are generally 10 g up to 2000 Hz although requirements are now being encountered at 20 g to 2000 Hz and occasionally as high as 30 g to 3000 Hz. Use of jet engines has brought on new vibration testing techniques and limits, such as random vibration and acoustical noise tests. Ambient temperature environments are higher, with +125°C being used generally as the upper limit.

Relays designed for these requirements are strictly unique military designs. Most have balanced armatures to resist shock and are hermetically sealed. High-temperature inorganic insulating materials or organic materials with minimum outgassing characteristics are employed. It is obvious that for these applications modified telephone or general purpose clapper type relays could not be used.

Military airborne navigation equipment is designed and built by contractors independent of the airframe manufacturers. For this equipment, MIL-R-5757 is increasingly being specified. Environmental requirements are essentially the same, and the relays used will be of of the same designs as for airframe applications. Since power requirements are less, a great many crystal can and multipole-type relays in small, round, hermetically sealed cans are in evidence.

For ground support equipment, environmental requirements are relaxed somewhat. Vibration and shock requirements are still applicable but with frequencies below 500 Hz and acceleration levels below 10 g. In many specifications, these are nonoperating requirements intended to simulate conditions met in transporting the equipment by military air and ground carriers. Field installations are often off beaten paths.

2.19 Ground defense systems

The various sentinel bases and missile launching sites such as Nike-Hercules bases, the DEW line, the SAGE system, and BEMEWS, to name a few, comprise complex radar detection equipment linked together by a vast communications network. Since these are permanent, manned, and well-controlled installations located in our northern hemisphere, military environmental specifications are less rigid.

Relays used in these installations differ little from those found in commercial communications or general electronic equipment. However, many relays are specified for convenience of logistics in accordance with MIL-R-5757 or MIL-R-6106.

2.20 Missiles and aerospace

This phase of the government program has been receiving the most attention and study in recent years. Certainly the requirements for relays are the most exacting and rigid. Unmanned missiles and spacecraft depend upon a most complex system of control and telemetry for their guidance and the execution of the mission. Relays play a most important part as switching devices in these circuits.

The key requirement for relays as well as other components is reliability, or surety of proper operation. With the value of a missile or spacecraft measured in millions of dollars and in human lives, and with the tremendous importance attached to a successful flight, the emphasis placed on reliability is readily understood. To obtain reliable military designs, tremendous effort, time and expense are expended on the control of manufacture, and elaborate test programs are set up to prove a given maximum failure rate on a statistical basis.

Specification MIL-R-39016 deals directly with established-reliability relays of the MIL-R-5757 type. In addition, work is underway to provide capability for testing to the reliability requirements that will be established in specification MIL-R-6106. Further information on these subjects will be found in Secs. 6 and 9.

Environmental requirements for missiles and spacecraft are severe. A full sinusoidal vibration limit of 30 g and 3000 Hz applies as well as random vibration and high acoustical noise levels. The normally specified conditions of up to 100 per cent humidity, thermal shock, high and low temperature operation, and salt spray also exist. An additional consideration is the ability of the relays to operate in a vacuum. Such would

be the case if leakage developed in a hermetically sealed enclosure installed outside of a pressurized compartment of the vehicle. One can also look forward to the use of materials that will withstand nuclear radiation and high energy particles. With the development of nuclear propulsion units for spacecraft, the need for such materials will be even greater.

The crystal can series of relays have been those most extensively used in missiles and spacecraft. Their small size and minimum weight are important advantages, besides their being hermetically sealed.

Ground support equipment requires the same degree of reliability as the components in the airborne gear, but the severe limitations of size, weight, and environmental resistance do not apply.

2.21 Naval shipboard

Modern naval craft merit attention as another singular military application. The gigantic aircraft carrier and nuclear propelled submarines include many control systems. Auxiliary relays are to be found in these electrical, hydraulic, and pneumatic systems as well as in supervisory applications where, through visual and audible signals, the status of operations is continually monitored.

As with other military applications, protection against severe environments must be emphasized. Such requirements and others can be found in MIL-R-19523 (Ships) dealing with relays for shipboard application. Environments of the most importance are salt-laden atmospheres and the high impact shock that may be encountered. Shock tests with impact energies as high as 2000 ft-lb are common. Vibration is present, also, although the magnitude and frequency will not be as great as found in airborne applications.

Relay types needed for shipboard use must employ a maximum of ruggedness to withstand the severe shock conditions without damage. They must be long-lived and provide adequate protection against corrosion, especially that produced by salt spray.

3
Relay Classifications

Introduction

This section is intended to assist the relay user locate the style of relay best suited to his requirements and to obtain information on the characteristics, functions, and purpose of the relay selected.

To accomplish this purpose, all styles of relays in general use have been listed in alphabetical order, and a functional description has been provided for each of them, along with a summary of typical applications. Admittedly, many relays have characteristics that are adaptable to a wide variety of applications. It should also be recognized that any one relay may be known by a variety of names.

For added relay information to assist in the formulation of specifications, the reader should refer to other sections of this handbook, with the final relay specification to be agreed upon between the user and the relay manufacturer.

3.1 Relay list (indicating preferred names)

The following is a listing of relay names, types, or styles intended to cover all those likely to be encountered. In many cases, several different names or terms are used to identify the same relay. In such instances, the preferred name is given as the main entry, and the nonpreferred names are cross-referenced to this entry. It must also be understood that there is a broad overlapping in basic styles resulting from modifications to achieve special purpose types.

Antenna switching relays
Armature type relays

Balanced armature relays
Bimetal relays
   Flasher relays

Clapper type relays
   General purpose relays
Coaxial relays
Contactor relays *(see* Solenoid actuated relays)
Crossbar switches
Crystal can relays
   Microminiature relays
Current sensing relays
   Sensing relays

Dashpot time delay relays
Delay slug relays
Differential relays
Dry circuit relays *(see* Low level relays)
Dry reed relays *(see* Reed relays)
Dual coil relays

Electrical reset relays *(see* Mechanical latching
   relays and Magnetic latching relays)
Electromagnetic relays
Electrostatic relays
Electrostrictive relays

Ferreed relays *(see* Reed relays)
Flasher relays *(see* Bimetal relays)
Frequency sensitive relays *(see* Resonant reed
   relays)

General-purpose relays *(see* Clapper type
   relay)

Heavy load relays *(see* Power relays)
Hermetically sealed relays *(see* Paragraph 3-4)
High speed relays

High voltage relays
Hot wire relays

Impulse type relays
Instrument relays *(see* Meter type relays and
    Moving coil relays)
Interlock relays *(see* Mechanical latching re-
    lays and Magnetic latching relays)

Latching relays *(see* Mechanical latching relays
    and Magnetic latching relays)
Linear expansion relays
Locking relays *(see* Mechanical latching relays
    and Magnetic latching relays)
Low level relays
   Dry circuit relays

Magnetic latching relays
   Electrical reset relays
   Interlock relays
   Latching relays
   Locking relays
   Memory relays
Magnetostrictive relays
Mechanical latching relays
   Electrical reset relays
   Interlock relays
   Latching relays
   Locking relays
Medium load relays
Memory relays *(see* Magnetic latching relays)
Mercury plunger relays
   Plunger (solenoid) relays
Mercury plunger time-delay relays
Mercury-wetted contact relays *(see* Reed
   relays)
Meter type relays
   Instrument relays
Microminiature relays *(see* Crystal can, Mil
   Spec and Rotary relays)
Mil Spec. relays
   Microminiature relays
Motor-driven relays
Motor-driven steppers
Motor-starting relays
Moving coil relays
   Instrument relays

Plug-in relays *(see* Mounting methods)
Plunger (solenoid) relays *(see* Solenoid actu-
   ated relays and Mercury plunger relays)
Polarized relays
   Telegraph relays
Power relays
   Heavy load relays

Printed circuit mounting relays *(see* Paragraphs 3.5 and 3.6)

R.F. switching relays.
Radiation resistant relays
Ratchet relays
   Sequential relays
Reed relays
   Dry reed
   Ferreed
   Mercury-wetted contact
Resonant reed relays
   Frequency sensitive relays
Rotary relays
   Microminiature relays

Sensing relays *(see* Current sensing and Volt-
   age sensing relays)
Sensitive relays
Sequential relays *(see* Ratchet relays, Stepping
   relays, Stepping switches)
Slave relays
Snap-action contact relays
Solenoid actuated relays
   Contactor relays
   Plunger (solenoid) relays
Stepping relays
   Sequential relays
Stepping switches (commercial)
   Sequential relays
Stepping switches (telephone type)
Strowger two-motion switches

Telegraph relays *(see* Polarized relays)
Telephone type relays
Thermal relays
Thermal time-delay relays
Time-delay relays

Vacuum relays
Voltage sensing relays
   Sensing relays

Wire spring relays

3.2   Relay descriptions

Antenna switching relays — These relays are
designed for switching radio frequency antenna
currents with minimum losses. The dielectric
materials used are selected for their insulating
qualities and low losses at frequencies up to 150
MHz (megacycles) or more. Particular attention
is given to the handling of the high voltages
present in the antenna circuits of transmitters.
The designs feature large contact gaps, long di-

electric leakage paths, and low capacitance between switching elements and other parts.

Antenna relays are used to switch an antenna between radio transmitters and receivers and to switch radio equipment from one antenna to another. The relays frequently have auxiliary contacts designed to perform additional switching functions in the radio equipment. Coaxial relays are often used as antenna switching relays. (*See* Coaxial relays and R.F. switching relays.)

Armature type relays — Broadly speaking, armature type relays cover the entire class of electromechanical relays that have a mechanical moving element which in turn either carries or actuates contacts. In common usage, however, armature relays are usually considered to be clapper type relays and are described thereunder.

Auxiliary relays — See Slave relays.

Balanced armature relays — Relays having armatures pivoted at the centers of their mass are thus balanced or in equilibrium with respect to both static and dynamic external forces. This design feature enables these relays to withstand vibration and shock to varying degrees, and they have become especially important as the use of airborne equipment has increased. This feature is also important if extremely sensitive relays are needed where even static forces on the armature could adversely affect their operation. Balanced armature relays are manufactured in a great variety of sizes from the smallest crystal can relays to relays for shipboard weighing several pounds.

Bimetal relays — These relays operate on the principle of the conversion of electrical power to heat and contact actuation by the differential thermal expansion of metals. If two metal strips with different coefficients of thermal expansion are laminated or bonded together (bimetal) with one end of the member anchored in position, the application of heat will cause the free end to deflect in the direction opposite the metal with the greater coefficient of expansion. However, this bimetal responds to *any* change in temperature no matter whether the change results from heat generated by adjacent components or equipment or from current through the heater. For many applications, therefore, it is necessary to offset the undesired deflection caused by ambient temperature variations since this motion affects the operating time. Compensation normally is accomplished by using a second bimetal with similar expansion characteristics so that both members maintain their relative position when the ambient is varied.

Bimetal relays are made in a great variety of sizes, shapes, and mechanical configurations. In their simplest form, they can be manufactured very inexpensively since they require only a bimetal strip, a heating element, and contacts. In this form, however, their application is limited to those loads adaptable to relatively slow moving contacts, where the operating power is not too critical and where ambient temperatures do not vary enough to affect operation. In contrast, some bimetal relays can be quite sophisticated devices, particularly when used as time relay units (*see* Thermal time delay relay). They embody ambient temperature compensation, close timing tolerance, instantaneous reset, snap-action contacts, and other important features. One form of bimetal relay is the self-interrupting type used for flasher applications. (*See also* Hot wire relays, Linear expansion relays, Thermal relays.)

Clapper type relays — This name applies to the large family of electromagnetic relays having armatures pivoted or hinged to a fixed part of the relay, usually, but not always, the frame or heelpiece. Although this is a broad classification, it nevertheless distinguishes this type of relay from the plunger type relay, bimetal relay, meter relay, and others having a totally different basic operating mechanism. This classification becomes a bit hazy when one considers some types of balanced armature relays, reed relays, and other borderline types. These latter relays are so well established under more descriptive names, however, that little or no confusion should result. Figure 3-1 illustrates a typical clapper type actuating mechanism.

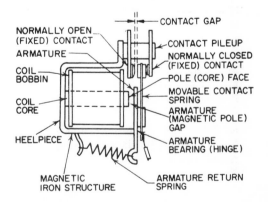

Fig. 3-1. Typical clapper type relay actuating mechanism

Coaxial relays — Like antenna switching relays, coaxial relays are designed for switching high frequency current with minimum losses. The name is derived from the fact that these relays are made for use with coaxial cables and for switching the types of loads coaxial cables transmit. Probably the most important feature of the coaxial relay, aside from its ability to carry the necessary load, is its voltage standing wave ratio (VSWR). If the characteristic impedance of the relay exactly matches that of its mating coaxial cable, the standing wave ratio is 1 to 1. Although this ideal ratio is seldom if ever reached, standing wave ratios of 1.02 to 1, or better, are common. This ratio varies and tends to get worse as the frequency increases, although it does not necessarily follow a straight line relationship. The contact mechanisms of coaxial relays are enclosed in a metal chamber with the dimensions chosen so as to form a cavity that will match the characteristic impedance of the coaxial cable connected to it as nearly as possible.

Coaxial relays are built in sizes ranging from relatively small units for handling 1 kw or less at frequencies of 500 MHz or less to fairly large vacuum units that handle quite large loads at extremely high voltages and frequencies. Probably the most common application of coaxial relays is to switch microwave antennas from transmitters to receivers. They are also used for switching from antenna to antenna in multiple antenna systems covering several frequency ranges. Television installations sometimes require coaxial relays for switching purposes.

Crossbar switches — Crossbar switches are multiple-contact devices for making grid or matrix connections, primarily for use in the telephone and communications industry but also in industrial control systems (*see* Fig. 3-2). The basic operating principles of the few different types are the same. They consist of a vertical row of electromagnets (usually in multiples of 10) mounted at right angles to a second horizontal row (also usually in multiples of 10). The vertical magnets are the selector magnets and the horizontal magnets are the hold magnets. Each pair of vertical magnets actuates an armature that rotates a horizontal bar extending the width of the matrix. Behind these bars are 100 sets of contacts. At each two sets of contacts, an actuating finger extends from the horizontal bar. Rotation of the horizontal bar causes the finger to select one of the two sets of contacts for actuation. Thus when a vertical coil is energized, a bar is caused to rotate and the fingers select 10 sets of contacts, any one of which may then be

FIG. 3-2. TYPICAL CROSSBAR SWITCH ARRANGEMENT

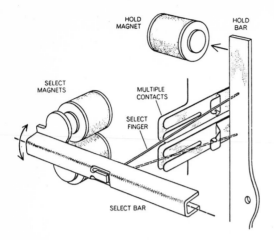

FIG. 3-3. CROSSBAR SWITCH OPERATING PRINCIPLE
The motion of the hold bar closes the contact only when the "select finger" has been placed in either of two positions by the movement of the select bar.

closed by action of the horizontal bar. Then when a hold magnet is energized, it moves a vertical bar that in turn moves the fingers horizontally and causes the contacts at the point where the vertical and horizontal bars intersect to close. Illustration of this operation is shown in Fig. 3-3. This mechanism allows 10 sets of connections to be made at one time per matrix. Other types of crossbar switches using ferreeds have been designed, but their cost is substantially greater than the type just described, and their usage is thus much more limited.

The term *crossbar switch* is sometimes applied to any grid or matrix array of switches that can select a common connection on the X and Y axis. For example, on some of the large radar installations a crossbar coaxial switch array is used for switching between antennas or segments of antennas.

Crystal can relay — This relay derives its name from the size of the enclosure that housed it in its early form. The great need for small, light, high performance relays for use in the aerospace program fostered this design. Its original size was approximately $3/8$ x $3/4$ x $7/8$ in. The enclosure was actually the same as that used to house the quartz crystals that are the frequency control element of an electronic oscillator. Very soon, however, relay manufacturers started modifying the size of the can to accommodate different features *(see Fig. 3-4)*. Virtually all these relays are hermetically sealed and usually have balanced

armatures for resistance to vibration and shock. Terminals are brought out through insulating beads (glass or ceramic) and provide for solder or plug-in connections. The majority of these relays have their terminals placed on 0.2-in. centers for insertion in printed circuit boards.

By far the largest number of the crystal can relays have two form C contact combinations. Load capacity of the contacts varies considerably, but for the most part the loads are relatively light. These relays are furnished in both conventional or on-off styles and polarized magnetic latch. They are made in both single-coil and two-coil designs. Coil power required varies from perhaps 75 to 500 milliwatts or more.

Since the introduction of the crystal can relay, the half-size and the one-sixth size were developed. Their characteristics are similar to the full-size crystal can relay. Although crystal can relays were originally designed for aerospace applications, their small size has also made them appealing for industrial and commercial use. A still newer and smaller design is the TO-5, housed in a transistor case. It includes an electromechanical relay and may include a built-in integrated circuit driver.

Current sensing relays — These relays are designed to function whenever a predetermined value of coil current is reached or exceeded. The differential between specified pickup (must operate) and nonpickup (must not operate) may have to be rather closely controlled. The same may also be true for specified dropout (must release) and hold (nondropout, must not release) where such characteristics apply. Generally such relays are exposed to relatively slow changing values of coil current (often referred to as "sliding current") and must be capable of positive and quick transfer once the operate value of

FIG. 3-4. TYPICAL CRYSTAL CAN RELAY

current is reached. Unless some snap action is provided by the contact actuator system or motor structure, the relay contacts would creep open in an indefinite manner, making for poor load switching and poor consistency of the operate point as contacts wear.

In the case of Form C contact combinations, it may be mandatory that once normally closed contacts open, closure of the open contacts must follow immediately. But even with snap-action transfer, such relays usually carry reduced contact load ratings as compared to units operated from suddenly applied voltage or current. Also, the relay's ability to withstand shock or vibration is impaired when the operate value is being approached, especially in the very near operate region.

Thermal relays are also employed as current sensing relays. These units respond to the heating effect, rather than to the electromagnetic effect, of their energizing currents.

Dashpot time-delay relay — Time delays for relays are achieved in a variety of ways and are described under several different headings in this chapter. Dashpot time-delays utilize pneumatic or hydraulic methods of operation. One common method is simply to connect the armature or plunger to a dashpot. The latter usually consists of a cylinder with close-fitting piston and an adjustable orifice that allows air to leak into or out of the cylinder at a controlled rate. The relatively slow transfer of the air volume regulates the piston movement, which in turn controls the movement of the relay armature, thus

producing a time delay when the relay is energized or de-energized. On the return stroke, a check valve allows the cylinder to fill or empty quickly, thus resetting the relay in a minimum of time.

Yet another form of pneumatic time delay employs a flexible bellows in the delay mechanism. The range of accurate time delays obtainable is quite broad, with 0.2 to 45 seconds being a typical range.

Other modifications of the dashpot principle are used. One device is a modified clapper-type relay using a movable magnetic core. The core is placed inside a tube filled with a liquid of selected viscosity and is supported endwise between two helical springs. When the surrounding coil is energized, the core moves toward the armature against the spring pressure, and when the flux path is sufficiently short, the armature will close. Variable time delays can be produced by using liquids of different viscosities and by varying the clearance or orifice formed between the magnetic core and the tube. This principle is also used on some makes of circuit breakers.

Another dashpot time delay relay combines the principle of the movable core with a dashpot using a cylinder and piston and adjustable air orifice. This device is unique in that the cylinder is made of accurately ground glass and uses a carbon piston held to very close tolerances. No lubrication is required, thus eliminating variances caused by the changes in viscosity *(see* Fig. 3-5).

Most dashpot relays operate on direct or rectified alternating current. A few versions operate directly on a-c.

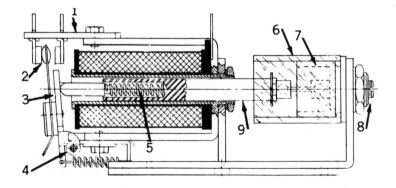

FIG. 3-5. ONE VERSION OF PNEUMATIC-TYPE DASHPOT TIME-DELAY RELAY
Elements: (1) Terminal board; (2) contacts; (3) armature; (4) pin type armature hinge; (5) compression spring (compresses when solenoid pulls out dashpot piston); (6) glass air dashpot cylinder; (7) graphite piston; (8) timing adjustment screw; (9) solenoid plunger.

Delay slug relays — A time delay can be produced on d-c relays by placing one or more shorted turns around the magnetic circuit (usually the core) so as to produce a counter mmf which retards the buildup of the operating flux, and upon de-energization, provides an mmf to retard the collapse of the flux. This shorted turn, or turns, is called a slug. Usually it consists of a copper collar on the core of the relay. In some designs, a copper sleeve is used over the full length of the core, and the coil is wound on the sleeve.

In order to produce a delay of any consequence, it is necessary to use a slug of considerable cross section, often equal to or larger than that of the coil itself. Although this method of time delay is applicable on any d-c relay with sufficient space to accommodate the slug, it is most commonly used on telephone-type relays, which have comparatively long coils and can thus more easily accommodate the slug. A copper slug on the armature end of the coil core causes the relay to be slow on both pickup and dropout, whereas a slug on the heelpiece end of the coil core has little effect upon pickup but does delay dropout. A copper sleeve the full length of the coil core makes the relay a little slow on pickup and delays it considerably on dropout.

The principle of operation of the slug is as follows:

When the relay coil is de-energized, the flux build up that pass through the slug and by self-inductance produce an mmf that opposes the coil mmf. This opposing mmf delays the buildup of the magnetic field in the air gap to a strength that will cause the armature to close. The time delay on dropout occurs in the opposite manner.

When the relay coil is de-energized, the field starts to collapse, thus inducing a current in the slug that provides an mmf oriented so as to sustain the magnetic field and thus delay the dropout.

Pickup delays up to 120 milliseconds and dropout delays up to 500 milliseconds can be achieved by the use of slugs. However, there are many other factors that affect the time delays produced by slugs, such as coil power, armature gap, heel gap, residual pin position, force required to move and close contacts, and the like. Consequently, it is impossible to predict that a given slug will produce a given time delay. All factors must be considered and sometimes it is necessary to use "cut and try" methods to produce the desired results.

Differential relays — In a broad sense, a differential relay is one having two or more windings that for various combinations of ampere-turns produce a net magnetic flux to determine the switching action. Differential relays can be separated into three different types: (1) conventional, (2) polarized-center off, (3) polarized-latching, and polarized monostable (i.e., side stable).

(1) *Conventional:* These are nonpolarized and may have two or more coils so arranged that the relay operates on the algebraic sum of the input currents regardless of net polarity.

(2) *Polarized-center off:* These may have two or more coils so arranged that the relay operates on the algebraic sum of the inputs but the direction of operation will be determined by the polarity of the net input.

(3) *Polarized-latching:* Operation from either bistable position is dependent upon the magnitude and polarity of the algebraic sum of the inputs.

(4) *Polarized monostable:* Similar to (1) above except polarity sensitive.

Simple differential operation involving two coils may use bistable windings on a common core for complete symmetry of operation or for identical coil effectiveness in certain applications.

Dry reed relays — These relays are a form of reed relay (*see* Reed relay). The term "dry" distinguishes this type from a mercury-wetted contact reed relay, which is also described under Reed relays. Also see Sec. 11.

Dual coil relays — Relays referred to by this term are relays having two coils, one on each leg of a U-shaped magnetic core. The term does not apply to the numerous telephone-type or polarized relays that use two coils on a single (straight) core. The size, shape, and variety of dual coil relays is almost infinite and used for a variety of reasons such as improvement in efficiency or simplification of manufacture.

Two coils usually are used in a U-shaped core. A U-shaped core can be quite efficient and is often used on sensitive relays with armatures that bridge the two pole faces. These pole faces can be made relatively large to overcome the effects of the additional air gap between poles and armature. This construction aids good armature bearing design since the bearing region is not utilized for a magnetic path, which can create high bearing load forces.

Dual coils are often used on polarized relays to establish the electromagnetic field in relation to the permanent magnetic paths. Many of the relays described in other parts of this chapter are dual coil relays.

Electromagnetic relays — This is the term applied to the original relays (dating back to the middle of the last century) that used electromagnets to provide mechanical motion to an armature and thus provide contact transfer. Today, they are used in almost every conceivable type of electrical equipment or system where remote or automatic circuit control is desired.

Electrostatic relays — Adjacent electrodes given an electric charge develop an opposing or an attractive force between them, depending upon polarities of the two charges. This force may be mechanically coupled to operate relay contacts. Such a device is in effect a capacitor with moving plates that transfer the contacts when voltage is applied and releases them when voltage is removed. A relay designed on these principles has characteristics similar to the electrostrictive relay but differs from it in that it responds to the root-mean-square value of the applied voltage and works on either alternating or direct current. (The electrostrictive relay works only on d-c.) Low-voltage operation is impractical; high-voltage operation is limited only by insulation breakdown and safety consideration. Low-loss insulation is used for operation in the megaHertz frequency range.

Electrostrictive relays — A dielectric body, especially when composed of piezoelectric or ferroelectric materials, changes its dimensions when placed in an electric field. The motion produced by this electrostrictive effect may be mechanically coupled to operate relay contacts. The resulting relay is in effect a capacitor that transfers the contacts when charged and releases them when discharged.

Several features follow from the electrostrictive operating principle. Operating power may be extremely low, only enough to charge the capacitor and support its leakage (resistance may be many megohms). Once operated, the relay will remain closed until the charge leaks off. Leakage can be accelerated by connecting an external discharging resistor. Short pulses of low energy may be accumulated, or one short high energy pulse may operate the relay. Operation at very low voltage is limited by available materials and mechanical problems. The device is polarized and operates on direct current.

Ferreed relays — The term *ferreed* is used to distinguish a form of reed relay in which dry reed contacts are combined with one or more remanent magnetic members whose state of magnetization can be changed by current pulses in associated coils. For a full description of its operation, *see* Reed relays. Also see Sec. 11.

Frequency sensitive relays — *See* Resonant reed relays.

General purpose relays — This name is given to a wide variety of relays with numerous applications as distinguished from relays that by their design are limited to relatively few applications. General purpose relays are sometimes referred to as clapper type relays. However, this reference is not necessarily accurate and is probably used because the clapper type relay exists in a greater variety of styles than other types and is manufactured in greater volume.

High speed relays — No specific operate time has been established to qualify a relay as being high speed in operation. However, d-c operated relays are available, ranging down to less than a millisecond. From a design standpoint, high-speed characteristics are obtained through use of low moving mass, low travel, low eddy current, and often by the use of polarized magnetic structures.

Operate time is also a function of the energizing circuit. Overdrive (abnormally high coil voltage or current) accelerates relay operation. A low-impedance energizing source also facilitates high-speed relay operation. In the case of polarized latching relays, very high energy coil pulses may be employed since their duration may be limited to the order of milliseconds. High coil voltages may be used with a current-limiting series resistor to improve the rate of coil current build-up (by reducing the L/R of the circuit). It should be borne in mind that coil overdriving or abnormal acceleration of the relay operation may result in increased contact bounce.

For conventional d-c relays, speed of dropout may be largely a function of the relay's magnetic circuit and the extent to which it permits eddy current generation to retard flux decay prior to dropout. Also, higher levels of energization, prior to de-energization, tend to reduce dropout speed slightly.

High speed a-c relays are also available. In spite of the randomness of the point on the sinusoidal voltage curve at which the a-c coil is energized, it is possible to ensure that operation will be effected within less than a half-cycle time duration, regardless of the starting point of energization.

High voltage relays — For relays with very high voltage and current switching capabilities, *see* Vacuum relays. *(See also* R.F. switching relays, Antenna switching relays, and Reed relays.) In general, high voltage relays switch up to 10,000 volts at 1.0 ampere or less a-c and 0.2 ampere or less d-c, or they switch at more conventional levels in circuits operating at a high reference potential. For these ratings, thick high-dielectric-strength insulation and large contact gaps are employed. Coil power requirements are comparatively high, around 5 watts d-c or 25 volt-amperes a-c, with solenoid construction quite common. For the upper voltage limits, ceramic pillar (standoff) insulators and rounded, polished tubular conductors are used to reduce electric stress and corona formation. The usual contact combinations are forms A, B, or C, with double break. Their double-contact equivalents (make and/or break) — known as forms X, Y, and Z, respectively — are often used.

Hot wire relays — This is a nonpreferred term for a form of linear expansion (thermal) relay in which the longitudinal expansion of a wire when heated by current passing through it is utilized to provide motion to open or close contacts. These relays, made in a variety of shapes and sizes, are frequently used as time delay relays since some delay is incurred in heating the wire. They are also used in series circuits where it is desirable to limit the current or to perform a switching function between two specific values of current.

Impulse type relays — Sometimes called flip-flop relays, these are single-coil relays having an armature-driven mechanism that alternately assumes one of two positions as the coil is pulsed. This mechanism transfers a contact system from one position to a second and back to the original position as pulses are received. The characteristics of impulse relays can vary greatly depending upon the complexity of the mechanism. They can be a-c or d-c operated and require a fair amount of power for operation; thus they are usually designed with intermittent duty coils. They are used for a variety of functions but probably their greatest use is in consumer-type remote control systems such as those on TV sets.

Latching relays — *See* Magnetic latching relays and Mechanical latching relays.

Linear expansion relays — This is a type of thermal relay that utilizes the linear expansion of materials to provide mechanical motion for the operation of contacts. One form is the hot wire relay discussed elsewhere in this chapter. Another common type contains a switching mechanism made up of two rigid similar metal members of equal length that expand longitudinally with temperature rise *(see* Fig 3-6). An electrical heater is included in one of two stainless steel members. Ambient temperature changes affect these two members equally, and no contact action results. But when the heater is energized, a simple but precise mechanism multiplies any difference in expansion of these two members to move a contact arm when a given temperature differential above the unheated member is

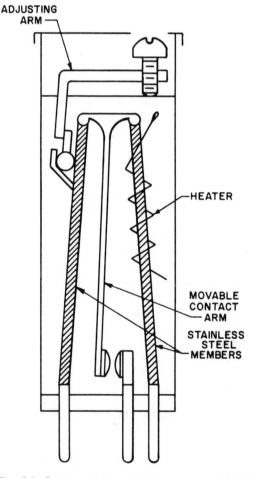

FIG. 3-6. OPERATING PRINCIPLE OF LINEAR EXPANSION THERMAL RELAY

reached. This relay is primarily a time-delay device, but it is also used for current and voltage sensing applications. It is available in both sealed and unsealed versions.

Low level relays — This term is applied to any relay type used to switch dry circuit or low level loads. Low level loads are considered to be loads on the order of 100 millivolts or less and 1 milliampere or less. Gold (or gold alloy) is the most common material used for the mating surfaces of the contacts, although various metals or alloys of the platinum group are also employed. Bifurcated contacts are often used for added reliability in low level switching. Dynamic contact resistance on low level relays is generally checked against a specified permissible voltage drop across the contacts (usually expressed in millivolts).

On the whole, low level relays are considered to be much longer life devices than their more heavily loaded counterparts. Life of a few million to over a billion operations is typical, depending on the load and relay design. The contacts of low level relays should be protected from high current or voltages that might damage the contact surfaces.

Magnetic latching relays — The latching function of armature-type electromagnetic relays may be accomplished by utilizing permanent magnets in conjunction with the normal soft-iron circuit so that the permanent magnet flux will hold the armature in the operated condition after the electromagnetic coil energy has been removed. The magnetic circuit is so configured that the armature may be reset by creating an electromagnetic field of opposite direction to that established by the permanent magnet. This may be done (1) by applying voltage of proper polarity to a separate reset coil, (2) by employing the same coil for both latch and reset but reversing the polarity of applied voltage for each function, or (3) by providing a mechanical reset. Characteristically, these latching relays are magnetically bistable, having relatively high armature holding forces in either extreme position of the armature.

Polarized relays inherently have efficient actuators and also high resistance to shock and vibration. They may be operated or reset with pulse voltages and will remain latched or reset indefinitely.

A special version of a magnetic latching relay employs a highly remanent core. Operation is obtained by strongly magnetizing the remanent member, and release is obtained by reducing this magnetization to a level insufficient to hold the armature closed.

Magnetic latching relays are all d-c relays that either must be polarized or require reverse polarity for operation. They can be built quite small, such as crystal can and half size crystal can, and have been widely used in aerospace applications. They are available in open or sealed versions, but at least dustproof protection is recommended on most types to prevent the permanent magnet from picking up iron particles that might interfere with operation.

Magnetostrictive relays — Certain materials, especially those strongly ferromagnetic in nature like high nickel alloys, change in dimensions when placed in a magnetic field. The motion produced by this effect may be mechanically coupled to operate relay contacts. Ampere-turns efficiency in terms of motion produced is very low compared to the more conventional electromagnetic relay. Little practical use is made of this phenomenon except in the acoustic transducer field.

Mechanical latching relays — All latching relays are designed to hold their contacts in a "locked in" position following switching, even though the energy is removed from their coils. Mechanical latching relays are of two basic styles: mechanical reset and electrical reset. Mechanical reset types employ a coil and armature mechanism plus a mechanical latching device. The latter locks the armature in the operated position after the coil has been de-energized. Reset is then accomplished by tripping the locking mechanism manually or by some means other than electrically. Electrical reset types employ a second coil and armature that will trip the latch mechanism and allow the relay to reset to its original position.

Almost all clapper or plunger type relays can be adapted to either of the above methods of operation; consequently, it is possible to obtain an extremely broad range of sizes, types, contact combinations, and load capacities. Their uses are almost as numerous as the different styles. One very common use is as an overload device. When a load exceeds preset conditions, one coil can function and the latch mechanism locks the relay in that position, thus requiring further action on the part of an operator or machine to reset to normal.

Medium load relays — This is a very broad term that usually refers to relays with load switching ability in the 2 to 15 ampere, 28 volt d-c, or 115/230 volt a-c ranges. They can be of almost any design or style.

Mercury plunger relay — This is a specialized form of solenoid-operated relay in which a floating magnetic plunger displaces mercury in a pool to effect contacting between fixed electrodes and thus make or break a circuit. The mercury plunger and contacts are hermetically sealed within a glass or metal envelope placed inside the actuating coil. Operation of this type of relay is accomplished by magnetically pulling the plunger into the pool of mercury, causing the mercury to rise and make contact. The normally closed version works similarly except the plunger is held down in the pool of mercury with a spring, and the coil pulls the plunger up out of the pool. This allows the level of mercury to fall and thus break the circuit.

Mercury plunger relays fall into two categories: (1) quick acting, and (2) time delay. The time-delay type will be discussed later in this section. Quick-acting mercury plunger relays are generally considered as heavy duty relays. They are available in the normally open contact arrangement from 30 to 100 amperes per pole and in the normally closed form from 30 to 75 amperes per pole. Inherently they are single-pole, single-throw devices with either open or closed contacts. Multipole relays are formed by mounting a plurality of contacts within one magnetic circuit or coil, thus providing actuation of all independent contacts at the same instant.

Mercury plunger relays are position sensitive and are not considered reliable under severe vibration and shock conditions. They are considered quite good for heavy loads, and being hermetically sealed, are excellent under those environmental conditions involving dust and high humidity.

Mercury plunger time-delay relays — These relays are similar to mercury plunger relays except a time delay element is introduced in the movement of the mercury. Time delays are available ranging from 0.5 seconds to 20 minutes on either the operate or release cycles of normally open, single-throw or normally closed, single-throw contacts. These relays also are inherently single-pole devices. They are available with slow-operate, slow-release functions in the same relay.

Operation of a *normally open slow-make relay* is essentially as follows: A plunger, floating in mercury, is pulled down into the mercury when the coil is energized. The displaced mercury may then enter an inert-gas-filled space through an orifice as the gas within this space gradually escapes through a porous ceramic plug. As the mercury finally completes filling this space, mercury-to-mercury contact is established between electrodes located therein. The degree of porosity of the ceramic plug determines the length of time delay and is, of course, fixed in any given unit.

The *normally open slow-break relay* operates on a variation of the above principle except that energizing the coil, which causes the plunger to be pulled down into the mercury, results in the displaced mercury's immediately filling a "thimble," overflowing into a ceramic cup within the thimble, and thereby establishing mercury-to-mercury contact between appropriately located electrodes. When the coil is de-energized, the plunger immediately returns to its floating position. However, the mercury in the thimble flows slowly back out through a restricting orifice, seeking its level with the mercury outside the thimble. When the mercury level within the thimble falls below the level of the lip of the ceramic cup, mercury-to-mercury contact between the electrodes is broken. The diameter of the orifice determines the lengths of opening time delay.

The *normally closed time-delay relays* work in a similar manner except the plungers are displaced downward by springs and the coils are placed so as to lift the plunger out of the mercury when energized. These are obviously fixed time-delay devices. Their applications are extremely varied, and they have the inherent advantages of hermetically sealed switching devices capable of carrying large loads.

Mercury-wetted contact relays — These are a special form of reed relay consisting of a glass-encapsulated reed with its base submerged in a pool of mercury and its free end arranged to move between two sets of stationary contacts. The mercury flows up the reed by capillary action and wets the contact surfaces of both the moving reed and the stationary contacts (the latter by transfer). The reed is generally actuated by a coil surrounding the glass capsule. For a complete description, *see* Reed relays. See also Sec. 11.

Meter type relays — As the name implies, these relays utilize modified D'Arsonval meter movements as the actuator for performing switching functions. The meter pointer or indicator is replaced with a moving contact arm and an adjustable stationary contact is added to a second arm. Both arms carry precious metal contacts and a very flexible pigtail is usually added to the meter arm for current carrying purposes. The contact pressures developed are so extremely small that it is often necessary to add some auxiliary means of providing greater pressure. Furthermore, since the movable arm could come to rest in any position proportional to the voltage or current imposed on the meter coil, it is necessary to provide some sort of quick, positive contact closing. One way of accomplishing these functions is to attach a small permanent magnet to the adjustable contact arm. The magnet will cause the meter element to close the contacts quickly and firmly as it nears the stationary arm. The contacts are released either manually or by some auxiliary means. Another method of quick closure is to add a pair of very light contacts on both arms in order to energize an auxiliary coil on the movable element that provides a surge of torque just before the main contacts are engaged. These contacts can be released by removing the current from the two movement coils. Meter type relays are extremely sensitive devices, capable of closing contacts over a wide and adjustable range, and are therefore used in applications requiring critical current or voltage sensing.

"Mil Spec" relays — This term may encompass any relay type built to meet stringent performance and environmental characteristics peculiar to military and aerospace requirements, such as high shock and vibration resistance, hermetically sealed enclosure, wide temperature and pressure ranges, quality assurance programs, and high reliability.

Among government specifications are MIL-R-5757, MIL-R-6106, MIL-R-19523, MIL-R-19648 and MIL-R-39016 (*see* Sec. 9). Marshall Space Flight Center MSFC-SPEC-339 is normally included in the Mil Spec Relay category because of application similarity.

These are general specifications covering wide ranges. There are other military specifications written to cover specific applications. For instance, individual specifications covering relays for usage in torpedoes, shipboard electrical service, and shipboard fire control equipment have been written by the Navy. The Air Force has several which cover relays for controlling generators and alternators. Army Ordnance has some for application to tactical military vehicles. All specifications are listed in the Department of Defense Index of Specifications and Standards (DODISS), available from the Superintendent of Documents, Washington, D. C., 20025. Individual copies of published specifications and standards appearing in DODISS may be obtained from the U. S. Naval Supply Depot, 5801 Tabor Ave., Philadelphia, Pa. 19120. (*See also* Crystal can relays and Hermetically sealed relays.)

Motor-driven relays — A few special types of motor-driven switching devices are sometimes classified as relays. The term "motor driven" refers to a variety of small electric motors, such as shaded-pole induction, hysteresis synchronous, a-c series, and d-c series. The motor usually drives a gear train and cam mechanism for contact switching. These units are often used as time-delay devices or for program switching applications where a motor provides the most suitable actuating mechanism.

Motor-driven steppers — Some stepping devices are driven by small conventional electric motors in place of the electromagnetic coil, armature, and ratchet mechanisms used in telephone-type stepping switches. For the most part, these devices are considered quite special and are usually more expensive than the coil type. Furthermore, they are usually slower in response than other stepping switches and relays. In recent years, a stepping switch has been introduced that can operate quite rapidly in a self-interrupting mode and will respond to pulses as fast as several hundred per second. It uses an impulse type motor, the armature of which moves a fixed number of degrees and stops in response to a pulse of current. The motor has an inherent magnetic detent and doesn't require a ratchet and pawls.

Motor-starting relays — This term is usually applied to two different functions performed in starting motors. One function is performed by the "across-the-line" starter, which is usually a common power relay that, when energized, connects the line to the motor terminals. The other function is designed to open the circuit to the motor start winding of a single-phase motor as the rotor approaches rated speed. Depending on the motor design, this switching function is performed by centrifugal switches, thermal relays, or voltage or current-sensing electromagnetic relays.

In the voltage-sensing method, the relay coil is connected in parallel with the starting winding of the motor. As the motor comes up to speed, the voltage built up in the start winding causes the relay to pick up, disconnecting the start winding. After pickup, the voltage at the start winding terminals reduces to some much lower value, but still sufficient to hold the relay in the energized position. This application requires a relay with a high pickup-to-dropout ratio and a close tolerance pickup voltage.

The current-sensitive relay types are connected in series with the motor winding. The initial locked-rotor current energizes the relay and causes contacts to close, thus placing the start winding into operation. As the motor comes up to speed, the line current diminishes and allows the relay to dropout.

Moving coil relays — Moving coil relays, with the exception of meter type relays *(see* Meter type relays) are usually quite special and not too commonly used. One such device, once quite popular, was a combination relay and transformer. A fixed primary coil was mounted on a laminated core, with a secondary coil free to move. Closing the winding on the secondary coil induced a current which generated a magnetic field which opposed the field of the primary coil. The secondary coil thus moved away from the primary, and this movement was used to operate a contact mechanism. Moving coil meter relays are in common use today, primarily where a high degree of sensitivity is required.

Polarized relays — Included in this category are many relay styles, including telegraph, crystal can, differential, ferreed, dry reed, magnetic latching, mercury-wetted contact, and armature type with a remanent core. They usually employ one or more permanent magnets to provide the polarizing magnetic flux that normally can flow in either of two symmetrical paths. The armature aligns itself according to the net force produced by the two flux paths. A small amount of permanent magnet flux present in an air gap will add to or decrease the forces produced by the coil flux in proportion to the square of the sum or difference of the flux values.

Utilization of the permanent magnet flux permits greater efficiency for a given size when compared to nonpolarized electromagnetic relays. This added efficiency is often used to make the relay more sensitive, to increase the operating speed, or to improve its resistance to vibra-

tion and shock. For magnetic latching (bistable) applications, there is the added advantage of no power consumption after contact transfer.

Depending upon the design, polarized relays may be operated by a series of high speed pulses as encountered in telegraph and pulse code equipment, by infrequent on-off signals, or by slowly varying signals found in controls and instrumentation circuits. Their operation depends on both the magnitude and direction of the coil energizing current. See also Appendix A.

Power relays — This is a general term interpreted differently from industry to industry, but usually it denotes relays capable of switching loads above 15 to 25 amps and 28 volts d-c or 115/230 volts a-c. Power relays encompass a wide variety of styles — armature, solenoid actuated, rotary balanced armature, and even microminiature.

R.F. switching relays — These relays are designed to switch radio frequency currents with a minimum of losses. The dielectric materials used are selected for their insulating qualities and low losses at frequencies up to 150 MHz or more. Large contact gaps and long dielectric leakage paths are employed to withstand the high voltages that may be encountered. *(See also* **Antenna** switching relays and **Coaxial** relays.)

Radiation resistant relays — A radiation resistant relay is one constructed using radiation resistant materials. Stated conversely, it is one in which the least radiation resistant materials have been eliminated. Of all materials, metals are by far the most highly resistant to radiation. Noticeable damage appears only at high levels of bombardment by heavy particles such as neutrons.

As a class, organic insulating materials are the least resistant of all materials to radiation. They become more conductive and experience permanent damage. Chemical bonds are broken and new chemical bonds are formed. Some organics stiffen and embrittle, some turn to a rubbery liquid, others to a powder. Gas may be evolved. The fluorides, such as polytetrafluoroethylene (Teflon) and polytrifluorochloroethylene (Kel-F), though heat resistant, are not very radiation resistant.

Inorganic insulators, such as ceramic oxides, glasses, and mica, fall in a class well above organics in radiation resistance but do not equal metals. They become temporarily conductive and are damaged, largely by atom displacement.

No radiation levels have been established as universal standards although several specifications have been written. The specific applications would quite naturally vary the requirements. The application specifications may (1) call out rad values and gamma and fast neutron counts, (2) specifically preclude the use of certain materials (especially particular organics), or (3) request a listing of all used materials for approval. The rad is the accepted modern unit of measure of *absorbed* radiation energy, or *dose*. (A rad is 100 ergs of absorbed energy per gram of material.) A given amount of rads absorbed from fast neutrons, for example, should have the same effect on a given material as the same number of rads absorbed from gamma photons. However, the absorption of either will vary independently from one material to another; therefore, gamma and fast neutron values are often called out as environmental factors instead of rads, especially where choice of materials is not in the control of the relay specifier.

Another consideration exists regarding radiation effects on relay performance. Although the total absorbed dosage of gamma or fast neutrons relates to a given degradation of a material, the *rate* at which these radiations are experienced can have thermal significance affecting both the operate values of the relay and its switching performance, as well as causing possible further degrading of the materials due to temperature increases.

Ratchet relays — A rachet relay, also known as an impulse relay, is basically a single electromagnetic motor (actuator) driving a rotating shaft by indexing a pawl into a star-wheel fixed onto this shaft. The shaft also supports an electrical member of a switch assembly. This rotating shaft typically would cause the movable switch member to come into contact with other electrical contacts, usually more than two. The switching arrangements and capabilities vary according to the requirements for which they have been designed. Many existing forms can be considered low-cost stepping relays, although they considerably differ from the telephone-type stepping switches in design and performance.

As in stepping relays, there are two main systems used in the driving mechanism: one called "direct driven," the other "spring driven" or "indirect." In the direct-action type, the switching action is carried out as the relay is energized. In the indirect-action type, a spring is compressed during relay energization and, upon armature release, the spring furnishes the energy for the stepping function.

Ratchet relays usually require more electrical power than the normal relay types and thus are quite often rated for intermittent duty whether a-c or d-c operated.

Reed relays — The term *reed relay* covers dry reed relays, ferreed relays, and mercury-wetted contact relays, all of which use hermetically sealed reed switches. They differ from the resonant reed relay, which is a frequency sensitive device. In all three types, the reeds (thin, flat blades) serve multiple functions — as conductor-contacts, springs, and magnetic armatures. In some designs they must also be compatible in a metal-to-glass seal. See also Sec. 11.

(1) *Dry reed relays:* In this basic design, two opposing reeds are sealed into a narrow glass capsule and overlap at their free ends. At the contact area they are usually plated with gold or rhodium or otherwise treated to produce a low contact resistance when they meet. The capsule, surrounded by an electromagnetic coil, is usually made of glass and filled with a dry inert gas. There is also a vacuum type. When the coil is energized in the basic form A contact combination, the normally open contacts are brought together; when the field is removed, the reeds separate from their own spring tension. Many variations of the original concept are being produced. Single-pole, double-throw contact combinations (form C) are available, as well as metal enclosed reeds. A variety of sizes are made. The original capsules were roughly 2 in. long by 0.200 in. in diameter without leads. Later models are $3/4$ in. long by 0.100 in. in diameter. Even smaller sizes are contemplated.

In some designs, contacts on compliant springs are added to the magnetic reed members to provide more rugged contact materials for the basic make-and-break functions. Current rating, which is dependent upon the size of the reed and the type and amount of plating, may range from dry circuit to 3 amperes. Effective contact protection is essential in most applications unless switching is done dry (circuit set-up only).

Relay packages using two or more dry reed switches are common, providing multipole switching arrangements, some of which may contain permanent magnets for magnetic biasing to achieve normally closed contacts. The reed relay may be built for a large variety of operational modes such as: pulse relay, latch relay, crosspoint relay, logic relay, or infinite margin. These re-

SUPPORTING   NORMALLY   GLASS   SUPPORTING
TERMINAL   OPEN   CAPSULE   TERMINAL
           CONTACTS

FIG. 3-7. CONSTRUCTION OF SWITCH CAPSULE OF A
TYPICAL DRY REED RELAY

lays may also be supplied with electrostatic or magnetic shields.

Because of the tremendous increases in low-level logic switching, computer applications, and other business machine and communications applications, dry reed relays have become an important factor in the relay field. They have the great advantage of being hermetically sealed and are thus impervious to atmospheric contamination. They are very fast in operation and when operated within their rated contact loads, they have a very long life. They can be manufactured automatically and therefore are relatively inexpensive. A typical dry reed switch capsule is shown in Fig. 3-7.

(2) *Ferreed relays:* The name *ferreed* is used to denote a form of reed relay in which the dry reed switch is combined with one or more remanent magnetic members whose magnetization can be changed by current pulses in associated coils. The device was originally designed for use in telephone systems where it performs functions comparable to crossbar switches. In one magnetic state, the remanent members supply a field

through the reed armatures strong enough to close them. In the other magnetic state, the field is too small to hold the reeds closed. An "operate" pulse through the coils produces the first state; a "release" pulse, the second. The pulse has to last only long enough to magnetize the remanent members and can be much shorter than the time for contact closure. In the conventional form of latching reed relay operation, the energizing pulse has to last long enough to commence the closing of contacts, which are then held closed by permanent or remanent magnets.

The outstanding characteristics of the ferreed are its extremely fast response (actuation by pulses down to 5 microseconds duration), and its ability to remain in either state without continued application of holding current.

The remanent material used in this application is a cobalt-iron-vanadium alloy developed by Bell Telephone Laboratories and called Remendur. A typical magnetization curve is shown in Fig. 3-8. It demonstrates the usual combination of "square loop," low coercive magnetizing characteristics, combined with high level residual flux density values.

(3) *Mercury-wetted contact relays:* Mercury-wetted contact relays are a form of reed relays consisting of a glass-encapsulated reed with its base immersed in a pool of mercury and the other end capable of moving between two sets of stationary contacts. The mercury flows up the

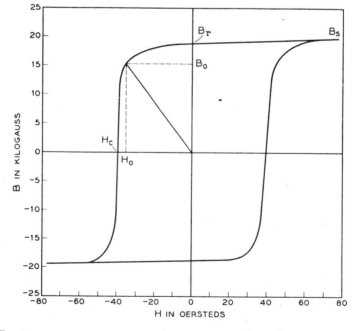

FIG. 3-8. TYPICAL MAGNETIZATION CURVE (HYSTERESIS LOOP) OF REMENDUR ALLOY USED IN
FERREEDS

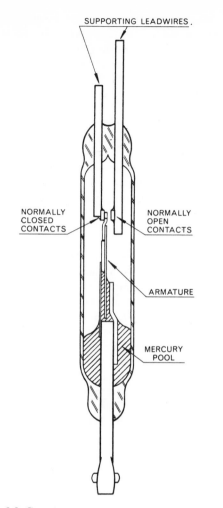

FIG. 3-9. CONSTRUCTION OF ORIGINAL TYPE OF MER-
CURY-WETTED CONTACT RELAY

the longer lead wires provide a better flux path, and the armature transfers to that pair of contacts. These contacts have a form D action (make-before-break) and will switch a maximum current of 5 amperes, a maximum voltage capacity of 500 volts, and a maximum load of 250 volt-amperes. These contacts must be protected by a resistor-capacitor network or other means of arc suppression, such as semiconductor diodes.

This relay will operate as fast as 3 milliseconds when energized at approximately 400 excess ampere-turns above its normal 190 ampere-turns. At 100 excess ampere-turns, the operate speed is approximately 6 ms. The release time is fairly constant around 3.8 ms under any conditions at coil disconnect. Permanent magnets can be added to the stationary contacts to provide single-side-stable, bistable, or chopper operation. These magnets roughly double the pickup power requirement.

In the second type of capsule, the armature consists of a magnetic alloy reed that is not spring biased and is adjusted to a neutral position between the stationary contacts in the externally unbiased condition (see Fig. 3-10).

The stationary contacts are each mounted in a single magnetic-alloy supporting leadwire. The movable reed is biased by means of permanent magnet or magnets. The contacts are furnished in either form D (make-before-break) or form C (break-before-make) combinations, and such contacts have a maximum load capacity of 100 volt-amperes, limited by a maximum current capacity of 2 amperes and a maximum voltage

reed by capillary action and wets the contact surface of the moving end of the reed as well as the contact surfaces of the stationary contacts. Thus a mercury-to-mercury contact is maintained in the closed position. The mercury-wetted relay is usually actuated by a coil around the capsule.

There are two basic types of mercury-wetted relay capsules. In one, the moving element is a magnetic armature carrying a platinum contact and supported by a flat steel spring welded to the stem at the bottom of the capsule (see Fig. 3-9). Four stationary platinum contacts are supported by two pairs of magnetic alloy lead wires sealed into the upper end of the capsule. The normally closed condition is maintained by initial spring pressure, which holds the movable contact against the two contacts affixed to the shorter lead wires. When the coil is energized,

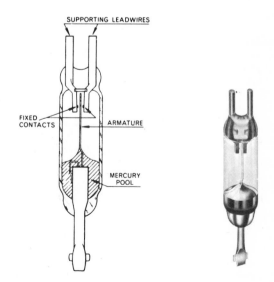

FIG. 3-10. SHORT MERCURY-WETTED CONTACT RELAY

rating of 500 volts. They must also be protected by suitable arc suppression devices. This relay is available with bistable or single-side-stable adjustment. This second type is of higher speed than the first and will operate as fast as 1 millisecond at 400 excess ampere-turns. It is also highly sensitive and will transfer on as little as 2.5 milliwatts.

Aside from being extremely fast in operation and having relatively good load-carrying capacity, mercury-wetted contact relays have extremely long life since the mercury films are re-established at each contact closure and contact erosion is eliminated. Since the films are "stretchable," there is no contact bounce (see Fig. 3-11). Contact interface resistance is extremely low. The disadvantages of this type of reed relays are poor resistance to shock and vibration and the need to mount in a near vertical position.

These relays are available in a metal can enclosure with plug-in base or in a more compact form for printed-circuit board mounting. Multipole versions are provided by putting additional capsules inside or about one coil. They are used for a great variety of high-speed switching applications such as found in computers, business machines, machine tool control systems, and laboratory instruments, such as digital voltmeters.

Resonant reed relays — This type of relay is designed to respond to a given frequency of coil input current. It consists of an electromagnetic coil that, when energized, drives a vibrating reed with a contact at its end. When the coil input frequency corresponds to the resonant frequency of the reed, the reed will vibrate and cause its contact to touch a stationary contact and thereby close a circuit once each electrical cycle. Otherwise, the reed does not respond. Sometimes the reed is surrounded for a portion of its length with a permanent magnet field to provide a constant magnetic bias. Since the vibrating reed closes its contact only for a portion of each cycle, it is often necessary to provide an output circuit that will store these pulses long enough to operate a conventional relay for control purposes.

Resonant reed relays can be built with a number of reeds having frequency responses in discrete steps, thus providing a device that will give signals on either side of a desired frequency for control purposes. Resonant reed relays are also used for a variety of applications where response to frequency only is desired, such as communications, selective signaling, data transmission, and telemetry.

Rotary relays — Rotary relays are relays whose armatures rotate to close the gap between two or more pole faces. Most rotary relays have balanced armatures and are used primarily under conditions of shock and vibration. Beginning with World War II, their use has grown tremendously, triggered originally by military requirements for mobile ground equipment and aircraft, and today for missiles. Rotary relays are manufactured in a wide variety of sizes and shapes, from the microminiature to very large relays designed to withstand the shock of gunfire on large naval vessels. Many of the relays discussed in this section may feature this type of construction.

Sensitive relays — Sensitive relays require small amounts of coil power to cause them to operate, usually 100 milliwatts or less. They encompass a wide variety of styles: Clapper or armature, crystal can or Mil Spec, dry reed, instrument, mercury-wetted contact, polarized, wire spring, etc. For a given style, it is often necessary to sacrifice one or more parameters in order to make the relay more sensitive. This trade-off of parameters might increase the oper-

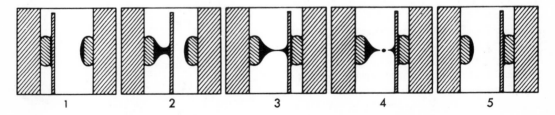

FIG. 3-11. MERCURY-WETTED CONTACT ACTION SEEN IN HIGH-SPEED PICTURES

(1) Mercury (shown in black) covers armature and contact points; (2) and (3) as armature moves from open to closed position, mercury filament joins both contacts momentarily; (4) ruptured mercury surfaces accelerate away from each other, providing rapid breaking action; (5) as contact surfaces join, mercury wetting dampens rebound, eliminates electrical chatter, and provides contact reliability.

ating time, reduce shock or vibration resistance, lower the output rating or life expectancy, or reduce contact pressures or gaps.

Slave relays — This term is usually used to denote any style of relay added to a circuit to step up its power switching ability or to provide additional isolated output switching functions; hence it is also called an *auxiliary relay*. For instance, since the contacts on a thermostat usually cannot handle a motor load, they actuate a relay instead, which in turn starts the motor. Secondary circuit functions, such as indicators, alarms, counters, and the like, might also be actuated by the relay. *(See* Auxiliary relay, Sec. 1, Paragraph 1.9.)

Snap-action contact relays — Snap action is a relative term but usually refers to the storing of energy during initial motion of an actuating member until a point is reached at which the contacts snap to a new position of equilibrium. This action can be achieved mechanically by over-center devices or armature pre-travel or electrically by storing energy from a sliding current source, triggered and applied to the relay for rapid contact transfer. The snap-action contact relay can incorporate an electromagnetic motor to operate directly on one or more precision snap switches, or it can use a mechanical linkage to actuate over-center stack switch assemblies. Polarized latching relays are often used in applications requiring fast operation since these devices have magnetic characteristics which produce rapid changes in contact equilibrium *(see* Polarized relays).

Solenoid actuated relays — Solenoid actuated relays are one of the oldest forms of relay structures and are manufactured in a wide variety of shapes, sizes, and characteristics. Because of this great variety, it would be tedious to go into detail for each type; some generalizations can be made that apply to most fields of interest.

Solenoid actuation of relay contacts is generally used where relatively large movement of the contacts is desirable or where considerable contact pressure is required. The solenoid provides relatively high pull in the open position, since by the nature of its structure, the coil can be virtually surrounded with magnetic material and the major air gap is often located inside the coil. This makes it an ideal method for actuating contacts carrying high power loads or multiple contact systems.

Solenoid relays are usually considered as on-off devices; they are not generally used where other characteristics are required, such as precise pickup voltage or sensitive operation. One exception is where solenoids are used in starter relays for capacitor-start motors in place of a centrifugal switch. This application requires rather close tolerances on pickup current as well as differential current between pickup and dropout.

Some phenomena associated with the connection and disconnection of a-c and d-c solenoids should be noted. In energizing either type, inrush current of extremely short duration (in the order of microseconds) occurs. This inrush is caused by the distributed capacitance within the winding and is normally neglected. When the armature changes from the open to the closed position, however, the accompanying large impedance change in a-c solenoids will result in surges much larger than rated current during actuation, decreasing to rated value upon closing. By contrast, in d-c solenoids, current will gradually build up to the rated value during the energization period and will not overshoot.

In disconnecting either a-c or d-c solenoids, if no protective devices are employed, stored inductive energy causes high voltage transients at the coil terminals at the time of disconnect. This energy will be dissipated in a number of ways. It will discharge through the disconnecting gap and other parts of the associated circuitry, be radiated, or bleed off through insulation, depending upon existing conditions. RC networks, semiconductor diodes, or short-circuited secondary windings are frequently used to absorb part or all of this energy and prevent generation of excessive voltage.

A-C solenoids require careful manufacturing procedures to provide proper seating of the armature and to prevent hum or chatter in the closed position. Many solenoid relays are position sensitive and can be used in only a limited range of positions. Some depend upon gravity to open the plunger. Solenoid relays are not usually used under conditions of vibration and shock, although there are some special designs manufactured that meet Mil Specs on shock and vibration.

Stepping relays — The stepping relay, sometimes called the rotary stepping switch, employs a driving mechanism similar to the stepping switch, but the contact springs take either of two positions (or at the most, one of three positions)

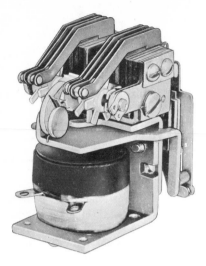

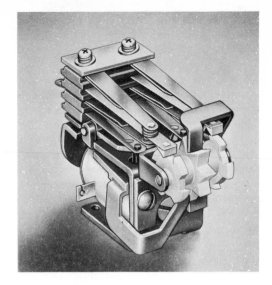

FIG. 3-12. TYPICAL STEPPING RELAYS

and are usually actuated by cams on the rotor assembly. Sometimes one or more multi-point bank and wiper levels are added to the stepping relay. Typical forms of stepping relays are shown in Fig. 3-12 *(see also* Stepping switches).

Stepping switches — Many switching devices perform sequential switching and are operated by a series of pulses. These devices are highly specialized for specific applications except in the telephone industry where the large quantities used over many years have resulted in a degree of standardization of some types. These same devices have found widespread use in other applications as automation of all types of equipment has progressed.

The bulk of these sequential switching devices falls under three categories: Stepping switches, commercial; stepping switches, telephone; and stepping relays (already described).

Stepping switches (commercial) — Various stepping switches are primarily designed for use in applications other than the telephone or communications industry. These commercial switches vary so greatly that no attempt will be made to describe each type. Their basic design is similar to that of telephone stepping switches in that they have an electromagnetic actuator which causes a contact wiping mechanism to rotate over a series of contacts arranged in a semicircle. They are also of two types: step-on-coil energization and step-on-coil de-energization. Some provide rather heavy button contacts for load-carrying purposes, whereas others use printed or etched circuit boards for the stationary contact system.

Various mechanical driving mechanisms are available. Some are bidirectional, having two coils and ratchet-and-pawl mechanisms arranged so that the wipers will be rotated either clockwise or counterclockwise. Other types rotate the wiper mechanism against a spring which returns the wiper to a home position when a pawl is released. Some are designed so the pawl can be released electrically, others manually. The electromagnetic driving mechanism may be a clapper type armature or solenoid. The number of steps varies considerably.

Stepping switches are used wherever a step-by-step switching device is required or where storage of a series of pulses is needed. Vending machines and business machines are typical applications.

Stepping switches (telephone) — The telephone stepping switch (Fig. 3-13), sometimes called a rotary stepping switch, consists basically of an electromagnetically operated mechanism having one (or more) wiping spring set(s) fixed on a shaft that is moved and controlled by a pawl and ratchet and actuated in response to current pulses through the armature operating coil. The stepping switch is composed of the following basic parts: the *frame* (the "platform" on which all parts are assembled and which is in turn fastened to the chassis of whatever equipment is using it); the *coil*, commonly called the "motor magnet," "MM," or "step coil"; the *armature assembly* (which includes the pawl spring), the *drive spring*, the *wiper assembly*, the *bank*, the *interrupter contact springs*, and the *off-normal contact springs*.

FIG. 3-13. TYPICAL TELEPHONE STEPPING SWITCH

On, or immediately following, each pulse of current to the coil, the pawl engages the ratchet, moving the rotor (wiper assembly) one step, and causing the attached wipers to contact, or break contact, successively with a semicircularly arranged row of contacts, called a bank level.

The basic wiper contact forms of the stepping switch can be either of the "make" or "break" variety. The make form is usually used and may be arranged to cause either "break before make" contacting (nonbridging), or "make before break" contacting (bridging). Bridging wipers have long flat tips to bridge successive contacts. (*See* Figs. 3-14 and 3-15.)

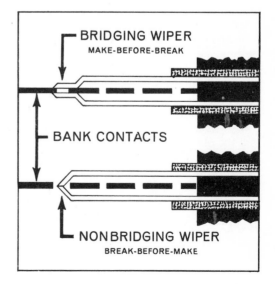

FIG. 3-14. BRIDGING AND NONBRIDGING WIPER CONTACTS OF A STEPPING SWITCH

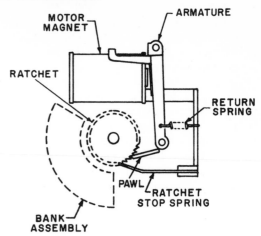

FIG. 3-15. BASIC SWITCHING PARTS OF UNIDIRECTIONAL STEPPING SWITCH

FIG. 3-16. PRINCIPLE OF DIRECTLY DRIVEN STEPPING SWITCHES

Stepping switches in industrial use are of the unidirectional rotating type. The basic switching parts are shown in Fig. 3-15. The arrangement in a single arc of independent contacts to which the wiper will be sequentially connected as it rotates is called a *physical bank contact level,* or more simply a *level.* The accumulation of levels into an assembly is called a *bank.* Frequently, more than one *physical* level must be employed to produce only a single *electrical* (circuit) level.

Banks are available in various switch types with 10, 11, 12, 20, 22, 24, 25, 26, 30, 32, 33, 36, 48, 50, and 52 contacts per level. Banks are built up to a maximum of 12 physical levels on the compact switches, and 16 to 24 levels for the larger switches.

Stepping switches are also made with nor-

mally closed contacts that are opened electrically as the rotor is stepped through the bank. Such a switch is referred to as having one or more levels of "normally closed" or "shorting" bank contacts. Both normally open and normally closed levels can be had on the same switch.

There are two types of driving mechanisms used in stepping switches: indirect and direct. When the armature-pawl combination acts directly on the ratchet under the power of the electromagnet, the stepping switch is said to be *directly driven (see* Fig. 3-16). When the pawl acts on the ratchet wheel from force stored in a drive spring, the mechanism is said to be *indirectly* driven. The indirectly driven stepping switch is the most common in industrial usage *(see* Fig. 3-17). The spring driven stepping switch is more consistent in performance, more efficient,

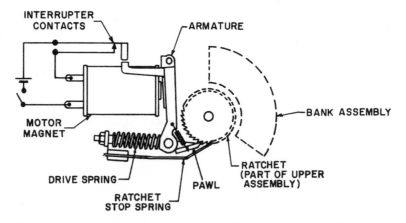

FIG. 3-17. OPERATING PRINCIPLE OF INDIRECTLY DRIVEN (SPRING DRIVEN) STEPPING SWITCH SHOWN IN THE SELF-INTERRUPTED MODE OF OPERATION

and capable of faster stepping than the directly driven stepping switch, besides having longer life.

There are basically two methods for stepping an indirectly driven stepping switch: *pulsed* and *self-interrupted*. When a circuit of proper voltage and power capabilities is closed to the motor magnet coil, the armature is attracted and holds the drive spring in the "cocked" position. When the coil is de-energized, the energy stored in the drive spring pushes the pawl against a ratchet wheel tooth, causing the wiper assembly to take a step. Repetitive pulses will cause the switch to take as many steps as the number of discrete pulses received. The length of time the circuit is closed (and opened) in a series of fast pulses is critical. In order to be certain of proper operation, the manufacturer should definitely be consulted.

Self-interrupted operation is used to step the switch rapidly from one point to another without use of discrete pulses from outside the switch. Under self-interrupted operation, a circuit is closed to the coil through a set of interrupter contact springs that are opened by an arm of the armature before it is fully seated. Breaking the coil circuit causes the armature to fall away, driving the wiper assembly one step and simultaneously reclosing the interrupter contacts. The armature is again attracted, re-cocking the switch and causing re-opening of the interrupter contacts. Thus the switch is made to run "self-interruptedly" until the circuit is opened permanently at the off-normal springs, at a bank level being used to furnish the self-interrupting potential, or by external control. Self-interrupted operation of the switch is sometimes referred to as "buzzing" or "door-bell" operation. For schematic representation, see Fig. 3-17.

For acceptable operation, a stepping switch coil must be supplied regulated direct current of the proper voltage. The maximum acceptable variation from nominal is plus or minus 10 per cent. The power available for each stepping switch should be at least 20 (preferably 30) watts. Standard voltages are 6, 12, 24, 48, and 110. Coils can be wound for any reasonable voltage, but the current-handling capabilities of the controlling contacts make the range of 24 to 110 volts the most practical, with 48 volts considered as ideal. By being so specified at the time of ordering, the switches may be powered from commercial a-c lines by use of a small rectifier. Unless the stepping switch is factory-adjusted to work with the rectifier selected, however, it may run raggedly, especially when being run self-interruptedly. Obviously, all switching is to be done on the direct-current (output) side of the rectifier.

Because the stepping switch coil is highly inductive, large (heavy-duty) contacts are recommended on controlling relays, and contact protection is required. Contact protection devices reduce the speed capability of a stepping switch and even the best of such devices represents a compromise. The relay manufacturer should be consulted on the kind and size of contacts required.

Stepping switches, like any mechanical device, require lubrication and some maintenance for maximum life. A check should be made with the manufacturer regarding the type of maintenance, the maintenance interval, and the proper lubricants to be employed.

Several kinds of enclosures are available for stepping switches, such as dust tight, protective only, and hermetically sealed. Ambient conditions and cost considerations should determine what type of enclosure is to be employed. Obviously, maintenance is not possible on a hermetically sealed switch, and life will be reduced as much as 70 per cent in some cases. Oil immersion is a possible solution to the need for long life with hermetic enclosure *provided the electrical contacts are to be switched with power off*. Otherwise rapid deterioration of the oil and switch failure will result from the generation of foreign deposits.

Strowger two-motion switch — The original stepping switch — and one that is still a major factor in telephone and other wired communications switching — is the Strowger or two-motion switch. On one series of pulses, a magnet coil and ratchet pawl raise a set of wipers to any one of ten bank levels. On a succeeding pulse series, the wipers are rotated in a plane perpendicular to the shaft to engage one of ten contact positions on the selected level. In this way a choice of one set of contacts out of 100 or 200 is quickly made. By means of ranks of such switches the selection of any point out of 100,000 or more is rapidly made with very simple control equipment. This is best exemplified by the commonplace "step-by-step" telephone exchange. The Strowger switch is also used in many nontelephone applications.

The X-Y switch is similar in performance and usage but employs a type of bank contact that sometimes offers an economy in first cost.

Telephone type relays — This is actually a misnomer since within the telephone industry different names are given for a variety of relays. Nevertheless, the telephone industry was the originator of the basic type and has produced great quantities of this type over a period of many years. During and since World War II, there have been a number of variations introduced, thus complicating the original concept and introducing additional qualifications, such as "short telephone relays," "small telephone relays," "midget telephone relays," "miniature telephone relays," and "wire spring relays." Perhaps these names should be abandoned, but they are still in common usage. With the exception of the wire spring relay, which will be covered in some detail a little later in this discussion, these names reflect variations primarily of size and proportioning. They still retain most of the same general features characteristic of the name "telephone type." However, it should be borne in mind that an exact description is impossible since the name is a very general term and means different types to different manufacturers.

The original telephone type relay is generally characterized by a relatively long coil compared to its diameter or cross-sectional dimensions. The frame or L-shaped heelpiece parallels the coil, and the armature pivots directly on the end of the frame or is suspended on a pin hinge. The contact assembly (or pileup) consists of flat stamped cantilever-mounted springs with contacts at the free end and connecting terminals extending from the fixed end. The contact springs are separated by stamped, laminated, or molded insulating spacers through which screws attach the contact assembly to the relay frame or heelpiece. The armature actuates the contact springs through insulating buffers. Similar insulating buffers are used between movable contact springs to actuate multiple contacts. The original telephone relays were designed for use on d-c although some a-c types are being made, which are less efficient. A typical telephone type relay is shown in Fig. 3-18. (*See also* Fig. 1-4b.)

The greatest advantage of the telephone type relay is the large variety of contact combinations obtainable by adding contact springs. It is also considered a relatively long-life relay and usually will function for many millions of operations. Slight time delays can easily be obtained by placing copper sleeves on the core. On the other hand, this is not an easy type of relay to manufacture. Parts must be made to fairly precise tolerances, and the manual adjustment of the

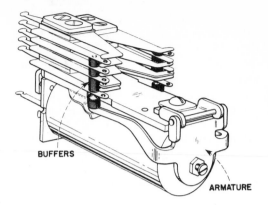

FIG. 3-18. TYPICAL TELEPHONE RELAY

contacts for proper gap and pressure can be done only by skilled operators after considerable training.

Many other telephone type relays introduced in recent years have the same general characteristics as described but vary considerably in size. A quite different type is the wire spring telephone type (*see also* Wire spring relays), which has found a number of uses outside the telephone field. In this relay, the contact arms are wire springs instead of flat strip springs, and the contact arms are actuated simultaneously by a perforated insulated card instead of by individual pushers. The wire spring contact arms are held in molded plastic instead of being clamped between insulating spacers. This relay is shown in Fig. 3-19. The greatest advantage of the wire spring telephone type is its adaptability to mass production methods and consequent relatively low unit cost. The contact springs can be preformed, making the final adjustment extremely simple.

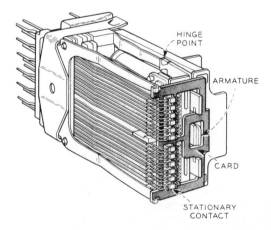

FIG. 3-19. WIRE SPRING TELEPHONE RELAY

Thermal relays — Thermal relays utilize a change in temperature to provide mechanical motion to operate a contact mechanism. *(See* Bimetal relays, Hot wire relays, Linear expansion relays, Thermal time delay relays.)

Thermal time delay relays — Most thermal relays have a heating element to provide the temperature differential for the thermal expansion and consequent movement to actuate the contacts. Since time is required for the heating element to attain the desired temperature and to transfer this heat to the expansion element, these devices are often used as time delay relays. A rather wide range of time delays, both fixed and adjustable, can be obtained. Their time tolerance depends upon the sophistication of a particular design; the better designs provide a high degree of accuracy even in a wide range of ambient temperatures. For further information, *see* Bimetal relays, Hot wire relays, Linear expansion relays.

Time delay relays — Time delay relays may be either electromagnetic or thermal types. They provide a time delay between the time that current is supplied to the coil or heating element and the actuating of the contact mechanism. They may also provide a delay between the time that the coil or heating element is de-energized and the contact mechanism is released. The variety of relays providing time delays is considerable. Several are described elsewhere in this chapter under the following names: Bimetal relays, Dashpot time delay relays, Delay slug relays, Hot wire relays, Linear expansion relays, Mercury plunger time delay relays, Thermal relays, and Thermal time delay relays.

Vacuum relays — This term is applied to relays having their contacts sealed in a high vacuum. They range from a simple dry reed single-pole, single-throw device, through small multipole relays, to rather large switching devices capable of carrying thousands of amperes at thousands of volts. The small dry reed type is actuated by an external coil in the same manner as the gas-filled dry reed relay. Other vacuum relays have their contacts actuated by mechanical means from an external source. The moving element is suspended on a metal bellows sealed into the glass enclosure and allowing sufficient movement to provide contact actuation.

Vacuum relays are characterized by their ability to carry high currents and high voltages for their relatively small size. They tend to be considerably more expensive than conventional relays, but they perform well where these characteristics are required.

Voltage sensing relays — The same general characteristics listed under "current sensing relays" also apply here, except that temperature compensating networks are required for voltage-sensing due to resistive changes in the coil as a result of self-heating or ambient temperature changes. Current sensitive relays, conversely, are relatively insensitive to temperature since relay operation is a direct function of coil current, whereas voltage, in d-c relays, is a function of the product of current and coil resistance. When thermal relays are used as voltage sensing relays, the problem of resistance change as described above is of little importance.

Wire spring relays — Relays having moving contact arms made of round-wire springs in place of flat springs are of three well-known types. One is a telephone type described under telephone type relays, two others were originally designed for use in setting up logic circuits in computers. The telephone type has a permissive-make contact system using precious metal contacts welded to the ends of the movable springs *(see* Fig. 3-20). The movable springs are twin springs, thus providing two normally open and two normally closed contacts for each pole. The stationary contacts are each a single spring positioned between the two pairs of movable springs. They have a precious metal double-faced contact welded on the spring end. When the coil is energized, the armature actuates a card made of insulating material, which lifts one pair of springs (per pole) away from the stationary contact and allows the second pair to "make" with the stationary contact, providing a permissive make, low-bounce contact action. This relay has many excellent characteristics in addition to the twin contacts. It can provide a large number of contacts in a relatively small space, it is well adapted to high production methods, and the method of contact adjustment is quite simple.

The other types of wire spring relays are fairly compact devices having double-throw contacts provided in four, six, and eight poles. The movable springs are also in pairs, thus providing twin contacts for each pole. These relays are characterized by relatively high speed, low contact bounce, long life, and relatively simple design. The load capacity of the contacts is low.

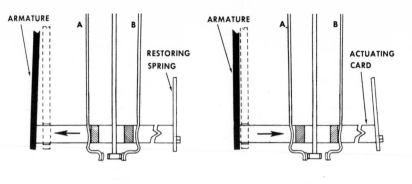

ARMATURE   A   B   ARMATURE   A   B

RESTORING   ACTUATING
SPRING   CARD

NORMAL POSITION   OPERATED POSITION

FIG. 3-20. PERMISSIVE MAKE CONTACT SYSTEM OF A WIRE SPRING RELAY, USING AN ACTUATING CARD.

Electrical and Mechanical Considerations Applicable to All Relay Types

3.3   Contact combinations

The current-carrying parts of a relay that are used for making and breaking the electrical circuits are available in various combinations of contact forms to make up the complete switching structure. Relay contact assembly designations are given in Paragraph 1.5 of Section 1 and will not be repeated here. Switching abbreviations are given in the following order:

Poles:	Single — SP	Double — DP
Throws:	Single — ST	Double — DT
Normal position:	Open — NO	Closed — NC
Double make	DM	
Double break	DB	

Single-throw contact forms have a pair of contacts open in one armature position and closed in the other. When the contacts are open in the normal or unoperated position of the relay, the position is designated "normally open," and when they are closed in the normal or unoperated position, the position is designated "normally closed."

Double-throw contact combinations have three contacts, of which one is in contact with the second but not with the third in one relay position, and in the reverse connection in the other relay position. The basic double-throw contact form is the "break-make."

Double-make and double-break contact forms have two independent contacts that are both connected to a third contact in one position on the relay, designated "double-make" when normally open and "double-break" when normally closed.

Classifications of compounded contact arrangements, such as for relays having more than two positions, are designated by the symbol MPNT. M signifies the number of poles and N the number of throws. Thus 8P20T identifies a relay with 8 poles and 20 throws (as in a 20-step relay with 8 banks of contacts).

In pileup contact arrangements, a set of contact arms, assemblies, or contact springs are stacked and fastened one on top of the other with insulation between them. Such multiposition relays must provide mechanical conditions that are satisfactory with respect to contact force, motion, mounting, and actuation. Because their primary development was for operation in telephone systems, relays with pileup contact arrangements are generally known as telephone type relays. However, their usual characteristics of extremely long life, multiple contact arrangements, sensitivity, and relatively fast operate and release time values make them useful in a wide range of applications.

Bifurcated contacts, also known as twin contacts, provide two separate contacts on a single, partially split contact arm or on separate arm members. The bifurcated arms, while flexing as a single unit, provide some degree of independence of movement between the twin contacts. Bifurcated contact arrangements are usually specified where environments may cause contact failures through deposit of dust or other foreign matter by sedimentation, thermal precipitation, or electrostatic attraction. With such contamination, one of the twin contacts will usually continue to function until the other contact is cleared by several make-and-break operations.

Contact reliability may also be greatly increased by wiring two separate contacts in parallel. Factors like ambient temperature, shock vibration, contact material, shape of contacts, the amount of contact force, and the wiping motion or slide of contacts will affect the occurrence of contact misses. An order of 5 to 10 operations is usually the average required for clearing contact surfaces of foreign matter to a satisfactory operating level. If on a "miss test" of one contact, five failures occurred in 100,000 relay operations, the failure rate per operation would be 5×10^{-5}. If the nature of the miss is truly random (Gaussian distribution), wiring two contacts in parallel would reduce the failure rate to (5×10^{-5}) $\times (5 \times 10^{-5}) = 25 \times 10^{-10}$. (Since other miss-producing factors — for example, coil failure — can exist, upon which the two contacts would be mutually dependent, such gains in reducing the failure rate by paralleling may not be fully achieved.) A generalized expression for the new failure rate resulting from paralleling any two independent systems having separate failure rates of $(FR)_1$ and $(FR)_2$, would be $(FR)_1 \times (FR)_2$. Similarly, the result of paralleling two independent systems having separate reliability ratings of R_1 and R_2 is $(R_1 + R_2) - R_1 R_2$.

Various special types of contact arrangements, usually designated by their method of operation, are: auxiliary, crossbar, wire-spring, cam-actuated (so-called), spring-buffer, lifter contacts, etc.

Auxiliary contacts are used when it is desirable to keep the coil energized after the original operating circuit is opened, to operate a visual or audible signal indicating the position of the main contacts, or to form interlocking circuits.

Each of the other types of contact arrangements covered usually provides operating characteristics to serve specific applications. Their basic forms function in accordance with one of the standard alphabetical indicators given in Paragraph 1.5 of Sec. 1.

3.4 Enclosures

Relays without covers are less costly than relays with enclosures. Most relay manufacturers provide finishes for coils and other parts of open relays that will protect them from adverse environmental conditions. Fumes caused by the outgassing of organic components (coil insulation and other insulating parts) do not settle on the contacts of open relays as frequently as they do if, for instance, hermetic sealing is specified.

Enclosures should be used if mechanical protection is needed to prevent the relay's adjustments from being upset, or if the motion of its parts could be disturbed by nearby moving parts, other equipment, or service personnel. Enclosures should be used if the relays are switching in an area filled with airborne dust, metal particles, or filmy fog. The protection of personnel against accidental contact with exposed current-carrying parts sometimes justifies their use.

Enclosures increase the size of relays and add to their cost. Relay manufacturers cannot always provide a low-cost dust cover for any given relay since another set of terminals, new mounting facilities, and markings may have to be provided.

Two types of enclosures are available, dust-tight and hermetically sealed. Both types may utilize metal cans, but dust-tight enclosures are often made of assorted plastic materials. Dust-tight sealing may be accomplished with gaskets or with potting materials. In the majority of applications, however, the normal fit of a molded plastic cover to a relay base will provide adequate protection. In some instances, as in reed relays, the contacts are hermetically sealed in a glass capsule, whereas the surrounding coil and other components are potted in a high melting point compound inside a metal case. The case and potting protects the coil against the entry of moisture or dust and minimizes injury to personnel in the event of breakage of the glass capsule.

The choice of enclosure depends on a number of factors. Hermetic sealing is indicated if (1) unusual atmospheric environments (chemical vapors, salt, high humidity, low pressure, and the like) are to be experienced; (2) explosion-proof switching is needed; (3) maximum inertness of contacts to chemical change over long storage periods is desired; or (4) hermetic sealing is required by Mil Specs. For many less severe environmental uses, hermetically sealed relays may not necessarily be superior to dust-covered units. In fact, unless the relay parts are extremely clean before sealing, and unless very stable materials that are well outgassed are employed, hermetically sealed relays may perform less satisfactorily in some applications than will their dust-covered counterparts. As a result of its higher cost, moreover, hermetic sealing is normally specified only when necessitated by requirements of the application. Prior to sealing, the hermetically sealed relay is thoroughly cleaned and outgassed by a vacuum bake process. Removal of air, moisture, and organic outgas from the enclosure, and the introduction of an inert gas such as dry nitrogen help provide a more stable environment essential to maintaining contact cleanliness, dielectric strength, insulation, etc., after the relay is sealed. When indicated (as for many types of military applications), hermetically sealed relays are tested for gas leakage to assure acceptable low leakage rates.

A variety of materials is used for molded plastic enclosures, such as polycarbonate resins, nylon, polypropylene, phenolics, and others. The kind of protection called for usually determines the type of plastic best suited for the purpose. High dielectric properties offered by plastics are desirable for personnel protection. A high-impact plastic, such as polycarbonate, is indicated where rough handling is a problem. Heat-resistant plastics are used when high temperatures are likely to be encountered.

Cases may be opaque, translucent, transparent, and in various colors. Transparent plastic covers serve best if frequent inspection of the moving parts of the relay is necessary. Different color finishes are convenient for color-coding circuits. Molded plastic enclosures in themselves provide a smooth, neat-appearing finish.

Metal enclosures for relays are usually made of sheet metal to provide a considerable degree of mechanical protection. When used as dust covers for industrial relays, the larger enclosures are equipped with conduit-knockouts, arrangements for fastening the relay inside the case, and some means for convenient access to inspect the relay. Some may be fitted with locking screws; others may have hinged covers. These enclosures may be finished with paint or electroplated.

Hermetically sealed metal enclosures are available for many types of relays normally furnished without enclosures. While the operational characteristics of open relays may be retained with minor differences when placed in enclosures, the wiring and mounting arrangements may change considerably, as may the life expectancy of the relay. Sealed terminals in the base plate, or header, together with mounting studs welded to the base, facilitate electrical connections and secure mounting to control panels. In some electronic assemblies, the relay may be encapsulated with other components.

Metals for hermetically sealed enclosures are usually copper-nickel, steel, nickel-steel, nickel-silver, or brass. To facilitate soldering of the base to the can, cases are hot-tin dipped or electroplated. Copper-nickel housings are used when the header is welded to the housing. Outside finishes for hermetically sealed enclosures may be paint, plating, or a natural finish in the nonferrous alloys.

3.5   Mountings

Relay mountings include simple brackets, studs, clamps, and the connecting terminals themselves. Most manufacturers offer several different mountings for each relay type. The crystal can relay, for example, is offered with bracket, stud, or clamp mounting. It can also be mounted by its terminals in sockets and printed circuit boards. For many other classes of relay, the press fit of plug-in terminals is sufficient to hold the relay in its socket.

Mountings are often modified to meet the particular requirements of a user, despite some attempts toward standardization. Relays having plastic molded bases present more of a problem for modification. Changes of the mold can be quite expensive. This cost can sometimes be reduced by adding a metal stamping or bracket that modifies the mounting to desired dimensions. The user can generally save money by using the standard types recommended.

3.6   Terminals

To connect the current-carrying parts of a relay to the external circuitry, some sort of termination is required. This termination varies greatly, but for the most part it will come under the following classifications:

(1) Lead wires.   Using lead wires for relay coil terminations allows the relay user to connect the coil directly to the terminals of other circuit devices or to other lead wires by twist connectors, clamps, or solder. Generally, lead wires are not supplied for contact terminals except by special requirement; to add them would increase the relay cost. One exception is in crystal can relays, where the wires coming through glass beads in the headers can serve as long leads, thus eliminating an extra set of solder joints.

(2) Terminals for printed circuit boards. In general, relays intended for mounting on printed circuit boards have short, straight-wire terminations coming through glass beads in a header, coordinately arranged in a grid pattern on spacings that are a multiple of 0.010 in. After insertion into the printed circuit board, the terminal leads are solder-connected.

(3) Solder terminals.   Such terminations vary from eyelets to stiff bent-wire terminals to flat-pierced tabs. They are generally characterized by a hook or a hole through which the connecting wires are looped around or through and thus accept mechanical stress. It is not good practice to depend upon a solder joint alone to absorb stress on the connecting wire.

(4) Screw terminals. The variety of screw terminals is great — from very small machine screws to large studs and bolts. They are all characterized by their mechanical means of making a compression connection without the use of solder. They are generally specified where the connections are likely to be changed frequently or where only screwdrivers or wrenches might be available.

(5) Quick connectors. Several varieties fall in this category. One type consists of a flat tab or terminal with a dimple or hole over which a spring-type fitting can be slipped to make the connection. The spring has a matching dimple and serves to lock the two parts together, although the spring portion is readily removable. The tab portion is usually connected to the relay and is frequently a part of the stationary or movable contact system. The spring part is attached to a lead wire. These connectors are available in a few different types and are widely used for appliance and automotive relay applications because the final connections are made so quickly.

(6) Taper tabs. These are a form of quick-connect terminal and consist of two small metal stampings with longitudinal taper designed so that one slips over the other and the two wedge together. Because of their thinness, these tabs are often used where a number of terminals are close together.

(7) Taper pins. These are similar to taper tabs except the female portion consists of a round tapered eyelet or sleeve and the male portion is a round tapered pin.

(8) Solderless wrap. This is a patented method of power-wrapping a conductor wire around a rectangular or square post or pin having relatively sharp edges. The special wrapping tool provides sufficient tension to give the lead wire a permanent set so that it will not unwind. This connection has the advantages of being inexpensive and fast. It is suitable for applications where a large number of terminals are required in a small area.

(9) "Termi-point." This is another patented method of connection consisting of a small metal-spring clip that clamps the lead wire against a rectangular post. As in the case of the solderless wrap, a special tool is required for application. It is also quite fast, inexpensive, and suitable for high density terminal areas.

(10) Plugs and sockets. Relays are available with plugs and sockets ranging from the miniature electron tube sizes to octal tube sizes and with a variety of coordinate grid terminal spacings. A great number of specials can be manufactured to accommodate a given relay. A possible disadvantage in using socket mounting is the additional contact interfaces added to the circuit. Sometimes, in addition to the plug-in interfaces, taper tab or other quick disconnect wiring is used to make connections to the socket terminals, further increasing the number of interfaces. The added resistance at the interfaces could be especially undesirable in very low voltage circuits. In certain atmospheres and environments, these contacting interfaces may become corroded or contaminated. Where there is extensive vibration, as in certain military applications, soldered or welded connections are more desirable than the plug-in type. Although plugs and sockets sometimes add a small amount to the cost of a relay, they greatly facilitate replacement and hence provide a substantial reduction in service costs.

Classifications of Relays

3.7 Commercial and industrial

Commercial and industrial relays are those considered for general use in commercial or industrial applications as contrasted to military or aerospace applications. Although they may be of the same design as military relays in some instances, they are more often designed for less severe environmental and operating conditions. This does not imply that they may be any the less reliable, for in many instances commercial and industrial relays must provide a very high degree of reliability and long life. However, the variation in the degree of design sophistication is probably greater in commercial and industrial types. They may vary from the simplest and most inexpensive design to very elaborate, complex types. Because cost is such an extremely important factor, there is less tendency for the user to overspecify commercial and industrial relays.

A list of typical commercial and industrial relays follows:

Armature type relays
Bimetal relays
Clapper type relays
Coaxial relays
Crossbar switches
Dashpot time delay relays
Delay slug relays
Dry reed relays
Electromagnetic relays
Ferreed relays

Frequency sensitive relays
Hot wire relays
Impulse type relays
Latching relays
Linear expansion relays
Magnetic latching relays
Mercury plunger relays
Mercury plunger time delay relays
Mercury-wetted contact relays
Meter type relays
Motor driven steppers
Moving coil relays
Plunger relays
Polarized relays
Resonant reed relays
Solenoid actuated relays
Stepping relays
Stepping switches
Stepping switches (commercial)
Stepping switches (telephone type)
Strowger two-motion switches
Telephone type relays
Thermal relays
Thermal time delay relays
Time delay relays
Vacuum relays
Wire spring relays

3.8   Military relays

Although there is no exact dividing line between commercial and industrial relays and military relays, the latter are generally classified as those designed specifically for military use. Typical of these are the following:

Balanced armature relays
Crystal can relays
Polarized relays
Radiation resistant relays
Rotary relays
Thermal relays
Vacuum relays

3.9   Other classifications

Efforts have been made to classify relays by various relay functions. Unfortunately, almost all functional classifications soon begin to overlap or encompass such a large number of types under each heading that the list becomes quite repetitious.

Relays have also been classified by methods of actuation. This is a workable classification but tends to lump a great many types into a few categories with the result that it becomes unwieldy and of questionable value to the user.

Performance characteristics present perhaps one of the best methods for relay classification since a user is enabled to select a relay based on the operational characteristics he is looking for. A typical outline of a performance classification follows:

Classification By Relay Operating Characteristics

(1) Contact load level
  (a) Low level relays
  (b) Medium load relays
  (c) Heavy load relays
(2) Low coil power (sensitive)
  (a) Under 1 milliwatt
  (b) 1 to 75 milliwatts
(3) Timing functions obtained by
  (a) Delay slug relays
  (b) Dashpot time delay relays
  (c) Mercury plunger time delay relays
  (d) Thermal relays
  (e) Sensitive relays with RC (capacitor-resistor) network
  (f) Sensitive relays with parallel diode
(4) Latching
  (a) Mechanical latching relays
  (b) Magnetic latching relays
(5) High speed
  (a) Armature
  (b) Polarized relays
  (c) Mercury-wetted contact relays
  (d) Dry reed relays
  (e) Ferreed relays
  (f) Wire spring relays
(6) High voltage
  (a) Armature relays
  (b) Vacuum relays
(7) Long mechanical life
  (a) Armature relays
  (b) Mercury-wetted contact relays
  (c) Dry reed relays
  (d) Wire spring relays
  (e) Telegraph relays
(8) Stepper or impulse devices
  (a) Stepping relays
  (b) Stepping switches
  (c) Strowger two-motion switches
  (d) Motor-driven steppers
  (e) Impulse type relays
(9) Special relays
  (a) Crossbar switches
  (b) Coaxial relays
  (c) Resonant reed relays
  (d) Radiation resistant relays

4
Principles of Relay Operation

Introduction

This section is primarily concerned with the fundamental operating principles of "light duty" electromagnetic relays such as those used for communication, control, monitoring, or alarm switching circuits in which load currents are normally fractions of an ampere, and 10-ampere currents or transients are considered heavy. The questions of importance in the use of such relays tend to be not only how much power they can switch but more importantly how often, how fast, how reliably, or how consistently. The electrical and mechanical operating characteristics of such relays can be best understood by considering the electromagnetic switching "actuator" and the contact performance separately.

The principles of operation discussed here are those that might reasonably be of concern to a user of relays or a circuit designer faced with the selection and specification of a relay that will satisfy to best advantage his needs in terms of functions to be performed and modes of operation and environments to be encountered. Since a relay always performs a switching function, an understanding of contact phenomena should also aid in the selection of a relay well suited to a particular application in terms of reliability and optimum life. Relay performance follows precise rules of physics, chemistry, and metallurgy. When these rules are observed or violated, the relay behaves accordingly.

A comprehensive treatment of relay design and contact theory is given in the texts listed in the bibliography.

Direct-Current Relay Actuator Systems

A relay is primarily a remotely controlled and electrically operated switch consisting of one or more contact pairs that serve to open or close external circuits. A detailed consideration of the electrical phenomena occurring at these contacts during the switching function is given in Paragraph 4.8. Some mechanical requirements for their operation must be considered first.

4.1 Mechanical requirements for operation

The switch usually consists of combinations of movable and fixed low-resistance contacts which do the actual circuit opening and closing. The fixed contacts are mounted on springs or brackets, which have some degree of compliance or springiness. The movable contacts are mounted on some form of spring that can be deflected or on a hinged arm. The force and travel needed for these motions must serve a number of purposes.

Before the switch is actuated, the movable contacts must be held against the normally closed fixed contacts by a spring force sufficient to establish good electrical connection. When the switch is actuated, a number of things happen. By some means, each movable contact is pushed or pulled away from the corresponding normally closed fixed contact. This requires a force sufficient to overcome one or more contact springs. Also, there is friction between the contacts if they slide before they separate, and also in actuator pivots if they are present. As contact motion takes place, various springs deflect according to Hooke's law, and inertial forces must be overcome.

After the accelerated motion of contact transfer, there is an impact and deceleration as the movable contact reaches its normally open fixed contact. Both must deflect or deform to some degree as the desired contact force builds up. In many designs, some further overtravel will occur to provide contact cleaning action through sliding and to compensate for contact wear or erosion. Also, when there are multiple sets of contacts, allowance must be made for manufacturing tolerances for the various stages of travel required and the spring forces associated with them.

Understanding these forces and travels requires a consideration of both the contact mechanism and the motions involved. The discussion below will deal in an elementary way with both the static and the dynamic characteristics required of a mechanism for providing these forces. Detailed analyses of design considerations are available in the reference mentioned at the end of this section.

4.2   Power–force–stroke relationship for d-c electromagnets

The commonest form of actuator or motor system for electromagnetic relays consists of an energizing coil and a permeable iron circuit that has both a fixed portion (open loop) and a movable member, called the armature, that completes the magnetic circuit by closing the air gap. This armature must be hinged, pivoted, spring-mounted, or somehow free to move within certain constraints so that its motion can do useful work, namely, causing the contacts of the controlled circuit to perform a switching function. In addition, it must normally store some energy in a spring (or springs) for the return stroke and for holding selected contacts closed when the relay coil is in the unenergized condition. The considerations of the greatest importance are the following:

(1) To provide, at a minimum reasonable expenditure of power, adequate magnetic pull to assure reliable closing of contacts.

(2) To provide sufficient separation between open contacts to withstand the steady state and transient circuit voltages.

(3) To provide the desired operate and release time characteristics.

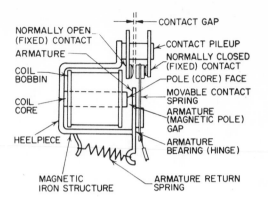

FIG. 4-1. CONTACT ACTUATING SYSTEM OF A SIMPLE RELAY EMPLOYING A CLAPPER-TYPE ARMATURE AND COMPLIANT CONTACT SPRING

Contact actuating systems. Actuation of contacts in electromagnetic relays is accomplished by four methods: (1) Direct armature clapper actuation (simplest construction); (2) multiple spring flexure (as in telephone-type relays); (3) card lift-off actuation (typical of wire spring relays); and (4) direct solenoid actuation (typical of power contactors). Only the first three systems will be analyzed here inasmuch as solenoid actuation is readily understood.

Direct armature clapper operation. One of the simplest contact arrangements employed in relays is the Break-Make or transfer (form C) contact combination employing a clapper type armature (see Fig. 4-1). It uses a flat or helical coil spring to provide the return or restoring force on the armature in the unoperated position. The break contact is then normally closed under action of the return spring. The sequence of spring forces to be overcome by the armature in transferring contacts to the fully operated position is graphed in Fig. 4-2 (broken curve 1, 2, 3, 4).

The moving contact spring attached to the armature is held against the break contact with a force created by the return spring, which also causes flexure in the movable contact spring. When the coil is energized, the armature will immediately begin to move in proportion to the energizing power. Between points 1 and 2, the flexed armature spring is being relieved, but the force to be overcome by the armature is also determined by the spring rate (deflection per unit loading) of the return spring. At point 2, the movable contact spring is completely relieved, and the normally closed (Break) contacts

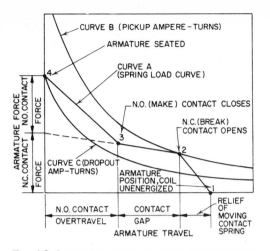

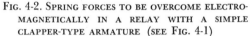

FIG. 4-2. SPRING FORCES TO BE OVERCOME ELECTRO-
MAGNETICALLY IN A RELAY WITH A SIMPLE
CLAPPER-TYPE ARMATURE (SEE FIG. 4-1)
*Contact forces and the contact gap can be varied by
changes in the lever arm ratio.*

open. The armature continues to overcome the
spring rate of the return spring until the normally open (Make) contact is met at point 3.
Load on this contact is built up at the combined
spring rates until the armature bottoms on the
core at point 4.

Flexure operation. In telephone-type relays, the basic spring arrangements are typically
those illustrated in Fig. 4-3. In this so-called flexure operation, a return spring is tensioned to
hold the armature in the unoperated position.
The moving contact spring is independently tensioned against the normally closed Break contact.
A slight separation, X_1, is provided between the
insulated buffer and the return spring to assure
that the full force of the moving contact spring

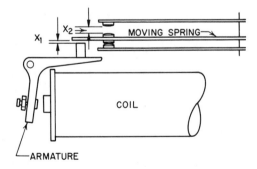

FIG. 4-3. FLEXURE CONTACT ACTUATOR SYSTEM OF A
TELEPHONE TYPE RELAY

is exerted against the stationary Break contact.
When the relay is energized, the armature,
through the buffer, lifts the moving spring contact off the Break contact and pushes it toward
the stationary, normally open (Make) contact.
After the contacts touch, further armature travel
builds up contact force until the armature seats
on the core or against the armature stop. The
force developed at the contact interface is a function of the flexure of the moving contact spring
and the stiffness of the stationary spring system.

In Fig. 4-4, at point 2, the moving contact
spring is picked up by the armature buffer, and
between points 2 and 3, the normally closed
constact preload is overcome. Between points 3

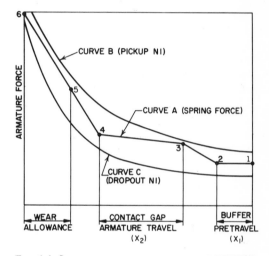

FIG. 4-4. SPRING FORCES TO BE OVERCOME ELECTRO-
MAGNETICALLY IN TELEPHONE TYPE RELAY
1   Armature position with coil unenergized
2-3   N.C. contacts open
3-4   Contact gap transfer
4-5   N.O. contacts close (initial tension)
5-6   Contact spring overtravel, or wear allowance.

and 4, the contact separation, X_2, is closed and
the normally open contact is met at point 4.
Pressure is built up on the Make contacts between points 4 and 5. Armature overtravel, or
contact wear allowance, ends at point 6, where
the armature is seated against the pole face.

It should be evident from this force curve that
contact pressures are the result of spring deflec-
tions caused by overtravel or built-in preload
(the adjustment process). It follows that contact
force will be reduced proportionally during relay life as a result of mechanical deformation,
electrical erosion of contacts, and armature bearing wear unless spring preloading is employed
in the relay design.

FIG. 4-5. COMPLIANT CONTACT SPRINGS PROVIDED
WITH INITIAL SPRING TENSION TO MAINTAIN
CONTACT FORCE ESSENTIALLY CONSTANT
THROUGHOUT LIFE

Figure 4-5 shows a contact construction in which initial tension or preload is built into the spring. With such an arrangement, any contact lift-off at all requires a minimum force equal to the initial tension. Furthermore, the contact force does not diminish appreciably during the wear-out process. On the other hand, the force to be overcome by the armature during the pickup stroke is a step function. This makes it possible for the pickup power measured at the start of the armature travel to be less than that required to complete the stroke after the engagement of the contacts. If this is the case, such a relay should not be used when the drive is a slowly changing current but only when at least the full specified pickup power can be abruptly applied to the coil.

Card lift-off actuation. This form of contact transfer is illustrated by Fig. 4-6. In this case, two moving springs and one stationary contact form a contact set or a transfer. The moving spring for the Break contact is tensioned against the stationary contact, and a slight separation is provided between it and the insulating actuator to assure that the full force of the pretensioned moving contact is exerted against the stationary

contact. As the armature moves toward the core, the moving contact is lifted off the stationary contact. The moving Make contact spring is tensioned against the insulating actuator with a force equal to the desired Make contact force. As the armature moves toward the core the actuating insulator follows. After a prescribed travel, it leaves the moving spring as the moving contact comes to rest on the stationary contact. The armature continues to move toward the core, thus providing separation between the actuating member and moving spring and thereby assuring that the full pretensioned force of the moving spring is exerted against the stationary contact.

The moving springs of the system usually are extremely compliant. Card wear and erosion of the contacts have virtually no effect on contact force until the erosion or wear has progressed to the point that the movable contacts rest on the card and their force is not exerted against the fixed conacts. This effect is independent of spring compliance. It should be mentioned that balance springs are required with lift-off actuation in order to overcome the force of the moving Make contacts in restoring the armature to its unoperated position.

Card lift-off actuation inherently provides considerably longer life than flexure actuation. Contacts, however, are more susceptible to contact chatter under the severe vibration and shock that are specified for many military applications. Another advantage of lift-off actuation is that any tendency of an individual contact to stick or weld is overcome, to a large extent, by the forces of the other contact springs acting on the system. In the case of the flexure system, only the restoring force of the moving spring farthest from the armature is available to overcome any sticking tendency of the outermost break contact.

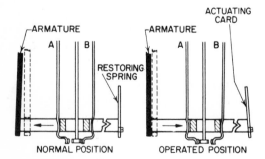

FIG. 4-6. CARD LIFT-OFF ACTUATION OF A FORM C
CONTACT COMBINATION, TYPICALLY ON A WIRE
SPRING RELAY

4.3 Matching mechanical and electrical characteristics

The area under the load curve is a measure of the work that the electromagnet is required to perform. Curve B of Fig. 4-2 represents a typical pull curve for an electromagnet. It shows the relation between pull and distance between the armature and core for a particular value of coil ampere-turns. From this figure it is evident that in order for the relay to operate, the force developed at all points of the armature travel will have to exceed the mechanical forces tending to restrain motion of the armature.

The force developed by the electromagnet may be expressed by

$$F = \frac{2\pi\,(NI)^2}{A\left(\mathcal{R}_0 + \dfrac{x}{A}\right)^2}$$

in which:

NI = ampere-turns

A = pole face area

x = distance between armature and core in the unoperated position

$\mathcal{R}_0$ = reluctance of iron portion of magnetic circuit

Thus the pull of an electromagnet of fixed dimensional constants varies with the energizing ampere-turns squared. The ampere-turn value at which the relay just operates is known as the ampere-turn sensitivity. However, for many circuit applications it is more convenient to express sensitivity in terms of the power, P, required to operate ($P = I^2R$, in which R is the coil resistance). Whereas ampere-turn sensitivity is independent of coil dimensions, power sensitivity varies with volume and the proportion of conductor space occupied by the winding. For a given coil volume and proportion, the ratio N^2/R is constant. It is known as coil conductance and is symbolized by G_c. By inversion, $R = N^2/G_c$ and $P = I^2R = N^2I^2/G_c$ watts, or the power required is inversely proportional to G_c. It can be shown (see Reference 3) that coil conductance may be expressed in terms of the dimensions of the coil by the equation

$$G_c = \frac{e}{\rho} \times \frac{lh}{\pi\,(d+h)}$$

in which

e = winding space factor (which decreases only slightly for fine wire windings)

ρ = wire resistivity

l = length of winding cross section

h = depth of winding cross section

d = diameter of core

Since power is N^2I^2/G_c, it is clear that the power required to operate varies inversely with coil length and directly with winding depth. It should not be assumed that power sensitivity will be the same for all values of coil resistance. It is not possible to obtain equal fullness of winding for all desired resistance values using standard wire sizes.

The required ampere-turns of magnetizing force to be generated in a coil of given available volume may be obtained by many turns of fine wire or much fewer turns of coarse wire carrying correspondingly larger currents. The resistance of the coil can be computed from the number of turns that can be wound in the particular dimensions available and their mean turn length, using wire of a given size and of a known resistance per unit length.

The coil constant, G_c, also relates to the amount of heat generated in the coil in providing a given magnetizing force, as well as to the inductance of the coil, which is the principle factor in determining the speed of response of a relay of given design to a given electrical drive.

Scaling down the size of a relay proportionally in all directions affects the performance in a number of ways:

(1) More magnetizing power (ampere-turns) is required for a given armature force and stroke.

(2) Magnetic saturation of the iron circuit is reached at lower armature force values and little further gain in pull is possible.

(3) The coil gives fewer ampere-turns of magnetizing force for a given power input.

(4) The ability of the relay to dissipate internally generated heat falls off sharply.

(5) The relay is more resistant to vibration, particularly at the higher frequencies because of the lower moments of inertia of its various parts.

Changing the coil wire one gauge size finer in a coil of given dimensions increases the coil resistance by approximately 60 per cent if the bobbin is wound to the same fullness. Such a change does not affect the power required for a given number of ampere-turns nor, therefore, the corresponding switching performance. It does reduce the current required for equal ampere-turns by 20 per cent and increases the voltage required by 25 per cent. Incremental changes of this order do not ordinarily introduce circuit mismatch inefficiencies of sufficient amount to be of concern, but the use of standard wire sizes (and resistance tolerances) automatically sets the resistance interval for fully wound coils at approximately 60 per cent and the resistance tolerance at $\pm$ 10 per cent for all but the very fine wire sizes (above B & S No. 45, a tolerance of 15 per cent is sometimes encountered).

Consideration of the force curves shown in Figs. 4-2 and 4-4 indicates that the ease of obtaining contact action with large forces and adequate travels is dependent on how low the dropout power may be as well as the value of pickup power available. Also, the choice of the return spring force and contact spring rates permit the designer to trade off between armature travel and the contact forces for given pickup and dropout values.

In such a trade-off, there are at least five variables related to the desired relay performance: (1) Pickup values, (2) dropout values, (3) contact gap, (4) pole gap (or wear allowance), and (5) spring (or normally closed contact) force. Three may be selected arbitrarily. The remaining two then become dependent variables and must be accepted, or else the first three choices must be revised until all five variables are satisfactory.

A simple relay with a compliant normally open contact has certain predictable characteristics:

(1) Pickup values are accurately adjustable within the limitations of spring force and contact position stability.

(2) Dropout values cannot be precisely adjusted without special provisions.

(3) Contact erosion results in variations in both pickup and dropout values and usually determines the effective end of contact life.

(4) Contact impact usually results in some bounce and provides some degree of contact wipe, roll, or scrubbing motion.

(5) The normally closed contacts become less stable as the relay coil current approaches the pickup value. This condition tends to make many relays prone to contact chatter when subjected to environmental vibration or coil current ripple when partially energized close to the pickup value.

(6) The normally open contact set, which commonly has greater overtravel, is less subject to chatter and bounce.

(7) Erratic pickup and dropout values can result from switching loads with heavy inrush current transients sufficient to cause contact sticking. Use of modern magnetic iron, annealing techniques, and relay design has resulted in relays which are seldom troubled with erratic performance due to magnetic hysteresis.

Dropout.   Curve C of Fig. 4-2 represents the pull of a relay electromagnet in the release or dropout range. As indicated, the armature will restore to its unoperated position when the energizing ampere-turns produce a pull that is less than the mechanical load throughout the release stroke.

Application considerations during design. The subject of application principles and techniques is covered in Sec. 5 of this handbook. However, application problems must be given some consideration during design.

4.4 Dynamic considerations

In addition to satisfying the requirements for operation under various steady-state conditions of circuit and environment, it may also be necessary to consider the relay's dynamic performance such as operate time, release time, tendency to chatter caused by current ripple, and bounce caused by contact impact.

Relay response to a step change in applied voltage is subject to delay due to two factors.

(1) The time required to change the flux in the magnetic circuit from some initial value to whatever value will cause the desired operation, either pickup or dropout. This delay is related to inductance L and resistance R in the coil circuit and to applied voltage E through the expression for current:

$$I = \frac{E}{R} \left(1 - e^{-Rt/L}\right)$$

However, since the value of L is quite variable as a function of the degree of magnetic saturation of the iron, an empirical solution is normally required.

(2) The mechanical transfer time of the moving elements. The time required for the accelerated motion of transfer in most small relays is short compared to the time required for the inductive current buildup except for applications in which the effect of the relay inductance is minimized by the other circuit parameters.

The pickup delay due to coil inductance, particularly for sensitive relays with a large value of coil constant, can be considerable — 5 to 50 milliseconds being common — whereas transfer times will usually fall within the range of 1 to a few milliseconds. For relays of a given design, the speed of response can be improved by:

(1) Increasing the power applied to the relay by increasing the source voltage or decreasing the coil resistance.

(2) Reducing the pickup value of the adjustment by minimizing spring forces and the various gaps.

(3) Increasing the source voltage and adding series resistance to lessen the circuit L/R ratio.

Although relay inductance is quite variable, dependable operate time curves can be made that are based on the coil constant relationship, $G_c = N^2/R$, in which the actual time for operation is plotted against coil "overdrive."

Coil overdrive is made up of two factors: the ratio of the final steady-state current to the relay pickup current, and the ratio of the open-circuit voltage to the voltage actually required for pickup of the relay. Graphical representation of coil overdrive versus operate time requires a family of curves, one form of which is shown in Fig. 4-7. Using these curves for a given design of relay, it is equally convenient to start with the desired performance and determine the necessary circuit power as well as the relay specifications, or to start with given circuit conditions and determine the speed of response that is to be expected.

Normally, dropout will occur following a delay of several milliseconds after the coil current is reduced below the dropout value. However, if a relay is shunted with a diode such as might be used for transient voltage suppression in transistor circuits, the delay can be as great as 20 to 30 milliseconds or longer. This is expressed approximately by the conventional logarithmic current decay curve from the steady-state value to the relay dropout value.

An additional dynamic characteristic to be considered in designing a relay for high-speed service is the bounce characteristic of the contacts as a result of the closure impact. In general, some mechanism for the absorption of the kinetic energy of the moving parts at the instant of impact must be provided in order to keep bounce time short compared to the operating time. This is normally accomplished by providing a small amount of spring compliance and contact rubbing action in addition to making the movable contact member as light as possible and its resonant frequency high. In any power switching application, bounce control is one of the most important factors in obtaining good contact life. Visible arcing at contact closure is normally evidence of contact bounce.

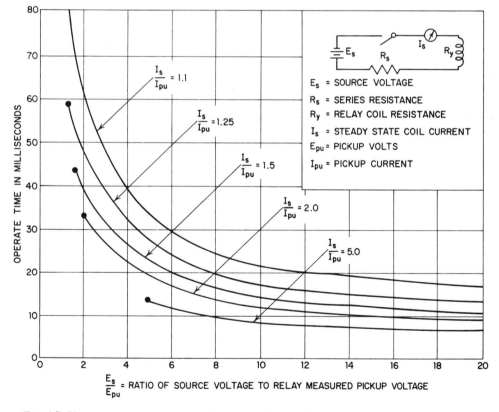

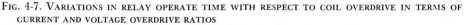

FIG. 4-7. VARIATIONS IN RELAY OPERATE TIME WITH RESPECT TO COIL OVERDRIVE IN TERMS OF CURRENT AND VOLTAGE OVERDRIVE RATIOS
Operate time is measured from closing of energizing circuit until normally open contacts engage.

Polarized Relays

A polarized relay is one that responds to the polarity as well as the magnitude of the energizing current. One way of accomplishing this type of operation is by connecting a blocking diode either in series or in shunt with the coil of a conventional d-c relay. When the energizing voltage is of the correct polarity, operation takes place as in a conventional relay; with opposite polarity applied voltage there is no response.

4.5   Magnetically polarized relays

In the simple magnetically polarized relay, the effect of a permanent magnet is introduced into the magnetic circuit, or circuits. The permanent magnet supplies flux to either of two permeable paths that can be completed by an armature. To transfer the armature and its associated contacts from one position to the other requires reversal of the polarity of the energizing current through the electromagnetic coil. This principle is illustrated by the two magnetic circuit configurations in Fig. 4-8. In one form, momentary energization of the coil by a current pulse of proper polarity reverses the flux in the iron structure of the relay; in the other, flux in the armature is reversed.

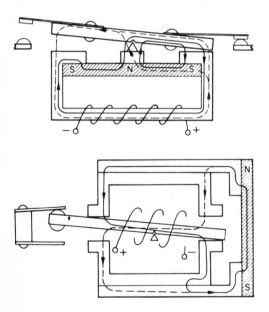

Fig. 4-8. Two forms of magnetically polarized relays
The solid lines indicate the magnetic latching flux from the permanent magnet, shown crosshatched. The dash line shows the redistribution of flux when the electromagnetic coil is energized at a high enough level to cause armature transfer.

To effect this reversal, the number of ampere-turns provided by the coil must be sufficient to overcome the reluctance of the open pole gap (see dotted line flux path). The advantage of this type of magnetic latching operation is that the contacts remain in the last position without continued application of electromagnetic power. It also augments the amount of armature force available with a given relay size and input power .

Polarized relays take many other design forms. For a listing of types, see Sections 1 and 3.

A-C Relay Actuator Systems

Alternating-current relays present the problem of obtaining a chatter-free contact closure when the energizing current passes through zero twice each cycle. One of the several ways of approaching this problem involves a modification of the magnetic structure (shaded pole); it is described below. Employing a-c rectification ahead of a conventional d-c relay is another method of actuating a relay from an a-c power source; it is described in Sec. 5.

4.6   Shaded-pole relays

Shaded-pole a-c relays are generally constructed like simple d-c electromagnetic relays with a portion of the core pole face separated from the rest of the pole face and enclosed in a loop of copper. This loop has the effect of producing a lag in the timing of the a-c magnetic flux in one portion of the pole face with respect to that in the unshaded portion. While the current in the coil passes through zero twice each cycle, the flux in the armature gap and hence the pull remains at a high enough level to hold the armature operated. If the minimum pull exceeds the mechanical forces (spring and gravity) tending to restore the armature to its unoperated position, there will be little buzzing of the armature or chattering of contacts.

The current drawn by a shaded-pole relay is determined by the a-c impedance of the coil at the power line frequency. This impedance depends upon the coil constants, the characteristics of the magnetic circuit, and the armature position. For example, the impedance of a relay may be twice as large with the armature operated (seated) as with it unoperated. It is customary to express the sensitivity or actual power required of such an a-c relay in volt-amperes, but the degree to which the iron is magnetized is better measured by V^2/R_c, the ratio of the square of the applied voltage to the coil resistance for a full coil. The degree of magnetization determines the inductance and impedance at various applied voltages for any particular frequency. From the applied voltage and impedance, the actual volt-amperes can be determined both for the energized and unenergized conditions. Some relays will not remain operated or may chatter badly if the coil current is reduced to half of the rated pickup value. Many a-c relays are intended to be energized at the rated voltage value even though there may be considerable margin between pickup voltage and rated voltage. This is sometimes referred to as *on-off* operation.

Contact Performance

Contact theory and its application to the design of relays constitute a complex subject that is treated comprehensively in texts. Since this section is intended to acquaint the reader with the factors that influence contact performance in service, the discussion is largely limited to presenting the practical aspects of contact design and circuit engineering. For a detailed discussion of constriction resistance, plastic flow, arc initiation glow discharge, tunnel effects, film breakdown and the like, see Reference 1.

4.7 Contact characteristics

Contact characteristics that affect switching performance are:

(1) Electrical conductivity

(2) Thermal conductivity

(3) Hardness; limit of elasticity; Young's Modulus

(4) Resistance to arc erosion, welding or electrical sticking, cold welding, mechanical wear, oxidation, atmospheric contamination (chemically active)

(5) Tendency to bounce on impact, gaseous adsorption, catalytic polymerization of hydrocarbons, metal transfer at contact closure and on arcing at opening.

Besides the physical and chemical properties of the metal, there are some geometrical and dynamic considerations:

(1) Shape of contacts

(2) Force between contacts

(3) Amount of slide or "wipe"

(4) Amount of rolling or twisting motion

(5) Resiliency of the supporting structure and its tendency to enhance or inhibit bounce or chatter.

When contacts meet, the metal at the point of the contact deforms until the actual touching area supports the contact force and provides metal-to-metal contact unless some foreign material interferes.[1] On a microscopic scale, many actual points of contact (often referred to as *a-spots*) form the electrical conductor and carry the current. The contact interface is also subject to mechanical abrasion, metal "galling" or "stiction" as it rubs, and "cold welding." The surface will adsorb a monomolecular layer of volatile molecules in direct proportion to the molecular weight and concentration of the volatile material and the ambient pressure, among other factors, and inversely proportional to the temperature. (Water vapor is also a particularly common substance forming very thin adsorbed layers.)

Each metal has its own pertinent chemical properties. Silver and silver alloys, which have excellent electrical and thermal characteristics, tend to combine chemically with gaseous compounds of sulphur, the halogens (fluorine, chlorine, bromine, and iodine), and silicones to form high-resistance, usually hard coatings. Unlike the other "noble" metals (gold, platinum, rhodium, iridium, palladium, and ruthenium, all of which are used in contacts) silver has no measurable catalytic effect (polymerization) in the sense of changing the adsorbed hydrocarbon molecules into some solid hydrocarbon material. Arcing, however, can accomplish the precipitation of solid carbon or carbonaceous products, usually in a ring around the actual point of contact.

Some more active metals, either pure or in alloys, find special areas of usefulness due to particular mechanical properties. Molybdenum, tungsten, nickel, and mercury, for example, are used alone or as alloying or sintering ingredients. Cadmium oxide, tungsten carbide, tin, magnesium, and carbon are sometimes added to silver to inhibit sticking or welding, particularly in high current relays or contactors. When contacts are surrounded by an inert gas, like nitrogen, consideration can be given to contact materials that could not be used in open style relays.

4.8 Effects of load currents

Physical conditions at the contact interface. The chemical and catalytic actions of these various contact materials are accelerated due to the fact that for an instant of time at each switching

---

[1]Deformation at the point of contact, which can be either elastic or plastic, is one of several factors that contribute to the amount of contact bounce.

operation the metal at the actual point of contact will be exceedingly hot, normally molten, and often vaporized. Arcing temperatures at the instant of circuit closure or interruption will be in the order of 3,000 to 6,000°K. In this temperature range, all metals melt and probably boil, and all common chemical compounds tend to decompose. Included among the compounds are hydrocarbons.

"Softening" voltage.   For each metal in the form of a short electrical conductor — such as a point of contact at a contact interface — there is a current density above which heat will be evolved faster than it can be conducted away until temperature equilibrium is reached at the melting point of the contact metal. The voltage drop across the contact interface is the electrical characteristic necessary for such a current density to maintain this metal softening temperature. This is commonly referred to as the "softening voltage." As the contact interface softens, the area in contact increases; any molecular thicknesses of film are vaporized, the resistance is reduced, and no further increase in voltage drop will occur as the result of further current increase unless there is particulate contamination that can interfere with this process.

Typical softening, melting, and boiling voltages (Holm) are as follows:

Material	Softening	Melting	Boiling
Silver	0.09	0.37	0.67
Gold	0.08	0.43	0.90
Palladium		0.57	1.3

These values drop off rapidly as the ambient temperature increases. Gold softens at 100°C and silver at 180°C as a result of mechanical considerations only. When the voltage drop at the contact interface exceeds the softening voltage of a particular contact material, fractional milliohm contact resistance at the interface will normally be established as the contact softens. Circuits in which there is no possibility of applying to the contacts either a steady-state or a transient voltage as great as the softening voltage are known as *dry* or *low-level* circuits.

4.9   Types of loads

The types of contact loads to be considered in relay design may be divided into four broad categories: (1) Dry circuits, (2) low level loads, (3) intermediate loads, and (4) heavy loads in the so-called rated-load range. Each of these categories presents its peculiar problems:

(1) Dry circuits are usually considered to be loads that are not opened or closed by the contacts, that is, current may flow through the contacts after closure and before opening, but the contact does not directly control the load. It is advisable, however, before concluding that the contact is dry to consider the possibility of the cable capacitance's being discharged through the contacts at time of closing.

(2) Low level switching ordinarily is considered to be in the range of microamperes or a few milliamperes, with the open-circuit voltage below the melting voltage of the contact material. This category covers a wide range of contact loads. The voltages and currents, however, are well below those at which arcing occurs.

(3) Intermediate contact loads are those for which the current is below the minimum necessary for a momentary arcing condition. Fifty to 400 milliamperes at 26 volts d-c is representative of this range.

(4) Heavy contact loads are those that cause some degree of contact arcing under normal operation.

Dry circuits.   The performance of contacts under dry circuit conditions is affected by many parameters. Contact material, contact force, contact wipe, cleanliness of contact surfaces, type of environment, and magnitude of current and voltage all influence their behavior. By definition, a contact is considered to be dry if it does not make or break current. There are, however, many applications falling within this category in which contacts may be required to carry appreciable current. If the initial interface resistance is high, appreciable voltage may appear across closed contacts at the instant of closure of some other part of the circuit. This resistance may decrease sharply or be affected very little, depending upon the surface condition. If organic films are the cause of initially high resistance, appreciable voltage may produce low and stable resistance. On the other hand, resistance may remain high if it is caused by particulate contamination. Over the wide load range encompassed by the dry contact concept, it is not possible to generalize on probable performance. It is possible, however, to evaluate contact performance for a particular set, or a limited range, of conditions within the broad dry contact category. Usually gold alloy contacts, or gold alloys working against palladium, offer the best performance under these conditions. The suitability of a contact material or combination of materials, however, depends on the interactions of the parameters mentioned earlier.

Low level loads. As in the case of dry circuits, contact performance at low levels is determined by materials, design parameters, and performance criteria. Within this range organic films may affect performance significantly. Although it is virtually impossible to eliminate the adsorption of organic films, cleaning techniques, controlled environment, and design may reduce their effects and assure satisfactory performance. It is within this range of low level contact loads that polymerization of adsorbed organic material or condensates on contact surfaces of materials in the platinum family can be particularly troublesome. When organic materials are present and microscopic sliding occurs between contacts of the platinum group, the heat developed by friction causes polymerization of the organic materials. These polymers, in the form of a powdery substance, cause high and unstable resistance. Increased contact force and greater wipe between contacts upon closure may alleviate but will not eliminate the trouble. The difficulty usually, but not necessarily, is associated with relatively large numbers of operations. Vibration of relay contact springs also has been responsible, on occasion, for considerable contact trouble of this type. The use of gold, gold alloys, or gold alloys in combination with palladium practically eliminates the polymer problem. However, gold or gold alloy contacts of 22K or higher gold content, when working against each other, can be susceptible to sticking or cold welding. This tendency must be considered in design and application.

Intermediate loads. In the intermediate load range, slight arcing may occur on closure or opening of contacts. Usually the erosion of contacts in the intermediate range progresses at a much slower rate than at voltages and currents close to the maximum contact rating. Loss of contact force, therefore, is not a problem. However, arcing in the presence of adsorbed or condensed organic material and the contact surfaces causes carbonization of these materials. The voltages and currents in the intermediate range are not high enough to break down completely the relatively high resistance of the carbonaceous deposits. As a result, appreciable contact resistance sometimes develops within several thousands of operations. In general, hermetically sealed relays are more likely to be affected than open type designs. High current contactors and circuit breakers are not affected significantly because of the high currents and voltages that are switched and the relatively high contact forces. The difficulty created by carbonaceous deposits can be minimized in smaller general purpose relay designs by choice of insulating materials and design of the contact actuating systems, and in hermetically sealed relays by baking and evacuating techniques or by isolation of the contacts from organic materials. Usually the resistance developed under intermediate load conditions, while significant, is tolerable from a circuit functioning standpoint. However, in certain critical cases the contact resistance may be troublesome. One set of conditions that should be avoided, if at all possible, is imposing arcing and low energy loads on the same contact.

Heavy loads. Ordinarily, contacts operating at, or close to, the rated load function satisfactorily for their required life. The amount of carbonaceous material formed under these load conditions may be considerably greater than the quantity observed at lower loads. However, the actual area of contact of the mating surfaces is usually relatively free from this material and the voltages and currents are high enough to break down the resistance of deposits in the immediate contacting areas.

Other considerations. Materials such as gold or gold alloys ordinarily are not suitable for currents in excess of approximately 0.5 ampere because of their relatively fast erosion rate. However, life requirements and relay design will determine the suitability of these materials. When contacts are to be used only to switch heavy loads, silver, silver cadmium oxide, and palladium have a longer erosion life. In most instances, if silver contacts are restricted to the load conditions for which they are particularly well suited, the slight resistance offered by sulphide films is of little consequence. Unrealistic and unnecessarily stringent contact resistance requirements that do not reflect actual circuit usage are sources of difficulty rather than the malfunction of the contacts.

The use of heavy contact forces and scrubbing action and the avoidance of exposure to volatile hydrocarbons by putting the contacts in a separate enclosure both tend to minimize contact trouble, particularly at the lower level of contact loads. The use of bifurcated or parallel contacts also helps.

Occasionally in hermetically sealed relays, if insufficient clearance is provided between contacts and a grounded case, flashover to the case due to gaseous ionization may occur upon repeated opening of the contact load. This condition, while undesirable, usually does not damage the relay when it is ungrounded. The effect is about the same as that of a repeated opening of the contacts on the contacts themselves. If the relay case is isolated from ground, however, consideration should be given to the personal hazard of possibly having a relay case at a potential well above ground because of a circuit trouble.

Much has been written concerning the use of relays to switch three-phase loads. Difficulties that have occurred were caused by misapplication. The transient and steady state voltages between contacts in a three-phase application may or may not be greater than those in a single-phase or direct-current application. Irrespective of the type of load, the voltages that may appear between adjacent contacts should be well below the dielectric withstanding voltage.

4.10   Contact gap characteristics

Voltage breakdown. Conditions for voltage breakdown of a contact gap depend on various geometric and environmental factors. For a static gap, initiation of an arc discharge can be related to the type of gas (air, nitrogen, hydrogen, argon, helium), gas pressure, and gap length. Secondary variables that influence this relationship are contact shape, material and surface texture, gaseous contaminants such as water content, and the degree to which the gas in the gap is being subjected to ionization. Discharge is initiated when ions that may normally exist in the voltage-charged gap are accelerated sufficiently to generate more ions and have a number of "mean free path lengths" in which to accomplish this. The minimum voltage for this kind of breakdown is of the order of 320 volts at any pressure for air, and at normal atmospheric pressure the gap length is approximately 0.0003 in. For both shorter and longer gaps, the breakdown voltage is greater unless the gap becomes exceedingly small (in the Ångstrom range). For materially shorter gaps, the voltage breakdown follows the rules for vacuum discharge or direct molecular ionization.

Arcs will form in a voltage stress of approximately one-half million volts per centimeter when the gap is small compared to the mean free path length of the gas molecules (or ions) in the gap. Therefore, when the gap is sufficiently small, much lower voltages are capable of initiating breakdown. Typical values are 100 volts for a gap length of 10,000 Ångstroms (0.001 mm), 10 volts for 1,000 Å, or 1 volt for 100 Å. At these extremely small gaps, the contact damage caused by the breakdown is accentuated by the discharge of the air capacitor formed by the very closely spaced contacts (and the nearby parts of the circuit). This discharge takes place as the closing contacts are about to meet. This arc is normally invisible and not to be confused with visible arcing (frequently seen on contact closure), which is actually caused by contact reopening during contact bounce.

Metal transfer. Since the high current density in contact a-spots at the first instant of closure can cause metal melting and probably boiling even at fractional ampere loads, there tends to be some metal transfer at contact closure. These phenomena become matters of practical concern when contact life must extend over many millions of operations, especially when significant circuit or line capacitance must be discharged in addition to the contact gap capacitance.

When contact separation takes place, the last instant of metallic conduction is subject to the conditions of small contact area and very light force. This results in molten or boiling metal (sometimes called a *bridge*) that becomes a copious source of electron emission and of the ionized, positively charged vapor of the contact metal immediately thereafter. These effects meet the requirements for generating the plasma (electrified particles) for an arc discharge when the circuit power can supply the energy needed at a rate sufficient to maintain the plasma. The amount of energy dissipated in the arc is the principle factor in governing the amount of metal transfer during arcing.

Inrush transients at contact closure. Contact damage is frequently caused by current surges at the instant of closure when the contact forces are light. Contact sliding and bouncing probably take place, and the load current is often many times the steady state value. A microscopic weld or "bridge" will frequently form at the point of contact closure. In d-c circuits this bridge usually ruptures asymmetrically at the next contact opening, resulting in metal transfer. In a-c circuits, there is usually a net loss of contact material. The metal vapor that condenses in the vicinity of the actual contact area is normally black and is frequently mistaken for carbon.

Loads that produce transients at contact closure are as follows:

(1) Tungsten lamps whose cold resistance is 7 to 10 per cent of their hot resistance.

(2) Transformers and ballasts that may cause transients 5 to 20 times their normal currents when switched in their inputs.

(3) A-C solenoids and some kinds of motors.

(4) Capacitors placed across contacts or loads with inadequate series-connected current-limiting resistance.

To meet these circuit conditions, the relay designer may elect to employ:

(1) Heavy duty contacts and a high contact force to minimize contact bounce on closure.

(2) Contact materials with the highest possible electrical and thermal conduction, usually silver or silver alloys.

(3) Contact material additives to inhibit welding, such as cadmium or cadmium oxide.

(4) Relay actuator mechanisms to enhance weld-breaking ability of contacts.

The circuit designer can add small values of series resistance to the circuit to reduce current surges.

Contact Protection

4.11 D-C circuits

When the circuit to an inductive load is opened, much of the energy stored in the load must be dissipated as arcing at the contacts unless some alternative means of energy absorption is provided. Some of the load energy is dissipated as heat in the load resistance, in eddy current losses in its magnetic circuit, and in the distributed capacitance of the coil winding. For d-c circuits, a number of simple solutions are available to lessen or inhibit contact arcing:

(1) A semiconductor diode may be connected across the inductive load (see Fig. 4-9), so that it blocks the applied voltage at contact closure but allows the stored energy in the load to recirculate through it at contact opening. The time for the load current to decay to 37 per cent of its steady state value equals L/R. The blocking diode will prevent any inductive transients from appearing across the contacts during the switch-

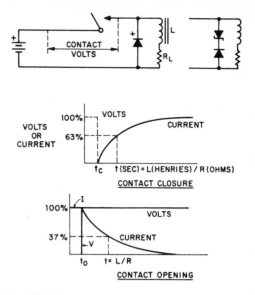

FIG. 4-9. METHOD OF USING SEMICONDUCTOR DIODE TO SUPPRESS VOLTAGE SURGE FROM INDUCTIVE LOAD AT CONTACT OPENING

ing operation. For loads below the minimum arcing current, the time required for load de-energization can be materially reduced by adding a Zener diode, resistor, or a varistor in series with the blocking diode, thus increasing R. The rate of energy dissipation after the contacts are opened is thereby increased as the load current circulates back through this additional voltage drop. The instantaneous voltage plus the source voltage should not exceed 320 volts.

(2) The load or the contacts may be shunted with a resistor-capacitor combination (see Fig. 4-10). For load currents in the stable arc range, the resistor, R_c, can be selected to match the load resistance, or it may be ½ or 1 ohm per volt of the power source. For smaller load currents than can cause a stable arc, the resistor can be higher in value. A reasonable value is one resulting in a voltage transient of less than 300 volts for the sum of the source voltage and the instantaneous voltage generated by the load current in the resistor, calculated thus:

$$R = \frac{300 - E_{\text{source}}}{I_{\text{load}}}$$

The resistor is essential and must be large enough to limit the current transient from the capacitor discharge (or charge) on contact closure to prevent contact welding. The capacitor should be large enough to accept the stored energy of the load without permitting an electric

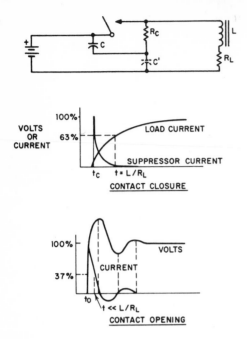

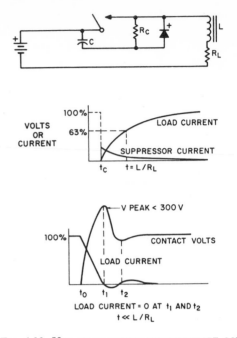

Fig. 4-10. Use of capacitor-resistor combination to suppress current surge from inductive load
Capacitor may be at either C or C'.

Fig. 4-11. Use of capacitor-resistor-diode combination for arc suppression with a highly
inductive load

breakdown of the contact gap, normally at
greater than 320 volts. An oscillograph is the
best way to determine when these transients are
adequately suppressed. In Fig. 4-10, the capacitor
can be connected either at C or C'. Connection
at C is preferred since it protects against
source and line, as well as load, inductance.

(3) A varistor (voltage-sensitive resistor) or
"Thyrite" may be used to shunt the load. If such
a device carries 10 per cent as much current as
the load, the maximum switching transient will
be about twice the source voltage. This method
is also suitable for a-c circuits.

(4) For extremely inductive loads, for the
longest possible life, or for load power and contact gap length above the minimums for a stable
arc, the circuit of Fig. 4-11 may be used. In this
circuit, the capacitor is charged through the diode but can discharge only through the resistor.
This arrangement gives essentially zero contact
voltage drop at the instant of contact opening.
The capacitor value should be such that when
the energy transfer from the load is complete, the
peak voltage to which it charges will not cause a
breakdown of the diode, the contact gap, or itself. Usually the peak voltage should not exceed
200 to 350. For d-c inductive loads for which the
conditions for a stable arc may be satisfied by the

partially opened contacts, the circuit of Fig. 4-11
permits the contact gap to be established without
drawing an arc, and the stored energy transfer is
accomplished more quickly than would have
been the case if the contacts had been allowed
to arc. The reason for this is that the integrated
inverse voltage to which the capacitor charges
is greater than the voltage drop in an arc, were
arcing permitted.

(5) Where the inductive load of a relay coil
presents a hazard to transistor drive circuits, coils
with dual windings wound together on the coil
bobbin (called *bifilar coils*) may be used with
one winding shorted. This arrangement provides
a pronounced damping effect on the rate of
change of magnetic flux in the iron and hence
provides a significant moderating effect on the
induced voltage. *(See also Sec. 5.)*

4.12 Switching a-c- inductive loads

Such loads are most commonly treated in a
different manner from d-c loads because of the
fact that a stable arc will normally be terminated
when the current passes through zero and reverses at the end of the first half cycle following
contact separation. Fairly common practice is to
use arc-resistant contact material, preferably in a
relay in which the contacts separate slowly, and

let arcing be terminated by the reversal of the current rather than by the continuing separation of the contacts. When load currents get too heavy for safe interruption by small relays (greater than 10 to 25 amperes), the current reversal effect can be supplemented by magnetic or air blowout, multiple break contacts, arc gap cooling labyrinths, or by evacuating the contact chamber.

Under moderate arcing conditions, contact life may be greatly increased by shunting the load with a resistor-capacitor-diode combination whose time constant is equal to that of the load:

$$R_c C = L/R_l$$

or, assuming R_c equals the load resistance R_l,

$$C = L/R^2$$

This network makes the load characteristics essentially resistive. When the maximum possible contact life is required, either of the capacitor-diode combinations shown in Fig. 4-12 may be justified. For 115-volt a-c service, the diodes should have a peak inverse voltage rating of 400, the capacitor should have a d-c working voltage of 200 volts d-c, and there should be a 100K-ohm resistor, which will dissipate nearly 1 watt. The capacitor discharge time after a switch closure may be as long as a second.

The transient voltages developed when the contacts open the load circuit may exceed the dielectric withstanding voltage between contacts and another part of the relay. In some circuits, these voltages may be high enough to cause breakdown of another circuit component. These transients often cause interference in adjacent or associated circuits. Usually a resistor-capacitor network, applied in accordance with the rules outlined in Sec. 5, will reduce the voltage to a level that suitably protects the contacts and avoids dielectric breakdown. However, it is sometimes necessary to use diodes to eliminate radio interference from arcing. For these latter cases, no general rules can be formulated because the interference is closely associated with the particular circuits.

In general, careful attention to contact protection can increase life expectancy as much as three orders of magnitude. System reliability may be greatly improved by elimination of high voltage transients, and the speed of response and its consistency is often substantially improved.

REFERENCES

(1) Holm, Ragnar, *Electric Contacts Handbook*, Springer-Verlag, Berlin, 1958.

(2) Jones, F. Llewellyn, *The Physics of Electrical Contacts*, Oxford University Press, London, 1957.

(3) Peek, R. L., Jr. and Wager, H. N., *Switching Relay Design*, D. Van Nostrand Company, Inc., New York, 1955.

(4) Roters, Herbert C., *Electromagnetic Devices*, John Wiley & Sons, New York, 1941.
Also:
Bell System Technical Journal
Collected Papers and Proceedings of National Conference on Electromagnetic Relays, Oklahoma State University, Stillwater, Okla., 1953-1966.
Proceedings for Engineering Seminar on Electrical Contacts, Pennsylvania State University, State College, Pa., 1956-1961.
University of Maine, Orono, Maine, 1962-1963 and 1964-1965.

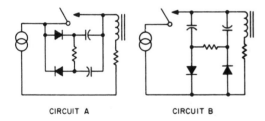

CIRCUIT A   CIRCUIT B

FIG. 4-12. RESISTOR-CAPACITOR-DIODE COMBINATIONS FOR SUPPRESSING CONTACT ARC ON A-C INDUCTIVE LOAD

5

Relay Application Considerations

D-C Armature Type Electromagnetic Relays

5.1 Introduction

The armature type electromagnetic relay is a complex electromechanical device in which electrical energy is converted through linkages into mechanical motion that actuates electrical contacts. Its performance and reliability, therefore, depend upon the interactions of many design parameters related to applications and performance criteria. It is essential, then, that the suitability of a design be evaluated in terms of the factors that may affect its performance under specified environments, winding circuit conditions, mechanical life requirements, and contact loads.

5.2 Design analysis

The initial phase in the evaluation and application of any relay should be an analysis of its design and a study of the controls exercised to assure consistent performance. Design criteria to a large extent depend upon the type of application, economic considerations, and consequences of failure. A design that is adequate for most applications might not be suitable for use in critical circuits requiring close controls and a high degree of stability. In such cases performance studies of limited quantities of relays cannot always be relied upon as the sole means of establishing the suitability of a design. It must also be determined whether a design is basically sound, employs quality materials, and is a product of good workmanship and controlled techniques.

Relay design analysis is an art involving good engineering judgment. This judgment must be based, to a large extent, on experience and an appreciation of cost factors related to performance requirements and the consequences of failure. It is not possible to present a comprehensive treatment of this subject in a handbook of this character. However, the following discussion outlines a few design factors that warrant consideration in specifying relays for critical applications.

(1) Friction. Frictional effects can significantly affect performance. Plated armature bearings or ferrous bearings that tend to rust often produce excessive friction. Excessive slide or wipe between actuating members, or actuated members, also may cause variable friction.

(2) Finishes. Some finishes intended for corrosion protection are susceptible to a whisker growth[1] that can cause voltage breakdown between plated parts and other metallic members of a relay having small clearances. Wear-resistant finishes on polefaces and backstop surfaces are often required for relays having long mechanical life or for which a high degree of stability in electrical characteristics is required.

(3) Contact adjustments. Contact force and contact overtravel may be affected significantly by environment, wear, and contact margins. It is essential, therefore, that the minimum adjustments provide sufficient margin to assure reliable contact performance for the required life and applicable environments. The design and contact adjusting techniques should assure

---

[1]Certain finishes, such as zinc, cadmium, and unfused electroplated tin, tend to develop whisker-like growth in the form of fine metallic filaments.

also that the full force of movable contact springs is exerted against the fixed contacts. With buffer-actuated contact springs, it is essential that there be a gap between the actuator and movable spring when the armature is fully released. If a buffer gap is not provided, appreciable contact follow is required to assure adequate contact force. For relays with armature card lift-off actuation, clearance is necessary between the card and movable springs of closed contacts in both the operated and unoperated positions.

In many instances, for example, normally open contacts of buffer-actuated designs, contact force cannot be measured directly. A study of the actuating system is necessary to determine the type of measurement required to assure reliable contact.

(4) Manufacturing cleanliness. Cleaning procedures should assure the highest degree of cleanliness consistent with the state of the art and the application requirements. Relay parts — particularly contacts, bearings, and polefaces — should be free from particulate contamination, and contacts, insofar as possible, should be free from organic films when controlling low energy circuits.

(5) Contact materials. The contact materials employed should be suitable for the contact load, environment, and other performance requirements. Wherever possible, materials that tend to stick should be avoided. Armature card lift-off actuation often tends to overcome contact sticking tendencies.

(6) Insulating materials. Insulating materials within contact chambers, or adjacent to contacts of open relays, should emit a minimum amount of vapors that might impair contact performance. Designs employing inorganic materials, or in which the contacts are isolated from organic materials, offer greater assurance of reliable contact performance.

Insulating materials should be: (1) free from corrosion promoting impurities, (2) dimensionally stable to minimize adjustment changes with fluctuation in temperature and humidity, (3) free from a tendency to shed particles that may contaminate contacts or become entrapped in bearings or air gaps.

(7) Soldering fluxes. Virtually all liquid or paste soldering fluxes and chemical strippers for enameled wire are highly corrosive. Unless the design lends itself to thorough washing and neutralizing processes, the use of these fluxes and strippers should be avoided. Sealing techniques for hermetically sealed relays should insure that flux or vapors are not entrapped within the contact chamber.

5.3 Winding circuit design

There are four operating characteristics for electromagnetic relays, namely, nonpickup and pickup on the operate stroke and hold and dropout on the release stroke. Whether only one or a combination of these characteristics is specified depends on circuit complexity and the relay's function. Definitions for these characteristics, which were given in Sec. 1, shall be restated here briefly. When a winding is energized:

(1) *Nonpickup* is the voltage (or current) at or below which: (a) The armature shall not move from its unoperated position, or (b) the normally closed contacts shall not open and normally open contacts shall not close.

(2) *Pickup* is the voltage (or current) at or below which: (a) The armature shall assume its fully operated position (seated against the core), or (b) all normally closed contacts shall open and all normally open contacts shall close.

When the energizing voltage (or current) of an operated relay is reduced:

(1) *Hold* is the voltage (or current) at or above which: (a) The armature shall not move from its operated position, or (b) the normally open contacts shall not open and the normally closed contacts shall not close.

(2) *Dropout* is the voltage (or current) at or above which: (a) The armature shall restore to its unoperated position, or (b) all normally open contacts shall open and all normally closed contacts shall close.

For most applications only *pickup* and *dropout* requirements are essential. Special circuit conditions or other applications considerations, to be discussed later, sometimes necessitate specifying *nonpickup* and *hold* requirements.

It is usually advisable to specify requirements in terms of the armature position. In some designs, however, such as certain sensitive relays or in hermetically sealed relays, the requirements are specified only in terms of contact operation.

Relays in which the armature hesitates while on the verge of just closing or opening contacts or in which the contacts have barely opened or closed could be in an extremely unstable state. Any slight mechanical disturbance or voltage fluctuation could cause intermittent opening or closing of the contacts. It is advisable, therefore, to specify requirements assuring that the desired performance will be obtained, that is, that the contacts will be fully operated. Specifying that the armature shall not move at a particular energizing value and shall complete its stroke at another value will provide this assurance. In some designs, such as certain sensitive relays under marginal requirements, it may not be possible to guarantee that the armature will operate fully.

5.4 Winding resistance and sensitivity

To define relays either as *voltage sensitive* or *current sensitive* devices is to use common misnomers. When a relay is to be operated from a power source with no series components, it is convenient to specify performance requirements in terms of voltage. When the winding circuit includes other fixed or variable components, however, it is preferable to specify relay and circuit requirements in terms of current. In either case, it is the ampere-turns — the product of turns and current *(NI)* — or power required that determines the sensitivity and operating characteristics of a relay. Only for convenience, or to reflect circuit usage, are relays designated voltage or current relays.

Efficiency or sensitivity of an electromagnetic armature type relay may be expressed in ampere-turns or power required to just pickup. For a particular design and contact arrangement, ampere-turn sensitivity is independent of wire size or fullness of winding. On the other hand, power sensitivity *(I²R or EI)* varies with the fullness of winding since it is a function of coil conductance, $G_c = N^2/R$.[1] In the absence of information on a desired winding, it is important that the manufacturer be consulted with respect to sensitivity or operating characteristics.

Almost all electromagnetic relay coils are wound with copper magnet wire. Since winding resistance is proportional to the absolute temperature for copper windings:

$$\frac{R_0}{R_1} = \frac{390 + T_0}{390 + T_1} \quad \text{or} \quad \frac{R_0}{R_1} = \frac{234.5 + T_0}{234.5 + T_1}$$

In these expressions, T_0 and T_1 are winding temperatures, and 390 and 234.5 are the inferred points of zero resistance on the Fahrenheit and Celsius scales, respectively. Since the current required to perform a particular function remains constant, assuming no instability,

the power required, I^2R, is proportional to absolute temperature. Ampere-turn sensitivity, again assuming no instability, is unaffected by temperature.

5.5 Winding corrosion

When a winding, particularly in the de-energized state at high humidity, is positive with respect to another winding, the core, or any other part of a relay structure, it is important that the coil insulation be free from impurities that form an electrolyte and cause electrolytic corrosion. Depending upon the type of coil insulation and wire size, the corrosion risk varies from serious to negligible.

In the early days of telephone switching design, the materials available were much more corrosive than the improved materials procurable today. In order to reduce the corrosion hazard, a positive grounded battery was used, and whenever possible, the positive ground connection was broken and the winding was kept negative during idle periods. This practice is still followed, although the materials now employed are far superior to former ones. In commercial or industrial use, however, Underwriters regulations may preclude breaking the ground side of the line where voltage is in excess of 50 volts.[2]

Before using a relay design that may be subjected to high humidity for extended periods under adverse circuit conditions, it is wise to refer to the literature on the corrosiveness of insulating materials. It should not be assumed that because a relay is hermetically sealed, corrosion will not be a problem. Some materials containing chlorides have a high affinity for moisture. Despite baking and evacuation techniques, these materials retain an appreciable quantity of moisture and are subject to hydrolysis. This fact may not be disclosed in accelerated tests.

Section 8 describes testing procedures for evaluating corrosion resistance. Experience indicates that relay coils should be capable of withstanding these tests if a corrosion hazard is to be avoided. It is important also that specifications adequately control the quality of the insulating materials to assure continued satisfactory performance of the product.

5.6 Dielectric considerations

Dielectric ratings for relays are a function of size and the separation between contacts and between various parts of the structure. The ability

[1] $G_c = (NI)^2/I^2R = N^2/R$. See Peek and Wagar, *Switching Relay Design,* D. Van Nostrand Co., Inc., Princeton, N. J. 1955.

[2] See footnote on page 117.

of a relay to withstand impressed voltage depends on the type of insulation employed and the severity of the environment to which it may be subjected in service. Cold flow of certain types of insulation at high temperature or prolonged exposure to extremely high humidity may result in a substantial reduction of the dielectric withstanding voltage.

It should be appreciated also that self-induced or externally developed voltage transients as well as the steady state voltages impressed on the winding or contacts should be well within the capability of a design.

5.7 Evaluation of operating characteristics

The margins between the operating characteristics of a relay and the most unfavorable circuit conditions may significantly affect performance. Mechanical and electrical adjustments of relays may be altered by temperature and humidity variations, dynamic environments, and repeated operation. The magnitude of these changes is a measure of the inherent stability of a design as well as the severity of the conditions imposed. Evaluation of a design to establish its stability therefore, is an important aspect of application engineering. The methods most commonly used in evaluation and application are: (1) the attributes method, and (2) the variables method.

The attributes method is usually suitable for relays used in relatively simple circuits as typified by many commercial and industrial needs. For more complex circuits, or for applications requiring a high degree of reliability, the variables method is to be preferred.

5.8 Attributes method of evaluation

This method consists essentially of measuring relays during initial evaluation and subsequent periodic sampling tests to determine whether they perform their specified functions at specified voltages or currents. Adjustment changes are not measured, and the inherent stability of a design is thus not evaluated quantitatively by this method.

Typical attributes requirements may state:

(1) Relays shall pickup at (E_1) volts (or I_1 amperes) and shall dropout at (E_2) volts (I_2 amperes) over a temperature range of $-T$ to $+T$ and during and after subjection to other applicable environments.

(2) Relays shall pickup at (E_1) volts (or I_1

amperes) immediately after the winding is de-energized following continuous energization at (E) volts (or I amperes) for time t.

(3) Operate time including (excluding) contact bounce shall not exceed (t_1) milliseconds when the winding is energized at rated voltage (or current) at temperature T.

(4) Release time including (excluding) contact bounce shall not exceed (t_2) milliseconds when the rated voltage (or current) is removed.

In addition to these requirements, winding resistance and nominal voltage rating are specified.

Attributes requirements are intended to provide sufficient margin to assure that a relay will pickup at rated voltage (or current) and dropout when the power is removed or reduced to a specified value. There are no restrictions, however, as to the range of fluctuations in energizing voltage (or current) that might be tolerated without incurring a risk of failure to operate at the minimum circuit voltage (or current), or of excessive deterioration caused by overheating at the maximum circuit voltage (or current).

In the absence of such information, it is imperative that the relay manufacturer be consulted with respect to the limiting circuit conditions for reliable performance. Test results may be misleading if performed on a few samples that may not represent the full spread in adjustment likely to occur in regular production.

Since timing characteristics of a relay may vary considerably with temperature, circuit power, relay characteristics, and adjustment changes, the manufacturer also should be consulted with respect to applications in which timing is important.

Data obtained from the attributes method of evaluation are suitable for noncritical circuits, but additional information is usually required for complex or critical applications. It is not feasible for a manufacturer to provide information in relay catalogs in anticipation of all types of applications. In instances where sufficient information is not available, it is unwise to proceed with the design of circuits without consulting the manufacturer with respect to special requirements and related relay capability.

5.9 Variables method of evaluation

This method involves measuring the actual values at which a relay performs a specified function at specified measuring intervals during evaluation studies. It offers a means of controlling the inherent stability of a design and provides the information required to engineer complex circuits. The basic inspection requirements may be essentially the same as those specified in the attributes method, for example, relays shall pickup at (E_1) volts (or I_1 amperes) and shall dropout at (E_2) volts (or I_2 amperes) at temperature t.

However, nonpickup and hold requirements are added to control the adjustments governing the operate and release strokes. On the basis of predetermined inherent stability established in evaluation studies, requirements are specified *in current* and measured *in current* rather than voltage to avoid the necessity of using correction factors to compensate for temperature effects. A typical specification might read:

(1) At all specified measuring periods during subjection of the relay to applicable environments, the operating characteristics shall not vary from the initial values by more than the following percentages:

Pickup current	$+a\%$
Hold current	$+b\%$
Nonpickup current	$-a\%$
Dropout current	$-b\%$

(2) At all specified measuring periods during mechanical life (or contact load) tests, the operating characteristics shall not vary from the initial values by more than the following percentages:

Pickup current	$+c\%$
Hold current	$+d\%$
Nonpickup current	$-c\%$
Dropout current	$-d\%$

(3) When measured during vibration tests,[1] the operating characteristics for missile or aerospace relays shall not vary from the values measured statistically before vibration by more than the following percentages:

Pickup current	$+e\%$
Hold current	$+f\%$
Nonpickup current	$-e\%$
Dropout current	$-f\%$

For purposes of illustration, the percentage changes for pickup and nonpickup, and for hold and dropout are shown as differing only in sign. In actual practice, the positive and negative values usually differ in magnitude.

With boundaries specified within which the product shall perform the required switching functions, it is now possible to determine circuit margins and timing characteristics, as explained in Paragraph 5.12.

5.10 Minimum reliable operating current or voltage

If I_0 is the specified pickup current and the stability factors are a%, c%, and e% for effects of environment, operation, and vibration, respectively then

$$I_0 \ (1 + a/100) \quad (1)$$
$$I_0 \ (1 + a/100) \ (1 + c/100) \quad (2)$$
$$\text{and } I_0 \ (1 + a/100) \ (1 + c/100) \ (1 + e/100) \quad (3)$$

are the respective minimum reliable currents that will assure reliable operation considering first the environmental factor alone, then environmental effects plus those of repeated operation, and finally all three effects, environment, operation, and vibration. For a relay that may accumulate few operations during its service life, the $(1 + c/100)$ term may be eliminated. The $(1 + e/100)$ term is applicable mostly for missile or aerospace relays.

It is desirable to provide some margin over these values for reliable operation. The current required to assure reliable operation is often referred to as *minimum reliable current*. Lack of manufacturing controls may be indicated when measured variations of a lot of relays, or of a particular sample, are appreciably larger than the established stability limits for a given design. If close control is exercised in manufacture, all lots should fall within the stability limits established.

The effect of linear acceleration on current required for pickup may be higher than the combined effects of environment and repeated operation. Many well designed relays exhibit rather large changes during acceleration because of an inbalance in the armature system. At high accelerations this effect may be so large for some relays that it may not be possible to provide sufficient current to assure reliable operation.

The minimum reliable voltage at any temperature is the product of the minimum reliable current and the maximum winding resistance (nominal resistance plus tolerance, corrected to the applicable ambient temperature and temperature rise). Thus, this method affords a means of engineering circuits on a current or voltage basis.

---

[1] The term as used here includes shock and centrifugal acceleration tests (see Sec. 8).

At the intermediate switching (partly energized) stage of some circuits, a relay may be energized at a current or voltage level at which it must not open or close contacts. This type of application makes it necessary to impose a nonpickup requirement and to control, by a negative stability requirement, any tendency toward operation at a value lower than that to which the relay was adjusted initially. In some designs, nonpickup requirements also are used to control the contact force of normally closed contacts or to control the armature back tension that restrains the armature motion when the relay is energized or subjected to vibration, shock, or acceleration.

The nonpickup requirement is absolutely essential, as will be explained later, for determining operate time capability and for controlling the operate time of the product.

erately. The hold point is also a factor, to some extent, in establishing release time. It is extremely important in controlling the release time of slow release relays. For these reasons, a hold requirement may be specified and hold stability limits imposed.

The procedure for calculating minimum reliable hold current or voltage is the same as that used for the operate values; it is summarized in Table 5-1.

The permissible percentage of deviations from initial hold values usually are greater than for pickup or nonpickup characteristics because changes in poleface alignments, wear of poleface finishes, or small quantities of wear products accumulating on the polefaces may have a pronounced effect on the holding force of the armature in the hold and dropout range. Wear of polefaces, which reduces closed gap reluctance,

Table 5-1. Effects of Environment, Operation, and Acceleration on Reliable Operating Currents

	Environment	Effect of environment and operation	Environment, operation, and acceleration
Pickup current	$I_o(1 + a/100)$	$I_o(1 + a/100)(1 + c/100)$	$I_o(1 + a/100)(1 + c/100)(1 + e/100)$
Nonpickup current	$I_{no}(1 - a/100)$	$I_{no}(1 - a/100)(1 - c/100)$	$I_{no}(1 - a/100)(1 - c/100)(1 - e/100)$
Hold current	$I_h(1 + b/100)$	$I_h(1 + b/100)(1 + d/100)$	$I_h(1 + b/100)(1 + d/100)(1 + f/100)$
Dropout current	$I_r(1 - b/100)$	$I_r(1 - b/100)(1 - d/100)$	$I_r(1 - b/100)(1 - d/100)(1 - f/100)$

Note: I_o, I_{no}, I_h and I_r are the specified initial, or inspection, values for pickup, nonpickup, hold, and dropout currents, and a, b, c, d, e, and f are the maximum permissible percentage changes established from evaluation studies. Hold and dropout requirements are not applicable for bistable magnetic latch-in relays.

The procedure for using stability factors to calculate the maximum voltage (or current) at which the winding may be energized without causing armature movement or contact actuation (nonpickup) is the same as that used in calculating minimum reliable pickup values. However, in this instance the stability factors and margins provided are negative (see Table 5-1).

5.11 Minimum reliable hold current or voltage

It is essential in some circuit applications to know the minimum value at which an energized relay will remain operated if the energizing voltage (or current) fluctuates or is reduced delib-

and the actuator or contact wear that comes from repeated operation usually cause decreases in hold values.

Armature realignment or any retention of wear products on the polefaces may cause increases in the voltage (or current) required to hold the armature in its operated position. Hold current variations also may be substantial if a relay is subjected to acceleration.

In most simple circuits, relays are required to dropout only when the energizing source is removed. However, in more complex circuits a relay is sometimes required to dropout when the energizing current, or voltage, is reduced gradually or abruptly to some value greater than zero. It is necessary, therefore, to know the value to which the energizing current (or voltage) must be reduced to insure dropout. (The minimum dropout value is of particular importance in establishing release time characteristics.) As in the case of hold current, the dropout point may vary considerably with environmental conditions and repeated operation. Acceleration effects may also be substantial.

The expressions for calculating the limiting values for pickup, nonpickup, hold and dropout currents are summarized in Table 5-1.

5.12   Evaluating timing characteristics

Operate time.   Determination of operate time of electromagnetic armature type relays is treated comprehensively in various texts.[1] This discussion is limited, therefore, to circuit applications using the circuit parameters and basic characteristics of a relay to predict the probable range of operate time. Although the method neglects some secondary factors, it is sufficiently accurate for most purposes.

Operate time is a function of relay adjustments and the coil conductance, $G_c = N^2/R$, which varies with fullness of winding but is substantially constant for a given fullness of winding. The resistance term includes any resistance in series with the winding. Operate time, then, becomes a function of total circuit resistance, which varies with temperature. It follows that operate time will vary with temperature.

The following discussion of operate time considers only time to first closure and disregards contact bounce time, which is influenced by many factors relating to the dynamics of a relay design.

Operate time of a relay is comprised of waiting time and transit time. Waiting time is the interval, after closure of the winding circuit, in which the flux builds up sufficiently to start the movement of the armature toward the core. Transit time is the interval between the start of movement of the armature and the completion of the switching function. As the energizing power is increased, waiting time decreases but finally levels off. Transit time also decreases somewhat with an increase in energizing power, but it, too, finally tends to become constant at a

certain power level. Thus, total operate time decreases with power and approaches a value at which there will be little or no benefit derived from increasing the driving power.

Figure 5-1 illustrates typical operate time curves obtained at three ambient temperatures on several samples of a particular type of four-transfer (4 form C) relay. The data were obtained using a bounce-free mercury-wetted contact to control the winding circuit. In this figure, Q is the ratio I_j/I_a (or E_j/E_a), in which I_j (or E_j) is the measured pickup point in current (or voltage) and I_a (or E_a) is the current (or voltage) at which the winding is energized. The upper and lower limits of operate time for a family of relays at given values of Q are illustrated by sets of curves, A and B. Curves such as these provide the basic data for predicting operate time. By a family of relays is meant a group of relays having essentially the same armature travel and load and the same fullness of winding or coil conductance ($G_c = N^2/R$). For another fullness of winding, the timing characteristic will be different. For example, for shallower windings, operate time will be shorter because the N^2 term of G_c decreases more rapidly than the resistance and varies directly with G_c.

As Q decreases, which is the equivalent of increasing power, operate time decreases until it approaches a minimum time. At this point very little increase in speed is derived from large increases in power. At the other extreme, operate time approaches maximum at $Q = 1$, the point at which energizing current (or voltage) is equal to the value at which the relay just picks up. It is inadvisable to operate a relay in the steep region of these curves if operate time is critical.

If a relay is to be used over a range of ambient temperatures, curves should be obtained at the applicable temperature extremes, as illustrated by Fig. 5-1. Likewise, if a winding reaches an elevated temperature as a result of internal heating and then is de-energized and reoperated shortly thereafter, timing data should be obtained for this condition. Heating effects are particularly important in rapidly pulsing circuits. It may be seen from Fig. 5-1 that for the same value of Q operate time is shorter at higher temperatures and longer at lower temperatures. The effect is explained by G_c, or N^2/R, being inversely proportional to resistance and therefore absolute temperature. As G_c decreases, operate time becomes faster.

With the nonpickup and pickup points controlled by initial requirements and stability

---

[1]Peek and Wagar, *Switching Relay Design*, D. Van Nostrand Co., Inc., Princeton, N. J., 1955. M. A. Logan, "Estimation and Control of Operate Time of Relays, Part II. Design of Optimum Windings," *Bell System Technical Journal*, Jan. 1954.

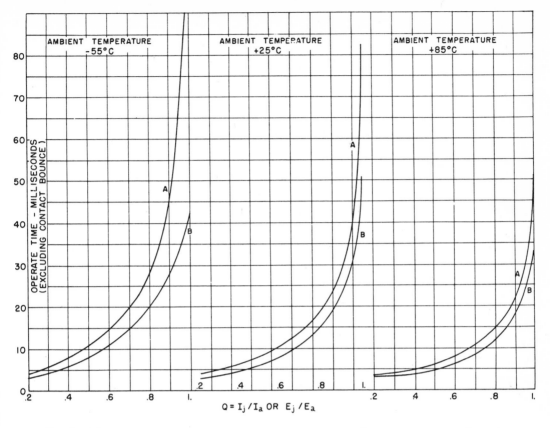

FIG. 5-1. TYPICAL OPERATE TIME CURVES FOR A FOUR TRANSFER (BREAK-MAKE, FORM C) RELAY AT THREE AMBIENT TEMPERATURES

limits, it is possible to utilize operate time versus Q data to predict, with reasonable accuracy, the range of operate time for relays adjusted within the specified nonpickup and pickup limits. Using curve A of Fig. 5-1, maximum operate time for this family of relays will result when a relay adjusted to pickup at the specified pickup value (I_j is maximum) is energized at the minimum circuit current. In a similar manner, minimum operate time is obtained from curve B when Q is minimum, that is, when a relay adjusted to pickup at the minimum value, just above the nonpickup requirement, is energized at maximum circuit current. The operate time range can be determined in this manner for any combination of ambient temperatures by obtaining Q curves at the applicable temperature extremes.

The curves of Fig. 5-1 were obtained with no resistance in series with the winding. For the series resistance case, $G_c = N^2/(R_c + R_s)$, in which R_c is the winding resistance and R_s is the series resistance. For a given Q and a given winding, the relay will be faster when resistance is in series with the winding. This method often

is used to reduce operate time and avoid the overheating that would result from applying a higher voltage directly across the winding. Operate time characteristics for the series resistance case can be obtained by using the method illustrated in Fig. 5-1.

Operate time curves expressed in terms of input watts often offer greater flexibility in circuit design. The Q data of Fig. 5-1 may be converted into watts versus time curves (*see* Fig. 5-2) as explained in the following paragraphs.

Case A: Maximum operate time at a given temperature (D curves of Fig. 5-2). An input wattage, W_a, is selected and a value for Q is calculated using either of the following formulas, depending on whether the operating characteristics are expressed in current or in voltage:

$$Q = \sqrt{\frac{I^2_{max}}{W_a} R_{max}} \quad \text{or} \quad Q = \sqrt{\frac{E^2_{max}}{R_{min} W_a}}$$

in which:

I_{max} = specified pickup current plus applicable stability limit

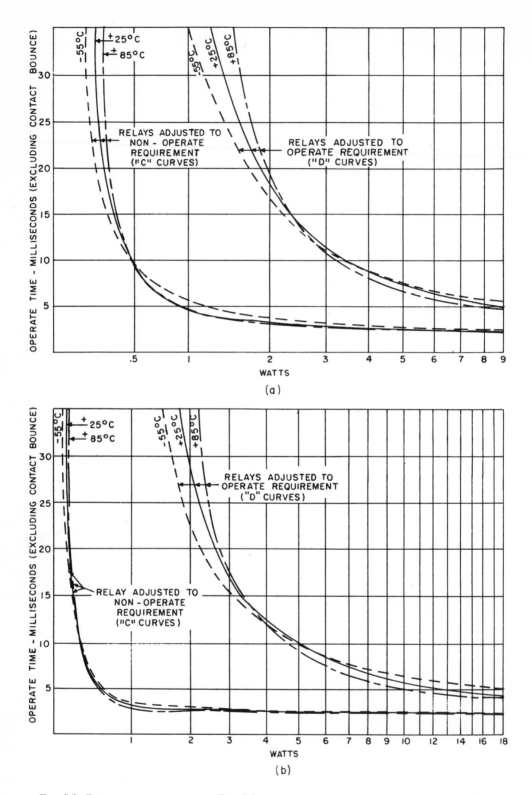

FIG. 5-2. OPERATE TIME CURVES OF FIG. 5-1 FOR A FOUR TRANSFER FORM C CONTACT RELAY
CONVERTED INTO CURVES RELATING TIME TO INPUT COIL POWER
(a) Ground and aircraft application; (b) aerospace application.

R_{max} = nominal winding resistance plus specified tolerance (corrected to applicable temperature)

E_{max} = specified pickup voltage plus applicable stability limit (corrected to applicable temperature)

R_{min} = nominal winding resistance minus specified tolerance (corrected to applicable temperature)

Using Fig. 5-1, an operate time value is obtained from curve B for the calculated Q. This value is plotted against W_a as one point on curve D of Fig. 5-2. In the same manner other points may be calculated using several values of W_a.

Case B: Minimum operate time at a given temperature (C Curves of Fig. 5-2). As in Case A, an input wattage is selected and the corresponding Q is calculated from the following formulas:

$$Q = \sqrt{\frac{I^2_{min} R_{min}}{W_a}} \quad \text{or} \quad Q = \sqrt{\frac{E^2_{min}}{R_{max} W_a}}$$

In this case, E_{min} is the specified nonpickup voltage minus the applicable stability limit (corrected to the applicable temperature).

Likewise, I_{min} is the specified nonpickup current minus the applicable stability limit.

Minimum operate time is obtained for the calculated Q from curve B of Fig. 5-1 and then plotted against W_a as one point on curve C of Fig. 5-2.

Having established the input power-operate time curves, it is possible to determine minimum and maximum operate time for the applicable temperature by calculating maximum circuit watts and reading from the minimum time from curve C and calculating minimum circuit watts and reading maximum time from curve D.

When timing is critical, a relay should be used only within the fairly flat range of the upper and lower curves.

The methods described also may be used to determine operate time of relays employing slugs, or shortcircuited turns to produce time delay.

Conditions requiring special study are:

(1) Timing during shock or vibration
(2) Operation in capacitor charging or discharging circuits
(3) Operation when a relay is in parallel with a capacitor and in series with a resistor.

Release time. Disregarding the dynamic considerations affecting contact bounce, release time of an electromagnetic relay is comprised of two stages, waiting time and transit time. The former is the time, after opening the winding circuit, for the flux to decay to a level at which the magnetic pull can no longer sustain the mechanical force acting on the armature and the armature starts to move from its operated position. Unless the relay is equipped with a sleeve, slug, or shortcircuiting winding to delay decay of flux, waiting time on dropout will be appreciably shorter than on pickup since the rate of decay of flux is faster than flux buildup. The second stage, transit time, is the interval between start of movement of the armature and contact actuation. Transit time usually is shorter during release than during operate because of the more rapid flux decay and because the forces acting on the armature aid release and oppose operation. Release time for many designs, therefore, is shorter than operate time. Contact protection in the form of semiconductor diodes, short-circuiting windings, or capacitor-resistor networks may substantially increase release time by retarding decay of flux but occasionally a capacitor-resistor network may decrease release time.

In a particular design, the parameters affecting release time are variations in the armature residual gap, armature load, contact separation, and the magnitude of the interrupted energizing current. Waiting time will be a maximum when the interrupted energizing current is maximum and the residual gap and armature load are minimum. It will be a minimum when the interrupted energizing current is minimum and the other parameters are maximum. In the case of unprotected windings, this effect usually is small. It may be appreciable, however, for protected windings.

Usually when protection is employed, the range of release current adjustments has an appreciable effect on release time. For unprotected windings the effect may be insignificant because waiting time then is relatively short. Transit time will be minimum when the armature load is maximum and the contact separation of normally closed contacts is minimum.

Thus in evaluating release time characteristics, it is essential that studies be conducted on samples representing the two extremes of adjustments for production relays. From this type of study it should be possible to obtain correlation between dropout current, or dropout ampere-turns, and release time.

By specifying dropout and hold requirements and controlling their stability, it is possible to predict the range of release time within limits suitable for practical application. Any variation in dropout current caused by environment, operation, or acceleration will inversely affect release time.

In determining release time capability of relays equipped with time delay features such as sleeves, slugs, or short-circuited windings, and the like, the maximum conductance sleeve, slug, or short-circuited winding should be used on relays adjusted for maximum release time. The minimum conductance sleeve or slug or short-circuited winding should be used on relays adjusted to provide minimum release time.

5.13 Magnetic interference effects

The pickup, nonpickup, hold, and dropout characteristics of a relay may be affected by leakage or stray flux from adjacent magnetic material or apparatus. The magnitude of this effect depends on:

(1) The magnetic circuit of the relay

(2) The ampere-turns at which the relay is energized

(3) Strength of the stray fields

(4) Polarity and proximity of adjacent interfering apparatus

(5) Shielding employed to reduce stray field effects

(6) Type of mounting

(7) Particular relay characteristics that may be involved.

Magnetic interference effects can be evaluated only by duplicating equipment mounting and circuit conditions for the interfering components and the affected relay or relays. The interference effect should be studied for the characteristics involved using relays adjusted to the extremes for each characteristic. It should be appreciated that magnetic interference may aid or hinder any characteristic, depending upon the energizing polarity of the relay and its interference.

5.14 Heating considerations

The primary heating considerations in the evaluation and application of relays are the effects of winding temperature on relay performance under normal circuit conditions and under trouble conditions.

Normal heating is the condition imposed on a coil with respect to duration of energization and wattage dissipation when the circuit is functioning in a normal manner. Relay coils should be capable of withstanding normal heating for their required life.

"Trouble" heating is a condition imposed on a coil when the circuit ceases to function normally, resulting in a dissipation of power greater than that for which the coil was designed. Circuit design should not impose a trouble-heating condition that could create a fire hazard, that is, the coil and circuit design should assure that the coil will be self-protecting.

Three factors should be considered in establishing normal operating temperature limits and corresponding maximum safe normal operating voltages, current, and power dissipation:

(1) Ability of the coil to withstand the cumulative hours of heating likely to be imposed during its required life.

(2) Ability of other parts of the relay structure — such as insulation, actuators, springs, and contacts — to withstand the temperatures imposed without impairing performance of the relay.

(3) The possibility of contamination of contacts from volatile substances in the coil and relay structure, and the effect on adjacent components.

Design criteria for trouble temperature limits may vary with the application. In many fields, it is imperative that fire hazards be avoided, and trouble heating is thus limited to a temperature that the coil will be capable of withstanding for a period of time well in excess of the likely duration of the trouble. The safe trouble temperature limit is set at a value below the temperature at which progressive short-circuited turns may develop as a result of deterioration of the wire or coil insulation. Relays that have experienced a trouble condition that causes heating above the normal operating temperature limit are not required to function satisfactorily thereafter. In fact, such relays should be removed from service even though they may still function satisfactorily, because the extent of deterioration and its effect on future performance is not determinable.

In some fields, relays are engineered on a different basis. The evaluation or applications engineer usually is not concerned with temperature limits and relies on the manufacturer's rating.

Methods of evaluating heat resisting properties of coil and wire insulations will not be discussed in this section. It should be mentioned, however, that finer gauge wires have a shorter life than coarser gauges. Safe operating limits, therefore, should be based on the heat resisting properties of the finest wire or should be determined for ranges of wire sizes.

Curves showing the relation between mean winding temperature and power dissipation are required for the application of relays in many systems. These curves are obtained at one or more ambient temperatures, depending on the application data required.

Typical curves showing final mean winding temperature (temperature at thermal equilibrium) related to power dissipation are plotted in Fig. 5-3. On the initial wattage curves, $W_0 =$ $E_0{}^2/R_0$, in which E_0 is the applied voltage and R_0 is the resistance at ambient temperature T_0. On the final wattage curves, $W_1 = E_0 I_1$, in which I_1 is the current at thermal equilibrium. Since the applied voltage remains constant, power dissipation is inversely proportional to absolute temperature, that is,

$$\frac{W_1}{W_0} = \frac{390 + T_0}{390 + T_1}$$

in which T_0 and T_1 are in deg F.

It will be noted that over a temperature rise range of $100°F - 150°F$ the relationship between final wattage and temperature is essentially

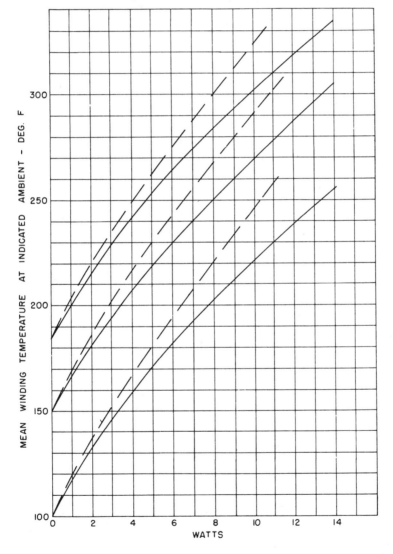

FIG. 5-3. TYPICAL CURVES RELATING FINAL MEAN WINDING TEMPERATURE TO COIL POWER DISSIPATION AT CONSTANT VOLTAGE (INDICATED AMBIENT AT 0 WATTS)

At the indicated ambient temperature, initial watts are indicated by solid lines and final watts by dashed lines.

linear. This linearity makes it possible to calculate with a reasonable degree of accuracy the temperature rise, θ, and final mean winding temperature for a variety of circuit conditions by determining the thermal conductance, ρ, of the coil, expressed in watts/degree rise. For purposes of illustration, thermal conductance of the coil of Fig. 5-3, obtained at the 250°F point on the 100°F ambient temperature curve, is 10.3 watts divided by 150, or 0.0681/ deg F.

Substitution of ρ in the applicable formulas of Table 5-2 permits calculation of limiting circuit conditions that will provide margins to assure reliable operation and to prevent overheating.

To avoid errors in calculating temperatures and circuit constants where the final watts/mean winding temperature curve departs significantly from a straight line, it may be necessary to choose a series of values for ρ, each over a limited range.

When a relay is energized under pulsing conditions, the allowable power dissipation is greater than for continuous energization. It has been found experimentally that for pulses up to one second duration at any duty cycle, allowable wattage dissipation is obtained from the expression, $P_2 = P_1 (a+b)/a$, in which a is the on time, b the off time, and P_1 the power that may be dissipated continuously. For other pulsing conditions, a more comprehensive treatment involving the load factor, thermal conductance, and thermal capacitance is required.[1] Unless such information is needed for a large variety of circuit functions, it would be more logical, for isolated cases, to conduct studies of several representative samples under the worst possible circuit conditions to determine the winding temperature and circuit margins for the limiting condition. The worst circuit conditions for heating are maximum voltage and minimum winding resistance, or maximum current through a maximum resistance winding. For determining pickup margin, the limiting case is excitation of the maximum resistance winding at maximum voltage or current, followed by application of minimum voltage or current when thermal equilibrium has been reached.

5.15   Evaluation of contact performance

Perhaps the most troublesome aspect of relay evaluation and application, particularly for hermetically sealed relays, is predicting contact performance under the multiplicity of contact loads and variety of performance criteria encountered in service. To a large extent the difficulty results from a lack of familiarity with the parameters affecting contact performance. Much of the trouble, however, is caused by reluctance to accept the limitations inherent in a design or contact material. There seems to be a lack of appreciation that higher reliability is attainable, although sometimes at an initial cost penalty. Often overlooked are the more severe economic penalties of increased maintenance and replacement and the consequences of catastrophic failure. Although the state of the art has not advanced sufficiently to eliminate contact troubles, a high degree of reliability can be achieved by adhering to a few basic principles and applying acquired knowledge. This knowledge, to the extent that it is applicable, forms the basis of this discussion.

The basic principles of contact action were discussed in Sec. 4 and will not be repeated here. The characteristics of certain contact materials primarily used in military type relays and in communications will be evaluated instead. It has been found that:

(1) Palladium, of the platinum family, is superior to other materials under eroding contact load conditions. As with all other materials, erosion will be greatly accelerated in the presence of organic vapors. The platinum family is particularly susceptible to the formation of insulating polymers under low energy or dry circuit conditions.

(2) Gold-plated contacts exhibit lower initial contact resistance than some unplated contacts, such as silver. However, the plating technique should be controlled to avoid porosity and creepage of the underlying material onto the contact surface. Gold plating has a short life under loads that cause electrical erosion. It is useful to the extent that it inhibits formation of sulphides and oxides during storage or in applications having relatively short operating life requirements. Gold-plated contacts, if thoroughly clean, may also tend to stick. This tendency is a function of the design of the actuating system.

(3) Solid gold contacts and some alloys rich in gold (20-22 karat), although excellent for low energy or dry circuits, may be extremely susceptible to sticking if cleaned to the degree necessary to obtain low and stable contact resistance. Armature card lift-off actuation can be used to

[1]P. Grice, "The Heating and Cooling of Electrical Machinery," *Institute of Electrical Engineers Journal*, vol. 51, pp 840-851, 1913. Peek and Wagar, *Switching Relay Design*, D. Van Nostrand Co., Inc., Princeton, N. J., 1955.

Table 5-2. General Temperature Rise Formulas for Coils of Electromagnets

Circuit Condition	Temperature rise, θ (°F) (W_o = initial watts)	Minimum series or shunt resistance permitted to keep temperature rise below θ	Maximum initial wattage permitted to keep temperature rise below θ
Constant power	$\theta = \dfrac{W_o}{K}$		$W_o = K\theta$
Constant current	$\theta = \dfrac{1}{\frac{K}{W_o} - a}$		$W_o = I^2 R = \dfrac{K\theta}{1 + a\theta}$
Constant voltage / (a) Simple winding	$\theta = \sqrt{\dfrac{1}{4a^2} + \dfrac{W_o}{aK}} - \dfrac{1}{2a}$	$r = \sqrt{\dfrac{E^2 R(1+a\theta)}{Ka}} - R(1+a\theta)$	$W_o = \dfrac{E^2}{R} = K\theta(1 + a\theta)$
(b) r = External series	$\theta = \dfrac{E^2 a - KR_s + \sqrt{(E^2 a - KR_s)^2 + 4aKR\,E_s^2 \frac{(R_s + R)}{R}}}{2aKR_s}$	$R_s = \dfrac{1}{\frac{K\theta}{E^2} - \frac{1}{R(1+a\theta)}}$	$W_o = \dfrac{E^2}{R(1+a\theta)} + \dfrac{E^2}{R_s} = K\theta$
(c) R_s = Internal shunt	$\theta = \dfrac{1}{2aR}\left[\sqrt{(R+r)^2 + \dfrac{4E^2 aR}{K}} - (R+r)\right]$	$r = \dfrac{E^2}{K\theta} - R(1+a\theta)$	$W_o = \dfrac{E^2}{R(1+a\theta)} + r = K\theta$
(d) r = Internal series			
(e) r = External series, R_s = External shunt		$r = \sqrt{\dfrac{R_s R(1+a\theta)\left[E - \sqrt{K\theta R(1+a\theta)}\right]}{\left[R_s + R(1+a\theta)\right]\sqrt{K\theta R(1+a\theta)}}}$	
(f) r = External series, R_s = Internal shunt		$r = \sqrt{\dfrac{R_s R(1+a\theta)}{K\theta\left[R_s + R(1+a\theta)\right]}\left[E - \sqrt{\dfrac{K\theta R_s R(1+a\theta)}{R_s + R(1+a\theta)}}\right]}$	

*Zero resistance–temperature coefficient

E = applied volts

I = current in amperes

R = main winding resistance at initial temperature (ϕ_0), in ohms

R_s = external or internal shunt resistance (zero temperature coefficient), in ohms

r = external or internal series resistance (zero temperature coefficient), in ohms

W_0 = initial watts

  = EI watts (constant power)

  = $I^2 R$ watts (constant current)

  = $E^2 R$ watts (constant voltage)

ϕ = temperature, in deg F

ϕ_0 = initial temperature, in deg F

θ = temperature rise above ϕ_0, in deg F

K = thermal conductance in watts per deg F

  = W_1/θ_1 = $\dfrac{\text{final watts to produce a } \theta_1 \text{ of } 150°F}{150}$

a = temperature coefficient of resistance of copper (based on inferred absolute zero resistivity of copper at −390°F)

  = $\dfrac{1}{390 + \phi_0}$

overcome sticking if the lift-off force is high enough. Gold contacts are less resistant to electrical erosion and mechanical wear than silver or palladium contacts.

(4) Silver-cadmium and silver contacts are suitable for relatively high currents and unprotected inductive loads. However, these materials have inherently higher contact resistance. Usually when sulphides are present on silver contacts, the potential drop across the contacts will be 0.12 to 0.20 volt, substantially independent of current. If silver contacts are used correctly, this voltage drop is tolerable, and sulphides will present no performance problem. The use of gold plating improves appearance but often offers no advantage whatsoever from a functional standpoint.

(5) In the presence of organic materials all contact materials erode at an accelerated rate under arcing loads. High contact resistance may occur under certain loads well before the end of normal erosion life. Hermetically sealed relays with organic materials in the contact chamber are particularly susceptible to this effect. Isolating contacts from organic vapors, or the use of inorganic materials, substantially reduces erosion and minimizes formation of carbonaceous material, thereby improving contact reliability over a wide range of contact loads.

(6) A combination of a 0.001-in. thick 22-karat gold overlay on palladium for one contact mating with a palladium contact has been found to offer excellent performance over a wide range of contact loads. At low energy and dry circuit conditions it is as effective, for practical purposes, as gold is in overcoming the polymer problem. Under eroding conditions, contact life is equivalent to that of palladium contacts.

(7) Contact cleanliness is essential to reliable and stable contact performance. For critical applications cleaning agents that leave film residues should be avoided.

(8) Bifurcated or twin contacts offer distinct advantages over single contacts at low energy or intermediate loads. At heavy loads single contacts may provide better performance. The advantages or disadvantages in either case are closely related to the relay design objectives, performance requirements, and contact load conditions.

(9) A single contact rating provides little information regarding the capability of contacts over a range of contact loads. Contact life under less severe loads may be less than that at rated load.

Suitability of a contact material or a relay for a particular application depends on life requirements; permissible contact resistance; contact load; environment; contact wipe, follow, and force; method of actuation; insulating materials employed in the relay; control of manufacture; and cleaning techniques.

The effects of lamp, transformer, motor, and other inductive loads may be severe because of the high inrush currents. Steady state currents for these loads are not a measure of the severity of the load, particularly if the contacts are subject to bounce on closure.

In view of all factors involved and the large variety of relays available, it is difficult to offer estimates of probable trouble-free life for various contact materials under a wide variety of load conditions. It is advisable, therefore, to consult the manufacturer for information concerning contact performance for special load conditions and application requirements.

Contact protection. If contact load conditions indicate a need for contact protection, the following procedures may be used:

(1) Inductive d-c loads (load current less than the arcing current): For protection consisting of an RC network across the contact or coil, the value of capacitance should be at least 1 mf per ampere of load current, and the resistance in series with the capacitance should not exceed the load resistance.

(2) Inductive and noninductive d-c loads (load current greater than the arcing current): The capacitance should be at least 1 mf per ampere of load current, and the series resistance should not exceed E_a/I_0, in which E_a is the minimum arcing voltage and I_0 is the steady state current.

In both load conditions (1 and 2), surge current I_s through the contact should not exceed the minimum welding current for the particular contact material. Surge current may be estimated from $I_s = E/R$, in which E is the energizing voltage and R is the resistance in series with the capacitance. It should be less than the minimum welding current.

The minimum arcing current, I_a, the minimum contact welding current, I_w, and the minimum arcing voltage, E_a, for the most commonly used contact materials are given in Table 5-3.

Diodes are also used quite extensively to protect contacts or reduce transients that produce noise or interference in adjacent circuits. The use of RC networks or diodes, particularly the latter, may have an appreciable effect on release time.

Table 5-3. Limiting Arcing and Welding Currents and Arcing Voltages for Some Contact Materials

Materials	I_a (amperes)	I_w (amperes)	E_a (volts)
Silver	0.4	19.0	12.0
Gold	0.4	11.0	15.0
Gold alloy (69% gold, 25% silver, 6% platinum)	0.4	11.0	9.0
Palladium	0.8-1.0	16.0	
Tungsten	1.0-1.4		16.5

Note: Values apply to contacts that are not activated by organic vapors.

Another method of suppressing arcing or reducing peak voltage is to wind over the core or inductive winding a bifilar noninductive winding connected in parallel with the inductive winding. This method was frequently used many years ago but has not been used extensively in recent years. It has some obvious shortcomings. Theoretically, the peak voltage developed upon opening the coil circuit is the product of the d-c resistance of the noninductive winding and the steady state current in the inductive winding. It is, however, virtually impossible to wind a pure resistance winding. Thus, at the steep wave front of the transient voltage, the impedance may be considerably greater than the d-c resistance and the peak voltage will be appreciably higher than the calculated value. Furthermore, to reduce the peak voltage to as low a value as can be maintained with an RC network or a semiconductor diode requires a low resistance winding that increases wattage dissipation considerably and often results in overheating.

Parallel windings with one winding short-circuited also have been used for arc suppression. The effectiveness of this method is a function of the resistance of the short-circuited winding as related to that of the energizing winding, a lower resistance winding having a greater effect than a high resistance winding. This method imposes a penalty on sensitivity because the space occupied by the short-circuited winding constitutes a substantial portion of the available winding space. Since the turns of the energizing and short-circuited windings are contiguous, the possibility of voltage breakdown or short circuits between windings should be thoroughly evaluated.

Contact maintenance. In the case of open type relays or switches, maintenance procedures can extend or shorten their life depending upon the practices adopted.

The manufacturer should be consulted with regard to accepted procedures. The use of corrosive cleaners or highly abrasive tools for maintenance of contacts frequently leads to increased troubles. Lubricants should be avoided unless specifically recommended by the manufacturer. Only trained personnel should attempt to perform mechanical readjustments. Many times relay troubles can be attributed to inexperienced personnel tinkering with the apparatus.

In open type relays, maintenance practices often provide for readjustment of contacts to compensate for the cumulative effects of millions of operations. It is a well-established practice to connect contact springs to battery and ground in such a way that the possibility of blowing fuses or other damage will be minimized if the adjusting tool should inadvertently short-circuit adjacent springs. All moving springs are maintained at positive or negative potential, and the fixed contacts are connected to the load.

A-C Armature Type Relays

5.16   Introduction
Armature type relays for a-c operation fall into two basic categories: (1) the shaded pole design, and (2) the conventional d-c armature type equipped with a diode rectifier. The operating principles of both are explained in Sec. 4.

5.17   Winding circuit design
Relays of the a-c type are not ordinarily used, nor are they particularly well suited, for complex switching circuits or for applications having critical timing requirements. Usually the contacts of these relays are required only to open and close reliably for the expected life under the specified load conditions.

The information that is most essential in the application of a-c relays is the minimum voltage at which the relay will operate reliably. Assurance also is required that the relay will release dependably. Usually the inspection and evaluation requirements of the type discussed under the attributes method (Paragraph 5.8) will offer this assurance, provided the requirements are representative of the worst circuit conditions. Ability of the relay to withstand prolonged energization periods must also be considered.

In some applications, impedance and phase angle may be important, at least to the extent that they determine the power supply required. It should be noted that these characteristics may be quite different for the unoperated and operated positions of the armature.

5.18   Contact performance
The factors influencing contact performance are basically the same as those outlined in Paragraph 5.15. However, in heavy-duty a-c type relays, contact resistance and activation effects may be relatively unimportant.

Power Relays or Contactors

5.19   Introduction
Power relays or contactors perform a wide variety of functions in the power field in industrial and military applications. They are used for switching heavy contact loads that may be highly inductive, such as motor, generator, and transformer loads. These devices are also used to switch heavy resistive and lighting loads.

In both military and industrial motor control systems, power relays are used for "across-the-line" applications, that is, the relay contact closure places the motor directly across the source power line. Across-the-line industrial motor starters are made in sizes up to those capable of carrying 600 amperes. Industrial motors are also started at reduced voltages, using series resistance, autotransformer action, or field control (in the case of d-c motors) to restrict current inrush. An additional set of relay contacts is required for reduced-voltage starting.

5.20   Winding circuit design
The same general considerations discussed in Paragraph 5.3 are applicable to power relays. Wattage dissipation is greater in these relatively large units than in the general purpose d-c relays. Because of this higher dissipation, heating can become a problem if power relays are operated in a confined space.

5.21   Contact performance
The most widely used contact materials in power relays are silver-cadmium oxide and tungsten. These materials require rather high currents to weld and are therefore well suited for heavy motor loads in which the inrush starting current may be five to six times the steady state current. Contacts of power relays must also be

capable of opening at six to eight times the rated steady state current in case a motor should stall. These contact materials are well suited for power applications but should be avoided for low energy applications.

Mercury-Wetted Contact Relays

5.22   Introduction
Space limitations in a handbook of this type do not permit a comprehensive treatment of mercury-wetted contact relays (*see* Secs. 3 and 11).

Mercury-wetted contacts are essentially glass-encapsulated reed designs having magnetic spring members. Many relays employing these contacts are magnetically biased designs in which power sensitivity and operating characteristics are a function of the winding, the magnetic circuit, and the strength of the biasing magnet. Some mercury-wetted contact designs, however, are not of the magnetic bias type.

Mercury-wetted contacts are adaptable to bi-stable, magnetic latch-in designs. They are also used for rapid pulsing applications, as in telegraph relay circuits. Considerable flexibility in following alternating current can be provided through the use of a biasing winding.

Mercury-wetted contacts are intended primarily for vertical mounting, although some designs will function satisfactorily when mounted at an angle as great as 45 deg from the vertical plane.

5.23   Winding circuit design
The discussion pertaining to winding-circuit design for armature type relays is applicable to mercury-wetted contact relays. In these designs the movable contact spring acts as armature.

5.24   Contact performance
Since the movable spring of a mercury-wetted contact is magnetic, the contact force of normally open contacts depends upon energizing ampere-turns, and the force of normally closed contacts depends on the magnetic, or in some cases the mechanical, bias. The mercury-wetted contact provides essentially bounce-free operation over a wide range of pulsing conditions and reliable closure over a wide range of contact forces. Under certain rapid pulsing conditions, however, mercury-wetted contacts may exhibit chatter. Relays using them may have to be screened to assure bounce-free performance.

Mercury-wetted contacts will not function below the freezing point of mercury (−38°F). The contacts are also susceptible to contact chatter when subjected to severe shock and vibration since the mercury behaves like a conducting flexible membrane once contact is established.

Mercury-wetted contacts offer extremely long reliable contact life over a wide range of contact loads. Because of their high operating speed and the fact that the glass envelope is pressurized, the transient voltages developed when the contacts control inductive loads may be much higher than the voltages produced in circuits controlled by other types of contacts. Therefore, contact protection should be used to assure long life and to avoid voltage breakdown of the wiring or other insulation in the load circuit.

The following values of resistance and capacitance to be used in protection networks were determined empirically. The capacitance, C, in microfarads, should be equal to $I^2/10$, in which I is the load current in amperes. The resistance, R_s, in series with this capacitance should be equal to $E/[10I(1+50/E)]$, in which E is the load voltage. Contact protective devices should be closely connected to the relay terminals.

Dry Reed Contact Relays

5.25 Introduction

Dry reed contacts varying in size, sensitivity, and capability have been incorporated in a variety of relay designs. The basic dry reed contact is normally open, but a few break-make transfer designs are available. By using magnetic bias, break contacts and transfers can be provided at a sacrifice in power and size.

Dry reed contacts offer fast operation, in some instances as low as 0.5 millisecond, neglecting contact bounce. They are also used in sensitive and fast-acting remanent magnetic designs, such as ferreeds and ferrods. See also Sec. 11.

5.26 Winding circuit design

The discussion pertaining to the winding circuit design of armature type relays is applicable to dry reed contact relays.

5.27 Contact performance

When used within their capability, dry reed contacts offer reliable contact performance. They do not, however, have the current carrying capacity or switching capability of the contacts of mercury-wetted or armature type relays. Little detailed information can be provided at this time on the capability of dry reed contacts. Per-

formance of these contacts can be affected considerably by contact force, which depends on energizing ampere-turns and on the strength of magnetic bias in the case of magnetically biased break contacts.

The contact surfaces of dry reed contacts usually have a thin plating, or thinly diffused layer, of precious metal. These contacts, therefore, could have a substantially shorter erosion life under certain load conditions than heavier precious metal contacts. It is important, in requesting information from manufacturers, that the circuit conditions be clearly defined.

Capacitance discharge of wire or cabling connected to dry reed contacts can have a pronounced adverse effect on contact life and over-all performance. This factor should be given serious consideration in the application of dry reed contacts.

Because of the fast operate and release times of dry reed contacts, particular attention should be paid to the effect of contact protection. In some cases the RC network used may produce circuit resonance that will result in repeated reclosure of contacts before the contacts permanently open. This effect may influence circuit performance and may also cause accelerated erosion of contacts.

Rotary Stepping Switches

5.28 Characteristics

The principle of operation of the rotary stepping switch is the same as that of the armature type relay. In these designs linear motion of the armature is translated through linkages into rotary motion. Pulsing speed is closely related to design and circuit conditions. These devices are quite flexible with regard to their pulsing characteristics and the functions they can perform. Manufacturers' catalogs usually provide considerable information on capability. It would be advisable, however, to consult the manufacturer concerning special applications.

Stepping switches are available with gold-plated base metal and precious metal contacts. The subject of stepping switches and their application is treated comprehensively in other publications.[1] It should be stated, however, that the application of different potentials to adjacent wipers of stepping switches should be avoided. *(See also* Sec. 3.)

---

[1] V. E. James, "How to Use Rotary Stepping Switches," Automatic Electric Co., Northlake, Ill., 1964.

Thermal Relays

5.29   Introduction

Thermal relays provide operate time delays of 0.1 second to 5 minutes, the operate time for a particular design being a function of adjustment and power dissipation, or applied voltage. The basic relay consists of a heater element, a moving heated member, and an actuating linkage that operates normally open or normally closed contacts. Because this device depends on thermal expansion and contraction effects to obtain the desired operate time delay, there is also an appreciable inherent delay on release. Rapid reoperation, therefore, is possible only with special circuit arrangements.

Thermal relays employ only inorganic materials in their construction, and hermetically sealed units are therefore relatively free from contact activation effects. The heater elements are wound with low-temperature coefficient wire to minimize resistance changes with temperature. Being dependent upon heating for operation, thermal relays may be used for d-c, or the equivalent a-c, rms operation.

The terms associated with the design and application of thermal relays are peculiar to these devices. These terms are defined in Sec. 1.

5.30   Application factors

Adjustments of thermal relays are subject to variation with exposure to temperature extremes and dynamic environments such as vibration and shock. Operate time depends on the magnitude of variation in energizing voltage.

The operating characteristics of thermal relays can be predetermined for various environmental conditions and adjustments from the "basic time" of a particular structure. Basic time is that setting of a particular relay structure at which the operate time and the saturate release time are approximately equal (Fig. 5-4).

The time interval of any thermal relay is a function of voltage applied to the heater element, as shown in Fig. 5-5. As indicated in Fig. 5-6, a thermal relay will operate at any voltage

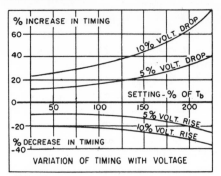

Fig. 5-5. Variation of thermal relay timing with voltage with respect to per cent of basic time, T_b

above the critical voltage. Below this voltage the relay will not operate no matter what the duration of applied voltage may be.

A thermal relay is said to have reached thermal saturation when it has been energized long enough for all elements to have reached thermal equilibrium. This saturation time may be 12 to 15 times the basic time.

Recovery and reoperation of a thermal relay depend upon the basic time of the relay and upon its adjustment within its operating range. A particular time delay can usually be provided by any of several different relays. Choosing the most suitable relay for a particular application, however, involves choosing a basic time that offers a balance between recovery and reoperation characteristics on the one hand and the effect of voltage change on the other.

The instantaneous release and recovery times are important factors for some applications. Normally the instantaneous release time is less than 1 or 2 seconds, but it may be a few seconds longer when a thermal relay is set to a small portion of its basic time. Any thermal relay will recover a fixed percentage of the time for which it has been adjusted after a definite cooling interval. The time after de-energization to regain a

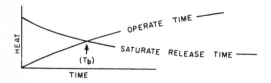

Fig. 5-4. Basic time of a thermal relay defined at T_b

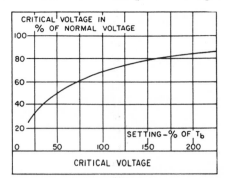

Fig. 5-6. Critical voltage below which a thermal relay will not operate

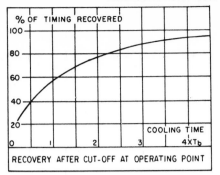

FIG. 5-7. RECOVERY TIME OF A THERMAL RELAY AFTER CUT-OFF AT OPERATING POINT

given percentage of initial operate time is a function of the adjustment and the basic time of the relay (see Fig. 5-7).

In some circuits it is necessary to have current applied to the heater of the thermal relay as long as the equipment is in operation. These applications sometimes involve reoperation after de-energization. In these cases it is important to know the time interval required, after removal of power from a saturated relay, for the relay to cool enough to permit reoperation. This time depends upon the basic time of the relay and its adjustment in the timing range. Figure 5-8 illustrates this factor. Obviously the longer the relay is permitted to cool, the longer will be its operate delay time. In effect, release time after saturation plus recovery time is the time required for reoperation.

Some typical applications for thermal relays are given in Paragraphs 5.41-5.45.

Typical Electromagnetic and Thermal Relay Circuits

The subject of relay circuits for switching systems and power applications is treated comprehensively in other publications. This presentation is limited, therefore, to a few simple circuits that are basic in the art of relay circuit design.

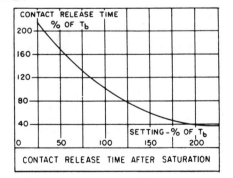

FIG. 5-8. CONTACT RELEASE TIME OF A THERMAL RELAY AFTER HEAT SATURATION

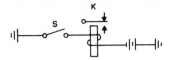

FIG. 5-9. BASIC RELAY CIRCUIT USING GROUNDED BATTERY (50 volts or less; *Tel. Prac.*)[1]

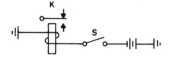

FIG. 5-10. BASIC RELAY CIRCUIT IN WHICH A FALSE GROUND AT SWITCH WILL BLOW A FUSE

5.31 Direct operation

The circuits of Figs. 5-9 and 5-10 are the simplest forms of electromagnetic relay circuits. When switch S is closed, the winding of relay K is energized and the contacts actuated. When S is opened, the winding is de-energized and the contacts restore to their original state. It will be noted that from the standpoint of relay operation, the circuit arrangements of Figs. 5-9 and 5-10 are equivalent. In the former, however, a false ground will not blow a fuse, and therefore this arrangement is more often used.[1]

5.32 Shunt operation

In some circuit applications a relay may be required to function when another part of a circuit is opened. Figure 5-11 illustrates such an arrangement. When switch S is opened, the relay winding K is energized, and when S is closed, the winding is shunted and therefore de-energized. A disadvantage of this type of operation is that it requires adding an additional component, resistor R, and thus is more costly than direct operation. There is the further disadvantage of constant current drain whether the relay winding is energized or de-energized. Release time is also increased because of the delay of current through the shunt resistor.

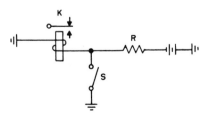

FIG. 5-11. SHUNT OPERATION OF RELAY[1]

[1]Warning: Not recommended for military or industrial practice, which should comply with National Electrical Code (personnel hazard).

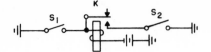

FIG. 5-12. BASIC RELAY LOCK-UP CIRCUIT

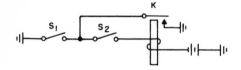

FIG. 5-13. MODIFIED RELAY LOCK-UP CIRCUIT

5.33   Lock-up operation

In direct and shunt operation the relay is controlled entirely by means completely independent of the relay. In locking circuits, however, a relay winding is connected to one or more of its contacts in such a manner that the relay contributes to its control. Figure 5-12 illustrates a basic locking circuit in which the relay winding is energized upon closure of S_1 and then is held operated or locked up through one of its make contacts and S_2. The lock-up circuit does not affect the relay prior to operation but controls it thereafter until S_2 is opened.

A variation of the lock-up circuit is shown in Fig. 5-13. Here closures of S_1 and S_2 are required to operate the relay, which is then held through its make contact and S_2.

Another form of lock-up utilizes a continuity make-before-break contact arrangement. In this type of circuit, illustrated in Fig. 5-14, the relay is operated through S_1 and the normally closed contact. After operation, the relay is held or locked up through the normally open contact and S_2. After the relay operates, S_1 is free to control other circuits without being affected by the ground on the winding of relay K. If the normally open contact is not adjusted to close before the normally closed contact opens, the relay will self-interrupt its winding, causing it to release. Buzzing will result.

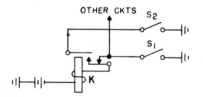

FIG. 5-14. CONTINUITY (MAKE-BEFORE-BREAK)
CONTACT LOCK-UP

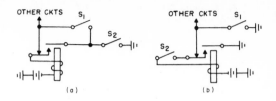

FIG. 5-15. ALTERNATIVE CONTINUITY LOCK-UP ARRANGEMENTS

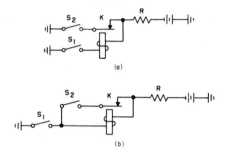

FIG. 5-16. TWO FORMS OF RELAY LOCK-DOWN CIRCUITS INVOLVING SHUNT RESISTOR PATH AROUND A RELAY COIL

Figure 5-15 illustrates variations in continuity lock-up circuits that require closure of both S_1 and S_2 before the relay will operate.

5.34   Lock-down operation

In a lock-down circuit a relay prevents itself from being operated through one circuit path until another circuit path has been opened. Figure 5-16 illustrates typical lock-down circuits in which the relay cannot be operated through S_1 until S_2 has been opened. After the relay has been operated through S_1, opening and closing of S_2 will not affect the operated state of the relay. These circuits dissipate power in the shunt resistor during the lock-down state. The resistor is in series with the relay winding during operation and can have an appreciable effect on operate time.

5.35   Circuits using multiwound relays

Multiwound relays are commonly used when operation of the relay through two or more electrically isolated circuits is desired. A circuit of this type is illustrated in its simplest form in Fig. 5-17. In this case, closure of either S_1 or S_2 or both will operate the relay. This method is sometimes used to isolate operating and locking circuits, as shown in Fig. 5-18.

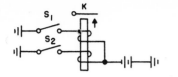

FIG. 5-17. SIMPLEST FORM OF TWO-COIL RELAY OPERATION ("OR" CIRCUIT)

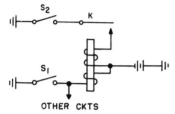

FIG. 5-18. METHOD OF ISOLATING AN OPERATING AND LOCK-UP CIRCUIT

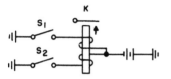

FIG. 5-19. TWO-WINDING RELAY IN SIMPLE DIFFERENTIAL CIRCUIT

Another application for a two-winding relay is the differential circuit shown in Fig. 5-19. Here two windings are connected in opposing directions. When both windings are energized, the flux will not operate the relay or hold it in an operated state. Closure of S_1 or S_2 will operate the relay, but when both circuits are closed, the relay will release. The windings must be so designed that the desired balance is obtained.

This arrangement is often used to determine whether two circuits open and close simultaneously. It may also be used to release a relay upon the closure instead of the opening of a control circuit. In order that the relay may release, it is essential that the operate control circuit remain closed until the second winding is energized. To prevent false reoperation, both winding circuits should be de-energized simultaneously, that is, the interval between opening

the two windings should not exceed the operate waiting time of the relay.

5.36 Forced release

It is possible to obtain rapid release of a relay by employing two windings wound in opposing directions. As shown in Fig. 5-20, the relay is operated upon closure of S_1 and remains locked up through a make contact after S_1 is opened. When release is desired, closure of S_2 energizes the stronger release winding. Opening of the make contact prevents reoperation of the relay by simultaneous de-energization of both windings.

5.37 Marginal circuits

Many times relays are used to detect two different circuit conditions in the same line. Figure 5-21 illustrates a typical circuit in which closure of S_1 will operate relay K_1 but not relay K_2, which is adjusted to operate at a higher current. Upon closure of S_2, however, the current limiting resistor R is short-circuited, and the current now increases and operates K_2. Relays in circuits of this type usually require a closer control of adjustments than is necessary in simpler circuits.

5.38 Polarized relay circuits

Polar relays are used to perform a variety of circuit functions. Some are quite sensitive and others quite fast, but all depend on direction of current for their operation.

The simplest form of polar relay is a design in which the armature is held in its unoperated position by a permanent magnet. This type lends itself to many of the same basic circuits as the neutral relay except, of course, that it will respond to polarity in only one direction. A polar

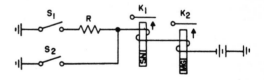

FIG. 5-21. OPERATION OF MARGINAL AND SENSITIVE RELAYS

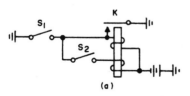

(a)

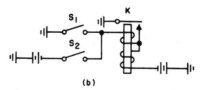

(b)

FIG. 5-20. TWO METHODS OF OBTAINING FORCED RELEASE OF A RELAY THROUGH A SECOND WINDING

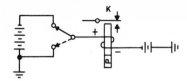

FIG. 5-22. CONTROL OF A POLAR RELAY

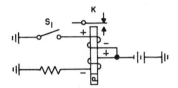

FIG. 5-23. OPERATION OF A POLAR RELAY THROUGH BIASING WINDING

relay with negative potential at the plus end of a winding is energized in the direction that will put the contacts in the normal condition. By using the basic circuit of Fig. 5-22, this type of relay may be used for the detection of polarity or for applications in which response to only one polarity is desired.

Another method of obtaining polar operation

nitude of the current in the operating winding.

Some polar relays are bistable, latch-in designs. These relays have two stable operated positions, that is, the armature may be operated in either direction by energizing one winding or either of a pair of windings at a polarity that will operate the relay to the desired position. When the winding is de-energized, the relay remains magnetically latched in the position to which it was operated until it is energized at reverse polarity. Figure 5-24 illustrates simple circuits for operating a single winding. Two winding bistable latch-in operation is shown in Fig. 5-25.

5.39　Slow operate and release

Relays with slow operate and slow release features are described in Sec. 3. Usually designs of this type are used to assure sequence of operation in a circuit containing several relays or to obtain a time delay of a definite interval.

The circuit arrangements may include relays operating in series or parallel, with one relay having a longer delay to satisfy circuit requirements. Slow operate and release time may also be obtained by other means (see Fig. 5-26).

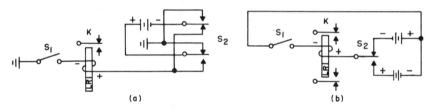

(a)　　　　　　(b)

FIG. 5-24. TWO METHODS OF OPERATING A SINGLE-WINDING BISTABLE LATCH-IN RELAY

is the use of a biasing winding, as shown in Fig. 5-23. When only the biasing winding is energized, the armature is held in its unoperated position, as shown. Upon excitation of the operating winding, the relay operates. In sensitive and fast-acting relays the operating winding may be energized from an a-c source and pulsed at a rapid rate. The time of closure of the contacts will depend on the amount of bias and the mag-

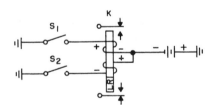

FIG. 5-25. DOUBLE-WINDING LATCH-IN RELAY OPERTION

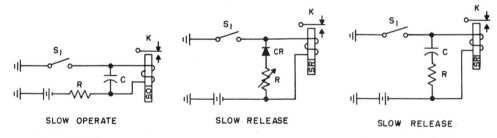

SLOW OPERATE　　　　SLOW RELEASE　　　　SLOW RELEASE

FIG. 5-26. METHODS OF OBTAINING SLOW OPERATE AND SLOW RELEASE TIMES OF RELAY

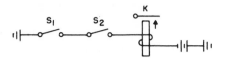

FIG. 5-27. SERIES "AND" CIRCUIT IN WHICH RELAY
OPERATES WHEN BOTH S_1 AND S_2 ARE CLOSED

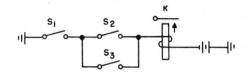

FIG. 5-29. CIRCUIT IN WHICH RELAY OPERATES
WHEN S_1 AND EITHER S_2 OR S_3 ARE CLOSED

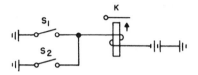

FIG. 5-28. PARALLEL "OR" CIRCUIT IN WHICH RELAY
OPERATES WHEN EITHER S_1 OR S_2 IS CLOSED

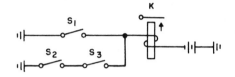

FIG. 5-30. CIRCUIT IN WHICH RELAY OPERATES
WHEN S_1 OR S_2 AND S_3 ARE CLOSED

5.40 "And," "Or," and series/parallel circuits

In Fig. 5-27 is shown a simple series circuit in which a proposition is true only when S_1 *and* S_2 are closed, whereas in Fig. 5-28 a proposition is true if S_1 *or* S_2 (or *both*) are closed. Thus, it is evident that an *and* proposition is equivalent to a series contact arrangement and that an *or* proposition may be represented by a parallel configuration.

Now, in Fig. 5-29 a proposition is true if S_1 *and* either S_2 *or* S_3 are closed, whereas in Fig. 5-30 a proposition is true if S_1 *or* S_2 *and* S_3 are closed. Although the circuits may be more complex, it is always possible to indicate closure of series connections by *and* and parallel connections by *or*.

5.41 Thermal relay circuits

Rapid reset. The inherent time delay in cooling a thermal relay precludes using a single relay for fast reoperation. However, two thermal relays in conjunction with an electromagnetic relay may be used to obtain instant reset. Typical circuits are shown in Fig. 5-31.

When switch S in Fig. 5-31 (normally open contact) is closed, both thermal relays start heating. At point A on the heating curve, the contacts of TR-1 open. Both thermal relays continue to heat until at point B the contacts of TR-2 close, thereby operating the magnetic relay, which locks itself in through contact M_1. Contact B_1 disconnects the heaters of both thermal relays, which immediately start to cool. The M_2 contact of the magnetic relay now is closed, but since the normally closed contact of TR-1 had

been opened previously, the load circuit contact remains open. The contacts of TR-2 also are out of the circuit. When TR-1 cools to point C, its contact will reclose, thus closing the load circuit through contact M_2. By the time the timing cycle is complete, both thermal relays will have effectively and completely cooled, and hence they will be ready to retime the cycle. No matter where the timing cycle is interrupted, the cycle will always return to a point on line AB, thereby assuring 75 per cent of the full timing cycle.

A variation of this circuit employing a normally closed contact to control the load is also shown in Fig. 5-31 (top).

5.42 Thermal timing element combined with double-pole double-throw magnetic relay for rapid reset

This method of obtaining rapid reset is used in industrial and communications systems but is not often used in military systems. The circuits employed for normally open contact control and for normally closed contact operation are shown in Fig. 5-32. The graph shows the timing cycle.

The thermal element has two independent sets of contacts. In the normally closed situation, these contacts close when the element is fully heated, thereby operating the electromagnetic relay which locks itself in and cuts off the heater of the thermal element. Operation of the electromagnetic relay also transfers control of the output circuit to the normally open 5-7 contacts in the thermal element, now closed. This pair of contacts reopens when the thermal element cools. When power is interrupted, the magnetic relay releases, and the output circuit is restored to its unoperated condition.

5.43 Current and voltage sensing

Thermal relays are adaptable to a-c and d-c current and voltage sensing applications when they have essentially no differential between contact opening and contact closing values. One of their important characteristics for this type of application is that they are insensitive to brief transients of considerable magnitude but respond to small fluctuations of any appreciable

duration. The length of the delay can be matched to the application by selecting a relay having the required basic time.

To protect equipment against excessive voltage, a voltage-sensing thermal relay with normally closed contacts is set to operate at the highest voltage that can be safely applied continuously to the protected equipment (see Fig. 5-33). For this type of service, the time constant should be long or short depending upon the ability of the apparatus being protected to withstand the overload imposed.

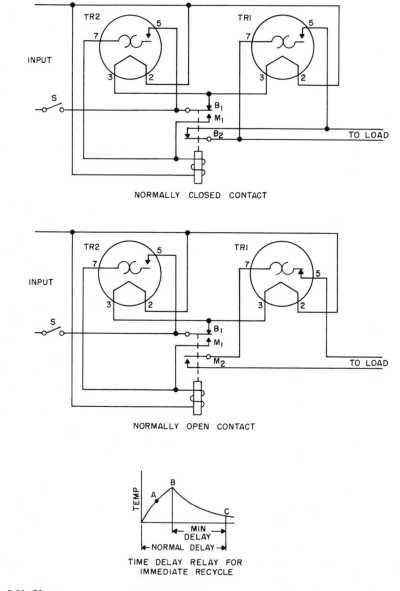

FIG. 5-31. USE OF TWO THERMAL RELAYS IN COMBINATION WITH AN ELECTROMAGNETIC RELAY TO OBTAIN RAPID RESET OPERATION

5.44 Stepped voltage regulation

Figure 5-34 illustrates a circuit in which a rather wide variation in supply voltage to a fixed load is controlled by inserting fixed resistance upon opening normally closed contacts.

5.45 Continuous regulation of voltage

Continuous regulation of voltage by thermal relays depends upon a characteristic not widely recognized. When a thermal relay with normally

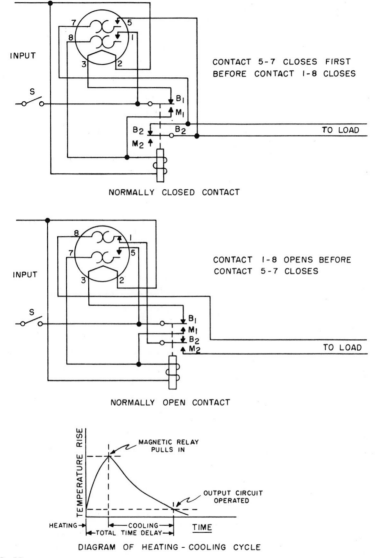

CONTACT 5-7 CLOSES FIRST
BEFORE CONTACT 1-8 CLOSES

NORMALLY CLOSED CONTACT

CONTACT 1-8 OPENS BEFORE
CONTACT 5-7 CLOSES

NORMALLY OPEN CONTACT

DIAGRAM OF HEATING - COOLING CYCLE

Fig. 5-32. Use of a dual contact thermal relay with an electromagnetic relay to obtain rapid reset operation

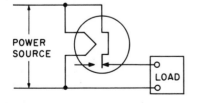

Fig. 5-33. Use of thermal relay for over-voltage cutoff

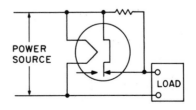

Fig. 5-34. Use of thermal relay for stepped voltage regulation

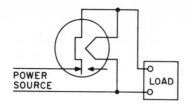

FIG. 5-35. ELEMENTARY VOLTAGE REGULATING CIRCUIT USING THERMAL RELAY

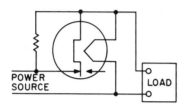

FIG. 5-36. A MORE SOPHISTICATED METHOD OF OBTAINING VOLTAGE REGULATION WITH A THERMAL RELAY

closed contacts is so connected that its heater circuit is supplied through its own contacts (Fig. 5-35), any voltage below the critical setting of the relay will not disturb its contacts. However, if the supply voltage is higher than that value, the relay will not disturb its contacts. However, if close, thus interrupting the current to the heater. The proportion of "on" to "off" time is automatically adjusted so that, irrespective of further rise in voltage, the heating will be the same as that of a continuous voltage equal to the critical voltage setting of the relay. The "on" and "off" time will be a function of the voltage applied to the heater. If the supply voltage is just slightly above the setting, it will be cut off for only a short portion of the time so as to reduce its heating effect to that of the critical voltage. If it is much higher, then it will be cut off for a longer portion of the time.

Figure 5-36 shows the circuit as it is normally used. It differs from the foregoing explanation in that the opening of the thermal relay contacts does not completely interrupt the supply potential but places a dropping resistor in series with it.

5.46 Two-relay pulse frequency dividers

A two-relay pulse frequency divider circuit is shown in Fig. 5-37. The first closure of the S contact operates relay K1, which latches electrically through its normally open contact to provide a make-before-break action. Simulta

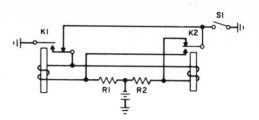

FIG. 5-37. TWO-RELAY PULSE FREQUENCY DIVIDER CIRCUIT

neously, relay K2 is inhibited from operating while contact S is closed. When contact S opens, relay K2 operates. The next closure of contact S short-circuits relay K1, causing its release. The K1 relay contact transfers the holding circuit for relay K2 to the control of the S contact. Meanwhile, relay K1 is inhibited by the S contact. When the S contact opens, relay K2 releases, and the circuit is normal.

Another frequency divider circuit is shown in Fig. 5-38. The first closure of the S make contact operates relay K1, which latches under control of relay K2. Release of the S contact operates relay K2. Both sets of the K2 relay contacts require make-before-break action. This allows relay K2 to latch to the relay K1 contact before opening the operating path and transfers the latching path for relay K1 to the break contact of the S contact. When the S contact is reoperated, relay K1 releases. The contacts of S also have make-before-break action so that the S make contact provides a latching path for relay K2 before relay K1 opens the latching path for relay K2.

This arrangement is capable of following faster pulsing than the circuit of Fig. 5-37 since each relay releases on open circuit instead of on short circuit.

Figure 5-39 shows an arrangement for counting pulses that are repeated by the S contacts. Relays K1 and K2 divide the pulses as described

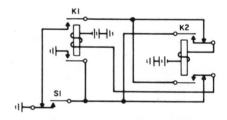

FIG. 5-38. ALTERNATIVE TWO-RELAY PULSE FREQUENCY DIVIDER CIRCUIT CAPABLE OF FOLLOWING FASTER PULSING THAN THAT OF FIG. 5-37

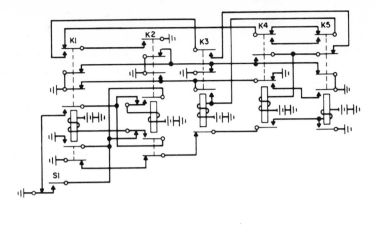

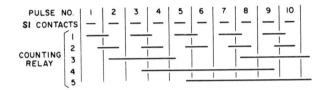

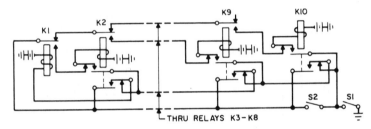

FIG. 5-39. PULSE-COUNTING RELAY CIRCUIT

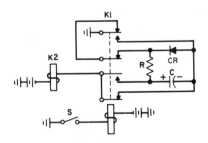

FIG. 5-40. CIRCUIT ADVANCE THROUGH SEQUENTIAL OPERATION OF RELAYS

for Fig. 5-38. Relays K3, K4, and K5 divide the output pulses of relays K1 and K2. The sequence chart at the bottom of Fig. 5-39 shows the relays operated for any number of pulses up to ten.

5.47 Circuit advance by sequential relay operation

This circuit, shown in Fig. 5-40, advances in a regular sequence with only one or two relays operated. The closure of ground at contact S1 operates relay K1. The closure of control contact S2 operates relay K2. Relay K2 latches to ground through succeeding break contacts and opens its operating path. Relay K2 also transfers control of the relay K1 winding from the S1 to the S2 contact. To accomplish these functions properly, two of the relay contacts must provide make-before-break action. When contact S2 opens, relay K1 releases. Subsequent cycles of closures and openings result in similar advances to succeeding relays in the chain.

5.48 Fast relay operation by voltage doubling

A circuit for doubling the relay supply voltage to obtain fast operation is shown in Fig. 5-41. When relay K1 is operated, relay K2 is operated by the charge on capacitor C in series-aiding with the voltage on its winding. Momentarily the voltage is 2E. Diode CR does not conduct until

FIG. 5-41. FAST RELAY OPERATION BY VOLTAGE DOUBLING

the voltage across capacitor C falls to a value equal to the drop across resistor R that results from the holding current for relay K2.

5.49 Bistable polar relay circuits

In the bistable polar slave relay circuit shown in Fig. 5-42, the contact conditions of relay K follow those of switch S. This arrangement requires the energy source to have low impedance.

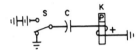

FIG. 5-42. BISTABLE POLAR SLAVE RELAY

Figure 5-43 gives an example of "pulse stretching" in which the original pulse is too short for effective relay operation. The energy source E and resistance R should have low impedance to store sufficient energy in capacitor C to operate relay K. In this arrangement, relay K is restored to the original position by a second winding (not shown).

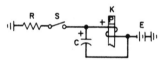

FIG. 5-43. PULSE STRETCHING APPLIED TO BISTABLE POLAR RELAY

A bistable polar relay pulse frequency divider is shown in Fig. 5-44. For each operation of control switch S, relay K transfers to its other position. If the relay winding and capacitor C are properly damped to prevent oscillation, this circuit has no tendency toward instability. However, resistors R1 and R2 must each be high enough so as not to operate relay K. Capacitor C must be capable of being charged with either polarity.

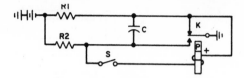

FIG. 5-44. BISTABLE POLAR RELAY PULSE FREQUENCY DIVIDER

The arrangement shown in Fig. 5-45 is a bistable polar relay multivibrator for times up to about 15 minutes. With the normally closed contact of relay K closed, terminal 1 of capacitor C is held to ground potential. A positive charge builds up on terminal 2 through resistor R2. When the potential is high enough, the neon tube NE conducts the charge through the winding of relay K, operating it to its other position. The neon tube is self-extinguishing. Capacitor C must have high capacitance, high voltage rating, and the ability to be charged to either polarity. This circuit is inefficient since considerable energy remains in the capacitor after the neon tube is extinguished.

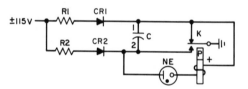

FIG. 5-45. BISTABLE POLAR RELAY MULTIVIBRATOR WITH LONG TIME CONSTANT

5.50 Time delay relay circuits

An RC controlled thyratron time delay circuit is shown in Fig. 5-46. While contact S1 is closed, no charge can build up on capacitor C if resistance R1 is made much higher than R3. If the S1 contact is open long enough, the voltage on capacitor C rises to the point where tube T ionizes its starter gap. The main gap then conducts, thereby operating relay K, which latches. In latching, relay K short-circuits the tube, thus

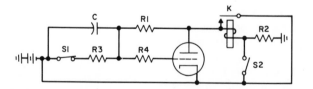

FIG. 5-46. RC CONTROLLED THYRATRON TIME DELAY RELAY

extinguishing it. To restore the circuit, contact S2 is closed long enough to allow relay K to release on the short circuit. When contact S2 reopens, the circuit is again ready to time the open period of contact S1.

A time delay relay employing a thermistor is shown in Fig. 5-47. This arrangement has the advantage of fast recycling. Each delay cycle first heats thermistor T very rapidly and then uses its slow cooling time to control the delay. Contact S closes three paths simultaneously:

(1) The secondary or biasing winding of relay K1 is strongly energized since resistor R3 is short-circuited by a back contact of relay K2.

5.51 Resistance comparison circuits

Shown in Fig. 5-48 is a resistance comparison circuit. It is sometimes desirable to determine whether an unknown resistance is above or below a predetermined value. Resistance R may consist of a number of resistors in series, each of which may or may not be short-circuited. Assume that R2 and R3 have equal values; then relay K operates when R is reduced below the value of the R1 resistor. For best results, the relay must be sensitive, and R1, R2 and R3 resistors should be the precision type with a low percentage tolerance. With R at the point of detection, the relationship between relay winding resistance

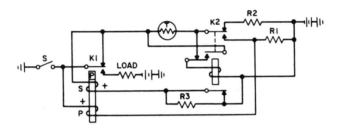

FIG. 5-47. TIME DELAY RELAY USING THERMISTOR COOLING EFFECT

(2) Primary winding P is energized in series with high resistance R1 but is inhibited by the heavy bias flux of the secondary winding.

(3) Thermistor T is energized in series with the parallel combination of relay K2 winding and low resistance R2.

Thermistor T quickly heats and lowers its resistance sufficiently to operate relay K2. Relay K2 latches through the normally closed contact of relay K1 before it opens its operating path through thermistor T. A contact of relay K2 opens the circuit to resistor R2 and connects the thermistor in parallel with the primary winding of relay K1. Another contact of relay K2 opens the short circuit around resistor R3. Now the low resistance of thermistor T depresses the current in the primary winding of relay K1. When thermistor T cools, its resistance rises, and relay K1 operates. The operation of this relay energizes the load, releases relay K2, and de-energizes the biasing winding of relay K1. The decay of flux in relay K2 generates a circulating current through the secondary winding of relay K1, but this current is in the direction that maintains relay K1 operated and thus has no effect.

and the bridge resistors should be approximately that shown in this formula:

Relay K winding resistance =

$$\frac{R \times R2}{R + R2} + \frac{R1 \times R3}{R1 + R2}$$

In the resistance comparison circuit of Fig. 5-48, the sensitivity of the circuit is limited by the gap between the point at which relay K operates to close its normally open contact when resistance R falls, and the value to which resistance R must rise in order to cause relay K to reclose its normally closed contact. The anticipation feature shown in Fig. 5-49 reduces this gap. When relay K1 operates as resistance R falls, it

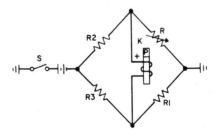

FIG. 5-48. RESISTANCE COMPARISON RELAY CIRCUIT

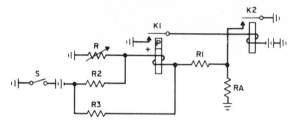

FIG. 5-49. RESISTANCE COMPARISON RELAY CIRCUIT WITH "ANTICIPATION" FEATURE

in turn operates relay K2, which short-circuits the RA resistor. This has the effect of lowering the point to which resistance R must rise in order to cause relay K1 to reopen its normally open contact. This feature minimizes "hunting" or "overshoot."

5.52   Circuits for checking

Shown in Fig. 5-50 (A) is a sequence method to check for latching of a relay where the time element permits. Relay K2 is energized by the operation of the S contact. If relay K2 does not operate and latch through its own contact to ground, relay K1 will not operate on return of contact S to its normal position. In Fig. 5-50 (B), a polar relay is so arranged that it will not operate until the latching ground is returned. In Fig. 5-50 (C), use is made of a neutral relay polarized with a shunting diode. Intermediate voltage from the divider operates relay K2 through the diode. When relay K2 latches, ground is returned toward the intermediate voltage but, being blocked by the diode, operates relay K1. Since K1 is a neutral relay, it usually has greater contact capacity than a polar relay.

The circuit of Fig. 5-50 (D) is used for a more difficult type of check. The closure of contact S1 operates relay K2 and in turn operates polar relay K1. When contact S1 opens, relay K1 would normally release but remains operated if a false ground is present. If no trouble is encountered, contact S2 is closed to provide a latching path for relay K2. This ground also reoperates relay K1.

A translating and checking circuit is shown in Fig. 5-51. This arrangement gives an output on one of the ten leads only if two of the five relays are operated. The designation of the relays and the translating network is so chosen that the numerical designation of the output is the sum of the designations of the operated relays, with the exception of lead O, which is energized when relays K4 and K7 are operated.

5.53   Crosspoint relay matrix

The crosspoint relay shown in Fig. 5-52 is operated by momentary simultaneous application of positive potential on a vertical S-lead and negative potential on a horizontal S-lead. A similar path for holding is then established between the corresponding H-leads. A path through a large switching network can be held by

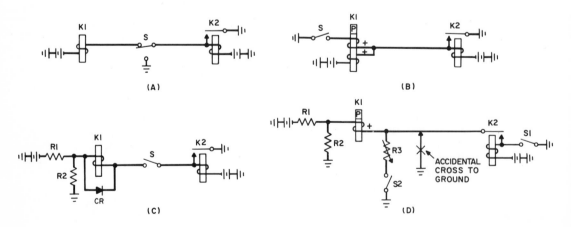

FIG. 5-50. CIRCUITS FOR CHECKING LATCHING AND GROUND FAULTS

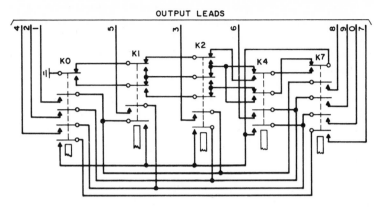

FIG. 5-51. TRANSLATING AND CHECKING CIRCUIT

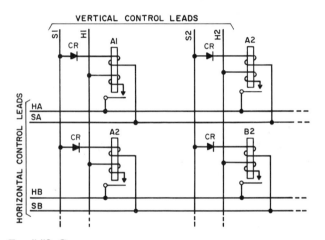

FIG. 5-52. CROSSPOINT RELAY MATRIX WITH HOLDING FEATURE

a series H-circuit through a number of cross-point matrices. A multiplicity of independent paths may be held provided that no attempt is made to operate more than one relay in each horizontal or in each vertical lead. The diodes connected in series with the S-leads prevent multiple shunt paths through the matrix.

5.54 Lockout circuit forces sequential priority

A lockout circuit is one that under the control of a number of external circuits provides an output indication corresponding to only one of the inputs at any one time. Under the control of an input signal, the lockout circuit establishes a unique path to one of the output leads corresponding to a particular control lead and prevents any further output until the first signal has been cleared. To do this, each control lead is connected to a corresponding

relay and the connecting paths to ground are closed through contact networks on the relays that form a transfer chain. As a result, an inherent order of preference is set up. The terminal circuit at the left in Fig. 5-53 has highest preference and that at the right the lowest, as designated by the subscripts H and L. The re-

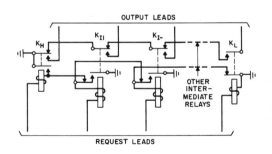

FIG. 5-53. LOCKOUT CIRCUIT, WITH RELAY K_H HAVING THE HIGHEST PRIORITY AND RELAY K_L, THE LOWEST.

lays are actuated by application of battery to the control leads, and the contact chain on the relays provide continuity to ground through a series of break contacts.

If relay K_{I1} first receives a signal, for example, relay K_{II} to its left is made inoperative by a break contact of K_{I1}. If a later signal appears on K_{I2}, it will pick up but will deliver no output as a result of the break in the output chain. As soon as K_{I1} releases, the signal from K_{I2} will go through. It should be noted that the relays of intermediate preference use form D (make-before-break) continuity transfer contacts for holding themselves in. If form C (break-make) contacts were used and if both relays K_{II} and K_L had been operated, the operation of a K_I relay would have resulted in relay buzzing, due to alternate release and pickup of relays as the continuity was broken.

This arrangement does not provide outputs in the same order in which the input signals originate.

5.55 Lockout circuit

If a circuit can serve a number of circuits only one at a time, requests for service are controlled by a lockout circuit. The circuit in Fig. 5-54 provides this function in accordance with

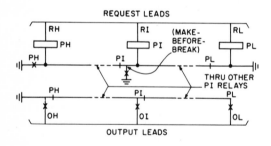

FIG. 5-54. LOCKOUT CIRCUIT

a wired-in priority ranging from PH having highest priority to PL having lowest priority. The reason for the make-before-break contact action can be seen if both PH and PL relays are operated and an RI lead is energized. If PI had

a discontinuous transfer, a "buzzing" action would result. This arrangement does not provide service in the same order as that in which the requests originate.

5.56 Typical power relay circuits

Typical power relay circuits are illustrated in Figs. 5-55 through 5-65.

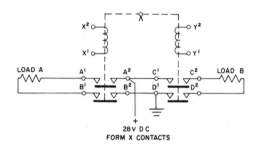

FIG. 5-55. LOAD TRANSFER, 28 VOLTS D-C, CENTER OFF

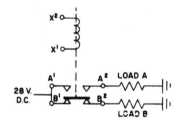

FIG. 5-56. LOAD TRANSFER, 28 VOLTS D-C, NO CENTER OFF (FORM Z CONTACT COMBINATION)

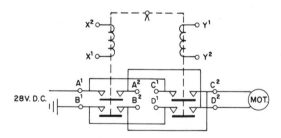

FIG. 5-57. REVERSING A 28-VOLT D-C MOTOR BY REVERSING ARMATURE CURRENT

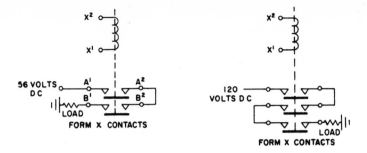

FIG. 5-58. MULTIPLE CONTACT, DOUBLE CONTACTS USED FOR BREAKING VOLTAGES HIGHER THAN 28 VOLTS D-C

Caution: Dielectric test voltages should be raised when using higher line voltages.

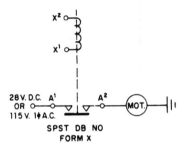

FIG. 5-59. "ACROSS-THE-LINE" STARTING OF 28-VOLT D-C OR 115-VOLT, ONE-PHASE A-C MOTOR

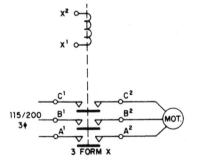

FIG. 5-60. "ACROSS-THE-LINE" STARTING OF 115/ 220-VOLT, THREE-PHASE A-C MOTOR

Single-break contacts may be used on 400-cycle, but double-break contacts are more common on power relays because of their higher peak interrupting capacity (particularly on 60-cycle circuits) and their suitability for 28-volt d-c circuits of comparable ratings.

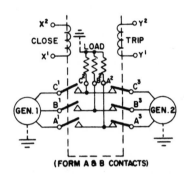

FIG. 5-61. SOURCE TRANSFER FROM TWO THREE-PHASE A-C GENERATORS, SINGLE-BREAK FORM A CONTACTS, NO CENTER OFF, LATCHED

Contacts should be rated at twice the line-to-line generator voltage across the air gap and phase-to-phase (for out-of-phase generator conditions).

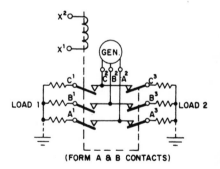

FIG. 5-62. LOAD TRANSFER FROM SINGLE THREE-PHASE GENERATOR, NO CENTER OFF, WITH ONE MAINTAINED COIL

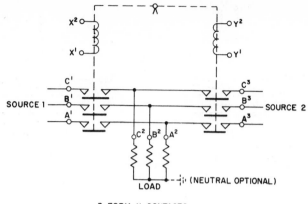

3 FORM X CONTACTS
3 PDT DM NO CONTACTS 3 POSITION

FIG. 5-63. TRANSFER FROM TWO THREE-PHASE SOURCES, CENTER OFF

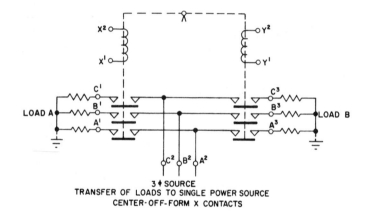

3 ⏀ SOURCE
TRANSFER OF LOADS TO SINGLE POWER SOURCE
CENTER-OFF-FORM X CONTACTS

FIG. 5-64. LOAD TRANSFER FROM SINGLE THREE-PHASE SOURCE

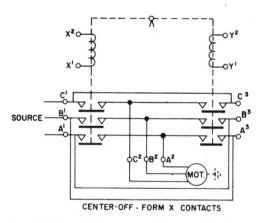

CENTER-OFF - FORM X CONTACTS

FIG. 5-65. REVERSING A THREE-PHASE A-C MOTOR BY
REVERSING TWO OF ITS PHASES (LINE C REMAINS
UNCHANGED)

6
Relay Reliability

Early Concepts of Reliability

It is difficult to single out for special mention any of the early programs for reliability. Some were part of the main stream of reliability development; some were plans destined for obscurity; still others that recognized the basic problems involved were much too *avant-garde* at that time and are only now being rediscovered.

6.1 Characteristics of early programs

These early programs were generally keyed to specific projects or departments within a governmental framework and found little support outside of the limited fields of interest for which they were intended. With few exceptions, they were concerned with the development of mathematical techniques and a governing philosophy and were not true reliability programs.

During this early period many technical papers devoted to particular aspects of reliability were published or presented at national symposiums of professional societies such as the IRE (IEEE) and ASQC. Concurrently, a much needed centralized source of engineering, statistical, and managerial data relative to reliability was being developed through papers published by the Research and Development Division, Ordnance Missile Laboratories, Redstone Arsenal.

Development of Present Reliability Concepts

6.2 AGREE recommendations

In its report of 1957, Task Group 5 of the Advisory Group on Reliability of Electronic Equipment (AGREE) recognized four basic needs for reliability:

(1) Additional requirements in electronic parts and tube specifications.

(2) Faster coordination of parts specification.

(3) Establishment of technical characteristic data on devices and systems for design and production personnel.

(4) Periodic review of parts specification programs to assure compatibility with the reliability program.

An *ad hoc* Study Group was established to analyze the recommendations of the AGREE Task Group 5 and to advise the Department of Defense of methods to implement these recommendations efficiently. The result was published in 1960 by the Department of Defense under the title, "Parts Specification Management for Reliability," more commonly known as the "Darnell Report" (from the name of the chairman of the Task Group). Volume II, Section 5, is devoted specifically to relay reliability and covers the entire range of the reliability problem. It takes into consideration the specific problems of the user and of both the systems and part manufacturers. The unifying or central theme of the report is twofold:

(1) Reliability of the system is dependent upon the component parts; therefore, to increase system reliability a concentrated effort is required to increase component reliability.

(2) A quantitative "yardstick of reliability" is needed to provide a means of comparison between groups of similar parts made by different manufacturers.

133

6.3   Development of standard life tests

The measure of reliability decided upon was the ability or inability of devices to pass certain standard life tests in addition to the requirements of the applicable military standard. The report recognized that a single-level reliability would not meet the various needs of the military. Therefore, a multilevel reliability requirement was developed. The basic concept behind this multilevel requirement is the fact that parts manufactured to existing specifications are often more reliable than the requirements of the specifications. It is, however, impossible to recognize these "more reliable" parts by the tests called for in existing specifications since they distinguish only between those parts that will or will not pass the minimum requirements.

To be consistent with levels recommended for time dependent parts, the report recommended that relay failure rates be expressed as a percentage of failure per 10,000 operations. It further recommended that the failure rate levels be established at 1.0, 0.1, 0.01 and 0.001 per cent per 10,000 operations.

6.4   Need for standard specifications

Reliability is something that everyone accepts as a necessity, but many times compliance varies. Specifically, there are numerous specifications covering reliability, and many of them are similar in some aspects. Consequently, suppliers are required to comply with many different specifications in their reliability programs. This points to the need for combining similar reliability requirements into one specification wherever possible.

Present Philosophy of Reliability

6.5   Statistical approach

The present philosophy of reliability uses a statistical approach that will be explained in detail later on in this section. Years ago, statistical methods were first applied in quality control procedures to predict the drift off tolerance of mechanical parts and to estimate the defects in a lot. The success of these methods made it reasonable to assume that reliability could be successfully predicted using some form of statistical approach. Obviously, the accuracy of any prediction depends upon the integrity of the data collected, and the sample size, as well as the prediction techniques. Reliability predictions are based on life tests in which the underlying statistical mechanism is that of random, or chance, failures that are independent of accumulated life and are individually unpredictable. Failure patterns follow one of several distributional forms, described in detail later. The use of such patterns is considered justified since many factors act to produce failures in a system. They establish a stress-strength relationship, which in turn causes a random distribution of the failures.

6.6   Sampling methods

Determination of the proper sample size when sampling groups of like parts (or "population")[1] for quality characteristics is usually achieved by means of the sampling tables provided in Military Standard MIL-STD-105. In sampling for reliability characteristics, however, the more frequently used sampling tables are those found in Military Handbook H-108. This handbook was prepared to provide sampling tables and procedures for life and reliability testing. The tables are based on the assumption of exponential distribution and should be used only when this assumption is deemed reasonable.

In sampling for reliability, a small sample is usually tested to stress loads that are meant to induce failures. The relays that pass this test are not considered acceptable for further use since a good part of their operational life has been used up. Screening differs from sampling in that all the units produced are subjected to some small increment of stress that will not adversely affect the "passing" units but still is severe enough to cause weak units to fail or to exhibit characteristics indicating that they would fail if stressed to the full specification requirements. These screening tests must be used judiciously so as not to be detrimental to the units that do pass and are shipped.

6.7   Process control

One basic premise of statistical testing is that the lots submitted for sample selection must be drawn from the same population. Although the effects of design changes on the sample are recog-

---

[1]See Glossary of Reliability Terms at the end of this section.

nized and methods provided to account for them, process changes originally were left to the discretion of the various manufacturers. It is now accepted that any reliability specification must contain provisions for establishing a basic process of manufacture from which deviation will be permitted only after tests have been performed to determine the effect of the change. This places a responsibility on relay manufacturers to provide a process manual that covers every step in the manufacturing process.[1] No changes should be made in this document until sufficient data has been accumulated to prove their worth, and the user has had a chance to evaluate their effect on his own system. This does not mean that the relay user should be able to dictate methods of manufacturing, but it does imply a joint effort by manufacturer and user to achieve a common goal in reliability.

Factors that Affect Relay Reliability

6.8   Complexity

Although relays themselves have not become more complex during the past few years, the systems in which they are used have become more complex with each new design. This increasing complexity shows no signs of abatement. In fact, as systems become more sophisticated, new areas of relay usage are opened up that demand more and more sophistication.

6.9   Miniaturization

Coupled with system complexity is an increasing demand for miniaturization. Smaller and smaller components are called for, and yet the performance demands made upon the relay are not relaxed.

6.10   Human error

Section 5 of this handbook describes the principles for the correct application of relays. Correct application will go a long way toward reducing relay failures. Improper selection and misapplication all too frequently affect relay reliability.

---

[1]In its simplest form, a process control manual can be construed to mean no more than a listing of operations in the sequence in which they are performed. High reliability programs require a more detailed and sophisticated description of the entire process.

About the mishandling of relays in the field much can be said. It is a cause of great concern to relay manufacturers to see solder-hook type relay terminals twisted and mangled beyond any ability to accommodate wire connections. Dumping trays of relays on a work bench prior to potting may be a good shock test, but unfortunately, no one checks the "failures" this may cause until after the relays are wired into a system. Relays are precision devices and should be handled as such. Care should be taken at all times to eliminate unauthorized shock and terminal pull tests, to say nothing of overload tests inadvertently caused by connecting the contacts to loads beyond rated capabilities. The relay manufacturer takes pains; so should the user.

Insuring Reliability Through Education

Since the desire for producing a reliable product must stem from management, reliability education must start at the top and filter down through the company chain of command. The educational approach must be tailored to the particular group being instructed. A reliability training program for management, for example, would be of no value to production personnel.

6.11   Management training

In selling a reliability program to management people, the emphasis should be on cost. The expenses incurred by unreliable equipment in terms of replacement, repair, interruptions of service, and even the loss of business can be measured and the cost of unreliability demonstrated in tangible terms. A management not fully convinced of the worth of such a program will doom it before it starts.

It should be obvious that product reliability is no longer the exclusive province of the reliability engineer. Awareness of the need for reliability must start with management before being implemented at the design stage and carried through production. Once production has begun, no life testing, no design of a statistical experiment, no fifth decimal place measuring of Mean Time to Failure will improve the reliability of a product. Because of this broadening of the reliability concept, management backing is the most important ingredient of any successful reliability program.

6.12 Engineering training

Every design and test engineer should have a thorough grounding in the basic requirements of reliability theory and practice. This knowledge should include an understanding of the statistics of reliability, of sampling techniques, and of testing requirements.

6.13 Procurement training

Purchasing agents should be instructed in how to determine relative values of different reliability requirements and what can be obtained for each reliability dollar.

6.14 Production training

Manufacturing personnel should be made aware of the cost of equipment failure to both the company and the nation. Every worker should be made aware of the need for reliability and his own importance to and responsibility for its achievement. Motivation programs are invaluable in creating the kind of atmosphere that is vital to the success of any program. "VIP" and Zero Defects Programs are examples of this type of motivation.

Reliability Administrative Techniques

6.15 Program requirements

The requirements of a good reliability program are the same whether they are the result of contractual agreement or an in-house desire to up-grade an existing product. These requirements include:

(1) Design goals
(2) Environmental factors (use conditions)
(3) Definitions of failure, including levels of degradation to the catastrophic.

Once goals have been defined, engineering designs can be developed and hardware produced. Tests can be performed to determine the degree of success attained by the design group. Evaluation of failures and subsequent changes in the initial design can be made to improve performance. This succession of design reviews and acceptance testing before development of a final configuration will generate a vast mass of performance data pertaining to various environmental conditions. Although the processing of collected data can be done by the engineering test department or any of the responsible design groups, the interpretation of the data in terms of attainment of reliability goals should be performed by the reliability group. The resulting report should identify the design goals in terms of the desired failure rate and confidence level, and it should pinpoint the level of achievement. It should not be necessary to wade through pages of test results to find the key information.

6.16 Testing procedures

In setting up testing procedures (see Sec. 8), satisfactory answers must be given to the following questions:

(1) Do the tests correctly simulate the environmental stress levels, duty cycles, and performance limits? Do they provide reasonable substitutes for what the unit will encounter during actual usage?

(2) Are the number of units tested and the length of time they are subjected to life and environmental conditions both sufficient to give an accurate appraisal of failure rates for 10,000 operations at the desired confidence level? Is the useful life sought for sufficiently long to give the required assurance of mission life?

(3) Are sufficient time and funding provided by management to carry out the tests? If either of these is lacking, some trade-off of engineering or statistical requirements may be required.

At all time, controls should be such that need for design or process changes can be readily determined. Once the unit reaches the field, any failures should be rigorously investigated, their causes isolated, and corrective action taken at the soonest possible time.

No amount of testing can make an unreliable product reliable (it can only be made to seem reliable). Tests are necessary to demonstrate that the reliability requirement has been attained.

In comparing reliability figures generated from various tests, it is important that the tests are indeed comparable. Their stress levels must be similar, and the number of units tested must be sufficient to give some confidence that the units are truly representative of the rest of the sample or population.

Theory of Probability and Statistics

This section has been compiled to provide systems engineers and equipment designers with a source of basic information on the mathematical tools used in reliability engineering. Particular emphasis has been placed on those mathematical disciplines used for reliability estimates of parts dependent upon load cycles. An attempt will be made to follow a middle course between a strictly empirical approach and the rigorous development of proofs of the various equations now used. It is hoped that this approach will provide an understanding of the analytical methods used by reliability engineers to obtain the desired product and systems reliability.

One note of caution: The statistical task of measuring reliability is often overemphasized. The engineering task of increasing reliability, which is incomparably more important, *must not be* overlooked.

Probability and statistics are two mathematical disciplines that are often coupled together and sometimes used interchangeably. Although they are interrelated, they are actually opposite sides of the same coin. In probability, starting with a known population, or total collection of units, the probable content, or parameters, of the sample is estimated or inferred. Statistics starts with the sample and deduces the content of the population.

There is a great deal more, of course, to statistics than the making of statistical inference. Generally, it is the science of gathering and analyzing data to make statistical inference from it. As such, it is a tool of invaluable aid to engineers in general and to reliability engineers in particular.

Since it is usually impossible to test an entire population, some method of sampling must be used. A knowledge of statistics enables the engineer to:

(1) Determine the proper sample size.

(2) Determine if a difference between two or more samples is significant or is merely sample error.

(3) Express the test results in some numerical statement.

(4) Express the degree of confidence in the result.

(5) Combine results and confidence in results in some quantitative statement.

6.17 Probability

Simply expressed, probability is the likelihood of an event happening, expressed as a value between zero and one. The probability of drawing an ace *and* a king with the draw of *one* card from a deck of cards would be zero; that of drawing any card from an ace through a king would be one. Thus, if an event can occur in N mutually exclusive ways (all equally likely), and if n of these outcomes has the attribute A, then the probability of A occurring is the ratio, n/N. The probability of a king being drawn from a deck of 52 cards would be 4/52, or 1/13.

As a start, a few basic rules and definitions of probability terms will be given, taking permutations and combinations first and progressing to the various rules of probability calculation.

Permutations. An arrangement of objects in a *definite order* is a permutation. The word "TWO," for example, is a permutation of the letters T, W, and O. Other permutations, or arrangements, of these letters are TOW, WOT, WTO, OTW, and OWT, or six in all. More basically, consider three letters — A, B, and C — representing three objects to be arranged in three boxes. In the first box, we have a choice of three objects: A, B, or C. The first box is thus labeled three. In the second box, there is a choice of only two objects; in the third box, of only one. Therefore, there are six (3x2x1) possible arrangements or permutations.

Factorial symbol. Obviously, the use of boxes to find or indicate the number of possible permutations of a large number of objects would be unwieldy and impractical. This fact has led to the use of a standard notation to indicate that such an operation is required; it is defined thus: "The product of all numbers from n to 1 is called n factorial and is denoted by the symbol $n!$" We may compute $n!$ as follows:

$$n! = n\,(n-1)(n-2)\ldots. \quad (1)$$

To give an example, 8 factorial is written 8! It may be computed as follows:

$$8! = 8 \times 7 \times 6 \times 5 \times 4 \times 3 \times 2 \times 1 = 40{,}320$$

Since they grow at such a tremendous rate, factorial values are usually taken from handbook tables.

Rules for permutations. The basic rules for permutations are as follows:

(1) The permutation of *n* things (all different) taken together is symbolized as *nPn*, or *nPn* = *n*!

(2) The permutation of *n* things taken *r* at a time is symbolized as *nPr* and is expressed by:

$$nPr = \frac{n!}{(n-r)!}$$

Consider a permutation of *n* different objects in which only a part of the total objects is to be used. For example, in how many ways can three books be chosen from seven books? Using the box concept, in the first box there is a choice of seven books; in the second, six, and in the third, five. Hence, the number of ways available is $7 \times 6 \times 5 = 210$. Factorially, the choice is expressed as:

$$\frac{7!}{4!} = \frac{7 \times 6 \times 5 \times 4 \times 3 \times 2 \times 1}{4 \times 3 \times 2 \times 1} = 210$$

Combinations. A combination is an arrangement, as is a permutation, with one important difference: In a permutation, *order counts;* in a combination, *order does not count.* For example, three books — A, B, and C — arranged on a shelf in order A, B, C or in order C, B, A would constitute different orderings; hence, we have a permutation. But a selection of the three books to read would be the same selection if arranged as B, C, A or as A, B, C; hence, we have a combination.

Rules for combinations. The combination of *n* things taken *r* at a time is found by the formula

$$C = \frac{n!}{r! \, (n-r)!}$$

For example, find the number of combinations of six things, all different, taken two at a time.

$$C = \frac{6!}{2! \, (6-2)!} = \frac{6 \times 5 \times 4 \times 3 \times 2 \times 1}{(2 \times 1) \, (4 \times 3 \times 2 \times 1)} = 15$$

Multiplication theorem. If an event can happen in *n* ways *and* then happen in *m* ways, the probability of both events happening is equal to *nm*. These are known as *independent events.*

Addition theorem. If an event can happen in *n* ways or *m* ways, then the probability of both events happening is equal to *n+m*. These are known as *mutually exclusive events.*

The key lies in the words "and" and "or." Thus, if the events are independent, we use the multiplication principle, and if the events are mutually exclusive, we use the addition principle.

6.18 Set theory

Before the probable characteristics of a distribution of test data are described, it would be best to introduce some of the vocabulary and ideas of the theory of sets, since sets define the character of devices subjected to test on a statistical basis. Mathematicians define a set in much the same way as the word "collection" is normally used. Thus a set can be defined as a group of objects with some common identifying characteristics.

For example, *my* collection of postage stamps is a set. Its identifying characteristic is possession; *I* own them. Within this general set may be any number of subsets: all the stamps I own that were issued by the United Nations, for example, or all the mint stamps owned by me.

One of two methods can be used in describing a set. The first, and least useful, is to list all of the elements of the set, known as the catalog method. The second method, of more practical use to mathematicians, is known as the rule method. Here the rule that defines the set is specified: "All the stamps owned by me" or "all numbers between 1 and 6 inclusive."

Universal sets and subsets. The universal set *U* is a set of all the possible elements of one definable nature: "All the postage stamps ever issued by any country in the world." A subset is then defined as that part of the universal set with one or more additional restrictions or rules: "All the commemorative stamps ever issued by the United States of America."

More generally, a subset is a set *A* composed entirely of elements contained in a related set *B* that may actually be the larger set or arbitrarily designated superior, though, in fact, identical to set *A*.

In a finite universal set where the number of elements is known, the number of subsets is found by the multiplication principle. To determine the number of subsets in a set, solve for the value of 2^n, in which *n* equals the number of elements in the set. *Example:* In set *U* there are four elements. How many different subsets has *U*? Obviously $2^4 = 16$ subsets.

In every set, two subsets are of special interest: (1) the subset with every element of *U* and (2) the empty, or null, subset.

Complementary sets. The set of all the elements of the universal set that is not in subset

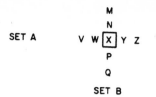

FIG. 6-1. INTERSECTION OF SETS DEFINED
Intersection composed of all elements common to both sets (in this case, X).

A is called the complement of A and is symbolized by $\overline{A}$ (read as A bar).

Mutually exclusive sets. Two sets are said to be mutually exclusive if they have no elements in common.

Intersection of sets. The intersection of A and B is the set of all the elements of U that belong to both A and B and is denoted $A \cap B$ (read as A cap B). See Fig. 6-1.

Union of sets. The union of A and B is the set of all the elements of U that belong to the intersecting sets A and B, including the elements common to both A and B (the intersection). It is denoted $A \cup B$ (read as A cup B). See Fig. 6-2.

Frequency Distribution of Data

It was indicated earlier in this section that reliability predictions are based on life tests in which the underlying statistical mechanism is that of random, or chance, failures that are independent of accumulated life and individually unpredictable. Hence, a major problem in reliability statistics is the analysis of random experimental data. A casual listing of raw test data is amorphous and of little value. Trends are difficult to see. Averages, ranges, frequency, and other information can be detected only with difficulty, or not at all. Life test data must be arranged logically to give meaningful information.

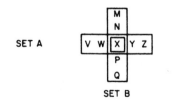

FIG. 6-2. UNION OF SETS DEFINED
Union composed of all elements (1) exclusively part of set A, (2) exclusively part of set B, and (3) common to both sets (in this case, MNPQVWYZ and X).

6.19 Data patterns

The following example of 20 random measurements illustrates the usual scattering of experimental data:

12	27	21	16	51
21	16	42	43	33
45	37	27	56	39
41	37	29	33	38

One method of arrangement is to place the data in a pattern called a "probability density distribution" or a "frequency distribution," which is grouped in fixed classes or sets according to a selected range of recorded values:

Class (range)	Frequency	Totals
0 - 10	0	0
10 - 20	xxx	3
20 - 30	xxxxx	5
30 - 40	xxxxxx	6
40 - 50	xxxx	4
50 - 60	xx	2

The frequencies or number of times a reading falls within a class gives a fair picture of the distribution of the data.

6.20 Histograms

The picture can be further clarified by plotting the frequencies in the form of bars. This form of plotting is called a *histogram*. By connecting the tops of the bars, a broken line is obtained as in Fig. 6-3. If the amount of data is large, the number of classes can be increased. This will give a smooth distribution curve.

In engineering problems, the amount of data is rarely great enough to obtain a smooth curve. It is important, therefore, to choose the optimum number of classes so that the class interval is neither too large nor too small, as is true of the histograms in Fig. 6-4.

For every set of data there is an optimum number of classes. The number of classes obviously increases with the increase in units of data. Trial and error is one way of determining the

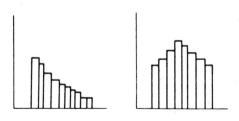

FIG. 6-3. EXAMPLES OF HISTOGRAMS OF CLASSIFIED EXPERIMENTAL DATA

optimum number, but with large groups of numbers, this may prove to be a long and tiresome process. A rule devised by Sturges simplifies the calculation of the class number, K (see Fig. 6-5):

$$K = 1 + 3.3 \ (\log_{10}N)$$

in which:

K = the number of classes
N = the total units of data

FIG. 6-4. CORRECT AND INCORRECT CHOICE OF CLASS INTERVALS

Example: For 20 measurements, determine the optimum number of classes, K.

$$N = 20$$
$$K = 1 + 3.3 \ (1.3010) \ = 1 + 4.29$$
$$= 5.29, \ \text{or 6 classes}$$

One further observation about the classes plotted as histograms in Figs. 6-3 and 6-4 should be made. They all have one *mode,* or peak. This unimodal curve tells us that the population of units from which the data was drawn was homogeneous. Were it not, it would have two or more modes, such as the curve of Fig. 6-6.

If many groups of data — such as heights, weights, intelligence quotients, births, deaths, variations in machine parts, and the like — were plotted, certain similarities would be observed between the various curves. In fact, most dis-

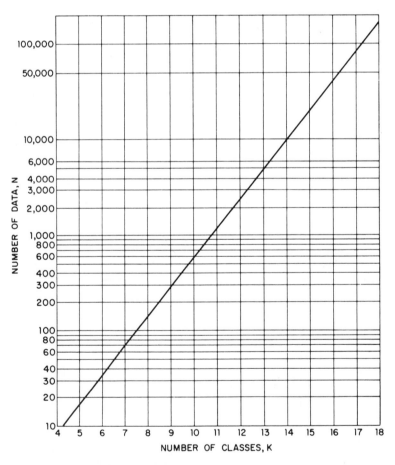

FIG. 6-5. GRAPH OF STURGES' RULE FOR DETERMINING THE OPTIMUM NUMBER OF CLASSES FOR A GIVEN NUMBER OF DATA
For values greater than those shown, use the formula: $K = 1 + 3.3 \ (\log N)$

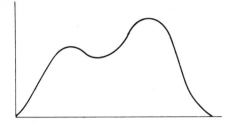

FIG. 6-6. DATA DISTRIBUTION CURVE WITH TWO OR MORE MODES

tributions can be assigned to one of several families of frequency distributions with curves fitting established mathematical expressions. Probability distributions are classified in two general categories: discrete and continuous. In the discrete distribution, the variable can take only specific values and can change only by set increments. The continuous frequency distributions most generally met in reliability studies are:

(1) Binomial distribution
(2) Poisson distribution
(3) Exponential distribution
(4) Normal distribution

6.21 Binomial distribution

If the probability of an event occurring in a single trial is p and the probability of its not occurring is q, then the probability of the event occurring exactly K times out of n independent trials is given by the binomial expansion $[(p + q)^n]$. The binomial distribution is a probability distribution involving two alternatives (p and q), the sum of whose probability outcomes equals one or unity. There are two possible outcomes, yes or no, acceptable or defective, white or black. In many engineering tests there could be any number of possible outcomes, but we may be interested in only one of them and can thus group all the others as a single alternative. For example, the pickup of a relay between 13 and 15 volts d-c may be regarded as successful and all other values as failures. The number of successes or failures can be 0, 1, 2, . . . n. To determine the probabilities of having exactly 1, 2 or 3 failures in a given sample, bimonial expansion is used.

A simple case would be to draw a sample of two units from a large lot that is known to be 10 per cent defective. Using the commonly accepted symbols, p = defective parts and q = good parts, then, by definition, the equation is

$$p + q = 1$$

Since $p = 0.1$ and $q = 0.9$, the probability of both units in the sample being defective would be p^2, or $0.1 \times 0.1 = 0.01$. The probability of two acceptable units would be q^2, or 0.81. The third possibility is finding the first sample defective and the second good or the first unit good and the second defective. By the multiplication principle, the first possibility would be $p \times q = pq$, and the second possibility would be $q \times p = qp$. Since we are interested only in the final result and not in the order of occurrence, the probability of finding one good and one bad unit in a sample of two would be $pq + qp = 2\,pq$, or $2 \times 0.1 \times 0.9 = 0.18$. Put in tabular form, this is:

Event	Two defective	One good, one bad	Two good
Probability	p^2	$2\,pq$	q^2

This is the expansion of the binomial term $(p + q)^2$, the exponent 2 being the number of units in this particular sample. For a sample of four units, the probabilities would be an expansion of the term $(p + q)^4$. Expansion of large sample terms is time consuming. Tables are available from various sources including the National Bureau of Standards, Mathematical Section.

6.22 Poisson distribution

This distribution is a discrete probability distribution in a denumerable infinite universe of test data. If points or intervals are established as 0, 1, 2, etc., then the probability of an event (a failure) occuring in the interval is defined as:

$$P\,(v=n) = \frac{\lambda^n e^{-\lambda}}{n!}$$

in which:

P = probability of failure
$\lambda > 0$ = gross mean failure rate
$n = 0, 1, 2, \ldots$
$e = 2.7183$ (base of Napierian logs)

The Poisson Distribution can be used when there is a large number, N, of units on test and the probability of an event happening in any specific observation or test is very small. As will be seen later, the Poisson distribution in this case serves as an approximation of the binomial distribution.

6.23 Exponential distribution

The exponential distribution or failure law is used to predict the probability of survival (success or reliability) of a part or device as a function of time. It is derived from the Poisson distribution and is expressed as:

$$P = e^{-\lambda t}$$

in which:

P = probability of success (reliability)
e = 2.7183 (base of Napierian logs)
λ = gross mean failure rate (a constant)
t = mission time for which reliability is being calculated

This formula can be expressed in another form:

$$P = e^{-t/m}$$

in which m = mean number of operations to failure (MOTF), which is defined thus:

$$\text{MOTF} = \frac{\text{Total number of cycles under test}}{\text{Total number of failures in test time}}$$

From this we can see that MOTF (m) is

$$m = 1/\lambda$$

Table 6-1 gives values for $P = e^{-\lambda t}$ and for the approximation, $P = 1 - \lambda t$, when P exceeds 90 per cent reliability. Values of λt range from 0.0001 to 0.10.

6.24   Normal distribution

The binomial and Poisson distributions enable the form of a distribution to be determined from a knowledge of one or two parameters. Both these distributions are concerned with the occurrence of distinct events. The normal distribution, or Gaussian distribution, deals with quantities that can take any value around some central value with the probability of occurrence decreasing as we progress further from the center

Table 6-1. Reliability Calculations Based on Gross Mean Failure Rates, λ

λt	Exact equation, $P = e^{-\lambda t}$	Approx. equation, $P = 1 - \lambda t$ (For $P > 90\%$)	Error
0.0001	0.99990	0.9999	-0-
0.001	0.99900	0.999	-0-
0.01	0.99004	0.99	0.00004
0.02	0.98019	0.98	0.00019
0.03	0.97044	0.97	0.00044
0.04	0.96078	0.96	0.00078
0.05	0.95122	0.95	0.00122
0.10	0.90483	0.90	0.00483

point, or *mean*. Here we find ourselves in the area of statistical inference, and before going further, some statistical concepts and terms will first be defined.

6.25   Variability of experimental data

If we flip a coin, either the head or tail must come up. If the experiment is repeated again and again, it will be found that there is a certain consistency in the nature of the results obtained. This consistency appears to be independent of who flips the coin. For a given coin, it appears that the observed ratio of the number of times that a head comes up to the total number of throws approaches a constant value, p. Expressed in a more formal way: If the number of trials, N, is increased, the probability of p can be made as small as desired. This rule is called the *law of large numbers*. It is also called the *swamping effect*. This does not mean in the coin trial that as N is made very large, p will become $\frac{1}{2}$. Rather, as the number of trials N gets very large, p will differ from $\frac{1}{2}$ by a smaller and smaller number, or the difference will approach zero as a limit. That is, if ten coins are tossed together again and again and the number of heads recorded, the number of heads in each trial will be different. To measure this difference, or variability within the trial, two important characteristics of the distribution of data must be known: (1) measures of central tendency, and (2) measures of general variability.

6.26   Measures of central tendency

Three different measures of central tendency are (1) arithmetic mean, (2) median, and (3) mode.

Arithmetic mean.   The arithmetic mean is a commonly used measure of central tendency. It is generally represented by the symbol $\bar{x}$. If the data are ungrouped, the mean is given by the formula:

$$\bar{x} = \frac{\Sigma\,(x)}{N}$$

The mean is strictly a mathematical measure of central tendency that is based on all the data. It is sometimes called the *expected value*. If the distribution shape were given physical form, the mean would be the center of gravity. If the distribution is unimodal and symmetrical, the mean will be at the point of heaviest concentration. If the distribution is skewed, the mean will be at the point that is "pulled" away from the point of the largest concentration in the direction of the tail of the distribution. In a skewed distribution, the mean is not a typical value.

Median. The median of a set of data is the value above which there are as many cases as there are below it. It is usually represented by the symbol M. The median is computed for ungrouped data by arranging the values in order of size. If the number of cases is odd, the median is the value of the middle case. If the number of cases is even, the median is taken as the arithmetic average of the two middle cases. The median is a position average that is unaffected by the values of the cases on either side of it. Unlike the mean, it is not affected by extreme values.

Mode. The mode is the value of a set of data that is at the point of greatest concentration. It is represented by the symbol Mo. Since the mode is the point of greatest concentration, it is thus the best measure of central tendency. Except for discrete data, it is hard to give an exact value for the mode. For this reason, the mean and the median are the measures of central tendency more commonly used.

6.27 Measures of general variability

Two measures of general variability are (1) range, and (2) standard deviation.

Range. This is the simplest measure of general variability. It is the difference between the highest and lowest value of a set of data. It applies only to ungrouped data and is represented by the symbol R. Thus, $R = (\text{high} - \text{low})$. In small samples, the range is a relatively sensitive measure of general variability.

Standard deviation. Ignoring of plus or minus signs during statistical computation makes the average deviation difficult to use in subsequent mathematical developments. For this reason, a more commonly used measure of general variability is the standard deviation. It is designated by the symbol σ and its formula is written:

$$\sigma = \sqrt{\sum_{j=1}^{N} (x_j - \bar{x})^2 / N}$$

This expression is defined as the positive square root of the average of the squared deviations from the mean. By first squaring the value and then taking the square root, the difficulty created by opposite signs is eliminated.

To construct the normal distribution curve of data grouped around a central value of highest frequency, a histogram can be made up of bars of varying height, y, but constant width along the X axis to represent a single class interval or range. The ordinate height will represent the frequency of occurrence. If the number of classes is increased, the bar width decreases (for a given histogram). Increasing the class number without limit thus decreases the class width to a mathematical line with a series of points along the X axis forming a smooth bell-shaped curve *(see* Fig. 6-7).

Mathematically, the equation for this curve is

$$y = \frac{1}{\sigma \sqrt{2\pi}} \, e^{-(x-\bar{x})^2 / 2\sigma^2}$$

in which:

y = ordinate of the curve at any point on the X axis

$e = 2.7183$ (base of Napierian logs)

In statistical work, the area under the curve is significant and ordinarily would be obtained by differentiation. This analysis has been done so often that usable data can be found in tables, such as the simple one under Fig. 6-7. Here "central percentiles" is interpreted to mean the percentage of data (area under the curve) for a given ± value of σ. Since 99.7 per cent of all values are found within the range of ± 3 σ, statistical analysis is rarely carried out beyond 3 σ.

A more refined approach to finding the areas under the normal curve or the cumulative probabilities of the normal distribution makes use of Table 6-2. Here the mean is 0, and the variance, or standard deviation σ, is 1. This is the standardized, or normalized, form and is arrived at by transforming the stated mean value, $\bar{x}$, into a variant z, where

$$z = \frac{x - \bar{x}}{\sigma}$$

Theoretically, the area of the normal curve is extended from ordinate z to minus infinity (as Table 6-2 states), although it is obvious that any area beyond 4 σ can be ignored. In actual practice, for a known mean $\bar{x}$ and variance of x, the probabilities can be found by computing z and checking the corresponding area from the table.

For example, suppose that it is known that a

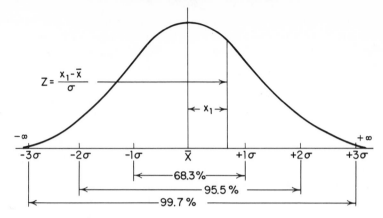

FIG. 6-7. PLOT OF NORMAL DISTRIBUTION CURVE

Values of areas under the curve (equal to the probability of the variable assuming a value in the corresponding region about $\overline{X}$) are as follows:

Region about $\overline{X}$, $\pm$ values of σ	Central percentiles	Area under curve
1	68.3	0.683
1.28	80.0	0.800
1.44	85.0	0.85
1.65	90.0	0.900
1.96	95.0	0.950
2.57	99.0	0.990
3.00	99.7	0.997
3.29	99.9	0.999
3.89	99.99	0.9999

Table 6-2. Cumulative Probabilities of the Normal Probability Distribution
(Areas under the Normal Curve from $-\infty$ to z)

z	0.00	0.01	0.02	0.03	0.04	0.05	0.06	0.07	0.08	0.09
0.0	0.5000	0.5040	0.5080	0.5120	0.5160	0.5199	0.5239	0.5279	0.5319	0.5359
0.1	0.5398	0.5438	0.5478	0.5517	0.5557	0.5596	0.5636	0.5675	0.5714	0.5753
0.2	0.5793	0.5832	0.5871	0.5910	0.5948	0.5987	0.6026	0.6064	0.6103	0.6141
0.3	0.6179	0.6217	0.6255	0.6293	0.6331	0.6368	0.6406	0.6443	0.6480	0.6517
0.4	0.6554	0.6591	0.6628	0.6664	0.6700	0.6736	0.6772	0.6808	0.6844	0.6879
0.5	0.6915	0.6950	0.6985	0.7019	0.7054	0.7088	0.7123	0.7157	0.7190	0.7224
0.6	0.7257	0.7291	0.7324	0.7357	0.7389	0.7422	0.7454	0.7486	0.7517	0.7549
0.7	0.7580	0.7611	0.7642	0.7673	0.7704	0.7734	0.7764	0.7794	0.7823	0.7852
0.8	0.7881	0.7910	0.7939	0.7967	0.7995	0.8023	0.8051	0.8078	0.8106	0.8133
0.9	0.8159	0.8186	0.8212	0.8238	0.8264	0.8289	0.8315	0.8340	0.8365	0.8389
1.0	0.8413	0.8438	0.8461	0.8485	0.8508	0.8531	0.8554	0.8577	0.8599	0.8621
1.1	0.8643	0.8665	0.8686	0.8708	0.8729	0.8749	0.8770	0.8790	0.8810	0.8830
1.2	0.8849	0.8869	0.8888	0.8907	0.8925	0.8944	0.8962	0.8980	0.8997	0.9015
1.3	0.9032	0.9049	0.9066	0.9082	0.9099	0.9115	0.9131	0.9147	0.9162	0.9177
1.4	0.9192	0.9207	0.9222	0.9236	0.9251	0.9265	0.9279	0.9292	0.9306	0.9319

data distribution is normal in form, the mean is 100, and σ is 10. Suppose that the problem is to find the probability of the variable x being less than 112. Then,

$$z = \quad = \frac{x - \bar{x}}{\sigma} = \frac{112 - 100}{10} = \frac{12}{10} = 1.2$$

Checking for the value of $z = 1.200$ in Table 6-2, we find that the cumulative probabilities will be 0.8849, that is, for 88.49 per cent of the time the variable x will be less than 112.

6.28 Confidence limits

In the dictionary confidence is defined as "trust in, or reliance upon, someone or something." This, in essence, is how the reliability engineer interprets the term except that he gives his confidence a numerical value. The confidence value helps to show how much better or worse one group of components or systems is when compared to another.

Now, since we cannot be right 100 per cent of the time, the confidence level chosen must be based on how often we are willing to be wrong. If we can afford to be wrong one out of 100 times, we have a 99 per cent confidence level, if 10 out of 100 times, a 90 per cent confidence level, and so forth. In other words, the confidence level specifies the percentage of times we expect to be correct.

When a group of components is tested to find a MOTF value (mean number of operations to failure), the value found is the best estimate, or point estimate. If every unit in the universe were tested, the true measure of reliability would be found. The difference between the true and the point estimate becomes less and less as more units are tested. However, regardless of sample or lot size, the point estimate is always the ratio of trials to the number of successes.

Unfortunately, the statistical terminology associated with reliability measurements has an aura of mystery about it so that the belief is often held that these measurements are in some way different from measurements of other parameters, say the length of an iron bar. Since this misinterpretation has led to such statements as 90 per cent reliability at a 95 per cent confidence, communication is often lost. If, however, it was stated than an iron bar measured 6.250 in. long with an instrument reading error of $\pm$ 0.002 in., there would be no communication problem. Everyone will accept the fact that 6.250 in. is a best estimate of some sort, with a range of possible error from 6.248 to 6.252. Tables for computing error values and other mathematical approaches are available to solve this type of statistical problem.

In much the same way, reliability measurements have associated with them certain errors that are inherent in the sample size used, and this defect gives rise to uncertainty about their own reliability. This uncertainty can be shown, however, to fall within a band on either side of the reliability estimate. This band is defined as the *confidence interval*. The limits of this band are called the upper and lower confidence limits and can be determined mathematically.

Confidence level. The χ^2 (chi square) distribution can be used to derive the confidence limits on the exponential mean life. The appropriate formula is:

$$\chi^2 = \sum_{i=1}^{n} \left(\frac{O_i - E_i}{E_i} \right)^2$$

in which:

O_i = observed value

E_i = some theoretical value

Table 6-3 gives multipliers of observed mean number of operations to failure to obtain lower and upper limits for various confidence levels. In this table the heading in the first column refers to the number of failures as n or $n+1$. If the test terminates at a failure the number of failures in the test is n. If the test terminates at a predesignated point, such as 100,000 operations, n is then equal to the number of failures encountered plus one $(n+1)$. Adding of an additional failure takes the pessimistic view that on the next succeeding operation there will be a failure.

6.29 Binomial confidence curves for small per cent defective

Many books on statistics verify the fact that the Poisson distribution serves as a good approximation to the Binomial distribution for very large N (sample size) and a very small p (per cent defective). Figures 6-8(a) through 6-8(d) are graphs of the Poisson limit to the binomial distribution on log paper for 90 per cent and 60 per cent confidence intervals for sample sizes ranging from 10^2 to 10^5 units and per cent defectives ranging from 0.0001 to 10 per cent. The 90 per cent confidence interval is defined by the upper and lower 95 per cent bounds, that is, the probable percentage of defects will come within

Table 6-3. Multipliers of "Observed" MOTF to Obtain the Lower and Upper Confidence Limits of an Exponential Distribution

| Number of failures, n or $n+1$ | One-sided confidence levels | | | | | | | | | |
| | Lower limit | | | | | Upper limit | | | | |
	0.95	0.90	0.80	0.70	0.60	0.60	0.70	0.80	0.90	0.95
1	0.334	0.434	0.621	0.831	1.090	1.96	2.81	4.48	9.48	19.42
2	0.422	0.514	0.668	0.820	0.990	1.45	1.82	2.43	3.76	5.63
3	0.476	0.564	0.701	0.830	0.966	1.31	1.57	1.95	2.72	3.67
4	0.516	0.599	0.725	0.840	0.958	1.25	1.45	1.74	2.29	2.93
5	0.546	0.626		0.849	0.952	1.20	1.38	1.62	2.06	2.54
6	0.571	0.647	0.759	0.856	0.952	1.18	1.33	1.54	1.90	2.30
7	0.591	0.665	0.771	0.863	0.952	1.16	1.29	1.48	1.80	2.13
8	0.608	0.680	0.782	0.869	0.952	1.14	1.27	1.43	1.72	2.01
9	0.624	0.693	0.791	0.874	0.952	1.13	1.25	1.40	1.66	1.92
10	0.637	0.704	0.799	0.878	0.952	1.12	1.23	1.37	1.61	1.84
11	0.649	0.714	0.806	0.882	0.955	1.12	1.22	1.35	1.57	1.78
12	0.659	0.723	0.812	0.886	0.956	1.11	1.20	1.33	1.53	1.73
13	0.669	0.731	0.818	0.889	0.956	1.10	1.19	1.31	1.50	1.69
14	0.677	0.738	0.823	0.892	0.957	1.10	1.18	1.30	1.48	1.65
15	0.685	0.745	0.828	0.895	0.958	1.09	1.18	1.28	1.46	1.62
16	0.693	0.751	0.831	0.897	0.959	1.09	1.17	1.27	1.43	1.59
17	0.700	0.757	0.835	0.899	0.960	1.09	1.16	1.26	1.42	1.57
18	0.706	0.763	0.839	0.902	0.960	1.08	1.16	1.25	1.41	1.55
19	0.712	0.768	0.843	0.904	0.960	1.08	1.15	1.25	1.39	1.53
20	0.717	0.772	0.846	0.905	0.961	1.08	1.15	1.24	1.37	1.51
21	0.723	0.776	0.848	0.907	0.962	1.07	1.14	1.23	1.36	1.49
22	0.727	0.780	0.853	0.909	0.962	1.07	1.14	1.22	1.35	1.48
23	0.732	0.785	0.855	0.911	0.963	1.07	1.14	1.22	1.35	1.46
24	0.736	0.788	0.857	0.913	0.963	1.07	1.13	1.21	1.34	1.45
25	0.741	0.791	0.859	0.914	0.964	1.07	1.13	1.21	1.33	1.44

those limits 90 per cent of the time. The 60 per cent interval is defined by the 80 per cent bounds. Because this is an approximation, these curves should not be used for a p greater than 10 per cent.

For a given sample size and number of failures observed, the per cent defective can be found in the following manner: The curve for the desired upper (bound) confidence or desired confidence interval is chosen. Starting with the vertical scale at the appropriate "sample size," one then proceeds across to the line corresponding to the number of failures observed. The per cent defective is read below from the horizontal scale. Obviously, one can reverse the procedure and obtain the sample size from a known percentage of defects. The horizontal scale is "per cent defective per some unit of time or operation," such as 1000 hours or 10,000 operations.

The following example explains the use of the binomial confidence curves for per cent defective less than 10 per cent. If the sample size is 500 and observed defects are 6, determine the 90 per cent confidence interval for the per cent defective.

Using Figs. 6-8(a) and 6-8(b), enter the "sample size" scale at 500. Proceed to the line marked 6 for the number of defects observed. From the horizontal scale, the value 2.3 per cent is read

from Fig. 6-8(a) and the value 0.52 per cent is read from Fig. 6-8(b) for per cent defectives. It can then be stated that the confidence is 90 per cent that the interval from 0.520 to 2.3 per cent will include the population per cent defective, written as follows:

$$C\ (0.52\% \leqslant \text{per cent defective} \leqslant 2.3\%) = 90\%$$

For confidence limits from 20 to 95 per cent and an explanation of their use, refer to "EETC Report No. 27," prepared by Aerospace Industries Association of American, Inc., Washington, D. C.[1]

Application of Statistical Principles to Reliability

Statistical analysis of complex systems or of systems components can be generalized in the curve shown in Fig. 6-9. Note that there are three discrete failure areas: (1) the early failure period, (2) the useful life (or random failure) period, and (3) the wear-out failure period.

---

[1]Distributed by National Standards Association, Inc., 1321 Fourteenth St., N.W., Washington, D. C. 20005 ($1.00 per single copy).

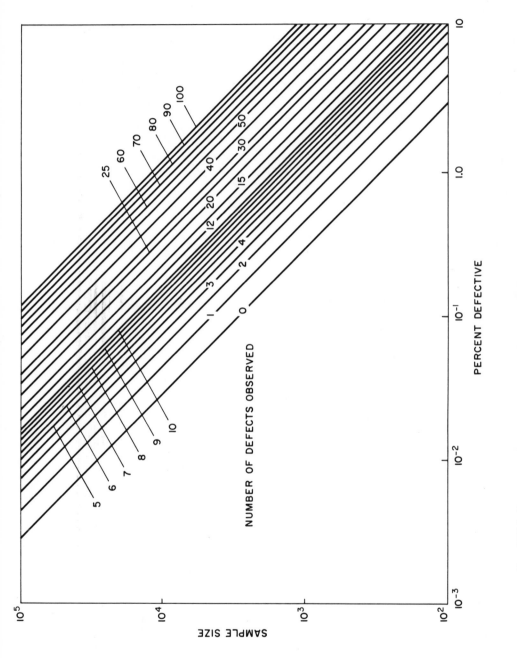

FIG. 6-8(A). BINOMIAL CONFIDENCE CURVES OF PER CENT DEFECTIVE FOR 90 PER CENT CONFIDENCE
INTERVAL — UPPER 95 PER CENT (*Courtesy, Aerospace Industries Assoc.*)

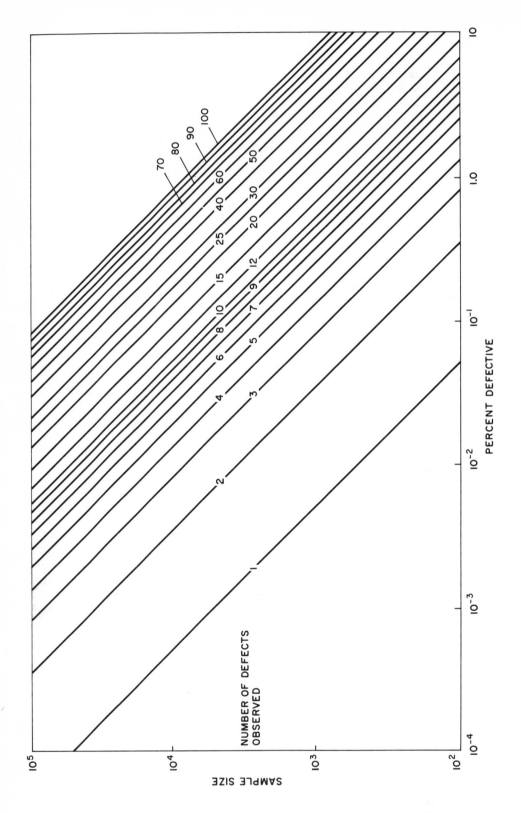

Fig. 6-8(b). Binomial confidence curves of per cent defective for 90 per cent confidence interval — lower 95 per cent. (Courtesy, Aerospace Industries Assoc.)

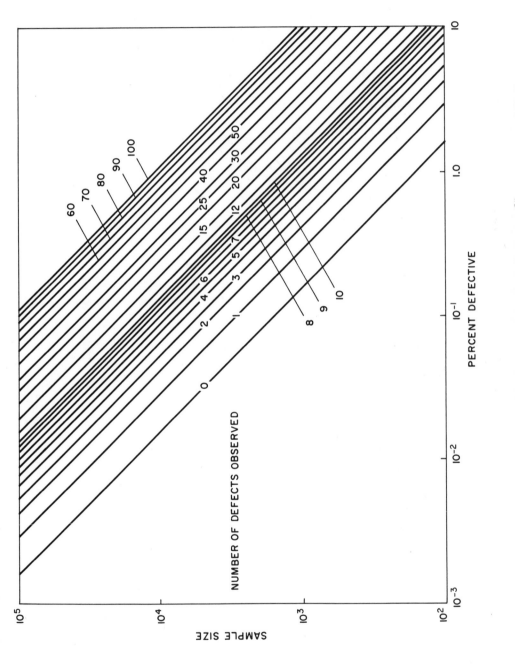

PERCENT DEFECTIVE

SAMPLE SIZE

NUMBER OF DEFECTS OBSERVED

FIG. 6-8(c). BINOMIAL CONFIDENCE CURVES OF PER CENT DEFECTIVE FOR 60 PER CENT CONFIDENCE
INTERVAL — UPPER 80 PER CENT. (*Courtesy, Aerospace Industries Assoc.*)

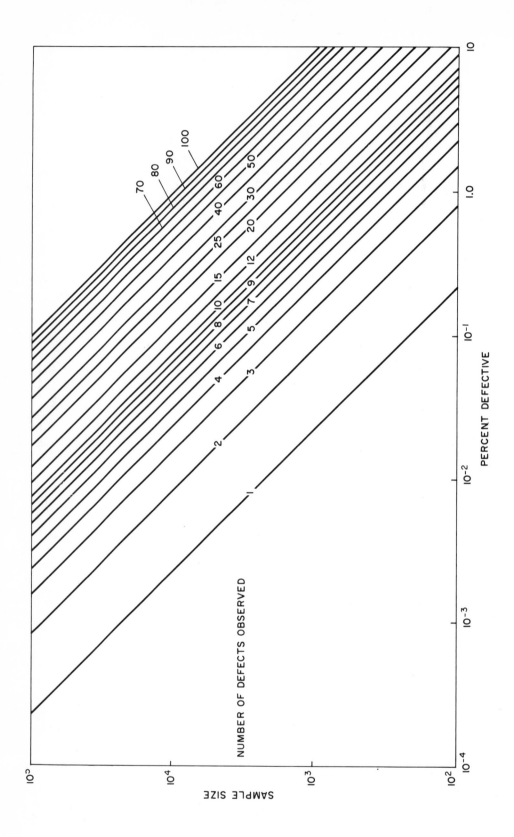

Fig. 6·8(b). Binomial confidence curves of per cent defective for 60 per cent confidence interval — lower 80 per cent. (*Courtesy Aeorospace Industries Assoc.*)

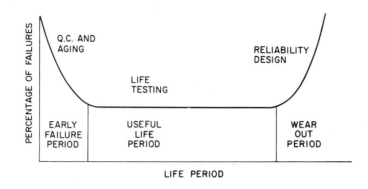

FIG. 6-9. CONTROL OF FAILURE RATE OF DEVICES IN THREE DISTINCT FAILURE AREAS

Many reliability studies are based on the characteristic behavior of a system or component as it passes from one portion of this curve to another. Do not, however, be lulled into any false sense of security by the presumed mathematical exactness of the various sections depicted on the curve. Though they may be carefully plotted, there is a considerable variety of opinion among reliability people concerning the point at which one period ends and another begins. This divergence of opinion is so wide that even the existence of the early failure period is denied by some.

In general, the start of each period is defined in terms of the end of the preceding period. However, for illustrative purposes, this discussion will define the end points more exactly than is generally done. It must be remembered that there is no hard and fast rule to follow; rather, the definitions given should be used as a basis of discussion. *To define a failure as a "useful life" or "early failure" is a rather academic consideration. The true objective is to find out what caused the failure and how it can be most efficiently corrected.*

Each failure period on the time axis will be analyzed and related to the other failure periods in the time domain.

6.30 Early failure

This type of failure is noted early in the life of the device and is generally considered to be the result of production errors. It will occur even in the most exacting manufacturing plant but can be reduced by the following measures: (1) Good design; (2) tight control of the manufacturing processes; (3) strong quality control; and (4) screening (wear-in).

Design. Unless reliability has been considered as a design parameter in the formative stages either through formal or informal design review, little can be done to effect greater reliability at a later stage. It is generally found that if there is a preponderance of early failures, a major design modification must be considered. If the component is of a critical nature, it might be wise to scrap the design and start again. In many instances, this is the least expensive approach and in most cases, the best. A well organized design group, having available the resources of a capable reliability section, can do much to eliminate the "early failure" caused by design weakness.

Control of manufacturing processes. As with early failures of design origin, a methods or industrial engineering group (aided by the reliability section) can go a long way toward a reduction of manufacturing failures by establishing proper production methods in which reliability is the goal.

Quality control. It is axiomatic that for a highly reliable product a strong, independent quality control department is an absolute necessity. In seeking increased reliability, the quality control department must go beyond its frequently static approach to quality rejects. A dynamic approach must be instituted, utilizing the full services of the reliability section in the never-ending task of exposing and eliminating the cause of rejects rather than merely recording the fact that they exist.

Screening (wear-in). Since an occasional mishap may occur even in the best of plants, some form of run-in may be required. Where the useful life failure rate is specified, a formula[1] for wear-in time, t, is available:

$$t = G \ ln \ \frac{N_i}{\lambda G}$$

in which:

G = 25 hours (approx.)
ln = natural log
N_j = number of initial defectives
λ = useful life failure rate (rated hours)

For cycle-dependent parts (those parts for which the rate or frequency of operation can vary), one must presently resort to studies made of the particular component involved, taking into consideration the degree of reliability required and the confidence needed. An old rule of thumb for the run-in period of cycle-dependent parts is 5 per cent of useful life. For relays, this test should be at circuit current levels low enough to minimize contact degradation.

6.31 Useful life (random failure) period

As the name implies, this is the period in the life of a device during which it is expected to perform as designed for the length of time required (see Fig. 6-9). Even in this period, failures must be expected, but their frequency should remain low. Such failures are classed as "without apparent cause" since the number of possible causes is so high that to investigate them all would be prohibitive, both in time and money. During this period, the failure rate will usually be constant for equal numbers of operations. This constant failure rate has been shown both by "use data" and by test to hold true for a great number of components and systems. For the present, the useful life period is expected to follow an exponential distribution.

6.32 Wear-out failure period

Wear-out failures can be attributed to a gradual deterioration of a device's original properties. This deterioration can be mechanical, chemical, or electrical in nature. Thus, as the various parts of the system receive slight overstress, there is a gradual reduction in their original strength until one or more devices are no longer functional.

The contributing environmental stresses are physical events such as temperature change, shock, vibration, and current or voltage surges. Since these stresses act in a random manner, they

[1]RADC *Reliability Notebook*, Sec. 4.

follow a normal distribution. The component strength is also random and thus normally distributed.

Wear-out failures are essentially a design characteristic. To reduce such failures, parts can be "beefed up" or the stress levels reduced. The difficulty starts when the systems design engineer must trade off this strength for reduction in weight or space. Safety factors of seven to ten times the expected requirements so common in structural or automotive engineering are not remotely approached in today's miniaturized electronic gear. In single-shot or short-life equipment, such as guided missiles, wear-out is not as important a consideration as is a low failure rate in the useful life portion of a system or component.

6.33 Life capabilities

For the purpose of analysis, it is acceptable to study the various portions of the lives of components or systems as separate entities (see Fig. 6-9), but it must be borne in mind that the periods are in a sense artificial. In reality, the sections are interrelated and interdependent. Recognizing this interdependence will prevent use of such meaningless phrases as "late early failure" or "early wear-out." Thus, during the period of useful life, failures might be expected to occur that a purist might classify as an early failure or a wear-out failure. The difficulty in determining the end points of the various periods can be resolved if the end points are defined as follows:

(1) *Early Failure:* Early failure ends when the rate of failure drops to the failure rate λ of the useful life period.

(2) *Useful life:* The useful life period ends when a point is reached three sigma units to the left of the mean wear-out distribution, M.

Glossary of Reliability Terms

Acceptance test — A nondestructive test to assure that certain operating characteristics are within required tolerance limits.

Binomial distribution — A discrete random variable has a binomial distribution if there exists the probability that the variable will be between 0 and 1 and a positive integer N so that

$$P\left(\frac{c}{N}\right) = \frac{N!}{C!(N-c)!} \ p'^c \ (1 - p')^{n-c}$$

in which $P\left(\dfrac{c}{N}\right)$ is the probability of the occurrence of the event c out of N trials and can take the value $0/N, 1/N, 2/N \ldots$ For example, $P\left(\dfrac{c}{N}\right)$ might be the probability of c failures in a sample size N taken from a universe that has a fractional p' defective units.

Catastrophic failure (chance) — A failure that occurs at random within the useful life period after unsound components have been eliminated (before wear-out failures start).

Characteristic — A trait, property, or quality of a specific item.

Component stress — Those stresses on component electrical parts that tend to affect the failure rate, such as voltage, power, temperature, time, shock, etc.

Confidence level — The statistical expression for the degree of trust in a given result. The confidence level measures the probability that a given assertion is true.

Consumer's reliability risk — The probability that a test will accept a device when in truth the device should be rejected. This is usually set at 10 per cent.

Double sampling — An inspection plan in which the first sample provides three decisions: (1) accept, (2) reject, (3) take another sample. If the second sample is required for decision, the number of rejects in both samples determines acception or rejection.

Early failure — The premature failure of components in quantities larger than those that will be observed when the system has been properly "de-bugged."

Environment — The aggregate of all the conditions that affect the operation of equipment.

Equipment failure rate — The ratio of the number of units that fail *(f)* within a given period of time *(t)* to the total number of units *(N)* at the start of the test period.

Exponential failure law — Components are said to follow an exponential failure law if:

(1) Their failure rate is constant *(see Failure rate)*

(2) The probability of their surviving to time t without failure is

$$P(t) = e^{-\lambda t}$$

Failure — The point at which an item fails to meet the minimum requirements essential to satisfactory performance. The failure can be a drift out of the specified requirements as a result of age or stress conditions, or it can be a catastrophic failure.

Failure mode — The physical description of the manner in which a failure occurs.

Failure rate — The failure rate is defined as:

$$\lambda = -\frac{R'(t)}{R(t)}$$

in which:

$R(t)$ = reliability for time t
$R'(t)$ = first derivative of $R(t)$

In the case of the exponential failure distribution, the failure rate is the reciprocal of mean-time-between-failures (MTBF).

Independent failure — A failure that occurs without being related to the failure of associated items.

Lot — That quantity of devices on hand for inspection or test from which a sample is drawn.

Mean — The arithmetic average of the characteristic values of the units under test.

Mean time to failure — The simple arithmetic average of the number of operations of a device from the time it is placed in service to the time of failure.

Poisson distribution — This distribution is a discrete probability distribution in a denumerable infinite universe. If points are established as 0, 1, 2, . . . then the probability of an event occurring at such points is defined as:

$$P(v=n) = \frac{\lambda^n e^{-\lambda}}{n!}$$

in which:

$n = 0, 1, 2, \ldots$
$\lambda > 0$

The Poisson distribution can be used when there is a large number of observations, n, and the probability of an event happening in any specific observation is very small.

Population — In statistics this term indicates the total collection of units from a common source.

Probability — The probability of an event is the theoretical relative frequency with which it will occur. This relative frequency is the ratio of the number of times the event is observed to the total number of observations made under the same conditions.

Probability of survival — A numerical expression of reliability with a range from 0 to 1.0, indicating the extremes of impossibility and certainty.

Producer's reliability risk — The probability that a reliability test will reject a device when in truth the device is of acceptable quality. This is usually set at 10 per cent.

Qualification test — This type of test attempts to answer the question of whether or not a device will operate under given environmental conditions.

Reliability — Reliability is the conditional probability of the successful performance of an assigned task under stated environmental conditions for a specific period of time.

Reliability test — A test whose purpose is to determine the type and amount of change in variables under environmental conditions.

Sample — A portion of the units from the total population. This sample may be considered representative or nonrepresentative of the population from which it is drawn.

Sequential sampling — A sampling plan that after each sample provides three decisions: (1) accept, (2) reject, (3) continue testing. Usually a maximum number of samples is employed.

Single sampling — A sampling plan in which a decision to accept or reject is based on the first sample taken.

Standard deviation — The positive square root of the average of the squared deviations from the mean, expressed as:

$$\sigma = \sqrt{\sum_{j=1}^{N} (x_i - x)^2 / N}$$

Statistics — The science or art of constructing a population based on a small segment (sample) of that population.

Wear-out failure — A failure that occurs as a result of deterioration processes or mechanical wear and whose probability of occurrence increases with time.

Reliability Symbols

e	Base of Napierian logs (2.7183)
λ	Gross failure rate
T	MTBF (mean time between failure)
t	Operating time (mission time)
R	Reliability, or probability of success
σ	Standard deviation
Σ	Summation of values
$\cap$	Cap (Boolean algebra for "and")
$\cup$	Cup (Boolean algebra for "either/or")
N, n	Number of samples, failures, tests, etc.
UCL	Upper limit (confidence limit)
LCL	Lower limit (confidence limit)
Q	Unreliability, or failure probability with the value, $Q = 1 - R$
R_S	Total system reliability
F_R	Generic failure rate
P_S	Probability of success
$\overline{x}$	Arithmetic mean

7
How to Specify a Relay

7.1 Basic rules

The detailed treatment of relay characteristics and performance factors in other sections of this handbook may lead to the conclusion that proper specification of a relay is a very complex task. Actually, it is not difficult if the specification writer is aware of all the application requirements of the particular relay being specified. If all this information is stated in the specification, the proposed supplier or bidder can offer the relay best suited to the requirements. The smallest detail may be significant to the supplier. The real key to a well written specification lies in inclusion of all the functional requirements of the relay and in exclusion of all perfunctory and superfluous items. Furthermore, the specification should not make restrictive demands based on a preconceived idea of how the relay should be constructed.

In brief, there are two simple rules to follow in writing a good relay specification: (1) *Include* all functional requirements of the relay. (2) *Exclude* all perfunctory and superfluous items. These simple points constitute the basic theme of this section of the Handbook.

In addition to the knowledge of what to specify and how to specify, it is important to understand the proper use of the documents that carry these requirements. Specifically, it is common practice to use a purchase order, a detailed specification, and various general specifications to describe relay requirements. Each document is a part of the complete relay description. All of the documents may not be necessary; their need is dependent on the sophistication of the application. To aid in the selection of these documents, the following briefly describes each:

(1) *Purchase Order* — The primary function of the purchase order is to provide the purchase relay part number and effectivity or revision, including contractual information, shipping information, and price. Use of the purchase order to define specific relay requirements is not recommended.

(2) *Detail Specification* — Once the purchase order defines the relay part number and effectivity, the detail specification must completely define the required relay. This may be accomplished by referencing supporting documents, such as general specifications. Since all referenced documents form a part of the detailed specification, it is necessary to indicate whether the entire referenced document is applicable or just a paragraph. Additionally, these references should include document effectivity (revision) and, when applicable, the date of issue.

(3) *General Specification* — The general specification is intended to be a support document to the detailed specification and must include all requirements not covered therein. Usually this document covers requirements that are not peculiar to one relay, but several. For example, these documents may include testing programs, quality assurance requirements, and packaging criteria. These documents may also reference other general specifications.

It is generally felt that a check list can be helpful in writing a specification, since its use often reduces errors of omission and points out areas of overspecifying. A single "general" or standard check list may not be practical for all applications of a specific user. Thus, five typical check lists representing broad areas of application are appended to this section. Many items may be dismissed by the specifier, but they should nevertheless be considered. The addition of columns titled Application Requirements, Specification Requirements, Detail Specifications and General Specifications provides information for the preparation of relay specifications.

By completing the Application Requirements column first and then the Specification Requirements column, the specification engineer has the entire picture. The remaining columns on Detail Specifications and General Specifications make it possible to choose which documents will be used to specify each relay requirement.

7.2   Establishing class of application

First of all we must establish the broad classes of relay application (see also Sec. 2). Knowing what "ball park" you are in helps identify the applicable industrial, commercial, and military standards and the types of relays designed to meet such standards. A check list including the following classes would be adequate:

(1) Military and Aerospace (Life Depe dent/Mission Critical)
(2) Industrial
(3) Commercial
(4) Commercial airborne[1]
(5) Air conditioning and heating
(6) Household electrical appliances
(7) Automobiles and trucks
(8) Business machines
(9) Coin operated machines
(10) Communications, radio
(11) Communications, telephone and telegraph
(12) Computer input-output devices
(13) Electric power control
(14) Electronic data processing
(15) Laboratory test instruments
(16) Lighting controls
(17) Machine tool control
(18) Production test equipment
(19) Street traffic control

In some cases, subcategories may be helpful, such as (a) ground, (b) vehicular, (c) shipboard and (d) airborne.

---

[1]Many relay users and manufacturers consider commercial airborne applications to be quite similar to military airborne applications. Use of military components and basic military specifications (with some deletions) is common.

7.3   Equipment or system description

A description of the specific piece of equipment or the system in (or with) which the relay is to be applied will also be of great help to the relay supplier, particularly if he has had previous experience with such applications. He may be aware of safety, operational, environmental, or other requirements that generally apply to such a case. For example, a specification might read:

(1) The relay shall be used in a machine tool control console.
(2) The relay shall be used in airborne life dependent/mission critical equipment.
(3) The relay shall be used in a digital computer.
(4) The relay shall be used in vehicular two-way radio equipment.
(5) The relay shall be used in a residential air conditioner.

7.4   Functional description

The specific function of the relay should be described. For example:

(1) The relay shall respond to a 120-volt a-c on-off type signal and switch a 120-volt a-c circuit from a 6-watt tungsten pilot light (connected to the NC contacts) to a $\frac{1}{2}$-hp capacitor-start motor (connected to the NO contacts).
(2) The relay shall respond to a slowly changing d-c current in a 24-volt d-c series circuit (including a light-sensitive variable resistance cell) to switch a 120-volt a-c circuit to a 150-watt tungsten lamp when the cell resistance increases to 1000 ohms.

7.5   Reference to general specifications

As a starter, a detailed specification may often be drawn up by citing a general specification from military or commercial sources and signifying those sections applicable to the relay being selected for a specific application within the area of the general one. Examples of general specifications that might be referred to are the following:

(1) Military (see also Sec. 9)
    (a) MIL-R-6106 (Aerospace Relays)
    (b) MIL-STD-202 (Test Methods)
(2) Underwriters' Laboratories Standards
    (a) Industrial Control Equipment (No. 508)

(b) Radio Receiving Appliances—Power Operated (No. 492)

(c) Temperature Indicating and Regulating Equipment (No. 873)

(d) Motor Operated Appliances (No. 73)

(3) American Gas Association Standards

(4) Canadian Standards Association Documents

(5) National Electrical Manufacturers Association (NEMA) Standards

(6) Electronic Industries Association (EIA & RETMA) Standards

(7) Quality assurance specifications

(8) Reliability specifications (see Sec. 6)

(9) Company proprietary specifications.

The order of preferential authority of various specifications and documents should be stated, particularly if there are conflicts in detail between them. It is also important to check for compatibility between the requirements of the detail specification and the general specification.

Since a general specification is seldom entirely applicable, it is important to note those portions that are to be included. Any variation from the general specification should be stated. Often a general specification contains ambiguities or multiple choices that must be clarified by the detail specification. For example, the general specification may mention several types of leak tests, vibration tests, or humidity tests. The specifier must make clear which types of test apply.

In some cases it may be of advantage to use a general military spec as a guide. Familiarity with such specs should be of mutual advantage to user and manufacturer. Calling out environmental test procedures from MIL-E-5272 or MIL-STD-202, for example, can be very helpful.

It would also be beneficial for the specification writer to go through each reference document in detail, thoroughly studying each section before deciding on those applicable to his case. Failure to do this will often result in confusion, unnecessary correspondence, lost time, and as a result, excessive costs. In addition to selecting only those sections that apply, it is also frequently necessary to specify detailed figures, such as exact values of pickup (pickup, specified) or dropout (dropout, specified), number of g's, or life expectancy. (See Secs. 1 and 3 for preferred nomenclature and definitions.)

7.6 Environmental requirements

If military specifications are used, it is almost certain that environmental requirements have been taken into account. When using other types of specifications, some assistance may be obtained from Secs. 8 and 9 of this handbook, the latter giving typical documentary types of environmental specifications.

Some of the environmental conditions to be considered are the following:

(1) High temperature

(2) Low temperature

(3) Temperature cycling

(4) Humidity (consider use of electrically polarized test for susceptibility to electrolytic corrosion)

(5) Corrosion (such as salt spray)

(6) Explosive atmosphere

(7) Sand or dust

(8) Oil, grease, and the like

(9) Sulfur fumes

(10) Ice, snow, road conditioning chemicals

(11) Vibration

(12) Shock

(13) Acceleration

(14) High-energy radiation

(15) Fungus

(16) External magnetic fields

(17) Ozone

These environmental considerations could be further classified as operational, nonoperational, static, dynamic, etc. The specification should state whether the device must operate under these conditions or just survive them and operate satisfactorily after being subjected to them. Without intending to repeat information covered in Sec. 8, a few comments on items sometimes overlooked will be included here.

Although ambient air temperature (and velocity) is generally recognized to be important, three items of equal importance should be given attention: (1) Mounting surface temperature, mass, and heat sink characteristics; (2) temperature, size, and proximity of adjacent bodies that could radiate heat to or absorb heat from the relay; (c) temperature, proximity, and orientation of adjacent hot bodies that could transfer heat by convection.

If the relay will be subjected to various operational temperatures, it may be economically advantageous to note what percentage of operations are required at each temperature.

The possibility of recurrent, cumulative, and nonreversible effects of temperature and moisture on insulation resistance and dielectric strength should be borne in mind. For this reason it may be important to specify storage conditions as well as operational conditions.

Military type shock and vibration specifications (see Section 9) are often used, but it may be equally or more important to note what special requirements are involved. If contact chatter or transfer is permissible during a shock or vibration test, for example, the allowable magnitude and duration should be specified. Specifying "no chatter or transfer" is not adequate. A value must be given such as "ten microsecond chatter maximum and one microsecond transfer maximum." Sometimes the operational requirements for shock and vibration are negligible, but shipment of components or equipment may introduce significant amounts of either or both. For such conditions, special tests should be devised to simulate actual field experiences. Other special tests may be set up to assure satisfactory performance after transportation of components or equipment.

Criteria for satisfactory performance or failure during or after environmental exposures should be considered in relation to the functional requirements of the relay. A 0.1 second fault might be insignificant in one application, whereas a 10 microsecond fault might be catastrophic in another. A reduction of insulation resistance to 100,000 ohms may not adversely affect one application, whereas a minimum of 500 megohms may be necessary to avoid field problems in another.

Environmental considerations have been discussed at this point because they play a very large part in determining the type of relay best suited for an application.

7.7 Enclosures, mounting, termination, and size

Specification of these mechanical factors (see Sec. 3) is related not only to field application requirements but also to the assembly of relays in a component or system and to the cost of maintenance of the equipment. Certain handling procedures or manufacturing processes may make advisable certain types of relay mounting and protective enclosure. One example might be an open-type relay suitable for field conditions but not for the assembly of the equipment of which it is a component because of the solder flux or

flux vapors that may unavoidably come in contact with it when adjacent components are soldered. In this case, a protective enclosure would prevent unnecessary contamination. Another illustration would be an open relay that can withstand all the field mechanical stresses but that is impractical to shield during equipment assembly, from some as yet unconnected heavy cables running nearby. Movement of the cables against or into its structure may damage this relay. In such a situation, an enclosure might permit faster handling. Still another example would be the relay that must be protected from paint spray or oil vapors. Exclusion of gaseous or particulate contaminants might also prevent enough problems to warrant enclosures of a relay.

Various methods of mounting may be used to reduce costs, facilitate field repairs, or alleviate problems within the equipment manufacturer's plant. The initial cost of the mounting should be weighed against installation and maintenance costs. Plug-in, sealed relays, for example, may have higher initial costs than devices intended to be connected by soldering leads. However, the labor cost of assembling plug-in components in the manufacturer's plant may be lower than that for soldered connections; the cost of correcting installation errors is also reduced.

Keying or polarizing methods may be required to prevent installation difficulties, particularly for symmetrical plug-in devices. Identification of terminals may be necessary as well as of the relay itself, particularly if it is sealed. If the marking is not necessary for proper installation of the relay or proper field service of the equipment, the cost should be avoided. On the other hand, there will be cases in which proper connection of the relay would be most difficult if each terminal is not clearly identified. In the case of multipole relays having one or more poles suitable for handling heavy duty loads and also one or more poles for low level loads, such marking could be warranted.

In specifying terminations, the following basic types should be considered: solder, screw, quick disconnect (various sizes), taper pin, lead wires, and printed circuit. Although it might be desirable to have all terminals of the same type, in some applications it is preferable to have coil terminals differ from contact terminals. Terminal spacing, pullout, and other space problems should be considered, as well as the method of connection, such as welding or soldering to the terminals. Voltage drops and current limitations of various termination methods should should also be evaluated.

In the relay drawing, only those dimensions *necessary* for proper factory installation or field application should be included, such as over-all dimensions. Options should be allowed wherever possible to give the relay manufacturer the widest latitude in making a proposal. Do not specify design details not related to relay performance or actual installation.

If the user permits options on some of the factors mentioned above (at least in the preliminary stage), his specification may allow several relay manufacturers to qualify. As a result, one of these suppliers may just have a mounting that will be more economical for the user's installation than the one he specified.

7.8 Coil or thermal actuator specifications

The following requirements should be taken into account in a coil or thermal actuator specification:

(1) *Resistance or impedance:* If the application dictates limitations on resistance or impedance, these should be noted, but options should be given to allow relay suppliers freedom in design that will result in performance gains or cost savings *(see* item 6).

(2) *Voltage or current:* It is not enough to state whether the source is d-c or a-c. Such details as the frequency, waveshape, pulse shape, nominal value, minimum value, and maximum value should also be included.

(3) *Actuator (coil) circuit diagram:* This is usually very helpful. Details that might otherwise be overlooked may be revealed to the relay engineer by such a drawing.

(4) *Duty cycle:* The three items below are intimately related and absolutely essential to the design of the relay actuating mechanism:
    (a) On-off ratio
    (b) On and off time limit (ratio alone is inadequate; absolute magnitudes are essential)
    (c) Rate of operation

(5) *Power consumption:* The maximum allowable power needed to operate a relay significantly affects cost and performance. This power should not be limited unless absolutely necessary.

(6) *Temperature rise:*
    (a) In specifying the ambient and mount-

ing surface conditions, refer to comments under "Environmental Requirements."

(b) Indicate ambient air temperature and state whether a still atmosphere or forced draft conditions prevail. This is particularly important for a "documentary" specification limiting maximum allowable temperature.

(c) Call out the exact voltage or current at which temperature rise is specified. If the device is used in a constant-current type of circuit, specify if the current is to be held constant during test. This would result in increasing wattage as coil temperature and resistance increase. The duration of the test must then be specified. When working with devices powered by control transformers, the voltage regulation of the transformer should be considered.

(d) Specify how rise is to be determined. One method is to attach a thermocouple to the coil (state exactly where and how). Another method is the resistance change method.

7.9 Operational specifications

Relay "input" factors are next to be considered. Operational specifications (which involve terminology noted in Sec. 1) should be correlated as much as possible to the functional requirements of the relay. Of the items listed here for convenience, include only those required by the particular application:

    (1) Nonpickup, measured
    (2) Nonpickup, specified
    (3) Pickup, measured
    (4) Pickup, specified
    (5) Hold, measured
    (6) Hold, specified
    (7) Dropout, measured
    (8) Dropout, specified
    (9) Operate time, measured
    (10) Operate time, specified
    (11) Release time, measured
    (12) Release time, specified
    (13) Transfer time, measured
    (14) Transfer time, specified
    (15) Contact bounce time, measured
    (16) Contact bounce time, specified

A number of important considerations arise when specifying any of the above factors, some of them related to test methods *(see* Sec. 8). Among the latter are these:

(1) Specify position of the relay with respect to gravity during check.

(2) Power source impedance, regulation, ripple, and waveshape are important.

(3) The type of instrumentation to be used is very important. Depending on waveshape, for example, a peak responding meter might indicate different results from those shown by a meter responding to rms values. Operate time measurements can be seriously affected by impedance of any portions of equipment connected in the relay coil circuit. Hence, one might obtain data using a cathode ray oscilloscope different from that obtained using a vibrating-reed galvanometer type recording oscillograph. When waveshapes other than pure d-c or sinusoidal a-c are involved, it may be necessary to include in the specification a requirement for specific measuring equipment. Such factors relating to test procedures cannot be ignored if the data of manufacturer and user is to be properly correlated.

(4) Be sure to indicate the temperature or temperature range at which or through which the specifications apply. If the relay's resistance varies with temperature (the usual case), some test correlation problems may be circumvented by specifying current instead of voltage values.

(5) Even room temperature variations and resistance changes due to self-heating during inspection may cause test correlation problems, particularly in marginal applications. (Marginal applications are those in which the actual operating points of the device will be very close to the specified limits, perhaps because of the difficulty in adjusting the device so as to provide a greater safety margin. This condition may occur because insufficient power is allowed or a variance from the device's inherent behavior is specified.)

(6) Specification limits should be established that allow for errors of repeatability and errors of measurement. However, to avoid excessive costs, safety factors should be fully understood by the user and supplier and not duplicated. Safety factors must be carefully used as they can affect producibility and reliability.

(7) Do not specify anything not required by the application.

(8) Be particularly sure the application actually *needs* both pickup and dropout limitations before including them in the specification. In many cases, only a maximum pickup limit or a minimum dropout limit is necessary.

(9) It is easy to write specifications based on the behavior of a few samples but this may result in excess costs when an entire production lot of devices must be adjusted to these specific limits.

(10 Timing specifications should clearly differentiate operate and release time from bridge, transfer, and contact bounce time. Often it may be advisable to specify a single maximum or minimum time limit including transfer and contact bounce periods, but this should be noted specifically. Coil energizing voltage and contact load is important here.

(11) Be very careful in analyzing applications in which one contact is required to open or close before or after another contact on the same relay. It is not enough merely to specify that contact A must close *before* contact B. The exact magnitude of time difference must be specified. Relay users should be aware of the typically short normal contact transfer time (a matter of microseconds).

(12) The same comments apply to applications in which one relay is required to pickup or dropout before or after another relay. Here the order of magnitude of time difference may be milliseconds instead of microseconds, but it is still necessary to determine the exact magnitude of difference that will be adequate to assure reliable circuit operation.

(13) A precautionary note is in order regarding the repeatability of contact sequence. Do not assume that the dynamic sequence of operation of contacts can be assured by static adjustments of spring positions or by checking the sequence while slowly operating the relay manually.

(14) In any timing tests, the impedance of the power supply and the means of switching the test circuit (including bounce of the switch) have serious effects on the results. The impedance of a device—cathode ray oscilloscope, galvanometer type recorder, electronic time interval meter, incandescent or neon lamps, meters of any type — in series or parallel with the test relay significantly affect its performance. These devices should be specified so that results may be properly correlated. The voltage or current and the temperature applicable to timing requirements should be specified. *Changes* of source impedance resulting from adjustment of voltage — such as the portions of a potentiometer in series and parallel with a test specimen—should be noted.

(15) The nature of some relay applications may be such that the test operation sequence for checking pickup and dropout voltages should be specified. For example: "With positive lead connected to terminal 1 and negative lead to terminal 2 and source voltage adjusted to zero,

close switch energizing relay. Slowly increase voltage from zero to pickup point (record this value). Continue increasing voltage to X (preferably maximum coil voltage). Then slowly reduce voltage to dropout point (record this value)." In some cases, the pickup point should be recorded only for a *second* increase of voltage. This procedure recognizes the effects of prior states of magnetization. Prior energization and the off time of thermal devices before test fall in a similar catergory. Another situation may warrant a simpler specification, such as this: "Adjust source voltage to X (maximum allowable pickup point considering regulation of source, loading of source by relay, and other factors that may require preloading of source). Then close switch connecting relay to source and determine if relay operates properly." Similar consideration must be given to magnetic latching relays.

(16) Off time before each operate cycle and ambient and mounting base temperature and mass should be considered when specifying thermal devices.

(17) Power source impedance, regulation, and waveshape are important not only in timing specifications but also in pickup or dropout specifications, particularly when pulse or surge type operation is required. By clearly defining power source characteristics as well as rise time and pulse width, one can prevent application errors such as those resulting from dependence on the inertia of the armature alone to integrate repetitive bits of energy or those based on the chance behavior of a few samples tested.

(18) If a-c or d-c relays are to be used for on-off functions, slowly rising or falling voltages or currents should not be specified to check their operating characteristics. For such tests (bearing in mind the power source details just discussed), it may be advisable to specify that the voltage be preset at a level 85 per cent of nominal (some applications require pickup at 75 per cent of nominal) and the switch then be closed to relay. This procedure will eliminate the noise complaints that may arise if a-c relays are taken too slowly through actual operate points (remote from specified limits).

(19) To check contact continuity and points of operation, a practical voltage should be specified. Do not specify low-voltage pilot lamps, for example, to check relays designed to handle 120- or 240-volt loads.

7.10 Electrical characteristics

Specifying electrical characteristics is an area in which a "black box" philosophy of including *functional items only* is extremely important. The following recommendations may be made:

(1) Electrical characteristics specifications, such as contact resistance, insulation resistance, or dielectric strength, should be related to the relay's functional requirements. Initial dielectric strength, for example, may be specified merely to assure some other minimum condition throughout product life.

(2) If it is desirable to specify a characteristic during or after life test or environmental exposure, it will almost always be necessary to establish less stringent requirements than the originals. Except for hermetically sealed relays, insulation resistance and dielectric strength normally are reduced, and contact resistance is normally increased by exposure or long time operation.

(3) For some applications it is unnecessary to specify high levels of insulation resistance. It may uselessly increase costs, for example, to ask for a 100-megohm insulation resistance on a relay used in a 6-volt, 10-ampere circuit. Although usually included in military specifications or in specifications for relays to be used in high impedance circuits, insulation resistance is not as frequently designated in commercial specifications as it is not always necessary. If electrolytic corrosion is a matter of concern, susceptibility to such attack can be evaluated by a humidity test, which often includes accelerated galvanic effects.

(4) Instruments made specifically for measuring insulation resistance are usually designed to make measurements at 100 or 500 volts d-c. The desired voltage should be specified. For most applications, 100 volts is adequate. For low voltage solid state circuits, 10 volts may be a practical value. Since insulation resistance varies with charging time, the measurement is usually specified to be made one minute after initial application of the voltage.

(5) Dielectric strength tests usually specify a one-minute exposure of the specimen to the stress. Sometimes, for economic reasons, a higher voltage is specified for shorter times of one or five seconds. Criteria of failure should be established at some maximum allowable level of leakage current. One important pitfall to be avoided is excessive transient voltages in the test set itself resulting from switching the high test voltage either at transformer secondary or primary level.

To prevent hidden damage to the specimens, the dielectric strength test voltage should not be specified at a level any higher than absolutely necessary.

(6) Insulation resistance and dielectric strength are both commonly specified (a) between all mutually insulated terminals, and (b) between insulated terminals and ground. Different values may be specified for the two basic cases. It may also be practical to specify one value for coils and another value for contacts. Caution must be exercised when dealing with any device incorporating solid state or other electronic components.

(7) The term "contact resistance" is generally interpreted as "terminal to terminal resistance" as it is seldom practical to measure resistance directly at the contacts. One should specify the points at which it is to be measured. The method of measuring contact resistance should also be specified (*see* Sec. 8). The test voltage is usually specified to be below nominal circuit voltage, but it is practical to use only a moderate safety factor. The current to be specified in measuring contact resistance should be a significant percentage of the nominal circuit current. In most cases, it would be prudent for the user to negotiate contact resistance specifications with the supplier.

(8) Caution and specific knowledge of a test device are required in specifying a "miss" test (usually associated with low level switching). Open and closed circuit voltage and current, maximum permissible contact resistance and time duration thereof, number of "misses" allowed, rate of operation, total number of operations, and ambient temperature should all be specified. For proper specification of a miss test, very close communication should be established with the relay manufacturer (*see* Sec. 8). For economic reasons, a miss test should not be specified unless absolutely required by the application.

7.11   Contact specifications

Considerations in drawing up contact specifications are as follows:

(1) Designation of *contact form* (defined in Sec. 1) is a good starting place.

(2) The importance of accurate specification of contact loads for each individual contact cannot be overstressed. "Standard" load specifications cannot be expected to assure field reliability. There is no such thing as a single ampere rating for a specific contact. Varied results will

be obtained from different types of relays, and even on the same relay one can expect varied results at different voltages, types of loads, ambient temperatures, and rates of operation. The nature of the load should be fully described — inductor, motor (type of motor), lamp, heater, and the like.

(3) In addition to stating nominal load voltages and currents or "steady state" values, the magnitude and duration of transient voltages and inrush currents should be indicated.

(4) Since contacts are most affected by the instantaneous load characteristics prevailing during the very short bounce period, an oscillogram is a recommended, accurate method that can be helpful in correlating inductive, motor, lamp, or capacitive load specifications.

(5) For inductive loads, the power factor or L/R ratio should be stated. Air core and iron core inductive loads should be differentiated.

(6) State type of contact protection that will or could be used, if any.

(7) Rate of operation, ambient air temperatures, mounting surface temperatures, impedance of power source (including lines), on-off ratio, all affect contact life and should be specified.

(8) Be sure to state what constitutes a failure. Specify whether test must be continuously monitored (usually quite costly) or whether periodic checks of the device during test shall suffice. (The latter is predominantly the current practice because of economic factors.)

(9) A complete circuit diagram should be included, with conductor types and sizes to be connected to the relay designated.

(10) Be sure to advise supplier of polarities to be switched. The possibility of electrolytic corrosion of devices switched should be considered. It is advisable to connect only one polarity to all movable or transfer contacts of a given relay. Then if make or break contacts should inadvertently come in contact (due to bounce or a service man working a "hot" circuit), short-circuit disaster may be avoided.

7.12   Life expectancy

Mechanical life expectancy.   It is common practice to specify a greater mechanical life expectancy than the life expected when the device is electrically loaded, provided:

(1) The electrical life expectancy specified is based on a fairly accurate estimate of a reasonable period of life in the field.

(2) The specified mechanical life expectancy is not unreasonably greater than the electrical life expectancy. (Consult the relay manufacturer for the proper magnitude for each type of device.)

Experience indicates the logic of relating the two since a significant percentage of failures occurring during electrically loaded tests is actually the result of mechanical causes. Therefore, specifying mechanical life tests is practical because such tests can be run faster, are less costly, and can give an indication of quality in a short time. Failure criteria should be carefully established *(see* Sec. 6).

Electrically loaded life expectancy. Electrically loaded life expectancy should be defined, noting whether loads are to be switched, made only, carried only, broken, or a combination thereof. The switching rate must be specified. Perhaps life expectancy should be specified by requiring different portions of the test to be run under different environmental conditions and at different cycling rates. This routine might better simulate actual field use. It is important to realize how severe is the stress put on relays by accelerated life tests. While establishing test cycling rates, it is recommended that the specification writer consult the relay engineer on specific products and their application.

7.13 Failure criteria

Failure criteria should be established with due consideration given to actual field functions. In each performance or characteristic area specified, failure criteria should be categorized as minor, major, or catastrophic. It would be practical to specify a decreasingly allowable percentage of defects with respect to the order listed above. Conversely, it would be practical to allow a higher percentage of minor defects than of major defects that can economically be allowed.

7.14 Qualification and acceptance test procedures

These procedures are so intimately associated with the relay specifications that they should be included therein directly or by reference to military or commercial specifications. Refer to Sec. 8 for information on test techniques.

7.15 Quantities, delivery schedules, cost requirements

These commercial factors may also help the relay supplier make the best selection for particular needs. They should be included with technical factors in "trade-offs" of characteristics. The user may be willing to reduce the life requirement at a higher temperature to reduce costs, for example, after due consideration of replacement costs and other factors in the specific case.

7.16 Specification check lists and sample specifications

Sample specification check lists with accompanying sample detail relay specifications follow. It is important that the relay user understand the purpose of these check lists. They are specification general guides for setting up a format for a specific device. While writing a specification for a particular relay, the components specification engineer would not necessarily include *all* items on the check list. Use of the list merely reminds him to *consider* each factor so as to reduce errors of omission and to eliminate areas of overspecification of relay requirements.

To be *really workable,* a check list must be tailored to a user's particular needs so that he may meet a real problem head-on with a realistic solution. Misapplication of relays — a major cause of malfunctions in the field — is often the result of incomplete or vague specifications. The tailored check list helps alleviate this problem.

Five different specification check lists are presented. Each is followed by a detail relay specification, related to a product, in which each item is cross-referenced to the applicable item in the check list. In an actual specification, these identifying codes would be omitted.

These sample check lists and related sample specifications illustrate different degrees of complexity. It will be noted that one of them is little more than a simple fill-in-the-blanks form. Such a form is practical when dealing with a definite purpose device.

SPECIFICATION CHECK LIST NO. 1

This check list might be utilized by a components specification engineer employed by a manufacturer of airborne communication equipment or electronic navigation aids. It should be noted that it is merely a list of items to be considered while preparing a specification. It is *not* a specification. It does *not* imply that *all* these items are to appear in *every* specification. Its purpose is to remind the specification writer, by the tailored check list system, to consider carefully a number of factors frequently important in *his* own usage. By proper use of this system, *no more* and *no fewer* requirements than are functionally related to the application will appear in the actual specification. Anything not required by the application should not be specified.

CHECK LIST FOR AIRBORNE APPLICATIONS

I. Relay function

II. Description of equipment in which relay is used

III. Class of application

  A. Military
  B. Commercial
  C. Industrial
  D. Electronic
  E. Communications
  F. Commercial airborne
  G. Other

IV. Applicable documents

  A. Military specifications
    1. MIL-R-5757E
    2. MIL-R-6106F
    3. MIL-STD-202C
    4. Other
  B. Underwriters' Laboratories (UL)
  C. Canadian Standards Association (CSA)
  D. National Electrical Manufacturers Association (NEMA)
  E. Electronic Industries Association (EIA/RETMA)
  F. Quality assurance specifications
  G. Reliability specifications

V. Environmental tests

  A. Nonoperative
    1. Thermal shock
    2. Sealing
    3. Salt spray
    4. Humidity
  B. Operational
    1. RF noise
    2. Vibration
    3. Altitude

    4. Shock
    5. Temperature range
      (a) −55°C to +85°C
      (b) −65°C to +125°C
      (c) Other
    6. High and low temperature operation
    7. Temperature cycling
    8. Acceleration
    9. Random drop

VI. Contact specifications

  A. Form designation
  B. Loads (specify each pole separately if loads are different)
    1. Current
    2. Voltage
    3. A-C or d-c
    4. Frequency
    5. Resistive
    6. Inductive
      (a) Power factor
      (b) L/R ratio
    7. Motor
      (a) Starting current transient
      (b) Locked-rotor current
    8. Lamp
      (a) Inrush current
      (b) Time to reach steady state current
  C. Transient conditions (provide calibrated CRO photograph)
  D. Circuit diagram
  E. Rate of operation
  F. Overload

VII. Coil specifications

  A. Resistance
  B. Impedance
  C. A-C or d-c
  D. Frequency
  E. Voltage
    1. Nominal
    2. Minimum
    3. Maximum
  F. Current
    1. Nominal
    2. Minimum
    3. Maximum
  G. Duty cycle
    1. ON-OFF ratio
    2. Magnitude of ON time
      (a) Minimum
      (b) Maximum
  H. Repetition rate
  I. Circuit diagram

VIII. Electrical characteristics specifications

A. Contact resistance
B. Insulation resistance
C. Dielectric strength
  1. Sea level
  2. High altitude

IX. Operational specifications

A. Pickup values
B. Dropout values
C. Operate time
D. Release time
E. Contact bounce
F. Contact chatter
G. Instrumentation
H. Temperature

X. Enclosures

A. Open
B. Dust cover
C. Hermetically sealed
D. Size limitations

XI. Mounting methods

XII. Termination

A. Terminal type
  1. Solder
  2. Screw
  3. Wedge
  4. Solderless wrap
  5. Pin type (printed circuit or plug-in)
B. Method of connection
  1. Welding
  2. Soldering
C. Terminal strength

XIII. Marking

A. Type designation
B. Part number
C. Date code
D. Manufacturer's code

XIV. Life expectancy

A. Mechanical
B. Electrical

XV. Failure criteria

A. Minor
B. Major
C. Catastrophic

XVI. Qualification tests

XVII. Acceptance tests

XVIII. Procurement factors

A. Quantity required
B. Delivery schedule
C. Cost limitations

SAMPLE DETAIL RELAY SPECIFICATION NO. 1

(Numerical identification after each item in this sample specification refers to the corresponding section of Specification Check List No. 1. In actual use, of course, these references would be omitted.)

PROCUREMENT SPECIFICATION FOR RELAY IN AIRBORNE ELECTRONIC EQUIPMENT

	Check list reference
Relay is required to switch audio frequency circuitry in radio receiver	I
Model 9999 Airborne Equipment	II
This equipment will be used on commercial airlines, and the following documents are applicable: MIL - R - 5757E, MIL - STD-202C, and MIL-R-6106F. Only those paragraphs specifically mentioned in this detail specification apply. In case of any discrepancy, the detail spec shall govern.	IIIF and IVA

The following environmental specifications apply:

1. Thermal shock per Test Condition B of Method 107 of MIL-STD-202C.	VA 1
2. Sealing Test II per Paragraph 4.8.4.2 of MIL-R-5757E.	VA 2
3. 100-hr salt spray test per Paragraph 4.8.13 of MIL-R-5757E.	VA 3
4. Humidity per Moisture Resistance Test Method 106A of MIL-STD-202C, except eliminate Paragraph 2.4.2	VA 4
5. Vibration Test I of Paragraph 4.8.11.1 of MIL-R-5757E.	VB 2
6. Shock Test of 30 g per MIL-R-5757E Shock Type 4, Paragraph 4.8.16.1.	VB 4
7. High altitude performance at 70,000 ft.	VB 3
8. Relay shall operate over ambient temperature range of —65°C to +125°C.	VB 5b

9. High and low temperature test per MIL-R-5757E, Paragraph 4.8.9 shall apply.   VB 6

This relay shall have a contact form C (SPDT).   VIA

Both A and B portions of the pole shall handle similar loads of audio frequency levels of 30 ma min. to 1 amp max. at voltages of 100 mv to 8 volts. Load will be basically resistive with power factor exceeding 0.8.   VIB

Normal rate of operation in equipment will be 4 cpm with equal on and off times.   VIE

The relay coil resistance shall be 250 ohms min. at 25°C.   VIIA

The nominal d-c coil voltage shall be 28 volts d-c with a range of 24-32 volts d-c.   VIIC and VIIE 1, 2, 3

Coil shall be capable of continuous duty over temperature range of −65°C to +125°C.   VIIG

Contact resistance shall not exceed 0.02 ohms initially when checked by voltmeter-ammeter method with an open-circuit voltage of 1 volt d-c and a closed-circuit current of 100 mA.   VIIIA

Relay contacts shall be closed before applying test circuit voltage.

Dielectric strength at sea level shall be required by Paragraph 4.8.5.1 of MIL-R-5757E.   VIIIC 1

Dielectric strength at 70,000 ft shall be in accordance with Paragraph 4.8.5.2. of MIL-R-5757E.   VIIIC 2

Insulation resistance of 1 megohm min. determined per Paragraph 4.8.6 of MIL-R-5757E.   VIIIB

Relay shall pickup at 20 volts d-c max. over the temperature range of −65°C to +125°C, and shall dropout at 1 to 10 volts d-c over the temperature range of −65°C to +125°C.   IXA and IXB

Relay shall be hermetically sealed.   XC

Size, mounting, and solder terminals to be per drawing 9999-1 (to be included as part of the specification).   XD, XI, and XIIA 1

Relay shall be marked per Paragraph 3.39 of MIL-R-5757E, items b, e, f, and g only.   XIII

Electrically loaded life expectancy shall be per Paragraph 4.8.34 of MIL-R-5757E.   XIVB

Failure criteria are categorized as follows: XV

1. Minor
    (a) Marking dimensions in error
    (b) 0.1 volt deviation beyond allowable limits of pickup and dropout
2. Major
    (a) Contact resistance exceeds 0.02 ohms but is less than 0.5 ohms
3. Catastrophic
    (a) Failure of normally open contacts to make contact when coil is energized at 28 volts
    (b) Open coil circuit

5,000 relays required, with delivery to begin 60 days after receipt of order at a rate of 100 relays per week.   XVIII

SPECIFICATION CHECK LIST NO. 2

This check list might be utilized by a manufacturer of air conditioning equipment or a domestic clothes washer. It should be noted that it is merely a list of items to be considered while preparing a specification. It is *not* a specification. It does *not* imply that *all* these items are to appear in *every specification*. Its purpose is to remind the specification writer, by the tailored check list system, to consider carefully a number of factors frequently important in *his* own usage. By proper use of this system, *no more* and *no fewer* requirements than are functionally related to the application will appear in the actual specification. Anything that is not required by the application should not be specified.

CHECK LIST FOR BOTH GENERAL
INDUSTRIAL AND DEFINITE
PURPOSE CONTROLS

1.0 Electrical requirements
 1.1 Load type
  A. Motor
  B. Solenoid or contactor
  C. Resistance
  D. Lamp
  E. Inductive (L/R)
 1.2 Load rating
  A. Nominal current, voltage, and horse-
   power (starter)
  B. Actual current, voltage, and horse-
   power (starter)
 1.3 Pole arrangement
  A. Termination, size and type
   1. Power
   2. Auxiliary
   3. Dummy binding posts
 1.4 Operate specifications
  A. Pickup value
  B. Dropout value
  C. No contact chatter position on slowly
   rising or falling coil voltage

2.0 Physical and environmental factors
 2.1 Mounting
  A. Position
  B. Method
  C. Sound absorbing
 2.2 Dimensions
  A. Over-all
  B. Mounting
 2.3 Marking
  A. Nameplate
  B. Pole marking
  C. Customer part No.
 2.4 Weight limitations
 2.5 Shock and vibration limits
  A. Operating
  B. Nonoperating
 2.6 Temperature
  A. Max. operating
  B. Storage
 2.7 Humidity
  A. Use
  B. Storage
 2.8 Salt spray
 2.9 Dielectric strength

3.0 Coil requirements
 3.1 Nominal rating, voltage, and frequency
 3.2 Termination

3.3 Marking
3.4 Inrush volt-amperes (Items 3.4 and 3.5
 should be stated at rated voltages on
 coil label or standard 24, 120, 240, 480,
 600 volts, or specify.)
  Max.   Nominal

  _____ _____

3.5 Sealed volt-amperes
  Max.   Nominal

  _____ _____

3.6 Max. temperature rise at specified voltage, frequency, and ambient temperature

4.0 Life expectancy
 4.1 Mechanical
 4.2 Electrical

5.0 Specifications
 5.1 Underwriters' Laboratories, Inc. (UL)
 5.2 Canadian Standards Association (CSA)
 5.3 Military
 5.4 Electrical
 5.5 Environmental (shock, vibration, temperature, humidity, salt spray)
 5.6 Other manufacturer's standards

SAMPLE DETAIL CONTROL
SPECIFICATION NO. 2

*(Check list reference would be omitted in ac-
tual use of this system.)*

PROCUREMENT SPECIFICATION FOR A
DEFINITE PURPOSE MOTOR CONTROL

	Check list reference
Electrical load requirements:	
Air conditioning compressor motor, 1 phase, 2 line, 60 cycle	1.1
Motor nominal rating	1.2
30 full-load amp, 150 locked-rotor amp, 250 volt	
20 full-load amp, 100 locked-rotor amp, 480 volt	
15 full-load amp, 75 locked-rotor amp, 600 volt	
Actual load, 24 amp, 240 volt	
Fan motor, 1 phase, 1 line, 3 amp, 220 volt	1.2
Terminations:	
3-pole pressure connect	1.3

Termination for No. 8 wire	1.3A1
Double quick disconnects on line side on L1 and L3	1.3A2
Relay shall pickup at 85% of nominal voltage	1.4A
Not to have a contact chatter position on slowly rising voltage when the rate of rise per sec is 5% of nominal voltage when within 10% of pickup voltage	1.4C

Physical and environmental factors:

3-hole mounting to clear No. 10 screw in either of two positions (see drawing)	2.1A,B
Mounting to be supplied with grommets	2.1C
Maximum height, width, and depth (see drawing)	2.2A,B
Nameplate to show FLA, LRA, and voltage	2.3A
Poles are to be marked L1, L2, L3 and T1, T2, T3 (see drawing)	2.3B
Must have customer and vendor part number marked on part (see drawing)	2.3C
Shock and vibration limits subject to shipping standards only	2.5
Temperature maximum operating ambient, 155°F	2.6A

Coil requirements:

240 volt, 50/60 cycle, screw terminals	3.1 and 3.2
Mark coil, "240V 50/60 Hz"	3.3

Power (volt-amperes) at 240 volts, 60 cps

	Max.	Nominal	
Inrush	100	95	3.4
Sealed	20	15	3.5

Maximum coil rise not to exceed 50°C when in a 50°C ambient with nominal voltage applied at both frequencies	3.6
Minimum life expectancy with all contacts electrically loaded at rated load shall be 100,000 operations.	4.2
All controls must be rated at UL and CSA for rating listed	5.1 and 5.2

on the label as intended for air conditioning and refrigeration use.	
In addition, all controls must have been tested and listed with Compressor Manufacturers Electrical Standard #XYZ	5.4 and 5.6

SPECIFICATION CHECK LIST NO. 3

This check list might be utilized by a manufacturer of electric heating devices. It should be noted that it is merely a list of items to be considered while preparing a specification. It is *not* a specification. It does *not* imply that *all* these items are to appear in *every* specification. Its purpose is to remind the specification writer, by the tailored check list system, to consider carefully a number of factors frequently important in *his* own usage. By proper use of this system, *no more* and *no fewer* requirements than are functionally related to the application will appear in the actual specification. Anything that is not required by the application should not be specified.

CHECK LIST FOR THERMAL RELAY CHARACTERISTICS[1]

I. Class of application

 1. Military
 2. Commercial
 3. Industrial
 4. Automotive
 5. Communication
 6. Other

II. Approvals agency

 1. Military
 2. Underwriters' Laboratories (UL)
 3. Canadian Standards Association (CSA)
 4. American Gas Association (AGA)
 5. National Electrical Manufacturers Association (NEMA)
 6. Electronic Industries Association (EIA/RETMA)
 7. None

III. Ratings

---

[1]See also Sample No. 4 covering a different type of thermal relay and different type of application.

1. Heater
   a. Maximum watts
   b. Nominal voltage
   c. Voltage range
   d. Duty cycle
2. Contacts
   a. Form
   b. Current
   c. Voltage
   d. Power factor

IV. Construction

   1. Mounting
   2. Terminal type
   3. Connections
      a. Heater common to contacts
      b. Heater isolated from contacts
   4. Size limitations
   5. Marking

V. Operation

   1. Operate delay
   2. Reset time
   3. Tolerance
   4. Life expectancy

VI. Environmental requirements

   1. Salt spray
   2. Humidity
   3. Shock
   4. Vibration
   5. Temperature range

VII. Sales information

   1. Approximate price
   2. Annual usage
   3. Delivery required
   4. Purchase of required new tools
   5. Inquirer's name, title, and date

SAMPLE DETAIL RELAY SPECIFICATION NO. 3

(Check list reference would be omitted in actual use of this system.)

SPECIFICATION FOR THERMAL RELAY[1]

	Check list reference
This inquiry pertains to a thermal relay to be used in domestic electric heat panels.	I 3
The device must be so designed as to be capable of approval by UL and CSA Testing Agencies.	II

proval by UL and CSA Testing Agencies.

The basic requirement is for a relay that will operate on a 240 volt, 60 Hz a-c line and consume a maximum of 5 watts of operating power. — III 1A,B

A normal +10%, −15% tolerance on line voltage can be expected. — III 1C

We would require the heater to be capable of continuous operation. — III 1D

A SPNO contact load will be 15 amp at 230 volts, 60 cycle resistive load. Please furnish the device with four quick-connect terminals with the relay heater and load contacts isolated. — III 2 and IV 2 and 3

Our part number and the supplier's part number are to be stamped on a suitable surface. — IV 5

Maximum physical size we can utilize is one that does not exceed 4 in. in length, 2 in. in width, and 1 in. in height. — IV 4

The single-pole contact must close in 2 to 4 sec at rated voltage and open in a maximum time of 15 sec under all conditions of voltage and ambient. We would require a minimum of 100,000 operations. — V 1, 2, and 4

Although this is a new product line with our company, we confidently expect the annual usage to start at 100,000 pcs. with increasing requirements to follow. We would be willing to pay for new tools provided a maximum price of approximately $XYZ would not be exceeded. — VII

SPECIFICATION CHECK LIST NO. 4

This check list might be utilized by a components specification engineer employed by a manufacturer of airborne communication equipment or electronic navigation aids. It should be noted that it is merely a list of items to be considered while preparing a specification. It is *not* a specification. It does *not* imply that *all* these items are to appear in *every* specification. Its purpose is to remind the specification writer, by the tailored check list system, to consider carefully a number of factors frequently important in *his* own usage. By proper use of this system, *no more* and *no fewer* requirements than are functionally related to the application will appear in the actual specification. Do not specify anything that is not required by the application.

CHECK LIST FOR THERMAL RELAY REQUIREMENTS[1]

I. Relay function

II. Description of equipment in which relay is used

III. Class of application

   A. Military
   B. Commercial
   C. Industrial
   D. Automotive
   E. Electronic
   F. Communications
   G. Commercial airborne
   H. Other

IV. Applicable documents

   A. Military
      1. MIL-R-19648
      2. MIL-STD-202
      3. MIL-STD-130
      4. Other
   B. Underwriters Laboratories
   C. CSA
   D. NEMA
   E. EIA/RETMA
   F. Quality assurance
   G. Reliability

V. Environmental tests

   A. Nonoperative
      1. Thermal shock
      2. Sealing
      3. Salt spray
      4. Humidity
   B. Operational
      1. RF noise
      2. Vibration
      3. Altitude

---

[1]See sample No. 3 covering a different type of thermal relay and different type of application.

      4. Shock
      5. Temperature range
         a. $-55°C$ to $+85°C$
         b. $-65°C$ to $+125°C$
         c. Other
      6. High and low temperature operation
      7. Acceleration

VI. Contact specifications

   A. Arrangement
   B. Loads (Spec each pole separately if loads are different)
      1. Current
      2. Voltage
      3. A-C or d-c
      4. Frequency
      5. Resistive
      6. Inductive
         a. Power factor
         b. L/R ratio
      7. Motor
         a. Starting current transient
         b. Locked-rotor current
      8. Lamp
         a. Inrush current
         b. Time to reach steady state current
   C. Transient conditions (provide calibrated CRO photograph)
   D. Circuit diagram
   E. Rate of operation
   F. Overload

VII. Heater coil specifications

   A. Maximum watts
   B. Nominal voltage or current
   C. Voltage or current range
   D. Repetition rate
      1. Intermittent
      2. Continuous
   E. Circuit diagram

VIII. Electrical characteristic specifications

   A. Contact resistance
   B. Insulation resistance
   C. Dielectric strength
      1. Sea level
      2. High altitude

IX. Operational specifications

   A. Operate time
   B. Saturate release time
   C. Instant release time
   D. Saturate recovery time
   E. Instant recovery time
   F. Voltage or current sensing
   G. Minimum hold-in voltage

X. Enclosure

  A. Open
  B. Dust cover
  C. Hermetically sealed
  D. Size

XI. Mounting

XII. Termination

  A. Terminal type
    1. Straight
    2. Hooked
  B. Terminal strength

XIII. Marking

  A. Type designation
  B. Part number
  C. Date code
  D. Manufacturer's code

XIV. Life expectancy

XV. Failure criteria

  A. Minor
  B. Major
  C. Catastrophic

XVI. Qualification tests

XVII. Acceptance tests

XVIII. Procurement

  A. Quantity required
  B. Delivery schedule
  C. Cost limitations

SAMPLE DETAIL RELAY SPECIFICATION NO. 4

(Check list reference would be omitted in actual use of this system.)

SPECIFICATION FOR THERMAL RELAY[1]

	Check list reference
Relay is required to control erection delay and caging delay in model 1234 airborne gyro automatic pilot equipment.	I and II
This equipment will be used on military aircraft and commercial airlines, and the following documents are applicable:	III A,B and IVA

[1]See also sample No. 3 covering a different type of thermal relay and a different type of application.

MIL-R-19648, MIL-STD-202, and MIL-STD-130. Only those paragraphs specifically mentioned in this detail spec shall govern.

The following environmental specifications apply:	
Thermal shock per test condition B, MIL-R-19648.	VA 1
Sealing test per MIL-R-19648.	VA 2
50-hour salt spray per MIL-R-19648.	VA 3
Vibration grade 2 of MIL-R-19648.	VB 2
High altitude performance at 70,000 ft.	VB 3
Shock test of 30 g per MIL-R-19648, shock test 4.	VB 4
Relay shall operate over ambient temperature range of −65°C to +125°C.	VB 5
The following contact specifications apply:	
Arrangement normally open.	VIA
Contact rating: resistive, 2 amps to 250 volts a-c; inductive, 25 volt-amps to 250 volts (1 amp max.)	VIB
The following heater coil specifications apply:	
The heater resistance shall be 190 ohms ±10% at 25°C.	VIIA
The nominal d-c heater voltage shall be 28 volts d-c, with a range of ± 5% d-c.	VIIB
The following electrical characteristic specifications apply:	
Contact resistance shall not exceed 0.050 ohms initially when checked by VM-AM method with an open circuit voltage of 28 volts d-c and a closed circuit current of 1 amp. Relay contacts shall be closed before applying test circuit voltage.	VIIIA
Insulation resistance of 100 megohm min. shall be determined per Paragraph 4.6.3.2 of MIL-R-19648A.	VIIIB

Dielectric strength at sea level shall be as required by Paragraph 4.6.3.1 of MIL-R-19648A. VIIIC

The following operational specifications apply:

Normal operate time: 60 ± 6 seconds at 28 volts d-c (±0.5%). IXA

Saturate release time: 52 seconds min. IXB

Minimum hold-in voltage: 23 volts d-c. IXG

Relay shall be hermetically sealed. XC

Size, mounting, and solder terminals to be per drawing 1234 (include as part of the specification). X, XI, and XII

Relay shall be marked per Paragraph 3.17 of MIL-R-19648A and MIL-STD-130. XIII

Electrically loaded life expectancy shall be per Paragraph 4.6.14 of MIL-R-19648A, except switching rate shall be 1 cpm. XIV

Failure criteria are categorized as follows:

(1) Minor XVA
  (a) Marking dimensions in error.

(2) Major XVB
  (a) Normal operate time exceeds 60 ± 6 seconds at 28 volts d-c.

(3) Catastrophic XVC
  (a) Failure of contacts to remain closed when heater voltage drops to 23 volts d-c.
  (b) Open heater circuit.

5,000 relays required with delivery to begin 6 weeks after receipt of order at a rate of 200 relays per week. XVIII

SPECIFICATION CHECK LIST NO. 5

This check list might be utilized by a components specification engineer employed by a manufacturer of coin operated vending equip-ment. It should be noted that it is merely a list of items to be considered while preparing a specification. It is *not* a specification. It does *not* imply that *all* these items are to appear in *every* specification. Its purpose is to remind the specification writer, by the tailored check list system, to consider carefully a number of factors frequently important in *his* own usage. By proper use of this system, *no more* and *no fewer* requirements than are functionally related to the application will appear in the actual specification. Do not specify anything that is not required by the application.

CHECK SHEET FOR VENDING MACHINE RELAY REQUIREMENTS

I. Relay function

II. Description of equipment in which relay is used

III. Applicable documents
  A. Underwriters' Laboratories (UL)
  B. Canadian Standards Association (CSA)
  C. National Electrical Manufacturers Association (NEMA)
  D. Electronic Industries Association (EIA/RETMA)

IV. Environmental requirements
  A. Nonoperative (storage)
    1. Temperature range
    2. Humidity
    3. Other
  B. Operational
    1. Temperature range
    2. Humidity
    3. Other

V. Contact specifications
  A. Arrangement (combination or form as described in Sec. 1)
  B. Loads (Specify each pole separately if loads are different)
    1. Current (nominal)
    2. Voltage (nominal)
    3. A-C or d-c
    4. Frequency
    5. Resistive (heater)
    6. Inductive
      a. Power factor
      b. L/R ratio
    7. Motor
      a. Starting current transient
      b. Locked-rotor current

8. Lamp
    a. Inrush current
    b. Time to reach steady state current
9. Solenoid or contactor
    a. Inrush current
    b. Steady state current
C. Circuit diagram
D. Rate of operation
E. Overload

VI. Coil specifications

A. A-C or d-c nominal voltage or current
B. Permissible power consumption in watts or volt-amperes
C. D-C resistance
D. Duty cycle
    1. Intermittent (list duration of ON and OFF periods)
    2. Continuous
E. Circuit diagram

VII. Electrical characteristics specifications

A. Maximum contact resistance
B. Insulation resistance
C. Dielectric strength (high-pot test)

VIII. Operational specifications

A. Maximum operate voltage or current
B. Minimum operate voltage or current
C. Maximum release voltage or current
D. Minimum release voltage or current
E. Operate time at nominal voltage or current
F. Release time at nominal voltage or current

IX. Enclosure

A. Open
B. Dust cover
C. Hermetically sealed
D. Size (maximum over-all)

X. Mounting

XI. Termination (list preferred types and sizes)

A. Solder lug
B. Quick disconnect
C. Screw terminals
D. Plug-in
E. Other

XII. Marking

A. Type designation
B. Part number
C. Date code

XIII. Life expectancy

A. Mechanical
B. Electrical

XIV. Noise level

XV. Procurement factors

A. Quantity required
B. Delivery schedule
C. Cost limitations.

SAMPLE DETAIL RELAY SPECIFICATION NO. 5

(Check list reference would be omitted in actual use of this system.)

SPECIFICATION FOR VENDING MACHINE RELAY

	Check list reference
Relay is required to control small vending and timing motors and logic circuitry in a commercial vending machine.	I and II
The following document will apply: Underwriters' Laboratories, Inc. Standard 306	III

Environmental requirements: IV
A. Nonoperative
    1. Storage temperature 50°F to 100°F
B. Operational
    1. Ambient temperature range, −40°F to +130°F
    2. Relative humidity range up to 98%
    3. Must withstand 10-day exposure

Contact specifications: V
A. 1 Form C, 1 Form A contact combinations
B. Load to be handled: 3 amps, 115 volts, 50/60 cps resistive

Coil specifications. VI
A. 115 volts +10%, −15%, 50/60 Hz
B. 6 volt-amperes
C. 690 ohms resistance (approximately)

D. Continuous duty

E. Circuit diagram per drawing no. B50001

Insulation resistance to be 100 megohms minimum at room conditions.   VIIB

Dielectric strength at 60 cps to be 1250 volts RMS minimum between all elements and ground.   VIIC

Must operate at 90 volts RMS 60 cps at 25°C.   VIII

Operate time within 30 milliseconds.   VIIIE

Relay to be mounted in nylon dust cover.   IX

Relay shall be mounted by means of guided-type 11-pin plug connected as shown on drawing B50002.   X and XI

Marking shall include: XII

1. Manufacturer's name and part number

2. Schematic diagram

3. Drawing no. B50002

4. Date code

Life expectancy to be 75,000 operations at rated load conditions.   XIII

No perceptible noise at 2 ft.   XIV

Quantity required will be 10,000 per month with a potential of 50,000 units over a 6-month period.   XVA

Delivery of 1,000 units within 30 days of receipt of order.   XVB

Cost must not exceed $XYZ per unit.   XVC

Note: See Chapter 12 for NARM "Standard of Electro-Magnetic Relays for Industrial and/or Commercial Applications" on pages 276 to 278.

8
Testing Procedures

Introduction

This section was written to acquaint the reader with procedures for inspecting and testing electromagnetic relays. It is concerned with relays that perform general switching functions in military and commercial systems. The recommended tests contain the technical substance of the Standard Test procedure prepared by the USASI Sectional Committee C83.

The subject of relay testing has many ramifications. As industry has become more highly automated, the duties of relays have become more complex. The result has been a great increase in testing by both relay manufacturers and users.

People unfamiliar with relay development have no conception of the myriad switching functions relays perform. The nature of the application dictates the type and rating of relay used. Inexperience has often caused the selection of the wrong relay. If the relay is not tested properly to the applicable requirements prior to use, it may fail as a result and be held responsible although the real cause was misapplication. It is highly important, therefore, that the relay selected have the desired capability and characteristics to fulfill the application requirements.

The tests performed should assure reliable performance. When the application is industrial, testing for general operating characteristics and safety requirements is usually sufficient. In military applications, however, testing becomes more extensive because of the critical nature of the applications. Military specifications

require that relays be tested to the maximum environmental condition they may experience in service. The rapid aerospace development has caused most relay manufacturers to develop complete environmental test laboratories and to orient their policy to make testing a highly important phase of manufacturing. In fact, the time devoted to testing frequency exceeds that of manufacturing.

The following tests are for both military and industrial relays. The user should omit those tests not specifically applicable to the end use of his own relay. Information given with each test includes:

(1) The purpose of the test
(2) Definition of the test (if not obvious)
(3) Requirements, or what data is needed to perform each test
(4) Procedure of test, including equipment to be used
(5) An example of how the data are to be recorded.
(6) Precautions or possible trouble areas that could affect the accuracy of results.

Test Procedures

8.1 Standard test conditions

Purpose. The reason for Standard Test Conditions is to insure repeatability of tests affected by atmospheric conditions.

Requirements. The standard reference conditions for characteristics that are affected by atmospheric conditions are:

(1) Temperature, 23°C

(2) Relative humidity, 20 to 50 per cent

(3) Barometric pressure, 29 to 30 inches of mercury.

Unless otherwise specified, actual test conditions may be normal room ambient as long as corrections can be made to the reference values whenever the environment may have a significant effect on the absolute values measured during the test.

The selection of 23°C is based on the international standard of temperature reference value and should not create any hardship to those who continue to use 25°C or 20°C so long as the correction factor can be applied.

Some of the characteristics affected are: Winding resistance, operating characteristics when measured in voltage, insulation resistance, and dielectric withstanding voltage. Values other than standard for atmospheric pressure, humidity, and temperature may be specified for specific tests if the values chosen are important to that test.

8.2 Visual and mechanical inspection

Purpose. Visual and mechanical inspection is made to insure that the relay and its parts conform with the requirements called for in the specifications.

Requirements. The extent to which visual and mechanical inspection requirements may be specified depends upon:

(1) The particular relay design

(2) Manufacturing techniques and materials employed

(3) Reliability and economic considerations.

Procedure. It is recommended that visual and mechanical inspection be conducted in areas in the manufacturers' and users' plants in which clean conditions are maintained to avoid contamination from dirt and other foreign matter.

When visual and mechanical inspection are specified, the following procedure shall be used. (Here and elsewhere, if tests are destructive, they are identified as such. Such tests should be applied on a sampling basis only).

(1) Workmanship: Factors that vary from one unit to another, depending upon the care exercised in the assembly and testing of a relay, are covered under this heading. Whenever necessary, the specification should indicate the stan-

dards of workmanship considered acceptable. A magnification of 10× shall be used to inspect the following:

(a) Cracks, burrs, chips, or filings; extraneous foreign material or oil; weld and solder splatter

(b) Clearance between fixed and moving parts

(c) Irregularities such as scratches and nicks on contact, or other, critical surfaces

(d) Contact alignment or registration

(e) Cracks in glass insulating parts

(f) Fracture of welded or brazed joints.

(g) Proper positioning of parts.

(h) Header glass for cracks and proper meniscus. (For example: Hi-Rel space applications, refer to NAS 728.)

(2) Materials and finishes: These shall be tested in accordance with applicable ASTM or MIL specification.

(3) Joined parts:

(a) Welded joints (destructive test): Strength of welded joints except contacts shall be tested by applying a force that causes the parts to be torn apart. Examination for conformity with weld strength requirements shall be made under 10× magnification.

(b) Brazed parts (destructive test): Brazed parts shall be tested for presence of HCl by using litmus paper or some other suitable pH indicator. The strength of brazed joints shall be tested by applying a force that produces deformation of the joined parts and then examining the joint for evidence of cracking.

(c) Contacts: In testing the shear strength of the joint between contacts and the body to which they are affixed, the specified shearing force shall be applied. As this specified force is applied, the contacts shall be observed under 10× magnification to determine whether any movement of the contact can be observed.

(d) Mating contact alignment: Contact alignment shall be observed under 10× magnification for conformance with the applicable specification controlling overlap and parallelism.

(e) Solder joints: These shall be inspected under 10× magnification for requirements covering smoothness, even flow, and absence of lumps or cold solder joints.

(4) Terminals of glass seal headers (destructive test): Three types of tests may be specified for determining the strength of the terminal-to-glass seal: pull, twist, and bend tests. When applicable, the test shall be performed

and the terminal and the glass headers shall then be inspected under 10× magnification for evidence of damage or looseness. Permissible damage should be specified. *Note:* Depending on the application, breakage of the meniscus of glass on the pin is normally not considered excessive damage after some of the severe twist and bend tests.

(a) Pull test (destructive test): A specified force shall be applied parallel to the longitudinal axis of the terminal using a force indicator having an accuracy of ±10 per cent. A perpendicular force test that is insufficient to bend the terminal may also be specified.

(b) Twist test (destructive test): The terminals shall be subjected to five cycles in which a torque producing rotation or twisting of the terminals about its longitudinal axis shall be applied at the point of connection. The distance away from the glass at which the force is to be applied should be specified. One test cycle shall consist of a 90° ±5° clockwise twist, a 180° ±5° counterclockwise twist, and a 90° ±5° clockwise twist to restore the terminal to its normal position. The number of degrees and cycles of rotation may vary depending upon pin size.

(c) Bend test (destructive test): The terminals shall be subjected to three cycles in which a force applied perpendicular to the axis of the terminal shall be of sufficient magnitude to bend it 90° ±5°C in one direction and 180° ±5° in the reverse direction before it is restored to its normal position. This test is severe. The angle to which the terminal can be bent without definite harmful effect on the glass seal is dependent upon pin size.

(5) Screws and Threads: The threaded parts shall be measured for class of fit in accordance with American Standard B1, 1949, or MIL-S-7742.

8.3 Mechanical adjustments

Purpose.   The purpose for measurement of the mechanical adjustment forces is to insure repeatability in design and workmanship of each specific unit of design.

Requirements.   In general, the extent to which mechanical adjustments may be specified depends upon:

(1) The degree of control the user desires.
(2) The relay design. In specifying displacement and force requirements, the point of application of force and the magnitude of force, as well as measurement point shall be defined.

Procedure.   When mechanical adjustment requirements are specified, the following measurement procedures shall be used.

(1) Armature travel and contact follow (or overtravel):

(a) Use of thickness gages: Gages of specified thickness shall be inserted between the armature and the fixed pole piece at the specified measuring point. The coil shall be energized at a voltage or current that causes the armature to operate fully. Opening and closing of the contacts shall be observed by means of an electrical indicator, using a voltage that will not produce visible erosion or carbonization of the contacts. All thickness gages shall be smooth and clean and within ± .0001 in. of the specified thickness. Significant factors in the armature travel may be controlled by the relay manufacturer, including (moving from the unoperated position): (1) The force at which the armature first begins to move from its unoperated position; (2) the points at which normally closed contacts open and normally open contacts close; and (3) the total displacement between operated and unoperated positions.

(b) Optical measurement: The significant points listed above may also be measured optically using sufficient magnification and calibrated grid lines as part of the optical system. The accuracy with this method shall be ± .0005 in.

(2) Contact separation: Gages of specified thickness shall be inserted between contacts, with care being exercised to avoid displacement of the contact springs. The gages shall be smooth and clean and within ± .0001 in. of the specified thickness. Because of a possible difference in the deflection of the normally open fixed contact as compared to the normally closed fixed contacts, there may be cases where this gaging of the contact separation may be necessary with the relay both energized and de-energized. Contact separation may also be gaged optically.

(3) Armature back force: This measurement is made by applying a force to the armature in the direction tending to move it from its unoperated position. The type of gage shall permit observation to an accuracy of ±10 per cent. The force at which the armature moves perceptibly when determined by 10× magnification shall be considered the armature back force. The point of application of force should be specified.

(4) Contact force: On many relays, contact force cannot be measured directly and must be calculated from contact follow (overtravel) and

the force deflection characteristics of the spring system. Before specifying a contact force requirement, it should be ascertained whether the design lends itself to this type of measurement. If contact force can be measured directly, the gages shall permit observations to an accuracy of ±10 per cent. The value at which the contact first opens shall be considered the contact force.

An optical instrument having a magnification of 10×, or an electrical indicator system that provides a contact voltage which does not cause erosion or formation of carbonaceous material shall be used to determine when the contacts open or close.

An example of a measurement that requires an indirect method to establish an exact contact force value is one where two compliant spring members make up a contact set. In this case, when a force is applied to lift either of the members, the other contact will follow. The measured value of force at which the contacts open would be greater than the actual force. An indirect method may be used, based on actual force-deflection rate of stiffness of the spring system.

8.4   Contact resistance

Purpose.   The purpose of the contact resistance test is to determine the resistance offered by electrically contacting surfaces to a flow of current. For practical reasons, leads and terminal resistances within the unit or test may be included in the measurement. In many applications, contact resistance is required to be low and stable to avoid voltage drop across the contacts, which adversely affects the accuracy of circuit conditions, and to prevent overheating at high currents.

Definition.   "Contact resistance" may be defined as the total electrical resistance of the contact system measured at the associated contact spring terminals.

Requirements.   Contact resistance requirements should specify:

(1) Maximum allowable contact resistance
(2) The voltage and current at which measurements are to be made
(3) If single or repetitive measurements are to be performed
(4) Whether the contacts should be switched with or without the rated load.

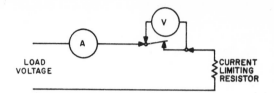

FIG. 8-1. VOLTMETER-AMMETER METHOD OF MEASURING CONTACT RESISTANCE

Procedure.   The resistance of the contact may be measured directly using a Kelvin bridge or indirectly using the voltmeter-ammeter method, as shown in Fig. 8-1 and outlined below:

(1) Normally closed contacts shall be measured individually at specified current before the relay is operated.
(2) The contact load shall be removed and the coil winding shall be energized at rated current or voltage.
(3) After the relay has operated, the contact load shall be applied to the normally open contacts and the voltage drop across each set of contacts shall be measured individually, as in Step 1.
(4) The contact load shall then be removed prior to de-energizing the coil of the relay on test.
(5) The maximum reading of the voltmeter and the minimum reading of the ammeter during the specified measuring period shall be used to calculate contact resistance, using Ohms law,

$$R = E/I$$

In performing contact resistance measurements, abide by the following regulations:

(1) As shown in Fig. 8-1, the voltmeter leads shall be connected inside the current leads to avoid including resistance of the current lead connection in the measurements.
(2) The resistance or impedance of the voltmeter shall be at least 100 times that of the resistance to be measured.
(3) Accuracy of the measurements shall be within 10 per cent.
(4) The voltage regulation of the power source from no load to full load shall be within ±2 per cent.

Recording of data.   In recording contact resistance data, it shall be stated whether readings are in ohms or millivolt drop, as indicated in the following table:

Contact resistance in ohms*

	Relay No.	1	2	3
Load current, 10 amp	NC1	0.012	0.016	0.012
Load voltage, 6v d-c	NC2	0.011	0.012	0.013
	NO1	0.014	0.016	0.011
	NO1	0.012	0.018	0.016

*Maximum allowable reading: 0.05 ohms

Precautions. In performing the contact resistance test, the following precautions should be taken:

(1) Make sure that the connection between the relay terminals and the test socket or probes is a good, clean one.

(2) The proper test socket for production measurement of contact resistance is the split pin test socket, as indicated in Fig. 8-2. One pin carries the current, and one lead is connected to the voltmeter. The resistance of the voltmeter connection will consequently be negligible compared with that of the meter.

(3) Measuring relays in test sockets facilitates production testing but is not as reliable as the use of probes or solder connections. Therefore, a relay that fails in a test socket should be rechecked by probing to insure the validity of the failure.

8.5 Insulation resistance

Purpose. The purpose of the insulation resistance test is to measure the resistance between mutually insulated members of a relay. Values of insulation resistance can be important in the design of high impedance circuits. Low insulation resistance may permit excessive leakage current that can affect isolation of independent circuits. Excessive leakage current can also be indicative of the presence of corrosive impurities that can cause deterioration by electrolysis or heating.

Definition. "Insulation resistance" is the electrical resistance between the insulated members of a device to a direct current voltage impressed across them, measured after the current becomes constant.

Requirements. Insulation resistance requirements should specify:

(1) Minimum allowable insulation resistance and time before reading.

(2) Voltage at which the measurements are to be made, usually 100 or 500 volts d-c.

(3) Insulated terminations between which measurements are to be made.

(4) Relative humidity and ambient temperature at which the measurements are to be made.

Procedure. A megohm bridge or megohmmeter shall be used in performing these measurements, and the instructions furnished by the instrument manufacturer shall be followed. Particular attention should be paid to the part of the circuit that is tied to the ground side of the megohmmeter to minimize the effect of parallel leakage paths.

(1) Measurements shall be made between all mutually insulated parts (as called out in the individual specification) with the relay winding de-energized.

(2) The measuring voltage shall be removed from the relay before the relay is energized at rated coil voltage or current. The test voltage shall then be impressed across specified parts with the relay in its fully operated position.

(3) Measurements shall be made between individual points of multiple members as required.

(4) The time of application of voltage shall be long enough to permit the reading of the meter to reach a reasonable steady state (usually a minimum of 5 seconds). The lowest reading

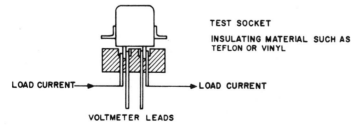

TEST SOCKET

INSULATING MATERIAL SUCH AS TEFLON OR VINYL

LOAD CURRENT →　　　　→ LOAD CURRENT

VOLTMETER LEADS

FIG. 8-2. SPLIT PIN TEST SOCKET FOR REPETITIVE TESTING OF CONTACT RESISTANCE ON PRODUCTION LINE

observed after 1 second shall be considered the insulation resistance.

(5) No cleaning shall be performed at any stage during these tests, nor shall there be any cleaning prior to testing, other than regular production cleaning. Care should be exercised to avoid contamination of insulated surfaces in wiring and handling. The unit may be cleaned after soldering wires to terminals by using standard production cleaning only.

(6) Standard reference conditions for this measurement shall be 23°C ±5° and the humidity shall be between 20 and 50 per cent.

Recording of data.   In recording data, insulation resistance shall be given in megohms and the measuring voltage in volts. Example of data:

Insulation resistance in megohms at 500 volts d–c

Relay No.	1	2	3	4
Coil to contacts	10,000	5,000	8,000	6,000
Coil to case	3,000	4,000	3,000	3,500
Contacts to case, coil energized and de-energized	5,000	5,000	6,000	5,000
N.C. to N.O. contacts, coil energized and de-energized	5,000	5,000	5,000	5,000
Between adjacent switching circuits	5,000	5,000	5,000	6,000

Precautions.   In performing the insulation resistance test, the following precautions should be taken:

(1) The accuracy of the measurements, including meter accuracy, and the effects of parallel leakage paths in wiring and fixture, shall be within ±10 per cent.

(2) Guarding techniques may be required to minimize leakage along undesired paths.

(3) A unit in a production fixture that fails the test because of low insulation resistance may be rechecked by probing point to point to determine whether the unit or fixture is at fault.

For production measurements of insulation resistance and where repetitive measurements are made on the same type of relay, high insulation test sockets, wiring, and switches may be used to shorten test time. The insulation resistance of production test circuits, without the relay, should be ten times the requirement for the relay. Use of a stepping switch to step off the check points for a typical test circuit is shown in Fig. 8-3.

8.6 Dielectric withstanding voltage

Purpose.   It is the purpose of this test to detect flaws in materials, design, or construction of the unit which might result in failure to withstand the specified test potential. It is a static test, conducted without contact switching and in the absence of contact arcing.

Definition.   "Dielectric strength" is the ability of the insulation portions of a relay to withstand the application of specified 60 Hz rms voltage without damage, arcing, breakdown, or excessive leakage.

Requirements.   Dielectric withstanding voltage requirements should specify:

(1) Voltage at which the test is to be performed.

(2) Barometric pressure, or altitude, at which the requirement is applicable.

(3) Time that the voltage is to be applied.

(4) Insulated terminations between which the voltage should be applied.

Procedure.   The dielectric strength tester shall impress a sinusoidal 60 ±2 Hz voltage having less than 5 per cent distortion. The voltage shall not vary more than ±5 per cent at a load of 0 to 1 milliamperes. The indicator used should be capable of responding to a specified level of current within a specified time. Typical values are 25 milliseconds response to a leakage current between 1 and 0.75 milliamperes.

(1) Voltage shall be applied between all mutually insulated parts (as called out in the individual specification) with the relay de-energized.

(2) The voltage from the dielectric tester shall be removed before the coil is energized at rated voltage or current. The testing voltage shall then be impressed across all specified parts with the relay in its fully operated position.

(3) The testing voltage shall be removed before the relay is de-energized after testing.

(4) The time the voltage is to be applied to the terminals on test shall be as specified. (Typically, 1 second may be specified for inspection testing and 30 seconds for evaluation on qualification testing. Usually the testing voltage for the 1-second test is approximately 20 per cent greater than that specified for the 30-second test. In applying voltage for the longer test period, the voltage shall be increased gradually to the specified test value at the rate of approximately 500 volts per sec. and maintained for 30 ±5 sec.)

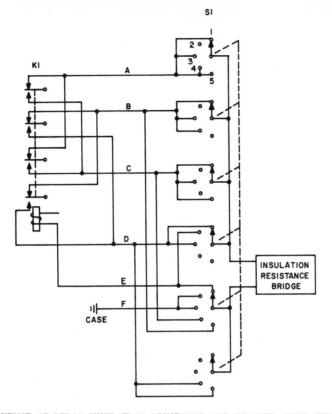

FIG. 8-3. SEQUENCE OF RELAY INSULATION RESISTANCE CHECKPOINTS, USING STEPPING SWITCH

Step 1: coil to contacts A, B, C, and D; Step 2: coil to case (ground); Step 3: all contacts to case; Step 4: normally open to normally closed contacts; Step 5: adjacent switching circuits (A to B, then C to D).

(5) When the dielectric withstanding voltage test is performed at simulated high altitude conditions, external connections should be comparable to what is normally encountered in service. Solder connections usually are covered with an insulating sleeving. Care should be taken in making the solder connections to avoid solder or flux spatter that might affect the breakdown point.

(6) No cleaning shall be performed at any stage during these tests, nor shall there be any cleaning prior to testing, other than regular production cleaning. Care should be taken to avoid contamination of insulated surfaces in wiring and handling. Cleaning of the unit after wires are soldered to terminals should be standard production cleaning only.

Recording of data. In recording dielectric data, the voltage at which breakdown occurred shall be indicated. A typical data sheet showing two failures during a test at 1000 volts, rms, 60 cps, a-c, follows:

Breakdown voltages

	Relay No.	1	2	3	4
Coil to contacts		>1000	800	>1000	>1000
Coil to case		>1000	>1000	500	
Contact to case, coil energized and de-energized			>1000	>1000	>1000	>1000
N.C. to N.O. contacts, coil energized and de-energized		>1000	>1000	>1000	>1000
Between adjacent switching circuits		>1000	>1000	>1000	>1000

Precautions. Since the voltages used in dielectric testing are dangerous, great caution should be exercised. Manual equipment should have properly insulated test prods and leads, and the operators should be well trained in their use. Testing equipment should include a safety interlock to avoid hazards to personnel. When breakdown occurs at simulated high altitude testing, ionization may result and cause a breakdown at lower voltages in subsequent testing. Therefore, after breakdown, the chamber should be returned to atmospheric pressure and then re-evacuated to the specified pressure before proceeding with the tests. In applying or removing voltage, switching transients are to be avoided.

For production testing of dielectric withstanding voltage or where repetitive measurements are to be made, test sockets and switches may be used to shorten testing time. The dielectric breakdown of the test circuit and components should be at least twice the specified breakdown requirement for the relay being tested. A stepping switch circuit similar to that shown in Fig. 8-3 may be used.

8.7 Winding resistance

Purpose. This test was devised for measuring the direct current (d-c) resistance of a relay coil winding.

Definition. "Winding resistance" is the d-c ohmic resistance of the coil measured at the coil terminals at 23°C, unless otherwise specified.

Requirements. Winding resistance requirements should specify:

(1) Resistance value and tolerance and temperatures at which the resistance measurement applies.

(2) That measurements are to be made after relays have stabilized at the specified ambient temperature. Two hours or longer at the ambient temperature will assure that the relays are at the thermal equilibrium.

(3) Whether the over-all reading should include other circuit elements such as series or parallel resistors that may be part of the winding circuit. If nonlinear circuit elements (such as semiconductor devices or thermistors) are associated with the winding, the true winding resistance may be unobtainable from measurements made at the external terminals. However, an equivalent resistance may be measured by the voltmeter-ammeter method.

Procedures. In the performance of this test, follow these procedures:

(1) A Wheatstone bridge, Kelvin bridge (for low resistance windings), voltmeter-ammeter method, or equivalent instrument capable of the required precision shall be used. The ambient temperature shall be measured and recorded. If the ambient temperature is different from the rquired value, resistance shall be corrected to the specified temperature.

(2) Although the voltmeter-ammeter method may be used, its accuracy is less than that obtainable by the bridge method. The proper connection of the voltmeter and ammeter, as dictated by good practice, is dependent upon the relative values of resistance of the instruments and the circuit being measured. The voltmeter should be connected across the ammeter and the winding if the resistance of the ammeter is 0.1 per cent or less than that of the winding resistance.

(3) When the voltmeter is connected across the winding alone, its resistance shall be at least 1000 times that of the resistance to be measured.

Precautions. Since the resistance of electromagnetic windings varies with temperature, temperature stabilization of the entire winding should be attained before measurements are attempted. In cases where the average temperature resulting from heating effects of applied voltage is to be determined by the change of resistance method, the unit should remain energized long enough to reach thermal equilibrium. When readings taken 15 minutes apart are of the same value, the winding temperature may be considered to have reached thermal equilibrium. In making the readings of the coil resistance under these conditions, the following precautions must be taken.

If a bridge is used, provision should be made for a fast transfer from the voltage source to the measuring bridge, and the bridge must be set close to balancing so that little time is required to effect a balance. The time between transfer from the energizing to measuring circuit and the measuring time should not exceed 5 seconds. If a balance is not reached within this period, the winding shall be re-energized and the process repeated after approximately 5 minutes.

The formula for converting resistance of a coil winding to a specified temperature in deg C is as follows:

$$\frac{234.5 \pm T_1}{234.5 \pm T_2} = \frac{R_1}{R_2}$$

in which:

T_1 = ambient temperature at which R_1 is measured

R_1 = measured d-c resistance at T_1

T_2 = specified temperature, deg C

R_2 = d-c resistance calculated for T_2

8.8 Winding inductance

Purpose. This test was devised for measuring the inductance of the coil winding. In relays, coil inductance is a function of the number of turns of wire and the geometry and reluctance of the magnetic circuit.

Definition. "Inductance" is the property of an electrical circuit (coil winding) whereby it resists any change of current during the build-up or decaying of a self-induced magnetic field. In relays, the delay produced results in operational delay (armature movement).

Requirements. Winding inductance requirements should specify:

(1) Voltage and frequency

(2) Whether the measurement is to be performed with or without superimposed d-c on winding

(3) The magnitude of superimposed d-c (if applicable)

(4) Whether the armature is to be positioned by mechanical means

(5) The ambient temperature

(6) Special mounting conditions or requirements relative to adjacent magnetic metal.

(7) Winding connections for multiple-wound coils. Inductance of one winding of a relay may depend upon what is connected across another winding. Unless otherwise specified, one winding is to be measured at a time with the other windings not connected to an external circuit.

(8) The prior magnetic history of the coil must be defined.

Procedures. In the performance of this test, follow these procedures.

(1) A conventional inductance bridge shall be used in accordance with its specified procedures.

(2) The relay shall be mounted in its normal operating position on a nonmagnetic plate with no other adjacent magnetic metal.

(3) If it is required to superimpose direct current on the winding during measurement, adequate provision for isolation of the a-c and d-c circuits shall be made, including use of a blocking capacitor between the a-c source and the bridge and a choke between the d-c source and the bridge.

(4) Unless otherwise specified, the voltage across the winding being measured shall be 2 ±.01 volts at 1000 ±5 cps sinusoidal.

(5) Measurement shall be made at the external relay terminals.

(6) Accuracy of this measurement shall be ±2 per cent.

Precautions. Inasmuch as the inductance of a relay coil is, in part, a function of the armature shape and position, any small variation in armature gap will greatly influence the reading.

8.9 Winding impedance

Purpose. This test method was devised for measuring the impedance of relay windings designed for use on alternating current.

Definition. "Impedance" is the opposition to a flow of alternating current. It may consist of any combination of ohmic resistance and inductive and capacitive reactance.

Requirements. Impedance measurement requirements should specify:

(1) The rated voltage and frequency, or other values, at which the measurements are to be made

(2) Ambient temperature, including tolerance

(3) The length of time the coil is energized prior to reading

(4) Whether a measurement should be made with the armature blocked open or closed (impedance will be lower for the open than for the closed state)

(5) Mounting conditions

(6) Winding connections

(7) Prior magnetic history.

Procedure. Impedance measurements shall be made with rated, or specified, voltage of rated frequency applied to the windings, and with no series impedance introduced.

(1) The relays shall be mounted by their normal mounting means on a nonmagnetic plate.

(2) The a-c source shall be low impedance sinusoidal with less than 5 per cent distortion at the required voltage and within ±2 per cent of the specified frequency.

(3) The measurements shall be made by the conventional voltmeter-ammeter method with instruments of suitable range.

(4) Measurements shall be made at the external relay terminals. If the relay has more than one winding, internal connections of the other windings shall not be disturbed. These windings shall not be connected to an external circuit.

(5) When a measurement is required with the armature open, a nonmagnetic insulating material shall be used to block the armature.

Procedure for complex impedance. If the power factor or complex impedance is to be determined, power measurements must be taken. The value of complex impedance Z can be calculated as follows:

(1) The absolute value of Z is equal to the voltage divided by the current.

(2) The power factor of the circuit is the ratio of power dissipated to the product of voltage and current or the wattmeter reading divided by the product of the voltage and current readings. Measurement can be made using the instrument connections shown in Fig. 8-4 and 8-5.

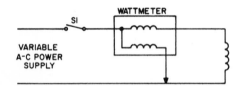

Fig. 8-4. Circuit connections for making watt-meter readings for measuring relay coil impedance

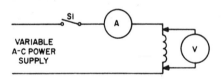

Fig. 8-5. Circuit connections for making volt-meter-ammeter readings for measuring coil impedance

(3) The phase angle, θ, is defined as the angle whose cosine is equal to the power factor.

(4) From the above data, a polar form of the complex impedance represented by Z at angle θ can be obtained.

Precautions. Care must be taken in selecting and using the correct wattmeter. Many relays dissipate approximately the same power as some types of wattmeters, thus making an accurate measurement impossible. A wattmeter of low power factor is preferable. Reference to a basic text on "long shunt" and "short shunt" connections will aid in eliminating wattage value errors. An oscilloscope is useful in making direct measurements of phase angle.

8.10 Contact bounce

Purpose. This test method was devised for the measurement of the duration of the intermittent opening or closing of contacts caused by contact bounce.

Definition. "Contact bounce" is the intermittent, internally induced opening of closed contacts or closing of open contacts caused by vibration of parts during relay pickup or dropout (*see* Sec. 1).

Requirements. Contact bounce requirements should specify:

(1) Voltage or current at which the winding should be energized

(2) Voltage and current for the contact circuit

(3) Maximum permissible contact bounce

(4) Number of contacts per relay to be measured, energized, and de-energized

(5) If photographs of oscillograph displays or recorded data are required

(6) Relay mounting position.

Procedure. The test method outlined below shall be used to measure contact bounce by means of an oscilloscope and the test circuit shown in Fig. 8-6.

(1) The contacts shall be connected to the specified voltage through a series resistor. Switch S2 shall be in position 1.

(2) The winding of the relay under test shall be energized at the specified voltage, or current, and the closure of the normally open contacts shall be observed on the oscilloscope, shown placed across the load resistor. Typically, the relay shall be operated three times per contact with observations being made at each operation.

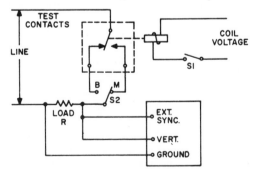

Fig. 8-6. Method of measuring contact bounce using an oscilloscope

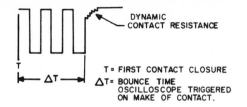

FIG. 8-7. TYPICAL CONTACT BOUNCE PATTERN AS OBSERVED ON AN OSCILLOSCOPE (SEE ALSO FIG. 1-1, SEC. 1)

The maximum duration of contact bounce shall be recorded.

(3) The load now shall be transferred to the normally closed contact through switch S2. The winding shall then be de-energized, and the closure of the normally closed contacts shall be observed on the oscilloscope.

(4) A typical oscilloscope pattern for contact bounce, as determined by the circuit in Fig. 8-6, is shown in Fig. 8-7. When the contact is closed, the full voltage appears across the resistor; any interruption of the contact under test will cause the voltage across the resistor to fall to zero. Toward the end of the bounce time, there may be a period of resistance fluctuation before contact resistance reaches a steady value. It may be necessary to operate the relay several times (varying the timing scale of the oscilloscope) to assure detection of the bounce caused by impingement of contacts and the bounce caused by armature rebound at a later interval.

In performing these measurements:

(1) Voltage and current shall be within 5 per cent of the value specified.

(2) Manufacturer's instructions for use of the oscilloscope shall be followed.

(3) Oscilloscope time base shall be calibrated and have an accuracy of ±3 per cent.

(4) Timing measurements shall be accurate to within 10 per cent.

Recording of data.   Bounce time data, in milliseconds or microseconds, and contact current and voltage shall be recorded. For oscillographic records, scope setting of time and voltage shall be noted. A typical method of recording data is shown in the following table:

Bounce time in microseconds

	Relay No.	1	2	3
Load current, 1 amp	NC1	100	150	100
Load voltage 6 volts, d-c	NC2	200	50	50
	NO1	100	50	50
	NO2	50	50	50

Precautions.   In performing this test, the following precautions shall be observed:

(1) The coil energizing switch should be essentially bounce free.

(2) Care should be taken not to exceed the maximum voltage and current rating of the contacts being tested.

8.11   Contact chatter

Purpose.   This test method was devised for monitoring contact chatter when relays are subjected to vibration, shock, and acceleration tests.

Definition.   "Chatter" is defined as the opening of closed contacts or closing of open contacts caused by some shock or vibration external to the relay.

Requirements.   The requirements controlling contact chatter should specify:

(1) The severity of the external environments — such as vibration, shock, or acceleration — to which the relays are to be subjected.

(2) The maximum permissible duration of contact chatter, that is, the longest allowable length of time for a single opening or the maximum duration of a series of openings.

(3) Whether the chatter requirement is applicable with the relay both energized and de-energized and for the voltage or current at which the winding shall be energized.

(4) The voltage and current in the contact circuit.

(5) The method of monitoring the contacts to be employed.

Procedures.   Procedures for the various test methods follow:

(1) The thyratron chatter detector: This detector was one widely used for chatter detection and is still employed in many cases. Recently, however, the low voltage chatter detector has been replacing the thyratron detector.

(2) Low voltage chatter detector: A typical circuit for a semiconductor chatter detector is shown in Fig. 8-8. The instrument shall be calibrated by suitable means to detect chatter of specified duration, usually 10 microseconds or longer.

The principle of operation of the detector is based on the characteristics of the silicon controlled rectifier. The gate of an SCR loses con-

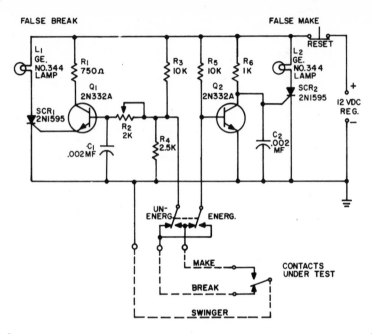

FIG. 8-8. SOLID STATE CIRCUIT OF INSTRUMENT USED TO DETECT CONTACT CHATTER (DUPLICATE CIRCUIT REQUIRED FOR EACH CONTACT TRANSFER TO BE MONITORED)

trol after the unit is turned on. A single transistor amplifier is used between the relay contacts and the SCR gate. This stage provides the necessary gate signal and introduces the desired time delay. The maximum open contact voltage is 2 volts, and the maximum closed contact current is 8 ma.

Resistors R_3 and R_4 form a voltage divider with their junction at about +2 volts. The closed contact of the test relay shorts R_4 and ties the base of transistor Q_1 to ground. When the relay contacts chatter (open), resistor R_4 is no longer short-circuited and capacitor C_1 starts to charge through R_2. The time necessary for C_1 to charge to a bias level of +2 volts is determined by the resistance of R_2. As Q_1 draws current through the gate of SCR_1, this unit will fire and turn on lamp L_1. The time delay, before turn-on, can be adjusted by varying R_2, which in this case is set to cause SCR_1 to fire should contact chatter exceed 10 microseconds. The stability of this timing is dependent upon the stability of the gate characteristics of the SCR. Any significant change in the gate current requirements would necessitate readjustment of R_2.

The contact position switch is first set for the test of an unenergized relay. If a momentary opening of the back contact occurs (greater than

10 μsec duration), lamp L_1 (false break) will light. Lamp L_2 (false make) will light if contact bunching (make contact closes while break contact remains closed) takes place. False transfers are indicated by the lighting of both lamps. Pressing the reset button will extinguish both.

When the contacts of an energized relay are to be monitored, the contact position switch is set for an energized relay. The lighting of lamp L_1 (false break) will now indicate chatter (longer than 10 μsec) of the closed front contact. Contact bunching would be indicated by lamp L_2 (false make) lighting. The simultaneous lighting of lamps L_1 and L_2 shows a complete transfer of the relay contacts.

(3) Oscilloscope method: The procedure shall be the same as outlined for contact bounce (see Fig. 8-6). This method shall be used when:

(a) The individual relay requirements specify that contacts shall be monitored for chatter at a particular load.

(b) Confirmation of the low voltage chatter detector is desired.

(c) Measurements of chatter time are required.

(d) A measurement of resistance fluctuation is required.

Precautions. In performing this test, the following precautions shall be taken:

(1) If chatter is observed when the contacts are connected in series or parallel, the contacts may be monitored individually if it is desired to ascertain which set of contacts chatter.

(2) Series wiring is to be used to detect the opening of closed contacts only.

(3) Parallel wiring is to be used to detect the closing of open contacts only.

8.12 Operating characteristics for d-c relays

Purpose. This test was devised for the following purposes:

(1) To determine whether specified pickup, nonpickup, hold, and dropout values are met.

(2) To obtain data on the stability of these characteristics during various types of tests.

Definitions. The following definitions apply:

(1) "Pickup" is the minimum voltage or current at which the relay armature actually seats against the coil core by assuming its fully operated position, or a specified position.

(2) "Nonpickup" is the maximum voltage or current at which a relay does not operate any contacts or only specified contacts.

(3) "Hold" is the minimum voltage or current at which the relay armature does not move perceptibly from its fully operated position after having been energized electrically.

(4) "Dropout" is the specified maximum voltage or current at which the relay must restore to its unoperated position.

Requirements. The requirements should specify the following:

(1) The pickup, nonpickup, hold, and dropout values as applicable

(2) Whether a forward or reverse soak (magnetic saturation) should be applied before measurements are taken

(3) Whether the relay is to be energized or de-energized gradually or abruptly during this test

(4) The ambient temperature at which the measurements are to be made

(5) Whether or not preheating of the winding is required prior to reading any of the values

(6) The mounting condition, if critical

(7) Any external magnetic field conditions, if applicable

Explanation. In measuring operating characteristics:

(1) The energizing voltage or current may be increased or decreased suddenly or gradually. In most relay applications, a sudden application or removal of the coil power source is the actual mode of operation. However, a gradual increase and decrease seem to be the accepted testing practice throughout the industry, because of their adaptability to production testing.

(2) The operate and release points of some relays may be affected significantly by the magnetic state of the iron. To assure reproducible results it is necessary, in some instances, to control the magnetic state prior to measurement of pickup or nonpickup by applying a soak in a forward or reverse direction. A forward soak tends to aid subsequent operation whereas a reverse soak may have the effect of increasing the pickup and nonpickup points. Releasing from a soak value may result in lower hold or dropout values than releasing from a lower energizing voltage, or current.

Procedure. After establishing the rate of application of the energizing source and the point at which prior soak must be applied, proceed as follows:

(1) Pickup value: The previous magnetic history having been established, the coil input power is gradually increased to the point at which the relay fully operates. That is, all the normally open contacts are closed, and all the normally closed contacts are open. This may be determined by visual observation on an open unit or by means of a monitoring system on a sealed unit. The lowest value of current, or voltage, at which the relay is fully operated is considered to be the pickup value.

(2) Nonpickup value: As was done for pickup, the source is increased until the first sign of a contact actuation is detected. The maximum value at which no normally closed contact opens, nor open contact closes, is the nonpickup value. That is, the value of current or voltage just below which some contact switching is observed will be considered the nonpickup value. Stating it in another way and starting with the relay in the de-energized state, energizing the winding at

the nonpickup value should not change the de-energized state of the contacts. Any value above will cause a detectable change in the system.

(3) Hold: The hold condition of the relay is determined by decreasing the energizing input to the coil from its rated value or soak value (or 125 per cent of rated in current units) until the first indication of contact action is observed, that is, the first normally open contact opens or the first normally closed contact closes. The closest value of energizing current or voltage observed prior to this change in the contact system is the measured hold value. Stated another way, with the relay in its fully operated or in the energized state, reducing the energizing source to the hold value should not change the operated state of the contact system. Further reduction will cause a detectable change in the switching system.

(4) Dropout: A continuing decrease in the energizing source will ultimately cause the contact system to restore to its normal unoperated state, that is, all normally open contacts will open and all normally closed contacts will close. The level of current or voltage at which this occurs is the measured dropout value.

Procedure for abrupt current or voltage changes. The following method is for testing relays where the source current or voltage is abruptly increased or decreased.

(1) Pickup (operate) and nonpickup (non-operate):

(a) Forward soak, measured values: After applying and removing the specified magnetic soak value, without changing polarity, the energizing current or voltage shall be increased in small increments, with the soak value abruptly reapplied after each incremental increase. This procedure shall be repeated until the measured nonpickup and pickup values are obtained.

(b) Forward soak, specified values: Using suitable resistors and switches the circuit shall be adjusted to the specified soak, nonpickup, and pickup values. After applying and removing the soak value, the specified nonpickup value shall be applied. The same procedure shall be followed in testing for the specified pickup value.

(c) Reverse soak, measured values: The procedure shall be the same as that for forward soak, measured values (a), except that the polarity is reversed after removal of the soak value.

(d) Reverse soak, specified values: The procedure shall be the same as that for forward soak, specified values (b), except that the polarity shall be reversed after removal of the soak value.

(2) Dropout (release) previous to dropout (hold):

(a) Forward soak, measured values: After applying the specified soak value, the current or voltage in the winding shall be decreased abruptly in small increments, alternately applying the soak value and decreasing current or voltage until the measured hold value is determined. The same procedure shall be followed in determining the measured dropout value.

(b) Forward soak, specified values: Using suitable resistors and switches, the current shall be adjusted to the specified soak, hold, and dropout values. After applying the specified soak value, the current or voltage shall be abruptly decreased to the specified hold value. The same procedure shall be used in testing for the specified dropout value.

Recording of data. Data shall be recorded as follows:

Operating data at +25°C after shock test, in d-c volts

Relay No.	1	2	3
Soak voltage	26.5	26.5	26.5
Pickup	13.5	12.5	12.2
Nonpickup	11.0	11.8	10.6
Hold	5.5	5.0	5.5
Dropout	5.0	4.5	5.0

Precautions. In performing this test, the following precautions shall be observed:

(1) The contact monitoring indicator shall not produce carbonaceous material on contacts that might affect their performance in low energy circuits. If lamp indicators are used, a solid state direct coupled amplifier shall be used with each of the lamps to prevent damage due to lamp inrush current.

(2) If a particular design is position sensitive, the relays shall be tested in a mounting position simulating actual field usage.

(3) If both an ammeter and voltmeter are used simultaneously in the test circuit, allowance shall be made for the effect of the meters on the reading.

(4) Stray magnetic fields that may affect the test values shall be avoided.

(5) The repeatability of voltage readings taken may be affected by the increase in coil resistance due to self-heating. The technique used shall avoid or minimize this measuring error.

8.13 Operating characteristics for a-c relays

Purpose. This test was devised to measure operating characteristics of a-c relays, including rectifier operated relays.

Definitions. Same as for Paragraph 8.12 except that the relays are a-c.

Requirements. Requirements should specify:

(1) All the factors listed for the d-c relay except that polarity of soak (forward or reverse) is not applicable

(2) Whether operating values are to be measured in voltage or current

(3) Frequency of voltage and current.

Other requirements are as follows:

(1) The voltage supply shall be sinusoidal with not more than 5 per cent distortion and shall be within ±2 per cent of the specified frequency.

(2) If operating values are required to be measured in current — as in relays used in sensing over-current or under-current — a-c resistance equal to 5 to 10 times the impedance of the relay (open armature position) shall be connected in series with the coil.

(3) Rectifier operated relays shall be energized at rated voltage or current prior to making measurements of electrical operating characteristics.

Procedure. In performing this test, the following procedure shall apply:

(1) Pickup and nonpickup values *(gradually* increasing voltage or current): The voltage shall be increased gradually to the specified nonpickup value by means of a variable auto transformer. All normally closed contacts shall remain closed at this value without chatter, and no normally open contact shall close. The pickup value shall be determined by further increasing the voltage until all normally open contacts close without chatter and all normally closed contacts remain open.

(2) Pickup and nonpickup values *(abruptly* increasing voltage or current):

(a) Specified nonpickup: The coil voltage shall be set to the specified nonpickup value and the switch opened. When the switch is reclosed, all normally closed contacts shall remain closed without chatter and no normally open contact shall close.

(b) Specified pickup: The voltage shall be set to the specified pickup value. The switch shall be opened and reclosed; all normally open contacts shall remain closed without chatter and all normally closed contacts shall be open.

(c) Measured pickup and nonpickup: To determine the measured nonpickup and operate values, the voltage shall be increased in small increments as the switch is opened and closed until the maximum value is obtained at which normally open contacts do not close and normally closed contacts do not open (measured nonpickup). To determine measured pickup, this procedure shall then be continued until a value is reached at which all normally closed contacts open and all normally open contacts close without chattering.

(3) Hold and dropout values: After applying the specified soak voltage values, the voltage shall be reduced gradually to the specified hold value. At this voltage, all normally open contacts shall remain closed without chatter, and no normally closed contact shall close (hold). The voltage then shall be further reduced gradually until all normally open contacts open and all normally closed contacts close without chattering (dropout).

(4) Sealing (seal-in value, when required): If the armature does not seat against the pole face or the stop at pickup value, the coil energizing voltage shall be further increased by method (1) or (2) until the armature does seat. On sealed relays, this test is usually not required; on open relays, it can usually be observed visually.

Recording of data. Same as for the d-c relay.

Precautions. In performing this test, the same precautions shall be observed as outlined for d-c relays, with the following ones added:

(1) Due to the inherent operating characteristics of a-c relays, contact chatter may occur prior to final pickup and dropout. Pickup and dropout points shall be considered those points at which all contact chatter has ceased.

(2) Although contact chatter may have ceased and the armature may be seated, audible hum may still emanate from the relay at or above the actual pickup point. The permissible level of this hum is to be determined by the application requirements of the relay.

8.14 Functioning time, or operate and release time

Purpose.   The purpose of this test is to measure the operate and release time of relays.

Definitions.   Operate and release time may be defined as follows:

(1) "Operate time" is the time interval from coil energization to the functioning time of the last contact to function (until the last normally open contact closes or the last normally closed contact opens). Unless otherwise stated, bounce time is not included.

(2) "Release time" is the time interval from coil de-energization to the functioning time of the last contact to function (until the last normally closed contact closes or the last normally open contact opens).

Requirements.   Requirements for operate or release time should specify:

(1) The maximum permissible pickup time and dropout time

(2) The circuit voltage or current at which time is to be measured (coil and contact circuit)

(3) The ambient temperature at which the measurements are to be made

(4) Whether or not contact bounce should be included in the operate and release time

(5) Whether the requirements apply to a particular set of contacts or to all contacts

(6) If any special circuit components are to be used, such as semiconductor diodes or capacitors, that may affect release time.

(7) Whether photographic records of oscilloscope traces are needed

Procedure.   In performing this test, the following procedure shall apply:

(1) Use of oscilloscope: Using the basic circuits of Figs. 8-9 and 8-10, make contacts shall be monitored individually or in series and break contacts individually or in parallel, depending on the nature of the time requirements. The oscilloscope shall be adjusted to read the total operate or release time including bounce. The oscilloscope shall be capable of a time base accuracy of ±3 per cent.

(2) Use of digital timer: This method is suitable only for measurement of initial time

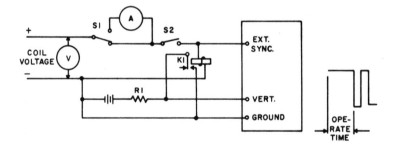

Fig. 8-9. Typical circuit for measuring relay operate time using an oscilloscope

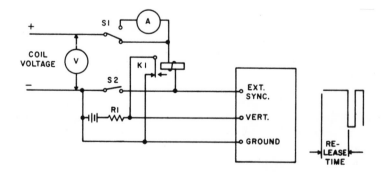

Fig. 8-10. Typical circuit for measuring relay release time using an oscilloscope

(not including bounce). Special precautions shall be taken to avoid having the transient in the relay coil circuit prematurely trigger the gate circuit of the timer.

(3) An elapsed time indicator or string oscillograph shall be used to measure long or intermediate time delay units.

Recording of data. In recording operate and release time, data shall be tabulated as shown in the following table:

Operate and release time measured in millisec at
26.5 volts d–c at +25°C, after vibration

Relay No.	1	2	3
Operate time	10.0	10.5	11.0
Release time	5.0	4.8	5.2

(Scope set at 2 millisec per division.)

Precautions. The power supply shall be well regulated, of low internal impedance, and shall have a fast recovery time.

8.15 Leak test for hermetically sealed relays

Purpose. The purpose of this test is to determine the effectiveness of the seal of an hermetically sealed relay, which either is evacuated or contains air or gas. Two methods of leak testing are outlined, namely helium detector, radioactive gas, and bubble test. (A defect in any portion of the surface area of a seal part can permit the entrance of damaging contaminants that could reduce the effective life of the relay.)

Definition. A "leak" is any opening that permits the entrance or exit of elements that is greater than the specified value.

Requirements. Requirements should specify:

(1) The test method to be used (of the three mentioned above). It is difficult to assign quantitative values to the bubble test. Therefore, it is usually used in conjunction with other methods for the detection of gross leaks.

(2) The maximum allowable leak rate in cubic centimeters per second per cubic inch of internal volume.

(3) The percentage of mixture if a tracer gas mixed with a back-fill gas is used.

(4) Whether the leak test is to be performed during production, acceptance, or before and after environmental tests.

Procedures. The following procedures are to be observed in using the different leak test methods. The equipment manufacturer's operating procedures shall be used.

(1) Helium detector (mass spectrometer):

(a) Explanation: In this method the relay enclosure is evacuated through a mass spectrometer while pure helium is sprayed or contained around the external surface of the unit. Any helium drawn through a leak in the relay will give a leak reading. When this test is performed after an environmental test, a small hole must be pierced in the relay to connect it to the vacuum system.

(b) Procedure: The relays shall be evacuated and then back-filled with 100 per cent pure helium. The relays shall be placed in a suitable chamber, which shall be evacuated to a specified pressure, and then, while the pressure is maintained, the chamber shall be connected to a mass spectrometer. Leakage rate from the relay into the chamber shall be determined.

A second method is essentially the same except that it is used more extensively for production testing. Relays are back-filled with a mixture of gas — dry nitrogen and 10 per cent helium are recommended, the helium being used for leak detection purposes. (A rich helium mixture in the internal part of a sealed relay may ionize at high potential and is therefore not recommended.) Calibration of the leak detector shall be based on the percentage of helium used.

(c) Precautions: It is periodically necessary to pierce a small hole in relay enclosures on a sampling basis to check for the presence or absence of the back-fill tracer.

(2) Radioactive gas:

(a) Requirements: Commercially available equipment shall be used for this method, including the proper activation and radioactive counting equipment. The detector system shall provide for a conversion of units to cubic centimeters per second.

(b) Procedure: The relay undergoing test shall be placed in a pressurized chamber with radioactive material such as Krypton 85 gas for a predetermined time, then thoroughly air washed and checked for leaks using the radioactivity counter. Detection of radioactive gas inside the relay indicates that leakage occurred during exposure period.

(c) Precautions: For consistent results the pressure, soak time, and activity of the test gas should be accurately controlled. An Atomic Energy Commission (AEC) license is necessary for the possession and use of Krypton 85 leak test equipment. AEC regulations should be followed, and the maximum permissible tolerance levels prescribed by the National Committee on Radiological Protection should be observed. The radioactive gas method is not suitable for relays having organic materials that will absorb the gas on the exterior surfaces.

(3) Bubble test: *not a complete test of hermetic sealing;* used mostly as a rough check to detect gross leaks:

(a) Procedure: The relays shall be completely immersed in fresh water containing a suitable wetting agent (such as aerosol) in a transparent container. The container shall be evacuated to an absolute pressure of 1.3 inches of mercury for a minimum of 5 minutes. The immersed relays shall be observed during this test for leakage as indicated by bubbles rising from the case. A steady stream of fine bubbles coming from one spot shall be indicative of leakage.

(b) Precaution: If a relay has a leak at low pressure and the pressure is restored to atmospheric pressure with the relay immersed, the liquid may be drawn into the enclosure of the relay. Therefore, for Production and Acceptance testing, the relays shall be raised out of the liquid and held there for 10 seconds or more prior to increasing the pressure in the chamber.

8.16 High and low temperature

Purpose. The purpose of this test is to determine the ability of relays to perform satisfactorily over the range of temperature likely to be experienced in service.

Requirements. Requirements should specify:

(1) The temperature extremes to which relays shall be subjected.

(2) The duration of exposure to each temperature.

(3) The characteristics to be measured during and after exposure to the temperature extremes.

(4) The rate of change of temperature.

Procedure. The chambers used for temperature test shall be capable of maintaining the specified temperature (within ±3°C) throughout the test. The test shall be conducted in the following manner:

(1) Relays shall be suspended in the approximate center of the temperature chamber by connecting leads or auxiliary supports of nonmetallic material.

(2) Relays shall be wired or plugged into a wired test socket to permit performing all specified measurements without opening the test chamber.

(3) During the exposure to maximum specified ambient temperature, the relay coil winding shall be energized at rated coil voltage with rated contact load on the normally open contacts for the required exposure period.

(4) After the high temperature exposure, the relays shall be removed from the test chamber and allowed to cool to room temperature prior to being placed in the low temperature chamber.

(5) The relays shall remain de-energized with no load on the contacts while at low temperature.

(6) Measurements normally made during each test condition are for operating characteristics, contact resistance, winding resistance, insulation resistance, and dielectric withstanding voltage. The procedures used shall be those previously outlined.

(7) The temperature cycling shall progress through the following steps and for the periods of time specified:

Step 1: 23°C ±2°C and 10 to 40 per cent relative humidity.

Step 2: Specified maximum ambient temperature with the coil energized at rated voltage or current.

Step 3: 23°C ±2°C and 10 to 40 per cent relative humidity.

Step 4: Specified minimum ambient temperature.

Step 5: 23°C ±2°C and 10 to 40 per cent relative humidity.

The temperature of the test chamber shall be raised or lowered slowly, and the required measurements shall be performed during the last two hours at each condition.

Recording of Data. Data shall be recorded as outlined in the section covering the particular characteristic being measured.

Precautions. In performing this test, the following precautions shall be observed:

(1) The doors of the test chamber shall remain closed; if the doors are opened, measurements shall not be made until sufficient time has

elapsed to assure that the units undergoing test have returned to the specified temperatures. Insulation resistance and dielectric withstanding voltage measurements may be affected considerably if the doors are opened at the low temperature and frost forms on the relays.

(2) If it is not possible to use the four wire method, lead resistance shall be measured and subtracted from the total resistance to obtain the value of contact resistance. This method introduces the possibility of considerable inaccuracy, however, because lead resistance is often many times the contact resistance.

8.17 Thermal shock

Purpose. The purpose of this test is to determine the ability of a relay to withstand the shock of sudden and rapid changes in surrounding temperature as might be experienced when relays are subjected to rapid changes during space flights.

Definition. "Thermal shock" is the effect of rapid changes from one extreme temperature to another.

Requirements. Requirements should specify:

(1) The high and low ambient temperature extremes and time of exposure

(2) Characteristics to be measured

(3) Degree of mechanical deterioration permissible

(4) Electrical performance requirements.

Procedure. In performing this test, the following procedure shall apply:

(1) One chamber set at the low limits and another at the high limits shall be used to perform these tests. The chambers shall be equipped with circulating air so that the specified temperature can be maintained with $\pm 2°C$ throughout the enclosure and shall be capable of restoring to the specified temperature within 2 minutes after being opened to insert test samples.

(2) Relays shall be subjected to five cycles of the following test conditions:

Step 1: $-65°C \, {}^{+0}_{-5}°C$ minimum for 120 minutes at minimum specified temperature

Step 2: Maximum of 5 minutes at room ambient $23°C \, {}^{+10}_{-5}°C$

Step 3: $+125°C \, {}^{+3}_{-0}°C$ minimum for 120 minutes at maximum specified temperature

Step 4: Maximum of 5 minutes at room ambient, $23°C \, {}^{+10}_{-5}°C$

Notes: (a) Repetitive thermal shock can produce progressive deleterious effects that may not be evident after one or two exposures; (b) no more than the 5-minutes maximum time at room ambient shall elapse between temperature extremes since the effect of rapid changes of temperature is the purpose of this test.

(3) Upon completion of the fifth cycle and after the units have stabilized at room ambient, they shall be examined for conformance with mechanical requirements, and specified electrical characteristics shall be measured.

Recording of data. Electrical and mechanical measurements shall be recorded as previously specified under the test procedure for the particular characteristic.

8.18 Mechanical life

Purpose. The purpose of mechanical life testing is to determine the ability of a relay to provide satisfactory mechanical service for a required number of operating cycles. Usually the required mechanical life is appreciably longer than that required under contact loads. This type of test is specified to assure that manufacturing techniques preclude early random mechanical failures.

Definition. "Mechanical life" is the number of operations without electrical contact load that the relay will perform without mechanical failure or adjustment changes that adversely affect its performance.

Requirements. Requirements should specify:

(1) The number of operations the relay is required to withstand

(2) The pulsing rate and duty cycle

(3) The measurements to be performed and the periods of the measurements

(4) The voltage or current to be applied to the coil

(5) The temperature if other than room ambient.

Procedure. In performing this test, the following procedure shall apply:

(1) Relays shall be mounted by their normal mounting means and in their normal mounting positions.

(2) Mechanical life tests shall be conducted at room ambient conditions.

(3) The relays shall be pulsed with the windings energized at rated voltage or at 1.2 times the specified operating current.

(4) The switching circuit controlling the windings shall be chatterfree and shall produce essentially a square wave.

(5) The pulsing rate may be as fast as the operate and release time of the relay will permit but shall not exceed five pulses per second for armature type relays.

Precautions. The following precautions shall be observed:

(1) Relays shall not be operated at a rate greater than that necessary to insure a full operation and release. The pulsing rate shall allow all vibration from the previous operate or release strokes to subside.

(2) Units under test should not be cleaned or adjusted during the test unless such attention is part of the normal maintenance routine.

(3) Measurement shall be made at intervals to determine the cumulative effects of repeated operation at various stages of the required life.

(4) The following characteristics shall be measured at the specified intervals:

    (a) Contact resistance
    (b) Operating characteristics
    (c) Dielectric withstanding voltage
    (d) Insulation resistance
    (e) Operate and release time
    (f) Mechanical adjustments
    (g) Winding resistance.

Recording of data. The time, date, and number of operations for each measuring period shall be recorded. Data obtained for the various characteristics shall be recorded in accordance with the applicable test procedure.

Measuring cycle. Relays shall be measured at the following intervals:

Extent of required life	Measurements to be made after
(1) 10^5 operations	5×, 10×, 25×, 50×, 75×, and 100×10^3 operations

Extent of required life	Measurements to be made after
(2) 10^6 operations	5×, 10×, 25×, 50×, 75×, 100×, 250×, 500×, and 750 × 10^3 and also 10^6 operations
(3) 5 x 10^6 operations	Same as (2) plus 2×, 3×, 4×, and 5 × 10^6 operations
(4) 10^7 operations	Same as (3) plus 7.5 × 10^6 and 10^7 operations
(5) Greater than 10^7 operations	As specified

8.19 Vibration

Purpose. The purpose of a vibration test is to determine the ability of relays to withstand vibration of specified frequency range and acceleration or amplitude. Although vibration encountered in the field may not be simple harmonic motion, sinusoidal vibration is often specified for commercial and industrial relays and always specified for military relays. Usually the requirements for commercial and industrial relays are not as severe as those for military systems, particularly in missile or aerospace applications. Random and complex vibration more closely approximate the kind of vibration encountered in the field, but these types of vibration are usually specified only for missile or aerospace relays.

Definitions. The following definitions apply:

(1) "Sinusoidal vibration" is repetitive cyclic vibration in which acceleration is a function of displacement and frequency *(see* Table 8-1).

(2) "Random vibration" contains all frequencies in a band, and the energy of each frequency changes continually. Random vibration is not cyclic or repetitive *(see* Table 8-2).

(3) "Complex vibration" consists of sinusoidal vibration superimposed on random vibration, resulting in a complex waveform *(see* Table 8-3).

Requirements. Requirements vary for each type of vibration.

(1) Sinusoidal vibration requirements should specify:

    (a) The frequency range and acceleration, or amplitude

Table 8-1. Sinusoidal Vibration

Procedure	Frequency range, Hz	Amplitude, inches, or acceleration, g	Traverse time, minutes Ascending	Traverse time, minutes Descending	Rate	Time of vibration, minutes (Each direction or plane) Total	Energized	De-energized
I	5–55	0.030 in.	1	1	L or U	120	60	60
II	5–55 55–500	0.030 in. 10 g	7.5	7.5	L	180	90	90
III	5–20 20–2000	0.25 in. 10 g	10	10	L	180	40	40
IV	10–55 55–2000	0.05 in. 15 g	10	10	L	120	120	120
V	10–55 55–2000	0.065 in. 20 g	10	10	L	80	40	40
VI	10–55 55–2000	0.10 in. 30 g	11	11	L	88	44	44
VII	10–44 44–2000*	0.25 in. 50 g	11	11	L	88	44	44

Note: L = logarithmic rate; U = uniform rate; g values represent peak values of acceleration; excursion is twice the amplitude.

*An increase in the frequency range to 3,000Hz, with indicated changes in amplitude to produce 30 g, is under consideration and may become a standard as Procedure VIII.

Table 8-2. Random Gaussian Vibration

Procedure	Flat frequency range, Hz	Acceleration spectral density, g^2/Hz	Time of vibration, minutes (Each direction or plane) Total	Energized	De-energized
VIII	10–2000	0.08	20	10	10
IX	10–2000	0.30	20	10	10
X	10–2000	0.80	20	10	10

Table 8-3. Complex Vibration

Procedure	Sinusoidal vibration Frequency range, Hz	Amplitude, inches or acceleration, g	Traverse time, minutes Ascending	Traverse time, minutes Descending	Flat frequency range, Hz	Acceleration spectral density, g^2/Hz	Time of vibration, minutes (Each direction) Total	Energized	De-energized
XI	10 2000	0.065 in. 20 g	10	10	10–2000	.08	80	40	40
XII	10 2000	0.065 in. 20 g	10	10	10–2000	.03	80	40	40

(b) The rate of change of frequency in octaves per unit time

(c) The duration of vibration with the coil energized and de-energized

(d) The number of positions in which vibration is to be imposed

(e) The maximum duration of permissible contact chatter and transfer during vibration and the method of detection

(f) Other requirements during vibration

(g) Measurements to be performed subsequent to vibration

(h) Relay mounting means

(2) Random vibration requirements should specify:

(a) The acceleration spectral density

(b) The shape of the random vibration frequency content

(c) Whether proof of equalization is required

(d) Steps c, d, e, and f of the sinusoidal vibration test

(3) Complex vibration requirements should specify:

(a) All the requirements of the sinusoidal vibration test

(b) The wave shape and acceleration spectral density of the random content.

Procedure.   In performing the test, the following procedure shall apply:

(1) The vibration exciter shall be capable of delivering the acceleration levels when driving a rigidly mounted load. It shall not exhibit transverse acceleration in excess of 20 per cent of the acceleration in the primary direction. The vibration control system shall be capable of maintaining the required level of vibration within an accuracy of plus or minus 10 per cent and the frequency shall be within ±2 per cent of the indicated frequency throughout the vibration range.

(2) Relays shall be mounted by their normal mounting means on a fixture that neither amplifies nor attenuates vibration. The accelerometer used to monitor the vibration level shall be placed on the mounting fixture as close as possible to the relay, or relays, under test rather than mounted on the table. The velocity of the vibration machine should not be used as a measure of vibration level. Acceleration in the two transverse planes shall be measured for conformance with the 20 per cent transverse vibration limitations.

For production vibration testing or where a series of vibration tests is performed, it may be economical to use sockets mounted in a specially designed mounting fixture, such as shown in Fig. 8-11, thereby eliminating the need for wiring individual relays. When such fixtures are used, it shall be determined that vibration severity is neither amplified nor attenuated thereby and that the results are comparable to those that would be obtained by mounting the relay by the normal means.

(3) Prior to vibration testing of relays, the vibration system shall be calibrated using the operating procedure recommended by the manufacturer. ·The calibration shall include:

(a) Frequency range.

(b) The g level or displacement, depending on which is specified. In the sinusoidal range from 5 to 34 Hz, the requirement may be displacement; at higher frequencies such as 30 g, it may be acceleration. For random vibration, calibration shall be in terms of acceleration spectral density (g^2/Hz).

(c) The rate of change of frequency in octaves per minute.

(4) Typical measurements specified for the relay being vibrated may include a check for contact chatter, as described in Paragraph 8.11, with the relay energized and again de-energized as the vibration frequency specimen is scanned.

An alternative method of monitoring contact opening includes the use of an oscilloscope across the contacts when they are carrying rated current.

(5) Requirements may be specified for vibration testing at low and high temperatures to uncover shortcomings not detectable at room temperature.

(6) If the vibration testing is either random or complex, a proof of equalization shall be made prior to any testing.

(7) Magnetic latch-in relays shall be subjected to vibration with the coil winding de-

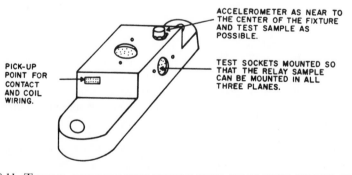

ACCELEROMETER AS NEAR TO THE CENTER OF THE FIXTURE AND TEST SAMPLE AS POSSIBLE.

PICK-UP POINT FOR CONTACT AND COIL WIRING.

TEST SOCKETS MOUNTED SO THAT THE RELAY SAMPLE CAN BE MOUNTED IN ALL THREE PLANES.

FIG. 8-11. TYPICAL VIBRATION TEST FIXTURE WITH RELAY TESTS SOCKETS MOUNTED INSIDE A SOLID ALUMINUM BLOCK

energized. Bistable relays shall be tested with the armature in each operating position.

Recording of data.   Before and after vibration, the specified measurements shall be made. Recorded data shall include a description of the vibration test and the nature of the failures.

Sample	Plane	Contact position	g level or displacement	Frequency range, Hz	No. of failures
1	Trans.	Energ. & de-energ.	30 g	---	None
	Vert.	Energ. & de-energ.	30 g	---	None
	Horiz.	De-energ.	30 g	1100–2000	2
		De-energ.	25 g	1150–1800	1
			20 g	---	None

Precautions.   The following precautions shall be observed:

·(1) During sinusoidal vibration, it is important to observe the waveform of the table output to make sure the waveform is smooth. A distorted waveform indicates trouble in the system.

(2) The mounting of the relay is critical in all forms of vibration testing, and extreme care should be taken to mount the relays by their normal mounting means with no distortion and at a specified torque on the mounting screws.

(3) Fixture design is also critical. All fixtures shall be made of one piece of aluminum or magnesium and be tested prior to use to insure that they have as few resonances in the test frequency range as possible, with little or no excursion in the planes perpendicular to the principal vibration plane.

(4) Since the location and mounting of the accelerometer is also critical, it shall be mounted

as close to the center of the vibration fixture and as near to the test sample as practical.

(5) A dry run with the test fixture under all specified conditions shall be made prior to mounting the test sample to insure the proper operation and performance of the test.

8.20   Shock

Purpose.   The purpose of shock tests is to determine the ability of relays to withstand mechanical shock experienced either during transportation or operation in service.

Definition.   "Shock" is primarily a unidirectional force pulse of a given magnitude (usually expressed in g's) and time.

Requirements.   Requirements should specify:

(1) Severity and duration of the shock impulse

(2) Number of shocks to be imposed along each of three mutually perpendicular axes of the relays, with the relay energized and de-energized

(3) Relay characteristics to be measured and the performance criteria

(4) Measuring periods

(5) Whether the relays shall be monitored for contact chatter, transfer and allowable duration.

Procedure.   In performing this test, the following procedure shall apply:

(1) The type of shock machine shall be that specified in the individual relay specification (free fall, and the like). The shock wave shall have the specified peak. *See* Fig. 8-12 for typical shock wave.

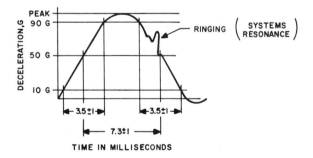

FIG. 8-12. TYPICAL SHOCK FORCE PULSE CHARACTERISTICS

Peak force (in g) and time are defined on the pulse. Ringing is superimposed on the basic shock wave and must be considered as part of the shock sustained by the relay on test. Efforts to reduce this resonance effect should be directed toward modification of the fixture structure rather than insertion of filters in the pickup circuit to dampen the observed wave only.

(2) Relays shall be mounted by their normal mounting means to a rigid fixture that does not distort the basic impulse of the shock machine. An accelerometer shall be placed as close as possible to the relay mounting and oriented so that its sensitive axis corresponds to the direction of the applied shock wave.

Where shock is needed in production testing and where repetitive shock on the same type of relay is made, it is recommended that test sockets be mounted in a one-piece shock fixture of steel, aluminum, or magnesium, as in Fig. 8-13. This will eliminate the need to wire the test specimen beforehand as well as to clean up the relay after wiring.

Recording of data. Recorded data shall include a description of test, results of electrical measurements, and a summary of failures and the nature of the failures *(see* Table 8-4).

8.21   Acceleration

Purpose. The purpose of this test is to determine the effects of centrifugal acceleration forces on the performance of relays during and after their subjection to constant acceleration such as is experienced in aircraft, missile, and aerospace applications.

Definition. The force resulting from acceleration is directly proportional to the acceler-

TEST SOCKET

ACCELEROMETER AS NEAR TO THE CENTER OF THE FIXTURE AND TEST SAMPLE AS POSSIBLE.

Fig. 8-13. Typical shock test fixture with relay test socket
The fixture is designed as a cube (all six sides equal).

(3) For calibration purposes, an oscillogram of the output of the accelerometer shall be obtained to evaluate the time and intensity of the shock wave.

(4) Where applicable, relays shall be monitored for contact chatter during shock testing, using the solid state monitoring device described in Paragraph 8.11 or an oscilloscope.

(5) The contacts should be wired in series when checking for opening of closed contacts and in parallel when checking for closing of open contacts.

(6) The relays shall be measured for applicable electrical requirements (operating characteristics, timing, insulation resistance, dielectric withstanding voltage, and contact resistance) before tests and at specified measuring periods.

ation (rate of change of velocity) and the mass of the body acted upon. In acceleration testing, a centrifugal machine is operated at an rpm calculated to produce an acceleration with a given number of g's.

Requirements. Requirements should specify:

(1) The magnitude and duration of the acceleration

(2) The relay axes along which the acceleration is to be applied

(3) The relay characteristics to be measured and the performance criteria

(4) Whether relays are to be monitored for contact chatter

Table 8-4. Sample of Recorded Shock Data (50g Shock for 11 milliseconds)

Sample No.	Plane	Contact position	g level	No. of drops	No. of failures	Nature of failure
1	Trans. 1	Energ., de-energ.	50	6	None	
	Trans. 2	Energ., de-energ.	50	6	None	
	Vert. 1	Energ., de-energ.	50	6	None	
	Vert. 2	Energ., de-energ.	50	6	None	
	Horiz. 1	Energ., de-energ.	50	6	None	
	Horiz. 2	Energ.	50	3	None	
	Horiz. 3	De-energ.	50	3	1	

Procedure. In performing this test, the following procedure shall apply:

(1) Relays shall be rigidly mounted by their normal mounting means to the machine or to a fixture that will not alter the acceleration.

(2) Acceleration shall be within ±5 per cent of the specified value.

(3) A linear differential displacement transducer shall be used for calibration and acceleration during the test.

(4) The relays shall be monitored for contact chatter using the same solid state device described in Paragraph 8-11. If applicable, the operating characteristics shall be measured during the acceleration test. The relays shall be tested energized and de-energized in two directions along the three mutually perpendicular axes.

Requirements. Requirements should specify:

(1) Limits for temperature and humidity at the temperature extremes

(2) Humidity cycle time and the number of cycles required for the complete test

(3) Measurements to be made before, during, and after the test

(4) Electrical performance criteria and permissible deterioration of finishes, and the like

(5) For open relays: the mechanical adjustment to be measured

(6) Corrosion resistance of relay parts and resistance of the winding to electrolytic corrosion.

Procedure. The humidity chamber shall be capable of meeting the following requirements:

Table 8-5. Sample of Recorded Shock Data (Relay Subject to Acceleration Force of 30g for 10 minutes)

Sample No.	Plane	Pickup	Nonpickup	Hold	Dropout	Chatter, both energ. & de-energ.	No. of failures	Nature of failure
1	Horiz. 1	18.0	16.0	7.0	6.0	None	0	
	Horiz. 2	17.5	16.5	7.5	6.1	None	0	
	Vert. 1	18.0	16.2	7.2	6.1	None	0	
	Vert. 2	18.2	16.2	7.2	6.2	None	0	
	Trans. 1	18.5	16.4	7.1	6.0	None	0	
	Trans. 2	19.0	16.5	7.0	6.1		1	Chatter, relay de-energized

Note: Operating values in current, milliamps

Precautions. In making measurements during acceleration tests, all connections to the relay are made through slip rings. It is essential, therefore, that the slip ring contacts be of low resistance, chatterfree, and capable of withstanding any high potential that may be applied.

Recording of data. Data for the acceleration test should describe the test, state the number and nature of failures, and present the results of the measurements required (*see* Table 8-5).

8.22 Humidity

Purpose. The humidity test of materials and the relay structure is performed for the purpose of simulating the effects of prolonged exposure to severe field conditions.

Definition. "Relative humidity" is the ratio of water vapor in the atmosphere to the amount of vapor required to saturate the atmosphere at the same temperature.

(1) Temperature control from +23°C ±2°C to +65°C ±2°C.

(2) Humidity control from 45 to 95 per cent RH.

(3) Maximum velocity of air through test chamber of 150 feet per minute.

(4) Chamber for water storage and heating shall not affect pH value beyond specified limits.

(5) Chamber capacity shall be at least 50 per cent greater than total volume of specimens on test.

There are two basic tests, A and B. Test A shall be conducted as follows:

(1) After setting the programmer for the desired cycle (*see* Fig. 8-14), the chamber shall be operated for one cycle before test specimens are introduced to assure that it is capable of providing the test conditions. The pH value of the vapor shall be measured by condensing a suitable amount of the vapor on a cooled sterile beaker. This beaker shall be inserted in the

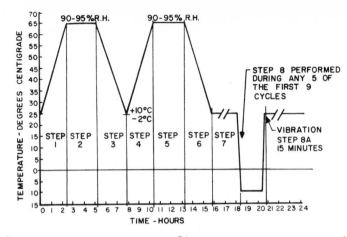

FIG. 8-14. GRAPHICAL REPRESENTATION OF A 24-HOUR HUMIDITY TEST CYCLE (MOISTURE RE-SISTANCE TEST)

chamber during step 2 of the first humidity cycle. The pH value shall be 6.5 to 7.5 at 25°C.

(2) After the relays have been mounted by their normal mounting means and wired for any measuring to be performed, initial measurements shall be taken. At this point the humidity test shall be started.

(3) Upon completion of the third, fifth, and tenth humidity cycles and while still at 90 to 95 per cent RH with the relays still in the humidity chamber, the required electrical measurements shall be made.

(4) Following the tenth cycle, the samples shall be removed from the chamber and allowed to dry for 24 hours at room conditions, after which electrical measurements are repeated.

Test *B* shall be conducted as follows. The test shall be the same as Test A except that during the second, third, fifth, seventh, and ninth cycles the relays shall be removed during the 25°C exposure and subjected to a subcycle of low temperature (−10°C ±2°) and vibration. The specimens shall be vibrated in a vertical plane for 15 minutes, using a simple harmonic motion having an amplitude of 0.03 in. The frequency shall be varied uniformly between 10 to 55 to 10 cps in approximately 1 minute. Upon completion of this subcycle, the relays shall be returned to the humidity chamber.

Recording of data. The temperature/humidity versus time charts made during the humidity test shall serve to show that the test was performed as specified. All other data shall be recorded as outlined under the characteristic test.

8.23 Winding corrosion (polarization)

Purpose. The purpose of this test is to determine the ability of the relay winding to withstand prolonged exposure to high humidity under circuit conditions that promote the electrolytic corrosion that destroys metallic continuity.

Requirements. Requirements shall specify:

(1) The d-c potential to be applied to the winding and case, frame, core, or other parts of the structure

(2) The humidity conditions under which the test shall be performed

(3) The number of days during which no failures shall occur

(4) The number of failures permitted for the total duration of the test.

Procedure. These are two basic tests, A and B, to be conducted as follows:

(1) Test A: Commercial relays shall be subjected to 90 per cent ±2 per cent relative humidity at 30°C ±2°C for a minimum of 14 days. Positive polarity shall be connected to the terminals of one coil winding and negative polarity to the frame, case, or core. Measurements of winding continuity shall be made daily for the first four days and every two to three days thereafter. A Wheatstone bridge having a battery supply of 1.5 volts in series with 10,000 ohms shall be used for continuity measurements. Note: This technique does not impose voltages that may bridge discontinuities in the wire re-

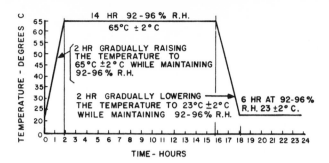

FIG. 8-15. ONE 24-HOUR TEMPERATURE/HUMIDITY CYCLE FOR TESTING WINDING CORROSION OF
MILITARY RELAYS

sulting from corrosion, nor will it destroy metallic continuity of reduced sections. The measurement, however, is not sensitive, being primarily a continuity test.

(2) Test B: Military relays shall be subjected to 10 cycles of temperature and humidity as outlined in Fig. 8-15. Positive polarity shall be connected to one terminal of the coil winding and the negative to the frame, case, or core. Measurements of winding continuity shall be made at the last phase of the first four cycles and during the seventh and tenth cycles.

8.24 High frequency effects

Purpose. The purpose of this test is to measure voltage standing wave ratio (VSWR), crosstalk, and insertion loss of coaxial relays used in transmission or high frequency circuits.

Requirements. The frequency range, signal level, temperature, and humidity at which these characteristics are to be measured should be specified. The type of coaxial connectors and cables to be employed in the actual application and their characteristic impedance (such as 75 ohms) should also be specified.

Procedures. In performing this test, these procedures shall apply:

(1) VSWR test: The relay is connected into the test circuit shown in Fig. 8-16, with the con-

tacts preferably connected in a signal direction corresponding to that in actual usage. Incident power (PI) is read on the directional power meter. Reflected power (PR) is read by reversing the meter. The VSWR is computed from the expression:

$$\frac{1 + \sqrt{PR/PI}}{1 - \sqrt{PR/PI}}$$

Note: The interconnections required for measurements of this type produce discontinuities and associated reflections within themselves. Therefore, maximum care must be exercised in the physical attachment of these connectors. Wherever possible, the cable lengths should approximate the actual lengths employed in the equipment. It is recognized that other methods of measurement, such as the use of slotted lines or time domain reflectometry, may be used.

(2) Crosstalk: Using the circuit of Fig. 8-17, the calibrated attenuator shall be set for zero db loss, and the signal generator connected to the terminated line through the closed relay contact. The attenuator is adjusted to obtain a reference reading on the meter. The open contact is then closed, and the attenuator is readjusted to obtain the same meter reading as before. The crosstalk level is read from the attenuator dial settings. The accuracy of crosstalk measurements shall be ±2 db.

(3) Insertion loss: Using the circuit of Fig.

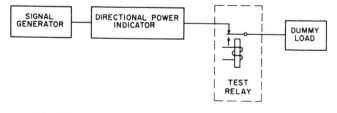

FIG. 8-16. METHOD FOR TESTING VSWR OF COAXIAL RELAY

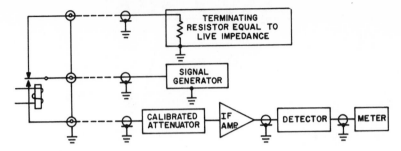

FIG. 8-17. MEASUREMENT OF CROSSTALK BETWEEN COAXIAL RELAY CONTACT LEADS

8-18, the calibrated attenuator shall be set for zero db loss and the signal generator connected to the attenuator through the closed relay contact. The attenuator is adjusted to obtain a reference reading on the meter. The relay contacts are then disconnected, and, using the same cables with an adapter, the signal generator is connected to the attenuator. The attenuator is adjusted to obtain the same meter reading as before, and the insertion loss is read from the attenuator dial setting. The accuracy of the insertion loss measurements shall be ±10 per cent.

8.25   Salt spray (corrosion)

Purpose.   The salt spray test is performed for the purpose of determining the ability of protective finishes of sealed relay enclosures to withstand corrosion in marine service or exposed shore locations. It is intended as a practical qualitative evaluation of the protective properties of metallic and other finishes.

Requirements.   Salt spray requirements should specify:

(1) The concentration of the salt solution, either 20 or 5 per cent by weight

(2) The duration of the test (96 or 48 hours)

(3) Special mounting instructions, if other than the standard mounting specified here

(4) Requirements to be met after exposure.

Apparatus.   The apparatus used for this test shall be as follows: (1) Exposure chamber with racks for supporting specimen; (2) means for atomizing the salt solution, including suitable nozzles and a compressed air supply; (3) salt solution reservoir; (4) means and control of chamber heating (immersion heater shall not be used); and (5) means for humidifying the air at a temperature above the chamber temperature.

(1) Chamber: The chamber and all accessories and parts that come in contact with the test specimens shall be made of material that will not affect the corrosiveness of the fog (such as glass, plastic, sulphur, wax string, and the like). The chamber and accessories shall be constructed so that there is no direct impinging or dripping of spray or condensate on the specimens. The spray shall circulate freely about all specimens to the same degree. No liquid that comes in contact with the relay shall return to the salt solution. The chamber shell be vented.

(2) Atomizer: The atomizer or atomizers used shall be designed and constructed to produce a finely divided, wet, dense fog. The compressed air entering the atomizer shall be free from all impurities, such as oil and dirt. The air shall be humidified and warmed to approximately 35°C. A suitable method is to pass the air at 12 to 18 psi above atmospheric pressure through a tower containing heated water with a barrier to break the water-laden air into fine bubbles.

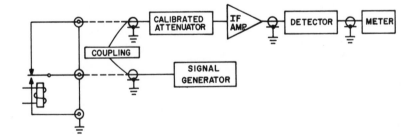

FIG. 8-18. MEASUREMENT OF INSERTION LOSS IN HIGH FREQUENCY RELAYS

(3) Salt solution: When sodium chloride is to be employed on a dry basis, it shall contain not more than 0.1 per cent sodium iodide and not more than 3 per cent total impurities. The solution shall be made by dissolving the specified salts in distilled water and shall be free of solids by subsequent filtration. The solution shall be maintained at a pH of 6.5 − 7.2 when measured at 92° to 95°F. Only reagent grade hydrochloric acid or reagent grade sodium hydroxide shall be used to adjust the pH. The pH measurements shall be made electrometrically using a glass electrode with a saturated potassium bridge or by a colorimetric method such as bromothymol blue, provided the results are equivalent to those obtained with the electrometric method. There are two ways of handling the salt solution:

(a) Type I test: The solution shall be prepared by dissolving 20 ±2 parts (by weight) of salt (sodium chloride) in 80 parts (by weight) of distilled water. The solution shall be adjusted to and maintained at a specific gravity of 1.126 to 1.157 when measured at 92° to 97°F. This solution shall be used if no other is specified.

(b) Type II test: The solution shall be prepared by dissolving 5 ±1 parts (by weight) of salt (sodium chloride) in 95 parts (by weight) of distilled water. The solution shall be adjusted to and maintained at a specific gravity of 1.027 to 1.041 when measured at 92° and 97°F.

Procedure. In performing this test, the following procedure shall apply:

(1) The specimens shall be given a minimum of handling prior to test and shall be prepared for testing with only normal production cleaning. Specimens having an organic coating shall not be solvent cleaned. No cleaning shall be performed during the test. The specimens shall be suspended by means of glass, wax string, nylon strands, or plastic hooks and positioned so that they are not in contact with one another and not shielded from the salt spray. No puddling shall occur, and corrosion products and condensate from one specimen shall not fall upon another specimen. The test shall be monitored at 33° to 36°C while in the exposure zone.

(2) The nozzle pressure shall be adjusted to atomize approximately 3 quarts of salt solution per 10 cubic feet of box, per 24 hours. Atomization shall be measured by placing at least two receptacles in the exposure zone, one near the nozzle and one as far away as possible from the nozzle. Collection shall be from 0.5 to 3.0 milliliters of solution per hour for each 80 square centimeters of horizontal collecting area, based on an average run of at least 16 hours. The solution collected shall have a sodium chloride content of 18 to 22 per cent (specific gravity of from 1.26 to 1.157 at 34° to 36°C) for the 20 per cent solution and from 4 to 6 per cent (specific gravity of from 1.028 to 1.0413 at 34° to 35°C) for the 5 per cent solution. The specific gravity of the collected liquid will indicate whether the initial solution was satisfactory or whether it shall be adjusted by adding salt or distilled water.

(3) The test shall be run continuously, except for adjusting the apparatus or inspection of the specimens for 48 or 96 hours as specified. If specified, applicable measurements may be made before or after the washing and drying period, following the salt spray exposure. Salt deposits shall be removed with a gentle wash or dip in running water, not warmer than 38°C, and by a light brushing with a soft hair or plastic bristle brush. After washing, the relays shall be shaken, air blasted, and permitted to dry for 24 hours at room temperature. Then they shall be examined by the unaided eye for evidence of corrosion, peeling, chipping, or blistering of the finish, legibility of marking, and exposure of base metal.

8.26 Winding temperature rise

Purpose. The purpose of this test is to determine the mean winding temperature of an energized coil winding.

Definition. "Temperature rise" is the rise above ambient temperature.

Requirements. Requirements controlling winding temperature rise and final mean winding temperature should specify:

(1) The voltage or current at which the winding is to be energized

(2) The ambient temperature at which the test shall be performed

(3) The maximum permissible temperature rise or final mean winding temperature

(4) The type of mounting plate and enclosure to be employed if the ambient is at an elevated temperature.

Procedure. In performing this test, the following procedure shall apply:

(1) The relay shall be suspended in still air at the specified ambient temperature until temperature stabilization of the entire winding is attained.

(2) Measurements of d-c resistance, using a d-c Wheatstone bridge, shall be made at 15 minute intervals until successive readings indicate that stabilization has been reached. This d-c coil resistance shall be recorded as R_1 and the temperature at which it is read as T_1. The relay shall then be energized, with the specified voltage and current applied to the coil windings and the rated resistive current load flowing through its now closed contacts. Resistance measurements are made until stabilization of the coil windings is reached. The measured winding resistance at stabilization shall be recorded as R_2.

Precautions.   In making the readings of the coil winding as part of this temperature rise, the following precautions must be taken:

(1) Preparation for a fast transfer from the voltage source to the measuring bridge must be made.

(2) The bridge must be set close to balancing so that no time is lost in searching for the correct reading.

(3) At the final reading, the transfer and reading time should be no greater than 1 second.

(4) The size of the chamber shall be such that its temperature is not affected by the winding temperature rise.

Formula for calculating coil temperature rise from 20°C and total or mean temperature of a coil winding. In the Appendix, this equation is given as:

$$T_1 + \Delta T = (234.5 + T_1)\frac{R_2}{R_1} - 234.5$$

$T_1 + \Delta T = $ total temperature (T_2)

in which:

$T_1 = $ ambient temperature at which R_1 is established

$\Delta T = $ temperature rise above T_1

$R_1 = $ cold d-c resistance

$R_2 = $ hot d-c resistance after energizing with full contact load

8.27   Capacitance

Purpose.   The purpose of this test is to measure the capacitance between mutually insulated parts of a relay. Capacitance affects the relay operating time and leakage currents in h-f circuits.

Definition.   Two electrodes or a set of electrodes separated from each other by an insulating material (dielectric) constitute a capacitor and store energy when there is a potential difference between the electrodes. In a relay, "capacitance" is set up between coil windings and across contact gaps.

Requirements.   Capacitance requirements should specify:

(1) The measuring voltage

(2) The measuring frequency

(3) The maximum permissible capacitance between each set of measurement points

(4) The points between which the measurements are to be made.

Procedure.   In performing this test, the following procedure shall apply:

(1) A capacitance bridge or other suitable instrument shall be used for making the measurements.

(2) All test leads shall be as short and as stiff as possible.

(3) The position of the test leads on the terminals shall be controlled.

(4) Stray capacitance shall be balanced out or measured and subtracted from the results.

Recording of data.   Capacitance shall be recorded in picofarads (micromicrofarads). Sample data:

Sample No.	1	2	3
Coil to case	30	29	31
Coil to contacts	18	18	19
Contacts to case, relay energized	26	25	27
Contact to case, de-energized	23	24	21
Across open contact gap, energized	10	10	10
Across open contact gap, de-energized	11	11	12
Adjacent switching circuits	26	27	25

8.28   Contact life

Purpose.   The purpose of relay contact life testing is to determine the ability of relay contacts to perform reliably the required number of operating cycles under a variety of contact loads.

Definitions. The "contact life" (electrical life) of a contact is the number of operations it will perform that will allow a relay to meet its specified requirements.

Requirements. Contact requirements should specify.

(1) Performance criteria, such as required life, maximum permissible contact resistance, and number of failures permitted

(2) Pulsing rate, duty cycle (per cent on time, per cent off time), and the voltage or current at which windings shall be energized

(3) Type of power and contact load (resistive, inductive, lamp, motor, minimum current and the like), voltage, current, polarity, and for a-c loads, the frequency and number of phases and whether or not intended for load transfer between unsynchronized a-c sources.

(4) The ambient temperature at which the test is to be conducted

(5) Measurements to be made before, during, and after life testing

(6) The method of monitoring the opening and closing of contacts.

Procedure. In performing these tests, the following procedure shall apply:

(1) General instructions: The following general instructions shall apply to all levels and loads:

(a) Prior to load testing, relays shall be measured for dielectric withstanding voltage, contact resistance, insulation resistance, and operating characteristics.

(b) Relays shall be wired with copper wire having a current carrying capacity that is consistent with the contact load rating.

(c) Relays, mounted by normal means on nonconducting material, shall be subjected to the specified ambient temperature. When a test chamber is used, it shall be a circulation type capable of maintaining the specified temperature within ±2 per cent.

(d) At each operation all contacts shall individually switch the specified current, voltage, and type of load.

(e) Power supplies shall have a voltage regulation of less than 10 per cent between no load and full load. Ripple of d-c supplies shall not exceed 2 per cent.

(f) Monitoring circuits shall be connected as close as possible to the relay contacts.

(g) Load currents shall be measured periodically by suitable instruments.

(h) The cycling program shall be timed for conformance with the specified pulsing rate and duty cycle.

(i) The coil power supply shall be interrupted with a bounce-free switch.

(j) Windings shall be energized at rated voltage or at 120 per cent of rated current.

(k) Resistive loads shall have a power factor of not less than 99 per cent. The resistors shall be of a size that prevents overheating. Provisions for adequate cooling shall be made for safety reasons.

(l) D-C load inductors shall be an air or magnetic core type having essentially constant inductance over the applicable current range. Iron cores shall be pre-aged to minimize changes in magnetic properties with time. Load inductance shall be adjustable by means of taps or by varying the air gap. Resistors shall be adjustable to provide the specified L/R ratio at the specified load, as determined by a direct measurement of the time constant, that is, the time in which current rises to 63 per cent of the steady state value (See Fig. 8-19). A-C load inductors shall be the same as the d-c inductors except that the power factor shall be adjusted between 40 and 50 per cent.

(m) Lamp loads shall consist of tungsten lamps operating at rated voltage. The load shall be monitored periodically to check for lamp deterioration. The cycling rate shall be slow enough to permit lamp filaments to cool sufficiently between operations to assure full inrush current at each operation. If a simulated resistor lamp load is used, the contacts shall close a current that is ten times the steady state lamp current. The cycling rate for a simulated lamp load shall be 0.35 ± 0.05 seconds on and 2.0 ± 0.1 seconds off. A resistor reducing the current to 10 per cent of the inrush current shall be inserted automatically in the load circuit 0.020 ± 0.005 second after the contact makes and shall be removed automatically after the contact opens (see Fig. 8-20).

(n) Relay contacts shall switch a resistive simulated motor load at rated voltage for the specified number of operations. For both a-c and d-c ratings the contacts shall make six times rated current and break rated current. The time cycle rate shall be 0.35 ± 0.05 second on and 2.0 ± 0.1 seconds off. The inrush current shall be maintained for 0.070 ± 0.020 second.

(o) The number of relay operations shall be determined by means of a counter that operates every time the coil of a relay is energized.

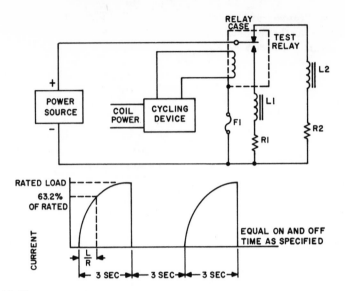

Fig. 8-19. Circuit and time cycle for contact life test with inductive loads

Opening and closing of each contact shall be checked automatically every operation. The device shall count closures and automatically stop the test when resistance exceeds the specified value or record the failure on a suitable recording device.

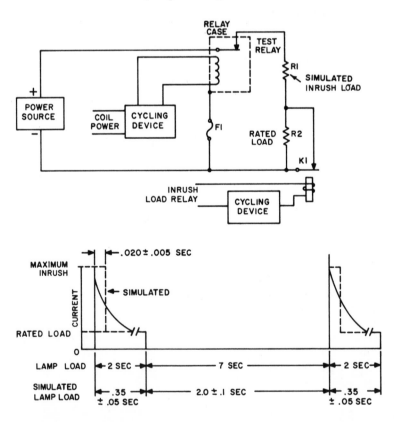

Fig. 8-20. Circuit and time sequence for load contact life test using a resistor to simulate inrush characteristic

The simulated lamp load condition can also be applied to motor loads.

(p) The usually specified maximum resistance values for various loads are : (1) several tenths of an ohm, at rated loads; (2) several ohms, at medium loads; and (3) several hundred ohms at low levels.

(q) The current in the monitoring circuit shall not be more than 5 per cent of the load current and the circuit shall be timed to prevent having the contacts open or close the monitoring circuit.

(r) Relay sensing circuits shall be provided to operate an alarm or cut off the test if the contacts of the relay on test fail to break upon the energizing or de-energizing of the relay coil.

(2) Rated loads: This test is intended to evaluate contact performance at rated current and voltage.

(a) The procedure shall be as outlined above for the applicable type of load.

(b) Normally grounded parts of relays undergoing test shall be connected to ground (or to the neutral when a three-phase system is used) through a "quick blow" 100 milliampere fuse. (The purpose of the fuse is to determine whether arcing to ground occurs. It also prevents excessive damage, and a blown fuse indicates that breakdown occurred during measuring intervals.)

(3) Medium loads (milliampere range) : This test is intended to evaluate performance under loads that are well below the rated load capability of contacts but considerably higher than the so-called low energy loads. The formation of carbonaceous materials in this current range may significantly affect contact performance sooner than at rated load. The procedure shall be the same as for the rated load test above, except that the contact loads shall be within the following ranges:

(a) Resistive loads: Between 50 and 400 milliamperes at voltages up to 28 volts d-c.

(b) Lamp loads: One 28 volt lamp having an inrush current of 400 milliamperes and a steady state current of 40 milliamperes (d-c) .

(4) Low level loads and miss tests (microampere range) : This test is sometimes specified for 100 per cent production testing for a limited number of operations. Its purpose is to detect the presence of organic films or particulate contamination.

(a) The general procedure with respect to mounting, coil energization, contact monitoring, and initial measurements shall be as previously specified.

(b) For 100 per cent production screening, relays shall be subjected to 5000 to 10,000 operations at a rate of two to three operations per second, the duty cycle being 50 per cent. The open circuit contact voltage shall be 30 to ±3 millivolts, rms, 1000 cycles, and shall not vary by more than 10 per cent from no load to full load. The contact current shall be 10 microamperes ± 10 per cent.

(c) For qualification testing, relays shall be subjected to 100,000 operations as follows:

50,000 operations at room ambient
25,000 operations at maximum ambient
25,000 operations at minimum ambient

The pulsing rate shall be 3 to 10 operations per second and the voltage and current shall be as specified in (b) .

(d) There shall be sufficient time allowed between operations to permit monitoring contacts after contact bounce subsides. The detecting circuit may either stop the test after a failure or count cumulative failures during the test.

(e) Contacts may be connected and monitored in series if specifications permit.

(f) A typical circuit for performing these tests is shown in Fig. 8-21.

8.29 Continuous contact current

Purpose.   The purpose of this test is to determine the ability of relay contacts to carry rated current for prolonged periods.

Requirements.   Continuous contact current requirements should specify:

(1) Voltage or current at which the winding shall be energized

(2) Current that the contacts shall carry

(3) Ambient temperature at which the test shall be conducted

(4) Contact resistance requirements, including measuring voltage and current

(5) Other performance criteria, such as stability of electrical operating characteristics, insulation resistance, dielectric withstanding voltage.

Procedure.   In performing this test, the following procedure shall apply:

(1) The following initial measurements shall be made at room ambient temperature:

(a) Winding resistance (corrected to reference temperature)

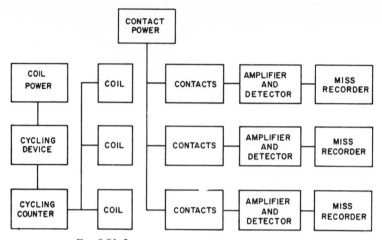

FIG. 8-21. LOW LEVEL TEST SYSTEM FOR MISS RECORDING

(b) Contact resistance at rated current and voltage

(c) Insulation resistance and dielectric withstanding voltage

(d) Applicable operational characteristics.

(2) The relays shall be suspended in free air at maximum rated ambient temperature with the winding energized at rated voltage, or 120 per cent of rated current, and the normally open contacts carrying rated current. After 24 hours of operation, contact resistance of the normally open contacts shall be measured before de-energizing the coil. The normally closed contacts shall be measured after de-energizing the coil. The relay shall then remain de-energized for 24 hours ·with rated current through the normally closed contacts, after which the contact resistance of these contacts shall be measured. Following these measurements the coil shall be energized, and the resistance of the normally open contacts shall be measured. The relays shall then be restored to room ambient temperature, and all initial measurements shall be repeated.

8.30   Overload and rupture

Purpose.   The purpose of overload and rupture testing is to establish the ability of a relay to perform satisfactorily under circuit trouble conditions that impose loads on the contacts that are considerably in excess of their normal rating.

Requirements.   Overload and rupture requirements should specify:

(1) Type and magnitude of the load and permissible contact resistance. Contacts should pass contact voltage drop tests after overload but may give impaired performance after rupture at higher current value.

(2) Method of mounting, such as by normal means

(3) Coil excitation through a bounce-free switch

(4) Whether a grounded case (in which moving contacts are at the highest potential above system ground, and the case of the relay is grounded through a "quick blow" fuse rated at 5 per cent of the contact rating) is applicable

(5) Ambient temperature at which the test shall be performed

(6) Measurements required before and after overload or rupture testing and performance criteria.

Procedure.   In performing this test, the following procedure shall apply:

(1) When overload is twice the rated current (MIL-R-5757 or MIL-R-39016), all contacts should be tested simultaneously at the various applicable loads using the testing procedure of Paragraph 8.28.

(2) When overload and rupture is four, six, or eight times the rated current, the contacts shall be tested independently at the specified on and off time (MIL-R-6106).

(3) The number of operations at these conditions shall be 50 or 100.

(4) Monitoring may be by visual observation of measuring instruments. Automatic facilities are not required.

8.31   Multiple load test

Purpose.   The purpose of this test is to determine the performance of relays on which several contacts individually switch different loads ranging from intermediate to rated loads.

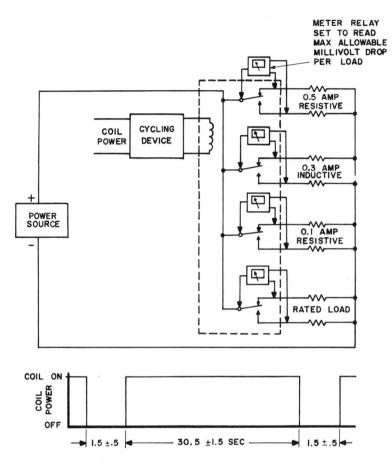

FIG. 8-22. CIRCUIT AND TIME SEQUENCE FOR MULTIPLE LOAD TEST

Requirements. The requirements to be specified are essentially the same as those listed in Paragraph 8.28.

Procedure. The testing procedure shall be the same as that specified in Paragraph 8.28 with the following exceptions:

(1) Normally open and normally closed contacts shall be divided equally, each contact making and breaking one of the following loads:
  (a) 0.5 ampere resistive at 28 volts d-c
  (b) 0.3 ampere inductive at 28 volts d-c
  (c) 0.1 ampere resistive at 28 volts d-c
  (d) Rated resistive load at 28 volts d-c
Associated normally closed and normally open contacts shall switch the same load. For relays having fewer or more than four sets of normally open and normally closed contacts, the loads shall be repeated in the sequence indicated for the number of contacts to be tested.

(2) Relay windings shall be energized for 29 to 32 seconds and de-energized for 1.0 to 2.0 seconds during each cycle.

(3) The test shall be conducted at rated maximum ambient temperature.

(4) Using the four wire voltmeter-ammeter method, contact resistance shall be measured initially and at intervals of approximately 5000 operations during the test.

(5) A typical testing circuit is shown in Fig. 8-22.

8.32 Minimum current

The intermediate load area between rated and low level loading can result in contact failure from contamination, especially in hermetically sealed or well enclosed relays. Where the application results in contact loading in this area, testing should be done in accordance with the ruling military or commercial specification.

9
Government Specifications

Introduction

This section reviews most of the active government and government-type specifications and standards (MIL, NAS, SAE, and NASA) that are applicable to relay evaluation and qualification. It will be useful in interpreting and applying these specifications. Although this section deals with military type specifications and standards, this information can prove helpful in preparing relay specifications for other applications. For some applications, it may be necessary to take exceptions or to add special requirements. It is important to remember that conformance to military specifications without exception may result in higher costs than the application justifies. This can result from the requirement of lengthy and expensive test programs as is frequently associated with these specifications.

Tables 9-1 and 9-2 compare the requirements of specifications that are similar in content. This information may be a valuable tool in selecting applicable portions of military specifications with which to describe relays for a particular application or requirement.

Government specifications and standards are revised from time to time, so at some future time the data herein may be obsolete. Therefore, a check should be made with the cognizant service, "Preparing Activity," regarding revisions made, or under way, prior to designing a system involving relays subject to military specifications and/or standards. Each specification discussed in this section includes the revision designation and date of revision. This makes it possible to determine the status of each document with respect to current revision status at any particular time.

Activity preparing — The military activity, or the activity in a Federal civil agency (for Federal documents only), responsible for document and study projects and for maintenance of the resultant Standardization Documents. See MIL-R-5757 activities chart (Fig. 9-1).

Custodian — The activity responsible for effecting coordination and other related functions for its own department in the DOD.

Department — The Department of the Army, the Department of the Navy, or the Department of the Air Force.

Qualified Products List — A list of products qualified under the requirements stated in the applicable specification, including appropriate product identification and test reference with the name and plant address of the manufacturer and distributor, as applicable. (*Source*: Department of Defense Directive 4120.3).

Activity Symbols—The following symbols are used to identify the preparing activity, custodians, and review/user interest on Federal and military standardization documents, and to identify the issuing activity on limited, coordination documents.

ARMY[1]

Electronics Command: EL
Missile Command: MI
Munitions Command: MU
Weapons Command: WC

[1]Partial listing.

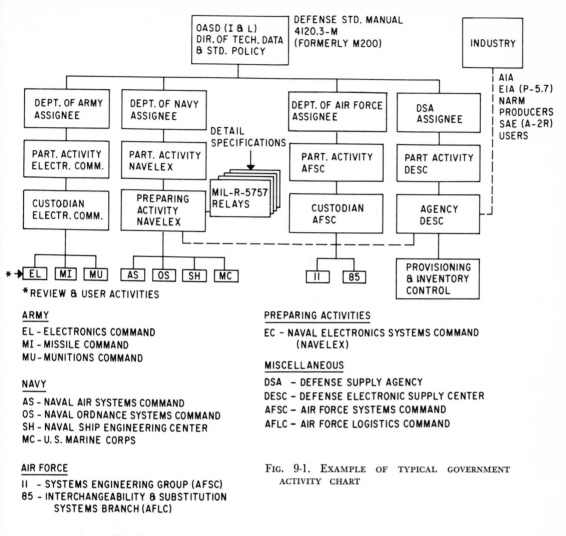

FIG. 9-1. EXAMPLE OF TYPICAL GOVERNMENT ACTIVITY CHART

*REVIEW & USER ACTIVITIES

ARMY
EL – ELECTRONICS COMMAND
MI – MISSILE COMMAND
MU – MUNITIONS COMMAND

NAVY
AS – NAVAL AIR SYSTEMS COMMAND
OS – NAVAL ORDNANCE SYSTEMS COMMAND
SH – NAVAL SHIP ENGINEERING CENTER
MC – U.S. MARINE CORPS

AIR FORCE
II – SYSTEMS ENGINEERING GROUP (AFSC)
85 – INTERCHANGEABILITY & SUBSTITUTION SYSTEMS BRANCH (AFLC)

PREPARING ACTIVITIES
EC – NAVAL ELECTRONICS SYSTEMS COMMAND (NAVELEX)

MISCELLANEOUS
DSA – DEFENSE SUPPLY AGENCY
DESC – DEFENSE ELECTRONIC SUPPLY CENTER
AFSC – AIR FORCE SYSTEMS COMMAND
AFLC – AIR FORCE LOGISTICS COMMAND

NAVY[1]

Naval Air Systems Command: AS
U.S. Coast Guard: CG
U.S. Marine Corps: MC
Office of Management Information: OM
Naval Ordnance Systems Command: OS
Naval Ship Engineering Center: SH
Naval Electronics Systems Command: EC

AIR FORCE[1]

Headquarters U.S. Air Force Standardization Group: 01
Rome Air Development Center (AFSC): 17
Quality & Reliability Assurance Branch (AFLC): 23

[1]Partial listing.

Headquarters, AFLC, Standardization Branch: 26
Interchangeability and Substitution Systems Branch (AFLC): 85

DEFENSE SUPPLY AGENCY

Headquarters, Defense Supply Agency: DH
Defense Electronics Supply Center: ES

OTHER

Other — If the issuance is applicable, only to the Naval Air Systems Command and the Department of the Air Force. In the aeronautical field, use the symbol "ASG."

Table 9-1. Practical Comparison of Military Specification Requirements

SPECIFICA- TION NO.	MIL-R-5757E	MIL-R-6106F(ASG)	MIL-R-39016
DATE	AMENDMENT 1, 30 DECEMBER 1968	20 AUGUST 1967	AMENDMENT 3, 10 FEBRUARY 1969
1. Scope	1.1 Scope — This specification covers the general requirements for electrical relays with contact ratings up to and including 10 amperes for use in electronic, communication, and for other type applications, including those used in telegraph equipment.	1.1 Scope — This specification establishes general requirements for electro-mechanical relays with nominal contact ratings from five amperes (resistive) and upward for use in electrical applications. Relays covered by this specification are capable of meeting the electrical and environmental requirements when mounted directly to the structure of aircraft and other primary vehicles.	1.1 Scope — This specification covers the general requirements for established reliability, electromagnetic, hermetically sealed (excluding thermal) relays for use in electronic and communication-type equipment. These relays are designed to operate in low and medium power switching circuits and contact ratings up to 10 amperes alternating current (ac) or direct current (dc). Relays covered by this specification will demonstrate a life failure rate level of 0.01 to 3.0 percent in 10,000 relay operations. This failure rate level is established at a confidence level of 90 percent for qualification and 60 percent for maintenance of qualification, established at 10,000 operations at 85°C, 125°C, and 200°C under rated load conditions specified herein.
2. Classifi- cation	1.2 Classification 1.2.1 Table I — Enclosure Design 1.2.2 Table II — Vibration Characteristic 1.2.3 Table III — Temperature Range 1.2.4 Table IV — Shock Type 1.2.5 Military Part Number Example: M 5757/01 — 001 Military Specification Dash Designator Sheet Number Number 3.2 Relay Categories 3.2.1 Category 1 — Relays completely defined by a military specification sheet. 3.2.2 Category II — Relays the same as Category I, except for minor differences such as terminals, mounting means or coil resistance, which do not change the basic design or construction of the qualified relay. Category II relays shall be procured from a source on the applicable qualified products list for the particular similar product of Category I. Category II relays are nonstandard. 3.2.3 Category III — Relays not covered by specification sheets. These relays are nonstandard.	1.2 Classification 1.2.1 Type Designators— Type I — Continuous duty, hermetically sealed. Type I ER — Continuous duty, hermetically sealed, established reliability, failure rate 1 percent per 10,000 operations. Type II — Continuous duty, nonhermetically sealed. Type II ER — Continuous duty, nonhermetically sealed, established reliability, failure rate 1 percent per 10,000 operations. Type III — Intermittent duty.	1.2 Classification 1.2.1 Table I — Vibration Level 1.2.2 Table II — Temperature Class 1.2.3 Table III — Shock Level 1.2.4 Table IV — Terminal Type 1.2.5 Table V — Failure Rate
3. Enclosure	1.2.1 Enclosure Design Table I — Symbol 1 = Open Symbol 2 = Enclosed Symbol 3 = Sealed (other than hermetically) Symbol 4 = Hermetically sealed		
4. Vibration	1.2.2 Vibration Table II — Symbol 1 = 0.06 in. D. A., 10–55 Hz Symbol 2 = 10g, 10–500 Hz Symbol 3 = 15g, 10–2,000 Hz Symbol 4 = 20g, 10–2,000 Hz Symbol 5 = 30g, 10–3,000 Hz Symbol 6 = random, 50–2,000 Hz 3.15.1, 4.8.11.1 Test I (not applicable to telegraph relays) per MIL-STD-202. No opening or closing of contacts in excess of 10 microseconds. 3.15.2, 4.8.11.2 Test II (telegraph relays only) per MIL-STD-202. Unless otherwise specified, 10 g's to 500 Hz. Chatter shall not exceed 0.167 milliseconds.	3.6.6.4, 4.7.6.5 Vibration — Range per figure 5. Double amplitude range 0.06 to 0.5, g level range 2–50 g's, frequency range 5 to 3,000 Hz. No opening or closing of contacts in excess of 10 microseconds.	1.2.1 Vibration Table I Symbol 1 = 10 g, 10–2,000 Hz Symbol 2 = 20 g, 10–2,000 Hz Symbol 3 = 30 g, 10–2,000 Hz Symbol 4 = 30 g, 10–3,000 Hz 0.03 g^2 per cycle random 3.11, 4.7.7 Vibration per MIL-STD-202. No opening or closing of contacts in excess of 10 microseconds.
5. Temper- ature	1.2.3 Temperature Range Table III — Symbol A = −55°C to +85°C Symbol B = −65°C to +125°C Symbol C = −65°C to +200°C Symbol D = 0°C to +70°C	Temperature range — As specified by the detail specification.	1.2.2 Temperature Class Table II — Symbol A = −65°C to + 85°C Symbol B = −65°C to +125°C Symbol C = −65°C to +200°C

Note: Paragraph numbers are from the referenced military specification.

Table 9-1. Practical Comparison of Military Specification Requirements (Cont'd)

SPECIFICA-TION NO.	MIL-R-5757E	MIL-R-6106F (ASG)	MIL-R-39016
DATE	AMENDMENT 1, 30 DECEMBER 1968	20 AUGUST 1967	AMENDMENT 3, 10 FEBRUARY 1969
6. Shock	1.2.4 Shock Type Table IV (per MIL-STD-202) — Symbol 1 = 50 g, 11 ± 2 ms, sawtooth (G of Method 213) Symbol 2 = 75 g, 11 ± 2 ms, sawtooth (H of Method 213) Symbol 3 = 100 g, 11 ± 2 ms, sawtooth (I of Method 213) Symbol 4 = Method 202 (not for new design) Symbol 5 = High impact (Method 207) Note: Specified 50 g, 75 g, and 100 g are considered nominally equal to 15 g, 30 g, and 50 g, respectively (Method 205) 3.20.1, 4.8.16.1 Types 1, 2, 3, 4, and 5 (not applicable to telegraph relays) Type 1, 2, and 3 = No opening or closing of contacts in excess of 10 microseconds. Type 4 = As specified. Type 5 = No opening or closing of contacts in excess of 20 ms unless otherwise specified. 3.20.2, 4.8.16.2 Type 6 (telegraph relays only) per Method 205 Condition B of MIL-STD-202.	3.6.6.4, 4.7.6.3, 4.7.6.4, Shock — per the detailed specification and Method 213 of MIL-STD-202. High shock — per the detailed specification and Method 207 of MIL-STD-202.	1.2.3 Shock Level Table III — Symbol 1 = 50 g Symbol 2 = Not specified 3.15, 4.7.7 Shock — per Method 213, 207 of MIL-STD-202
7. Seal Test	3.8.1, 4.8.4.1 Seal Test I (Enclosure 3 relays only) — condition A or B (depending on temperature characteristics of Method 112 of MIL-STD-202. 3.8.2, 4.8.4.2 Seal Test II (Enclosure 4 relays only) — condition C procedure IIIb or IV of Method 112 of MIL-STD-202 Test Condition B for Gross Leak Test. Sealed volume of case / Max. allowable leakage: > 2 cubic inches 1 X 10⁻⁶ atm cc/sec; ≤ 2 cubic inches 1 X 10⁻⁸ atm cc/sec	3.6.1.3, 4.7.1.3 (Hermetically sealed relays only) — Mass spectrometer leak detection per Method 112 of MIL-STD-202. Relay volume > 2 cubic inches = 1.04 X 10⁻⁵ cc/sec Relay volume ≤ 2 cubic inches = 1 X 10⁻⁸ cc/sec	3.5, 4.7.2 Seal — per Method 112 of MIL-STD-202 Test Condition C, Procedure III (1 X 10⁻⁸ cc/sec). Test Condition B for gross leak test (use water)
8. Insulation Resistance	3.10, 4.8.6 Insulation Resistance — 1000 megohms minimum. Test per Method 302 of MIL-STD-202. Test Condition A for relays with coil and contact rating below 60 volts. Test Condition B for telegraph relays and all others.	3.6.2.1, 4.7.2.1 Insulation Resistance — 100 megohms minimum at 500 VDC with 30 to 50 percent humidity.	3.6, 4.7.3 Insulation Resistance — Method 302 of MIL-STD-202. 1,000 megohms minimum; 500 megohms minimum at maximum temperature
9. Dielectric Strength	3.9, 4.8.5 Dielectric Withstanding Voltage per Method 301 of MIL-STD-202. Maximum leakage current 1.0 mA. Test voltage 60 Hz. Telegraph relays — 700 VRMS all points except 450 VRMS between normally open contacts, between dual coils, and no requirement between poles. All other relays — 1000 VRMS all points unless otherwise specified. At altitude (above 10,000 ft) — per Method 105 Condition C of MIL-STD-202. Test voltage 350 VRMS all points.	3.6.2.2, 4.7.2.1 Dielectric Strength Table IV — Test voltage range at sea level = 1,050-1,500 VRMS for 1 minute and 1,250-1,800 VRMS for 2-5 seconds. Test voltage range at high altitude (80,000 ft) = 500-700 VRMS for 1 minute. Maximum leakage 1.0 mA. Test voltage varies with system voltage rating.	3.7, 4.7.4 Dielectric Strength — Per Method 105, 301 of MIL-STD-202. Test voltage range = 500-1250 VRMS at sea level and 350-500 VRMS at high altitude.
10. Contact Resistance	3.11.1, 4.8.7.1 Static Contact Resistance (or voltage drop) per Table VI and Method 307 of MIL-STD-202. Allowable contact resistance range 0.05 ohms-100 mV before life and 0.10 ohms-200 mV after life. Acceptable level depends on contact rating.	3.6.2.3, 4.7.2.2 Contact Voltage Drop or Resistance — Table V (volts max). Types I & II = 0.125 avg, 0.150 individual before life and 0.150 avg, 0.175 individual after life. Type III = 0.150 avg, 0.175 individual before life and 0.175 avg, 0.200 individual after life. Contacts loaded with rated resistive at 6 VDC.	3.8.1, 4.7.5.1 Static Contact Resistance — Method 307 of MIL-STD-202. Contact rating ≤ 3 amps = 0.050 ohms max (any reading). Contact rating < 3 amps = 0.125 volt drop max (any reading). Contact rating low level per 4.7.5.1.3.
11. Pickup	3.11.2, 4.8.7.2, 4.8.7.2.1 Pickup and Dropout Voltage (or Current) (not applicable to telegraph relays) per the detail specification. Soak for a period of 1 to 3 sec with rated voltage. Gradually increase from zero. Relays mounted in three mutual perpendicular planes for qualification.	3.6.3.1, 4.7.3.1, 4.7.3.1.1 Pickup (Operate) Voltage (or Current) per detail specification within temperature limits of class, de-energize for 30 minutes prior to starting test. Then energize for 30 minutes with nominal coil voltage.	3.8.2, 4.7.5.2, 4.7.5.2.1 Pickup and Dropout Voltage (or Current) per detail specification. Soak for 2 sec max with rated voltage (or current). Gradually increase from zero.

Note: Paragraph numbers are from the referenced military specification.

Table 9-1. Practical Comparison of Military Specification Requirements (Cont'd)

SPECIFICA-TION NO.	MIL-R-5757E	MIL-R-6106F (ASG)	MIL-R-39016
DATE	AMENDMENT 1, 30 DECEMBER 1968	20 AUGUST 1967	AMENDMENT 3, 10 FEBRUARY 1969
12. Dropout Voltage	3.11.2, 4.8.7.2, 4.8.7.2.2 Pickup and Dropout Voltage (or Current) per the detailed specification. Gradually reduce from rated coil voltage (or current).	3.6.3.2, 4.7.3.1.3 Dropout (Release) Voltage (or Current) per detailed specification. Gradually reduce from maximum operating.	3.8.2, 4.7.5.2.2 Pickup and Dropout Voltage (or Current) per detailed specification. Gradually reduce from rated coil voltage (or current).
13. D-C Coil Resistance	3.11.3., 4.8.7.3 D-C Coil Resistance — Per the detail specification. Test per Method 303 of MIL-STD-202.	3.6.2.4, 4.7.2.3 D-C Coil Resistance — Per the detail specification. Stabilize for 2 hr at test temperature.	3.8.5, 4.7.5.5 D-C Coil Resistance — Per the detail specification and Method 303 of MIL-STD-202.
14. Contact Bounce	3.11.6.1, 4.8.7.6.1 Contact Bounce Test I (not applicable to telegraph relays). 2 msec max unless otherwise specified. Contact load rated voltage or current. 3.11.6.2, 4.8.7.6.2 Contact Bounce Test II (telegraph relays only) — Duration 0.5 ms, effective bounce 0.2 ms max. Contact current 6 mA at 12 VDC max.	3.6.3.3, 4.7.3.2 Contact Bounce — Per the detail specification. Contact load 100 mA. Average of 5 consecutive readings.	3.8.3, 4.7.5.3 Contact Bounce — Per the detail specification. Contact load 6 mA at 10 VDC max (not to exceed rated contact load).
15. Operate and Release Time	3.11.5, 4.8.7.5 Operate and Release Time (not applicable to telegraph relays) — Per the detail specification. Exclusive of bounce time.	3.6.3.3, 4.7.3.2 Operate and Release Time — Per the detail specification. Contact load 100 mA max exclusive of bounce time. Multi-pole relays must function simultaneously within 1 msec for relays $\geq$ 15 amps and 2 msec for relays $<$ 15 amps.	3.8.6, 4.7.5.6 Operate and Release Time (when applicable) — Per the detailed specification exclusive of bounce time. Contact load 6 mA at 10 VDC max (not to exceed rated contact load).
16. Thermal Shock	3.12, 4.8.8 Thermal Shock (high and low temperature operation) (not applicable to telegraph relays) — Per Method 107 of MIL-STD-202. Test Condition A, B, or C per Table III.	3.6.6.1, 4.7.6.1 Temperature Shock — Per Method 107, Procedure 3 of MIL-STD-202.	3.10, 4.7.6 Thermal Shock — Per Method 107 of MIL-STD-202.
17. Acceleration	3.16, 4.8.12 Acceleration (when specified) — Per Method 212 of MIL-STD-202. Test Condition A, 17 g unless otherwise specified. Apply in three mutually perpendicular axes. Coil de-energized 5 minutes, momentarily energized with rated voltage (or current), and reduced to one-half rated for 5 minutes.	3.6.6.5, 4.7.6.6 Acceleration — Per Method 212 of MIL-STD-202. Test Condition A with a force of 15 g. Apply in three mutually perpendicular axes. Coil de-energized, energized with pickup voltage and one-half pickup voltage.	3.13, 4.7.9 Acceleration (when applicable) — Zero to specified value in detail specification in 2 minutes and held 10 minutes max. Operate 10 times with rated voltage (or current). Neon test lamp for proper contact positioning. Test in all six orthogonal directions.
18. Salt Spray	3.17, 4.8.13 Salt Spray — Per Method 101 Condition A (for telegraph relays) or Condition B (all other types) of MIL-STD-202 using 5% salt solution. Drying time = 25 hr.	3.6.6.6, 4.7.6.7 Salt Spray — Per Method 101 Condition B of MIL-STD-202 using 5% salt solution. Drying time = 6 hr at $-65°C$.	3.14, 4.7.10 Salt Spray — Per Method 101 Condition B of MIL-STD-202. Drying time = 24 hr. Exposure time = 48 hr.
19. Over-voltage	Not by this title — See Coil Life in this table.	Not by this title — See Coil Life in this table.	Not by this title — See Coil Life in this table.
20. High-Low Temperature Operation	3.13, 4.8.9 High and Low Temperature Operation (telegraph relays only) — Unless otherwise specified, test temp = 70°C and 0°C, 2 hr exposure at each temperature. Bias distortion shall not differ at each temp by more than 2%. High and Low Temperature Operation (not applicable to telegraph relays) — See Thermal Shock in this table.	4.7.3.1.2 High Temperature Pickup Voltage — Subjected to operate test at max ambient temp. Test time 1 hr. This requirement is covered under Pickup Voltage in the specification. 4.7.6.2 Low Temperature Operation — Subject to specified low temp for 48 hours. The relay will then meet specified pickup voltage, dropout voltage, and contact drop requirements. This requirement is covered under Thermal Shock in the specification.	3.19, 4.7.14 High-Low Temperature Operation — 2 hr at rated coil voltage and contact current at high temp and de-energized for 15 hr at minimum low temp prior to measuring pickup, dropout, operate and release times.
21. Overload	3.36, 4.8.32 Overload (when specified) (not applicable to telegraph relays) — 100 Hz for D-C contact loads and 200 Hz for A-C contact loads. Case grounded. Overload per the detail specification.	3.6.5.1, 4.7.5.1, 4.7.5.2 Overload — per Table XIII for 50 operations.	3.20, 4.7.15 Overload — 100 Hz at rated voltage (or current). Resistive = 2X rated. Inductive = 2X rated. Lamp = 2X rated.
22. Rupture		3.6.5.2, 4.7.5.1, 4.7.5.3 Rupture — Per Table XIV for 50 operations min.	
23. Loads — Resistive	3.1 per detail specification 4.8.34.1 Life	3.1 per detail specification 3.6.5.3, 4.7.5.1 Endurance (Life Load)	3.1 per detail specification 4.7.18 Life
23. Loads — Inductive	3.1 per detail specification 4.8.34.1 Life	3.1 per detail specification 3.6.5.3, 4.7.5.4 Endurance (Life Load)	3.1 per detail specification 4.7.18 Life 4.7.18.1.1 Load Impedance
23. Loads — Motor	3.1 per detail specification 4.8.34.1 Life	3.1 per detail specification 3.6.5.3, 4.7.5.4 Endurance (Life Load)	

Note: Paragraph numbers are from the referenced military specification.

Table 9-1. Practical Comparison of Military Specification Requirements (Cont'd)

SPECIFICATION NO.	MIL-R-5757E	MIL-R-6106F (ASG)	MIL-R-39016
DATE	AMENDMENT 1, 30 DECEMBER 1968	20 AUGUST 1967	AMENDMENT 3, 10 FEBRUARY 1969
23. Loads — Lamp	3.1 per detail specification 4.8.34.1 Life	3.1 per detail specification 3.6.5.3, 4.7.5.4 Endurance (Life Load)	3.1 per detail specification 4.7.18 Life 4.7.18.1.1 Load Impedance
Minimum Current	3.22, 4.8.18 Minimum Current (Intermediate Current) (not applicable to telegraph relays) Contact load: First pole — 0.1 amp resistive at 28 ± 1 VDC Second pole — 0.3 amp inductive (200 millihenries) at 28 ± 1 VDC Third pole — 0.5 amp resistive at 28 ± 1 VDC Fourth pole — Rated resistive at 28 ± 1 VDC Level I = 100,000 operations at 20 ± 2 sec, on-off time equal. Level II = 100,000 operations at 29 ± 3 sec on and 1.5 ± .5 sec off. Quality inspection test = 10,000 operations.	3.1 Minimum Current 3.6.5.3, 4.7.5.4 Endurance (Life Load)	3.8.1.3 per Table VI Minimum current 0.100 amp. Contact resistance 2 ohms when rated ≤ 3 amps and 0.200 ohms when rated > 3 amps.
Low Level	4.8.34.1.5 Low Level — 10 mA max at 30 millivolts max dc or peak ac open circuit voltage.	4.7.18.2 Low Level — 10 mA max at 50 millivolts max dc or peak ac open circuit voltage.	
3 Phase AC	3.1 per detail specification 4.8.33 Load Transfer	3.1 per detail specification 3.6.5.3 Endurance (Load Life)	
24. Coil Life	3.27, 4.8.23 Coil Life (not applicable to intermittent duty & telegraph relays). Test for 1,000 hr in still air. Rated coil voltage shall be applied continuously. See Figure 5, ambient temperatures.	3.6.4.3, 4.7.4.3 Continuous Current — Per the detail specification. Type I & II relays shall be energized continuously for 96 hr and Type III per the detail specification and Table XV.	3.16, 4.7.17 Coil Life — Energized continuously with max specified coil voltage. Cycle per Figure 14. Test duration 100 hr.
25. Endurance	Not listed by this title — See Life in this table.	3.6.5.3, 4.7.5.4 Endurance (Load Life) Duty cycle per Table XI. Min operations for life = 100,000. Loads: Resistive DC Inductive DC Motor DC Lamp Minimum Current (50,000 Hz) 3 Phase AC (when specified)	Not listed by this title — See Life in this table.
26. Life (Minimum Operating Cycles)	3.38.1, 4.8.34.1 Life Test I (not applicable to telegraph relays) — 100,000 operations minimum. Case grounded. Loads (case grounded): Resistive — cycled 400,000 operations with current reduced 25%) Inductive Lamp Motor Low Level 3.38.2, 4.8.34.2 Life Test II (telegraph relays only)	3.6.4.1 Mechanical Life — 4X minimum operations for relays < 25 amps and 2X for relays ≥ 25 amps. 3.6.4.5, 4.7.4.5 Operational Reliability — 500 Hz for relays < 25 amps. 1,000 Hz for relays ≥ 25 amps. See Table XV for Resistive Load. See Endurance above.	3.21, 4.7.18 Life — 100,000 Operations Minimum. Loads (case grounded): High Level Low Level High and Low Level combination Pre- and post life measurements per Table XV
27. Ozone		3.6.6.10, 4.7.6.11 Ozone — (not applicable on hermetically sealed relays) Exposure time 2 hr at room temperature. Ozone concentration per ASTM-D-470-59T.	
28. Grounding		3.4.5.3 Grounding Enclosure — Mounting holes shall provide electrical ground.	
29. Marking	3.39 Marking — Includes the following: Military Part Number (Category 1 only) Rated Coil Voltage (or current) Coil Resistance Coil Inductance Contact Rating Circuit Diagram Terminals	3.7 Identification of Product — Per Mil-STD-130, including the following: Name of Relay M, MS or a Part Number Manufacturer's Part Number Type Coil Volts Manufacturer's Name or Trademark	3.22.1 Marking — Per MIL-STD-130, including the following: Part Number JAN Brand Rated Volts or Coil Current & Operating Frequency Coil Resistance for D-C Relays Contact Rating

Note: Paragraph numbers are from the referenced military specification.

Table 9-1. Practical Comparison of Military Specification Requirements (Cont'd)

SPECIFICA-TION NO.	MIL-R-5757E	MIL-R-6106F (ASG)	MIL-R-39016
DATE	AMENDMENT 1, 30 DECEMBER 1968	20 AUGUST 1967	AMENDMENT 3, 10 FEBRUARY 1969
29. Marking (Cont.)	Source and Date Code Per MIL-STD-456	Date Code per MIL-STD-456 Contact Rating AC and/or DC and Frequency Serial Number (when specified) Wiring Diagram	Circuit Diagram on Case Suppliers Name or Code Date Code per MIL-STD-456 Serial Number
30. Radio Interference	3.24 Radio Interference (when specified) – Per MIL-STD-461 for Equipment Class 1C.	3.6.4.4, 4.7.4.4 Radio Interference – Per MIL-I-1681 for a-c coils.	
31. Internal Moisture	3.14, 4.8.10 Internal Moisture (when specified). Static contact resistance shall not exceed 0.1 ohm or 0.4 ohm for dry reed delays. Expose for 1 hr at max rated temp and 1 hr at min rated temp.	3.6.6.7, 4.7.6.8 Humidity Test (unsealed relays) – Per Procedure I of MIL-E-5272. Max leakage 50 mA at 150 VRMS after drying for 6 hr at −65°C.	
32. Moisture Resistance	3.23, 4.8.19 Moisture Resistance – Per Method 106 of MIL-STD-202.		3.18, 4.7.13 Moisture Resistance – Per Method 106 of MIL-STD-202.
33. Sand & Dust	3.25, 4.8.21 Sand and Dust (Enclosure 2 and 3 relays only) – Per Method 110 Test Condition A of MIL-STD-202	3.6.6.9, 4.7.6.10 Sand and Dust – Per Method 106 Test Condition A of MIL-STD-202.	
34. Capacitance	3.34, 4.8.30 Capacitance (when specified) (not applicable to telegraph relays) – Per Method 305 of MIL-STD-202.		
35. Thermal EMF	3.35, 4.8.31 Thermal EMF (when specified) (not applicable to telegraph relays) – Thermal EMF voltage per detail specification.		
36. Contact Noise	3.32, 4.8.27 Contact Noise (when specified) (not applicable to telegraph relays) – Contact noise shall have delayed to less than 0.05 millivolts peak-to-peak in less than 10 msec.		
37. Cross-Talk	3.33, 4.8.29 Cross-Talk (dry reed relays only with other types when specified, except telegraph relays). Equipment input impedance = 1 megohm min, paralleled with a capacitance of 20 picofarads max. 1.0-10.0 volts peak-to-peak input signal at 10 MHz.		

Note: Paragraph numbers are from the referenced military specification.

9.1 Format

The format of relay specifications may vary from one type of document to another. For example, the format of military specifications differs from the format of military standards.

Military relay specifications are written in six sections, and many systems manufacturers have adopted the same format. A format of this type would include the following:

Section 1 — Scope. An over-all picture of the requirements can be obtained from this section, which provides classifications and general information.

Section 2 — Applicable documents. Each of these documents is applicable to the extent specified in the general specification and should be read to obtain a complete picture of the requirements of the specification. Many a pitfall can be avoided by having the complete information.

Section 3 — Requirements. This section spells out exactly what is required for compliance. As a rule, the following subjects are outlined:

(1) Detail requirements for general relay types. This paragraph usually states that individual relay requirements are covered by the general and detail specifications. The detail specification takes precedence over the general specification.

(2) Qualification requirements

(3) Preproduction prototypes (when applicable)

(4) Material

(5) Design and construction

(6) Physical requirements

(7) Mechanical requirements

(8) Electrical requirements

(9) Environmental requirements.

(10) Marking

Most of the paragraphs in items 6, 7, 8, and 9 refer to paragraphs in Paragraph 9.3. To obtain full information, the reading of both paragraphs is *essential.*

Section 4 — Quality assurance provisions The documentation and necessary test information are found in this section. As a rule, the following subjects are outlined:

(1) Responsibility for inspection

(2) Classification of inspection

(3) Qualification inspection (complete information necessary to qualify a unit, advising the user as to which tests will be performed on a particular relay and where information from the detail specification must be applied)

(4) Tables of test sequence

(5) Preproduction inspection or first article inspection

(6) Quality conformance tests or acceptance inspection

(7) Test methods.

Test paragraphs often bear reference to the requirement paragraphs in Sec. 3, above. These should not be ignored. Some of the test methods include many different procedures or test levels. The detail specification pinpoints the exact procedure or test level for the particular relay. This should be kept in mind when reading a general relay specification. For example, if a specification calls for a relay that will meet the vibration requirements of a general specification, instead of referring to a specific test level, the result could be a test that is not properly defined. This impression can lead to the exchange of many letters or telephone calls before the requirements are clarified.

Section 5 — Packaging and preparation for delivery. The subject is self-explanatory. Various packaging levels are given that should be further defined in the detail specification or in the procurement document.

Section 6 — Notes. Additional information, intended use, and data requirements are included in this section. These paragraphs do not necessarily call for mandatory actions. However, this section is often overlooked and can be a source of trouble.

Not all specifications applicable to relays require the six sections. Where no information is to be given in a section, the words "Not Applicable" are printed. Thus, the format is maintained and information finding is facilitated regardless of the type of specification. Government standards may not follow this type of format. MIL-STD-105, for example, contains 11 sections. The format variations of Government standards make it impractical to cover in this section.

Table 9-2. Practical Comparison of Military Specification Requirements

SPECIFICA-TION NO.	MFSC-SPEC-339	MIL-R-19648B	MIL-R-19523A
DATE	31 OCTOBER 1967	AMENDMENT 1, 6 JANUARY 1969	30 DECEMBER 1966
1. Scope	1.1 Scope — This specification covers hermetically sealed, direct-current (d-c) relays with contact ratings up to and including 10-amps resistive load. These relays perform general purpose and magnetic-latch switching applications. Class "S" relays are qualified, screened, and acceptance tested for use in criticality category applications. Class "U" relays are qualified, screened, and acceptance tested for use in criticality category applications 3 or C. The major differences between Class "S" and "U" relays are that the Class "S" relay has more comprehensive screening tests (100% internal inspection, vibration scan, run-in, and radiographic inspection) and larger lot acceptance sample sizes.	1.1 Scope — This specification covers the general requirements for thermal, time delay relays.	1.1 Scope — This specification covers relays intended primarily for use in control circuits where a number of relays are interconnected to control the proper sequencing and functioning of a complex electrical, hydraulic, or pneumatic system or combination of such systems. Such relays are also required to provide suitable indication and alarm circuits directly associated with these systems. The relays are also intended for use in motor controllers, and related electrical equipment aboard naval ships.
2. Classification	1.2 Classification S — Class (1.2.1.1) 6 — No. of Poles (1.2.1.2) G — Coil (1.2.1.3) H — Terminals (1.2.1.4) −2 — Coil Resist. (1.2.1.5) −1 — Detail Specification & Vib. Level (1.2.1.6) 1.2.1.1 CLASS — Class "S" relays may be used in any application. Class "U" relays shall be used only in criticality 3 or C applications. 1.2.1.2 NO. OF POLES — The second symbol is a digit to designate the number form "C" contacts. 1.2.1.3 COIL SERVICE — Indicated by one of the following: General Purpose — G Magnetic Latch — L Sensitive — S Bifilar General Purpose — BG Bifilar Magnetic Latch — BL Bifilar Sensitive — BS 1.2.1.4 TERMINALS — Types shall be designated as follows: Solder Hook — H Plug In — P Wire Leads — W 1.2.1.5 COIL RESISTANCE — Multiplied by 100, shall specify the coil resistance in ohms. 1.2.1.6 SPECIFICATION SHEET NO. & VIB. LEVEL — The digits designate the applicable specification sheet. A letter preceding the number digits designates vibration level as follows: (a) When no letter is used, Level 2. (b) "C" designates Level 3. (c) "D" designates Level 4.	1.2 Classification 1.2.1 Military Part Number M — Military Designator 19648/1 — Specification Sheet Number − 001 — Dash Number 1.2.2 Levels & Classes 1.2.2.1 Shock — Table I 1.2.2.2 Temperature — Table II 1.2.2.3 Vibration — Table III	1.2 Classification Category A — 500,000 operations Category B — 100,000 operations Category C — 25,000 operations
3. Enclosure			
4. Vibration	1.2.1.6 Specification Sheet No. & Vib. Level | Level	Acceleration	Frequency
---	---	---
2	20 g	10-2000 Hz
3	30 g (sine) 0.3 g² (random)	10-2000 Hz
4	30 g (sine) 0.6 g² (random)	10-3000 Hz		1.2.2.3 Vibration — Table III | Level	Acceleration Range	Frequency Range	MIL-STD-202 Method	Condition
---	---	---	---	---
1	10 g	10-55 Hz	201	−
2	10 g	10-500 Hz	204	A
3	15 g	10-2,000 Hz	204	B
4	20 g	10-2,000 Hz	204	C		3.4.2.9.4 Vibration — Relays shall be designated to withstand Type I Vibration of MIL-STD-167

Note: Paragraph numbers are from the referenced military specifications.

Table 9-2. Practical Comparison of Military Specification Requirements (Cont'd)

SPECIFICA-TION NO.	MFSC-SPEC-339	MIL-R-19648B	MIL-R-19523A
DATE	31 OCTOBER 1967	AMENDMENT 1, 6 JANUARY 1969	30 DECEMBER 1966
5. Temperature	−65°C to +125°C	1.2.2.2 Temperature Class Table II — Class Operating Range A −55°C to +85°C B −65°C to +125°C	3.4.2.2 Ambient Temperature Ambient Range 50°C 5°C to 50°C 65°C 5°C to 65°C Special Higher than 65°C
6. Shock		1.2.2.1 Shock — Table I Level Test Condition Method of MIL-STD-202 1 G 213 2 I 213 3 High Impact 207	3.4.2.9.3 Shock Proofness — Class I — Relays whose contacts will not chatter. Class II — Relays whose contacts will not chatter long enough to either drop out the relay or chatter of 4 msec maximum; no transfer. Class III — Relays whose contacts will not chatter 4 msec or more; no transfer. Class IV — Relays whose contacts will not chatter long enough to either drop out the relay or chatter of 20 msec maximum; no transfer. Class V — Relays whose contacts will not chatter 20 msec or more; no transfer. Class VI — Relays whose contacts will not close from the open position. Class VII — No requirement for electrical operation.
7. Seal Test	3.7.7 Seal Leakage — Seal leakage shall not exceed an equivalent rate of 1 X 10^{-8} atm cc/sec.	3.7.1 Seal Test I (hermetically sealed relay). Method 112 of MIL-STD-202 Test Condition C. Procedure I, leakage rate of 1 X 10 cc/sec. 3.7.2 Seal Test II (nonhermetically sealed relays). Method 112 of MIL-STD-202 Test Condition B.	4.5.2 Sealing — 4.5.2.1.1 Seal Test I — Immersed relays in a saturated solution of sodium chloride and subject to absolute pressure equal to 2.5 in. of mercury for 4 hr. Subject relays to test which will determine if leakage rate is in excess of 3 cc of gas in 10 yr at a pressure differential of 1 atm. 4.5.2.1.2 Seal Test II
8. Insulation Resistance	3.7.5 Insulation resistance shall have a minimum of 1,000 megohms at 25°C with 500 VDC potential.	3.9 Insulation resistance shall have a minimum of 100 megohms per Method 302 of MIL-STD-202 Test Condition A.	3.4.2.4 Insulation resistance shall have a minimum of 100 megohms at 25°C.
9. Dielectric Strength	3.7.6, 4.10.3 Dielectric Strength — Leakage current 1 mA max. Sea Level — 750 VRMS all points, except 500 VRMS between open contacts. High Altitude — 300 VRMS all points.	3.8, 4.8.5 Dielectric with Standing Voltage — Leakage current 1 mA max. Sea Level — 1,000 VRMS all points, except 500 VRMS between open contacts. High Altitude — 350 VRMS all points.	3.4.2.5 Dielectric Strength — A-C Relays — Rated at 600 volts or less twice the rated voltage plus 1000 VRMS. — Rated over 600 volts, $2\frac{1}{2}$ times the rated voltage plus 2000 VRMS. D-C Relays — 10 times the maximum operating voltage plus 1000 VRMS.
10. Contact Resistance	3.7.2.3, 4.10.6.3 Contact resistance shall not exceed 100 milliohms.	3.6.1, 4.8.3.1 Contact Resistance — Initial — 0.050 ohm max After Life — 0.150 ohm max Minimum Current — Initial — 0.5 ohm max After Life — 1.0 ohm max	Per detail specification
11. Pickup	3.7.2.1, 4.10.6.1 Operational Voltage or Current. Per detail specification, soak 2 sec max with rated voltage gradually increased from zero.		3.4.2.10 Operating Voltage — Pickup — At not more than 80% of rated voltage.
12. Dropout Voltage	3.7.2.2, 4.10.6.2 Release Voltage or Current. Per detail specification, rated voltage reduced gradually.		3.4.2.10.3 Dropout Voltage — Dropout not less than 10% of rated voltage.
13. D-C Coil Resistance	3.7.2.4, 4.10.6.4 Coil Resistance — Maximum variations shall be ± 5% provided the specified limits of the detail specification are met.		4.5.4 Resistance — Plus or minus 10% of detail specification.
14. Contact Bounce	3.7.2.6, 4.10.6.6 Operate and Release Time (including bounce) — Shall not exceed the values of the detail specification.		

Note: Paragraph numbers are from the referenced military specifications.

Table 9-2. Practical Comparison of Military Specification Requirements (Cont'd)

SPECIFICATION NO.	MFSC-SPEC-339	MIL-R-19648B	MIL-R-19523A
DATE	31 OCTOBER 1967	AMENDMENT 1, 6 JANUARY 1969	30 DECEMBER 1966
15. Operate & Release Time	3.7.2.6, 4.10.6.6 Operate and Release Time – Shall not exceed the values of the detail specification.	3.6.2, 4.8.3.2 Normal operate time, operate time tolerance shall be as specified on the detail specification. 3.6.4, 4.8.3.4 Release time shall be as specified on the detail specification.	
16. Thermal Shock	3.7.1.6, 4.10.5.8 Thermal Shock – Water at 85°C for 20 minutes, then water at 5°C for 20 minutes; perform cycle three times	3.11, 4.8.8 Thermal Shock – Per Method 107 of MIL-STD-202. Test Condition A (for Class A relays). Test Condition B (for Class B relays)	
17. Acceleration	3.7.1.7, 4.10.5.9 Centrifugal Acceleration – 100 g's six directions, closed contacts chatter 10 microsec max. Energized and de-energized at 30 sec intervals.	3.13, 4.8.10 Centrifugal Acceleration (when applicable) – Per the detail specification.	
18. Salt Spray	3.7.1.1, 4.10.5.3 Corrosion – 5% salt, Method 101, Test Condition B of MIL-STD-202. Drying time 24 hr.	3.18, 4.8.15 Salt spray per Method 101, Test Condition B of MIL-STD-202.	
19. Overvoltage	3.7.1.2, 4.10.5.4 High Temperature/Overvoltage. 28 VDC nominal coil voltage, energize with 32 VDC for 2 hr at 125°C. For coil voltages other than 28 VDC, 120% of rated nominal coil voltage.	3.14, 4.8.11 Overvoltage – energize at room temperature for 8 hr at 110% of rated operate voltage.	
20. High-Low Temperature Operation	3.7.1.2, 4.10.5.4 High Temperature/Overvoltage – See overvoltage above. 3.7.1.3, 4.10.5.5 Low Temperature – De-energized 6 hr at −65°C, measurements and test at both exposures.		
21. Overload		3.17, 4.8.14 Overload – 50 operations. Contact current twice the rated, voltage shall be rated voltage. Following test, contact resistance shall not exceed 0.100 ohms.	
22. Rupture			
23. Loads — Resistive	1.1 Covers relays with contact rating up to and including 10 amps resistive. Per detail specification.	3.4.2 Contact arrangement and contact rating per detail specification.	
Inductive		3.4.2 Same as above.	
Motor			
Lamp		3.4.2 Same as above.	
Minimum Current			
Low Level	3.7.4, 4.10.8 Low Level Run-in. 10 microamps max at 30 mV max a-c or d-c open circuit voltage.		
3 Phase AC			

Note: Paragraph numbers are from the referenced military specifications.

Table 9-2. Practical Comparison of Military Specification Requirements (Cont'd)

SPECIFICA-TION NO.	MFSC-SPEC-339	MIL-R-19648B	MIL-R-19523A
DATE	31 OCTOBER 1967	AMENDMENT 1, 6 JANUARY 1969	30 DECEMBER 1966
24. Coil Life		3.19, 4.8.16.3 Heater Life Test — 200 hr rated heater voltage at maximum rated temperature.	
25. Endurance	Not listed by this title — See Life in this table.	Not listed in this title — See Life in this table.	3.2.4.9.2 Endurance — Category "A" 500,000, "B" 100,000, "C" 25,000 operations.
26. Life	3.7.3, 4.10.7 Life Test — 100,000 operations, rated contact load, 125°C,18-20 cpm, with case grounded.	3.19, 4.8.16 Life — Operations determined by normal operate time, coil voltage shall be nominal, and contacts loaded with rated load.	
27. Ozone			
28. Grounding			
29. Marking	3.11 Marking — Per MIL-STD-130 and include the following: 　Type Designation 　Rated Voltage or Current 　D-C Coil Resistance 　Contact Rating 　Circuit Diagram 　Date Code 　Radiflo Symbol 　Serial Number	3.20 Marking — Per MIL-STD-130 and include the following: 　Manufacturer's Name 　Date Code 　Heater Voltage 　Specification P/N 　Contact Rating 　Circuit Diagram 　Time Delay Rating	3.6 Identification Plates — Per A, B, or C of MIL-P-15024 and MIL-STD-130 and the following: 　Federal Stock No. 　Manufacturer's Name & P/N 　Government Inspector's Stamp
30. Radio Interference			
31. Internal Moisture			
32. Moisture Resistance		3.16, 4.8.13 Moisture Resistance — Method 106 of MIL-STD-202.	
33. Sand and Dust			
34. Capacitance			
35. Thermal EMF			
36. Contact Noise			
37. Cross-Talk			

Note: Paragraph numbers are from the referenced military specifications.

9.2   Detail specifications

Each general relay specification gives reference to a number of applicable detail specifications. The detail specifications are designated as "−/" or MS (Military Standard) numbers. The phrases "unless otherwise specified" and "when applicable" often appear in general specifications. The detail specification indicates any requirement which differs from the general specification and lists applicable requirements.

9.3 Specific General Specifications for Relays

9.3.1   "MIL-R-5757, Military Specification. Relays, Electrical (for Electronic and Communication-type Equipment), General Specification for" (Preparing activity: Navy-EC, Project 5945-0064)

Scope (MIL-R-5757E, Amendment 1, 30 Dec. 1968)

1.1 This specification covers the general requirements for electrical relays with contact ratings up to and including 10 amperes for use in electronic, communication, and other type applications, including those used in telegraph equipment.

MIL-R-5757 uses slash numbers to identify the detail sheets, that is, MIL-R-5757/1, MIL-R-5757/2, and the like. Revisions to the detail sheets are denoted by letters (A, B, etc.). Each detail sheet is written in the same format as the general specification. The relay type designations (e.g., RY4XX4B3L11) used in previous revisions of MIL-R-5757 have been excluded from this revision. A relay classification system has been included in the section that provides information applicable to the individual relay.

Classification. Relays shall be classified as called for in the specification.

Enclosure Design. The enclosure design is identified by a single digit, as follows:

Symbol	Type
1	Open
2	Enclosed
3	Sealed (other than hermetically)
4	Hermetically sealed

Vibration Characteristic. The vibration characteristic is identified by a single digit as follows:

Symbol	Maximum Acceleration Level	Frequency Range (Hz)
1	0.060″ D.A.	10 to 55
2	10 G	10 to 500
3	15 G	10 to 2,000
4	20 G	10 to 2,000
5	30 G	10 to 3,000
6	Random	50 to 2,000

Temperature Range. The temperature range is identified by a single letter as follows:

Symbol	Range (°C)
A	−55 to +85
B	−65 to +125
C	−65 to +200
D	0 to +70

Shock Type. The shock type is identified by a single digit as follows:

Symbol	Shock Type (In accordance with MIL-STD-202)
1	50 G, 11 ± 2 MS, sawtooth (Test condition G, Method 213)[1]
2	75 G, 11 ± 2 MS, sawtooth (Test condition H, Method 213 modified)[1]
3	100 G, 11 ± 2 MS, sawtooth (Test condition I, Method 213 modified)[1]
4	Method 202 (Not for new design)
5	High impact (Method 207)
6	Medium impact (Method 205)

Military Part Number. The military part number shall consist of the letter "M," the basic number of the specification sheet, and an assigned dash number as shown in this example.

[1]Specific shock pulses of 50 G, 75 G, and 100 G are considered nominally equivalent in severity to former designations 15 G, 30 G, and 50 G, respectively (Method 205).

Requirement section 3 of this document specifies the general requirements, design and construction, physical characteristics, and electrical characteristics. If a requirement is other than that stated in the general specification, it will be shown on the detail sheet. For example, contact bounce and dielectric strength specifications are often changed, depending on the relay type. The detail sheet must be used in conjunction with the general specification. One is not complete without the other. The revision to MIL-R-5757 included relays for telegraph equipment. These relays were formerly specified MIL-R-83722 (USAF).

QPL 5757-27 is a Qualified Products List for MIL-R-5757. The activity responsible for this Qualified Products List is the Naval Electronics Systems Command. Each issue is denoted by the last number, that is, the next issues will be QPL-5757-28, -29, etc. Relays that have been qualified under the requirements for the product as specified in the latest effective issue of the applicable specification are listed. The list is subject to change without notice. Changes are made by amendments to the list or revisions. Government designation, manufacturer's designation or type number, test or qualification reference and manufacturer are noted. The address of each qualified manufacturer is on the last page.

MIL-R-5757 has been approved by the Department of Defense and is mandatory for use by all departments and agencies of the Department of Defense.

9.3.2 "MIL-R-6106, *Military Specification. Relays, Electric, General Specification for*" (*Preparing activity: Air Force—85*)

Scope (MIL-R-6106F, (ASG) 25 August 1967)
1.1 This specification establishes general requirements for electro-mechanical relays with nominal contact ratings from five amperes (resistive) and upward for use in electrical applications. Relays covered by this specification are capable of meeting the electrical and environmental requirements when mounted directly to the structure of aircraft and other primary vehicles.

MIL-R-6106 uses MS (Military Standard) and numbers to identify the detail sheets. The older type relays used AN designations, such as AN3303. Revisions are denoted by letters — A, B, etc. The detail sheet takes precedence over the general specifications. The newer detail sheets use the following format:

Drawing with dimensions
Schematic wiring diagram
(A) Operating characteristics
(B) Contact rated load
(C) Environmental characteristics
(D) Minimum dielectric strength requirements
(E) Maximum weight
(F) Mating socket.

If a requirement is other than that stated in the general specification, it is called for on the detail sheet. For example, dielectric withstanding voltage or overload requirements are often changed, depending on the relay type.

The type designator included in section 1 of this specification classifies the relays covered by MIL-R-6106. The type designators are as follows:

Type I — Continuous duty, hermetically sealed.

Type I ER — Continuous duty, hermetically sealed, established reliability, failure rate 1 percent per 10,000 operations.

Type II — Continuous duty, nonhermetically sealed.

Type II ER — Continuous duty, nonhermetically sealed, established reliability, failure rate 1 percent per 10,000 operations.

Type III — Intermittent duty.

Unless otherwise specified on the detail specification or military standard, all relays are type I.

QPL-6106-18 (Feb., 1969) is the Qualified Products List for MIL-R-6106. The activity responsible for this list is the Engineering and Technical Branch (EWBE-E), Material Identification and Engineering Division, Directorate of Air Force Support, Wright-Patterson Air Force Base, Ohio.

Each issue is denoted by the last numbers, that is, the next new issues will be QPL-6106-19, -20, etc. Relays that are listed have been qualified under the requirements for the product as specified in the latest effective issue of the general specification. The list is subject to change without notice. Changes are made by revisions or amendments to the list. Government designation, manufacturer's designation, test or qualication reference, and manufacturer are noted. The address of each manufacturer is listed on the last page.

Amendment to QPL's can be issued without reissuing the entire QPL.

This specification is an ASG (Aeronautical Standards Group) and has been approved by the Departments of the Air Force and the Naval Air Systems Command.

9.3.3 "MIL-R-39016, *Military Specification. Relays, Electromagnetic, Established Reliability, General Specification for*" (*Preparing activity: Navy-EC, Project 5945-0049*)

1.1. *Scope* (MIL-R-39016, amendment 3. 10 Feb. 1969). This specification covers the general requirements for established reliability, electromagnetic, hermetically sealed (excluding thermal) relays for use in electronic and communication type equipment (*see* 6.1). These relays are designed to operate in low and medium power switching circuits with contact ratings up to 10 amperes alternating current (AC) or direct current (DC). Relays covered by this specification demonstrate a contact life failure rate level of 0.01 to 3.0 percent in 10,000 relay operations. The failure rate level is established at a confidence level of 90 percent for qualification and 60 percent for maintenance of qualification, established at 100,000 operations at 85°C, 125°C, and 200°C under rated load conditions specified therein.

Paragraph 6.1, referred to in the scope, states: "Intended use — Relays covered by this specification shall not be used in plug-in socket applications. Terminal solderability requirements are not specified.

MIL-R-39016 is the first military specification of this nature. The demand for highly reliable parts in the ever-expanding communications, missile, and spacecraft fields created the need for such a specification. Some relay manufacturers had already written their own reliability specifications.

A rundown of the subparagraphs of the specification provides a good idea of the type of relays covered by this document:

Table I. Vibration level

Level 1	10g	10 to 2000 Hz
Level 2	20g	10 to 2000 Hz
Level 3	30g	10 to 2000 Hz
Level 4	30g	10 to 3000 Hz and 0.3g^2 per Hz random

Table II. Temperature class

Class	Operating ambient temperature range (°C)
A	−65 to +85
B	−65 to +125
C	−65 to +200

Table III. Shock level

Level	Test condition	Applicable test method of MIL-STD-202
1	H (75g)	213
2	......	207

Table IV. Terminal type

Symbol	Type of solder terminal
L	Lug (solder)
W	Wire lead
P	Pin

Table V. Failure rate level[1]

Symbol	Failure rate level (Percent per 10,000 operations)
M	1.0
P	0.1
R	0.01
L	3.0

This specification has three life tests: High level (4.7.18.1), low level (4.7.18.2), and combination high and low level (4.7.18.3) contact loads. (High level loads are rated as 0.1 amp at 25 to 30 volts d-c and low level loads as 10 ma at 50 millivolts d-c or peak a-c.) The equipment necessary to monitor the life tests is much more elaborate than that required by other military relay specifications. Table XV of this specification calls for the initial and post life measurement and lists post life test limits. This kind of information is not found in many specifications.

[1]The failure rate levels apply to electrical life within the rated number of relay operations as called for by the specification sheet at maximum ambient temperature and applicable load.

The supplier must submit evidence of compliance of the qualifying activity to MIL-Q-9858 as a prerequisite for qualification and maintenance of qualification. Compliance to MIL-C-45662 is also required. Qualification shall be granted at the "M" failure rate initially and shall be based on the results of qualification inspection, and on compliance with the prerequisite mentioned above.

There are provisions for the following:

(1) Extension of failure rate level qualification

(2) Maintenance of failure rate level qualification

(3) Verification of qualification.

The various reliability tables provided are in accordance with the general approach and procedures described in MIL-STD-690.

The specification includes sample data forms showing the minimum information required and furnishes a suggested format. MIL-R-39016 uses slash numbers to denote the detail sheet (example: MIL-R-39016/3). The detail sheet lists the following requirements: Dimensions, physical characteristics, electrical characteristics, contact ratings, contact bounce, life, duty, and insulation resistance.

Applicable notes specify any precautions or unusual features. The part number consists of the basic number of the specification sheet and a dash number taken from the part number table (example: M39016/03-0001). The table is a list of all the applicable dash numbers and characteristics. The columns include the following typical data:

Dash number	Mount	Vibration	Temperature
−0007	Flange	3	B

Shock	Terminals	Failure rate level
1	L	M

This specification has been approved by the Department of Defense and is mandatory for use by all departments and agencies of the Department of Defense.

9.3.4 "MSFC-SPEC-339, Relays, DC, Hermetically Sealed, For Space Vehicles and Associated Support Equipment, General Specification for" (Preparing activity: George C. Marshall Space Flight Center — NASA)

Scope. (MSFC-SPEC-339A, 31, Oct. 1967) 1.1 This specification covers hermetically sealed, direct-current (d-c) relays with contact ratings up to and including 10 amperes resistive load. These relays perform general purpose and magnetic-latch switching applications. Class "S" relays are qualified, screened, and acceptance-tested to meet all critical category applications. Class "U" relays are qualified, screened, and acceptance-tested for use in critical category application 3 drawings, the major differences between prehensive screening tests (100-percent internal inspection, vibration scan, run-in and radiographic inspection), and larger lot acceptance sample sizes.

This specification does not cover contact load ratings for minimum current, a-c loads, motor loads or lamp loads. Caution must be exercised where these are encountered.

This specification has been approved by the George C. Marshall Space Flight Center (MSFC) in Huntsville, Alabama, and is available for use by MSFC and allied contractors.

Before the establishment of this specification, the George C. Marshall Space Flight Center used ABMA-PD-R-187, Army Ballistic Missile Agency Purchase Description, as a procurement specification. The scope of MSFC-SPEC-339 indicates the need for this new specification since previous specifications had not made provisions for general purpose switching applications. MSFC-SPEC-339 includes dry circuit (low level) cycling and life tests as well as life tests for rated loads.

Some of the wording from ABMA-PD-R-187 has been carried over into this document, but on the whole it is new. The similar type designation and the color-coding systems are two of the recognizable features. The type designation has one change in that the prefix letter "S" is used to identify relays covered by MSFC-SPEC-339. The complete breakdown of the type designation S6GH21, for example, would be:

S   *Component.* Relays covered by this specification are identified by the one-letter symbol "S."

6   *Number of poles (switching circuits).*

G   *Coil service.* There are three types, identified by a one-letter symbol as follows:

     G   General purpose
     L   Magnetic latch
     S   Sensitive
   BG   Bifilar suppressed general purpose
   BL   Bifilar suppressed magnetic latch
   BS   Bifilar suppressed sensitive

H   *Terminals.* There are three types, identified by a one-letter symbol as follows:

     H   Solder hook or eyelet
     P   Plug-in
     W   Wire leads

2   *Coil resistance.* This number multiplied by 100 specifies the nominal coil resistance in ohms.

1   This number indicates the applicable specification sheet.

Considerable information is given in this system of type designation. Other specifications using a similar system perform the same service.

MSFC-SPEC-339 uses slash numbers to identify the specification sheets (example: MSFC-SPEC-339/53). The sheet is written in the same six-section format as the general specification. As in the case of all other specifications, the detail sheets specify the requirements of the individual relays and must be used in conjunction with the general specification to be complete. In the event of conflict, the detail sheet takes precedence over the general specification.

9.3.5   "MIL-R-19648B, *Military Specification. Relays, Thermal, Time Delay, General Specification for*"

Scope (MIL-R-19648B, amendment 1, 6 Jan. 1969)
1.1 This specification covers the general requirements for thermal, time delay relays.
MIL-R-19648 is a specification to fill the void in the coverage of MIL-R-5757, which previously (D rev.) excluded thermal types in the title. The format is similar to MIL-R-5757, and the sampling plan is very much like the older MIL-R-5757C specification.

MIL-R-19648 uses slash numbers to denote the detail sheets. The detail sheets are written

in the same six section format as the general specification. Revisions to sheets are noted by the letters A, B, etc. Detail requirements or exceptions applicable to individual types are specified on the detail sheet. In the event of conflict between requirements of the general specification and the detail specification, the latter shall govern.

The type designator of previous revisions is replaced by a military part numbering system like MIL-R-5757. A classification system has been included in this section that provides information applicable to the individual relay.

Military Part Number. The military part number shall consist of the letter "M," the basic number of the specification sheet, and an assigned dash number as shown in this example:

Levels and Classes. Relays covered by this specification shall be of the following levels and classes, as specified.

Shock. The shock level shall be in accordance with the following, as specified:

Level	Test Condition	Applicable Test Method MIL-STD-202
1	G	213
2	I	213
3	High Impact	207

Temperature Class. The temperature class shall be in accordance with the following, as specified:

Class	Operating — Ambient Temperature Range, °C
A	−55 to +85
B	−65 to +125

Vibration. The vibration levels shall be in accordance with the following, as specified:

Level	Acceleration Value	Frequency Range (Hz)	MIL-STD-202 Method/ Condition	
1	10G	10 to 55	201	
2	10G	10 to 500	204	A
3	15G	10 to 2000	204	B
4	20G	10 to 2000	204	D

QPL-19648 is the Qualified Products List for MIL-R-19648. The format and information given are the same as explained in the paragraphs for MIL-R-5757 and MIL-R-6106.

Information pertaining to qualification of products covered by MIL-R-19648 may be obtained from the Commanding Officer, Naval Electronic System Command, Specifications and Standardization Branch, Department of the Navy, Washington, D.C. 20360.

This specification is mandatory for use by all departments and agencies of the Department of Defense.

9.4 General Specifications Applicable to Relays

9.4.1 "MIL-Q-9858, Military Specification, Quality Program Requirements" (Preparing activity: Air Force — Hq. USAF)

Scope (MIL-Q-9858A, 16 Dec. 1963)

1.3 *Summary.* An effective and economical quality program, planned and developed in consonance with the contractor's other administrative and technical programs, is required by this specification. Design of the program shall be based upon consideration of the technical and manufacturing aspects of production and related engineering design and materials. The program shall assure adequate quality throughout all areas of contract performance; for example, design, development, fabrication, processing, assembly, inspection, test, maintenance, packaging, shipping, storage and site installation.

All supplies and services under the contract, whether manufactured or performed within the contractor's plant or at any other source, shall be controlled at all points necessary to assure conformance to contractual requirements. The program shall provide for the prevention and ready detection of discrepancies and for timely and positive correction action. The contractor shall make objective evidence of quality conformance readily available to the Government Representative. Instructions and records for quality must be controlled.

The authority and responsibility of those in charge of the design, production, testing, and inspection of quality shall be clearly stated. The program shall facilitate determinations of the effects of quality deficiencies and quality costs on price. Facilities and standards such as drawings, engineering changes, measuring equipment and the like which are necessary for the creation of the required quality shall be effectively managed. The program shall include an effective control of purchased materials and subcontracted work. Manufacturing, fabrication and assembly work conducted within the contractor's plant shall be controlled completely. The quality program shall also include effective execution of responsibilities shared jointly with the Government or related to Government functions, such as control of Government property and Government source inspection.

MIL-Q-9858 was written to cover the requirements of a Quality Assurance Program at the relay manufacturer's plant. This program does not pertain only to quality control personnel. Controls are specified for every phase of manufacture and engineering, and a continuity of interdepartmental cooperation is necessary for implementation of MIL-Q-9858. The extent of the requirements of any individual paragraph in this specification can only be determined by the specific contract. The program director should interpret the stringent requirements so that their general intent is met and the desired quality level is in no way compromised. The requirements of MIL-Q-9858, when interpreted economically, can prove beneficial to the entire organization.

A previous revision of MIL-Q-9858 required a quality assurance plan that would detect and eliminate rejects before use. MIL-Q-9858 now requires a quality assurance plan that will not only detect and eliminate rejects but also provide for the institution of corrective action, by the most economical means, to prevent recurrence.

9.4.2 "MIL-E-5272, Military Specification, Environmental Testing, Aeronautical and Associated Equipment, General Specification for" (Preparing activity: Aeronautical Standards Group)

Scope (MIL-E-5272C, Amendment 1, 20 Jan. 1960)

1.1 *General.* This specification establishes generally applicable procedures for testing aeronautical and associated climatic and environmental conditions. Procedures prescribed herein are to be utilized in subjecting equipment to simulated and accelerated environmental conditions in order to insure satisfactory operation and to reduce deterioration when the equipment is operated or stored in any global locality. In the case of any particular item of equipment, test procedures are to be followed to the extent specified in the applicable equipment specification.

MIL-E-5272 is one of the older environmental test specifications. Many of the test procedures have been discontinued. This document is one of the few test specifications that includes tables for suggested sequence of environmental tests for various types of aeronautical equipment.

9.4.3   MIL-I-45208, *Military Specification, Inspection System Requirements" (Preparing activity: Army-Munitions Command)*

1.1 *Scope* (MIL-I-45208A, 16 Dec. 1963) This specification establishes requirements for contractors' inspection systems. These requirements pertain to the inspections and tests necessary to substantiate product conformance to drawings, specifications and contract requirements and to all inspections and tests required by the contract. These requirements are in addition to those inspections and tests set forth in applicable specifications and other contractual documents.

MIL-I-45208 is an inspection system requirement specification and should not be confused with MIL-Q-9858, of which MIL-I-45208 is a part. An organization meeting the requirements of MIL-Q-9858 should require conformance to MIL-I-45208 by all suppliers of product components. Conformance to this specification also requires conformance to MIL-C-45662.

9.4.4   "MIL-C-45662, *Military Specification, Calibration System Requirements" (Preparing activity: Army-Ordnance Corps)*

1.1 *Scope* (MIL-C-45662A, 9 Feb. 1962) This specification provides for the establishment and maintenance of a calibration system to control the accuracy of the measuring and test equipment used to assure that supplies and services presented to the government for acceptance are in conformance with prescribed technical requirements.

Minimum requirements to establish and maintain calibration systems are outlined in this specification. Only the method of conformance and the calibration intervals are left to the discretion of the user. Many general specifications refer to this document. In most cases (MIL-Q-9858A, for example), it is to be used to the extent specified in the general specification.

9.4.5   "NPC-200-2, *NASA Quality Publication, Quality Program Provisions for Space Systems Contractors"* (April 1962)

1.1 *General.* The "Quality Program Provisions for Space System Contractors (NPC 200-2)" sets forth general requirements for contractor quality programs necessary to ensure that complete space systems, launch vehicles, spacecraft, and associated ground support equipment meet the quality requirements of the contract. These requirements include the establishment and maintenance of an effective quality program from the design conception to the delivery of articles of satisfactory quality level meeting the intended design.

This publication was "established to provide *common, general* requirements for contractor quality programs to ensure the required quality of NASA space systems and elements thereof."

NASA installations shall invoke the requirements of this publication *contractually* to the *extent needed* and consistent with program planning for procurements of complete space systems, launch vehicles, spacecraft, and associated ground support systems. NASA space system contractors will also invoke requirements of this publication in selected *major* subcontracts.

The above sentences are quoted verbatim from the preface of NPC-200-2, and certain words are italicized only for emphasis. This specification, basically more stringent than MIL-Q-9858, requires specific clarification for each contract and should not be invoked in whole unless specified.

9.4.6 "NPC-200-3, *NASA Quality Publication, Inspection System Provisions for Suppliers of Space Materials, Parts, Components and Services*" (April 1962)

1.1 *General.* The 'Inspection System Provisions for Supplies of Space Materials, Parts, Components, and Services (NPC 200-3)' sets forth the minimum requirements for supplier's inspection systems necessary to ensure that materials, parts, components, and services for launch vehicles, spacecraft, and associated ground support equipment meet the requirements of the contract. Procedures used to implement the provisions of this publication shall be subject to the disapproval, except as otherwise specified, of the cognizant NASA installation or its designated representative.

This publication was "established to provide common, general requirements for suppliers' inspection systems to ensure the required quality of materials, parts, components and services for end use in NASA Space Systems."

NASA installations shall invoke the requirements of this publication *contractually* to the *extent needed* and consistent with programs planning for procurements involved. NASA space system contractors will also invoke the requirements of this publication as *appropriate*.

The above sentences are quoted verbatim from the preface of NPC-200-3, and certain words are italicized only for emphasis. This specification, basically more stringent than MIL-I-45208, requires specific clarification for each contract and should not be invoked in whole unless so specified.

9.5 General Standards Applicable to Relays

9.5.1 "MIL-STD-790, *Reliability Assurance Program For Electronic Parts Specification*" (*Preparing activity: Navy-EC, Project 5900-00013*)

Scope (MIL-STD-790C, 18 April 1968)
1.1 *Purpose.* This standard is for direct reference in electronic parts established reliability (ER) specifications and establishes the criteria for a reliability assurance program which are to be met by manufacturers qualifying electronic parts to the specification.

1.2 *Application.* This standard is applicable when:
(a) Referenced in ER specifications where attainment of specified failure rate levels and assurance of homogeneity of parts require control of product facilities, materials, and processes.
(b) The qualifying activity evaluates, accepts, and monitors the reliability assurance program as required for qualification approval.

The referenced documents in Section 2 of this specification are "MIL-C-45662, Calibration System Requirements," "MIL-STD-721, Definition of Effectiveness Terms for Reliability, Maintainability, Human Factors, and Safety," and "Fed-Std-209, Clean Room and Work Station Requirements. Controlled Environment."

The format of this Military Standard differs from the usual arrangement of the sections. Section 3, for example, contains definitions that help to clarify and standardize interpretation.

Section 4 is General Requirements. It outlines the manufacturer's responsibility for establishing a reliability assurance program and maintaining the capability of demonstrating to the qualifying activity that the documented reliability assurance program is in effect.

Section 5 is Detailed Requirements. It outlines in detail the reliability assurance program and documentation requirements. The two main paragraphs are 5.1, "Documentation to be submitted to the qualifying activity," and 5.2, "Documentation to be retained at the manufacturer's plant and available upon request by the qualifying activity."

9.5.2 "MIL-STD-105, *Military Standard, Sampling Procedures and Tables for Inspection by Attributes*" (*Preparing activity: U. S. Army Munitions Command*)

Scope (MIL-STD-105D, Change Notice 2, 20 March 1969).
1.1 *Purpose.* This publication establishes sampling plans and procedures for inspection by attributes. When specified by the responsible authority, this publication

shall be referenced in the specification, contract, inspection instructions, or other documents and the provisions set forth herein shall govern. The "responsible authority" shall be designated in one of the above documents.

1.2 *Application.* Sampling plans designated in this publication are applicable, but not limited, to inspection of the following:

a. End items.
b. Components and raw materials.
c. Operations.
d. Materials in process.
e. Supplies in storage.
f. Maintenance operations.
g. Date of records.
h. Administrative procedures.

These plans are intended primarily to be used for a continuing series of lots or batches. The plans may also be used for the inspection of isolated lots or batches, but, in this latter case, the user is cautioned to consult the operating characteristic curves to find a plan which will yield the desired protection. . . .

1.3 *Inspection.* Inspection is the process of measuring, examining, testing, or otherwise comparing the unit of product (see 1.5) with the requirements.

1.4 *Inspection by Attributes.* Inspection by attributes is inspection whereby either the unit of product is classified simply as defective or nondefective, or the number of defects in the unit of product is counted, with respect to a given requirement or set of requirements.

1.5 *Unit of Product.* The unit of product is the thing inspected in order to determine its classification as defective or nondefective or to count the number of defects. It may be a single article, a pair, a set, a length, an area, an operation, a volume, a component of an end product, or the end product itself. The unit of product may or may not be the same as the unit of purchase, supply, production, or shipment.

This is an international specification that is not actually a "general" document. It is a document dealing with statistical quality control procedures, leaving very little margin for misinterpretation. Use of the designated tables leaves little chance of misconstruction.

The versatility of MIL-STD-105 is emphasized by the fact that the application is generally within the relay manufacturing facility, but the levels, risks, and AQL's are designated by the relay user.

The following is a list of the major changes incorporated in MIL-STD-105D:

(1) Increased scope of application
(2) Elimination of administrative instruction
(3) Improved AQL definition
(4) Specific instruction on the use of the inspection level
(5) Reduction in the number of "Special Inspection Levels"
(6) Change in the sample sizes and sample-to-lot relationship
(7) Changes in the switching rule for tightened and reduced inspection
(8) Reduced severity in shifts in inspection levels
(9) Adoption of samples of equal size for double sampling
(10) Modification of reduced inspection rate
(11) Elimination of very large acceptance/ rejection number sampling plans
(12) Acknowledged improvement of better risk performance of C-1 plans
(13) Authority to adjust sample size.

The following is a list of additions to MIL-STD-105D:

(1) Special tightened sampling plans
(2) Tables for AQL values
(3) Tables of limiting quality
(4) Average sample size (ASN) curves
(5) Tabulated select probability values.
(6) Conversion from small sample inspection level of revision C to the special inspection levels of revision D.

MIL-STD-105D contains more supplementary information than MIL-STD-105C in fewer pages. In addition to the tables and operating characteristics (O.C.) curves previously given in the Code Letter portion of the standard, tabulated values of the data given by the O.C. curves have been added for convenient reference. A change in format in the Code Letter portion of the standard has resulted in fewer graphs of the O.C. curves and in the elimination of the "folding down" of the sampling plan tables (made necessary in previous issues because of the limited page width). Another innovation that makes the standard easier to use is the addition of bold letters and reference codes in the lower corners of each page to function as a built-in index.

The following article gives a detailed description of all changes in MIL-STD-105D: "MIL-STD-105D, An International Standard for Attribute Sampling," O. A. Cocca, *Industrial Quality Control,* vol. 21, No. 5, Nov. 1964.

9.5.3 "MIL-STD-202, *Military Standard Test Methods for Electronic and Electrical Component Parts*" (*Preparing activity: Defense Supply Agency, Cameron Station, Alexandria, Va.*)

1.1 *Scope* (MIL-STD-202C, Change Notice 4, 20 January 1967).

This standard establishes uniform methods for testing electronic and electrical component parts, including basic environmental tests to determine resistance to deleterious effects of natural elements and conditions surrounding military operations, and physical and electrical tests. For the purpose of this standard, the term "component parts" includes such items as capacitors, resistors, switches, relays, transformers, and jacks. This standard is intended to apply only to small parts, such as transformers and inductors, weighing up to 300 pounds or having a root-mean-square test voltage up to 50,000 volts unless otherwise specifically invoked. The test methods described herein have been prepared to serve several purposes.

(a) To specify suitable conditions obtainable in the laboratory which give test results equivalent to the actual service conditions existing in the field, and to obtain reproducibility of the results of tests. The tests described herein are not to be interpreted as an exact and conclusive representation of actual service operation in any one geographic location, since it is known that the only true test for operation in a specific location is an actual service test at that point.

(b) To describe in one standard (1) all of the test methods of a similar character which appeared in the various joint or single-service electronic and electrical components-parts specifications, (2) those newly-developed test methods which are feasible for use in several specifications, and (3) the recognized extreme environments, particularly temperatures, barometric pressures, etc., at which component parts will be tested under some of the presently-standardized testing procedures. By so consolidating, these methods may be kept uniform and thus result in conservation of equipment, man-hours, and testing facilities. In achieving these objectives, it is necessary to make each of the general tests adaptable to a broad range of electronic and electrical component parts.

(c) The test methods described herein for environmental, physical, and electrical and electronic parts shall also apply, when applicable, to parts not covered by an approved military specification, military sheet-form standard, specification sheet, or drawing.

Many military and civilian relay specifications refer to this military standard. The test methods included in this standard are divided into three classifications: Environmental tests (100 class), physical-characteristics tests (200 class), and electrical-characteristics tests (300 class). When MIL-STD-202 is referred to by the individual specification, the method number and the details required in the summary paragraph of the applicable method must be specified. When there is a conflict, the individual specification takes precedence over this standard.

9.5.4 "MIL-STD-810, *Military Standard Environmental Test Methods*" (*Preparing Activity: Department of the Air Force — Aeronautical Systems Division*)

Scope (MIL-STD-810B, 15 June 1967).
1.1 *Purpose.* This standard establishes uniform environmental test methods for determining the resistance of equipment to the effects of natural and induced environments peculiar to military operations. This specification is sometimes passed on to the relay vendor in error. It does not apply to components only, such as relays.

9.5.5 "MIL-C-24010A (AS), *Contactor, Electric Power Line, Aircraft,*" (*15 August 1968*) Naval Air Systems Comand

This specification covers electromechanical switching devices for use in aircraft primary power circuits without backup protection.

9.5.6 *New Relay Specifications and Standards*

The military relay program as set forth by

the military at the January, 1969 A-2R Relay Committee meeting included the following:

Specifications for:

(a) Photo-Sensitive Devices

(b) Hybrid Relay/Assemblies

(c) Solid State Relays

(d) Vacuum Relays

(e) Time Delay Relays (Excluding Solid State Thermal Devices)

Development/Coordination of Military Standards

(a) Preferred Relays and Circuit Application

(b) Standard Test Procedures

Drafts of some of the above were circulated for comments at the time of printing, but the numbers were not assigned.

A joint EIA/NARM committee, known as the P5.7 Committee, is at work on a specification for military relays that will presumably be given a MIL. SPEC. number, but at present this cannot be verified.

For additional information see *Bibliography*.

9.5.7 "MIL-STD-454-B, *Standard General Requirements for Electronic Equipment*" (*June 1968*)

MIL-STD-454B, Requirement 57, Relays, covers selection of relays and is being referenced by such general equipment specifications as MIL-E-5400.

1. *Purpose.* The purpose of this requirement is to establish criteria for the choice application of relays.

2. *Documents applicable to Requirement 57:*

MIL-R-5757   Relays (Electrical—Excluding Thermal — for Electronic and Communication-type Equipment), General Specification for

MIL-R-6106   Relays, Electric, General Specification for

MIL-S-12883   Socket for Plug-In Electric Components, and Accessories, General Specification for

MIL-R-19648   Relays, Thermal, Time Delay, Hermetically Sealed, General Specification for

MIL-R-39016   Relays, Electromagnetic, Established Reliability, General Specification for

3. *Low current relays (up to 10 amperes).* Low current relays up to 10 amperes shall conform to MIL-R-5757. However, relay applications requiring high in-rush current capabilities (e.g., motor and con-troller functions) may be in accord with MIL-R-6106, as applicable.

4. *High current relays.* Relays used in high current applications shall conform to MIL-R-6106.

5. *Time delay relays.* Thermal time delays relay shall conform to MIL-R-19648.

6. *Solid state electromagnetic relay assemblies.* Solid state electromagnetic relay assemblies with an electro-magnetic relay output shall conform to MIL-R-5757.

7. *Established reliability relays.* Established reliability relays shall conform to MIL-R-39016.

8. *Reed relays.* Reed relays shall conform to MIL-R-5757.

9. *Relay sockets.* When relay sockets are required, they shall conform to MIL-S-12883.

9.5.8 *Summary On Government Specifications*

The government tries to define items so that adequate standards assure that components can be produced, procured, cataloged, and maintained. To this end, Federal Handbook H6-1 covers Federal Item Identification (FII). Supplementing this is Federal Handbook H4-1, which covers Federal Supply Classification (FSC).

FSC 5945 covers "Relays, Contactors, and Solenoids." Classification problems exist, because the demarcation is sometimes hard to establish, as for a "Solenoid, with contact added." Equally confusing is "Relay, Stepping" in FSC 5945, with a quite similar device designated "Switch, Stepping" in FSC 5930. Obviously, standardization by definition, in order to differentiate between stepping relays and stepping switches, as done in the Definitions section of this handbook (Section 1), did not come soon enough to help in this case.

9.6 *Nongovernmental Documents Applicable to Relays*

9.6.1 NAS-728, *National Aerospace Standard. Test Methods for Electromagnetic Relays (Preparing Activity: National Standards Association, Inc., Aerospace Industries Association)*

Scope (NAS-728, Oct. 1962)

This document provides standard test

methods and procedures for relays which are to be qualified for use in military equipment. This does not, however, preclude its use for relays intended for use in commercial equipment. Test methods have been included for those requirements known to exist in the military application of hermetically sealed relays, e.g., MIL-R-5757, but not MIL-R-6106. Alternate procedures have been included for the different test conditions or severity levels required by the ultimate usage of equipment being designed. Complete step-by-step procedures have been provided including details on apparatus, calibration, test circuits, mounting, interconnections, measurements and performance limits. The procedures are intended to assure duplicable results regardless of where the tests are performed or who performs them.

The tests are divided into five classifications, and the table of contents is so detailed that any test is readily found despite the size of the standard (139 pages). "Visual and Mechanical Inspection" (1.1) and "Terminal Strength" (1.2) are in classification or Section 1; "Coil Resistance" (2.1) and other electrical tests are in Section 2, and so on.

The test methods (1.1, 2.1, etc.) are divided into three sections: Scope, Procedures, and Performance Limits. All information necessary to perform each test is outlined in the test method.

The scope section of each method explains the value of the test, what information is provided to perform the test, and any precautions to be taken concerning the test.

The procedure section of each method includes a description of the apparatus or equipment necessary for testing, the test steps and figures, and the final measurements or inspections, if applicable. Only a few of the test methods have only one procedure, as the standard was written to provide standardized test methods for all requirements for hermetically sealed relays.

The performance limits give the criteria for the test. These limits apply unless otherwise specified in the detailed specification.

When this standard is specified, the required procedure must be specified as well. For example, Test Method 2.4, Contact Transfer Characteristics, includes the following procedures:

I   Operate time of normally closed contacts

II   Operate time of normally open contacts

III Release time of normally open contacts

IV   Release time of normally closed contacts

V   Operate transfer time

VI   Release transfer time

VII Contact bounce of normally open contacts

VIII Contact bounce of normally closed contacts

IX   Composite test of contact transfer characteristics.

In most instances, not all of this information will be required, and therefore only the specific procedures should be specified. It does not seem likely that Test Method 2.4 of NAS-728 would be required for acceptance testing, for instance. MIL-STD-202 and MIL-STD-810 apply to various components, but NAS-728 is strictly a test method standard for relays. This test procedure does not cover load tests for minimum current, motor, and a-c polyphase loads. AIA is considering a revision based on A-2R recommendations.

9.6.2   GSFC-S 601.100 (NASA Goddard Space Flight Center, Greenbelt, Maryland). Relays, DC, Hermetically Sealed, Grid Header, For Space Flight Applications, General Specification for

Aim is zero defects for properly applied relays. This specification includes plug-in relays. A-c applications do not cover three-phase. Effect of various type loads (e.g., motor, lamp, inductive, etc.) are not covered. Specification requires failure analysis including photography and radiography.

9.6.3   STD-R-001 (NASA, MSC, Houston, Texas). General Specification for Acceptance Testing of Electromagnetic Relays for use in Manned Space Flight Applications

MIL-R-5757 and 39016 are referenced, thereby limiting relays to 10 amperes and less without motor or three-phase capability tests. Specification requires three year traceability records and clean room facilities. High and low run-in

Table 9-3. Comparison of Military Specification Qualification Requirements

EXAMINATION OR TEST	MIL-R-5757E			MIL-R-6106F	MIL-R-19523A	MIL-R-19648B				MSFC-SPEC-339A		MIL-R-39016		
	1	2	3			1	2	3	4	1	2	1	2	3
Visual and Mechanical Examination (Internal)	X	X		X	X	X⁹				X	X	X		
Visual and Mechanical Examination (External)	X	X		X	X	X				X		X	X	X
Solderability	X					X¹⁰								
Electrical Characteristics	X		X			X				X	X	X		
Seal	X	X		X		X		X		X	X	X	X	X
Dielectric Withstanding Voltage	X				X	X		X		X	X	X		
Insulation Resistance	X			X	X					X	X	X		
Terminal Strength		X		X			X	X		X				X
Thermal Shock		X				X							X	
Shock			X	X⁷	X	X¹¹								X
Centrifugal Acceleration (when applicable)						X¹¹				X		X		
Overvoltage						X¹¹								
Vibration		X	X	X⁴,⁸		X¹¹				X			X	
Moisture resistance			X	X										X
Salt Spray (Corrosion)		X		X		X				X			X	
Overload				X		X	X						X	
Life									X					X¹²
Mounting Stud Strength				X						X				X¹³
Low Temperature										X				
High Temperature/Overvoltage											X			
Mechanical Shock											X			
Coil Resistance	X		X											
Creepage and Clearance Distance					X									
Heating					X									
Pickup and Dropout Voltage					X									
Inclination					X									
Endurance					X									
Random Drop (when specified)													X	
High Temperature Operation		X		X										X
Low Temperature Operation		X												X
Coil Life														X¹⁴
Contact Drop (resistance)	X			X	X									
High Temperature Pickup Voltage				X										
Radio Noise⁵				X⁵										
Temperature Shock				X										
Operating Characteristics				X										
Mechanical Life				X										
Humidity²				X²										
Ozone				X										
Acceleration		X		X										
Sand and Dust				X										
Explosion-proof				X⁵										
Inductive Load				X³,⁶										
Motor Load				X³										
Resistive Load				X³,⁶										
Lamp Load				X³										
Rupture				X³,⁶										
Continuous Current				X										
Minimum Current			X	X										
Mechanical Interlock				X³										
Accoustical Noise			X	X³										
Load transfer, 3 phases				X³										
Vibration Scan				X										
Low Level Run-in														
Conditioning														
Coil Induction	X													
Operate and Release Time	X													
Contact Bounce	X			X										
Sensitivity	X			X										
Break Time	X			X										
Bias Distortion	X			X										
Bias Compensation	X			X										
Contact Overload and Input Overdrive	X			X										
Operating Speed	X			X										
Internal Moisture		X												
Magnetic Interference				X										

[1] Additional sample or samples may be required.

[2] All sealed and Class A5 relays shall be tested in accordance with 4.7.6.8. Nonsealed relays of other classes shall be tested in accordance with 4.7.6.9.

[3] Omit tests that do not apply.

[4] Resonance or cycling endurance tests shall be conducted for 1 hr in one plane only.

[5] Additional samples may be provided for performing these tests.

[6] If d-c ratings are not involved, these tests shall be performed on samples 1, 3, 4 & 5, instead of the corresponding d-c tests.

[7] Additional sample may be provided when high shock is specified.

[8] Additional sample may be provided when random vibration is specified.

[9] One additional sample unit (unsealed) for internal examination. No testing required for the unsealed sample unit.

[10] Two sample units only.

[11] For operate time tolerance, see 3.1 and 3.6.2.1.2.

[12] Two sample units per load rating but not less than three total.

[13] Cycle IV — Life.

[14] Cycle V — Life (Heater).

Table 9-4. Comparison of Military Specification Acceptance Test Requirements

EXAMINATION OR TEST	MSFC-SPEC-339A Q1	Q2	Q3	MIL-R-39016 A	B	C	MIL-R-5757E A	B	MIL-R-19523A Routine	Periodic	MIL-R-6106F A	B	C	MIL-R-19648B A	B
Conditioning (run-in) (when specified)													X		
Visual and Mechanical Examination (External)	X		X	X			X8	X	X		X		X	X	X10
Visual and Mechanical Examination (Internal)	X		X				X	X	X						
Seal	X	X	X	X			X		X	X	X5			X9	X
Dielectric Withstanding Voltage	X	X	X	X		X	X	X8	X	X	X2		X	X	X
Insulation Resistance	X	X	X	X		X	X	X8	X			X		X	X
Electrical Characteristics	X	X	X				X								X
Static Contact Resistance (or voltage drop)				X			X7	X8	X	X				X	
Pickup and Dropout Voltage (or current)				X			X7				X1				
D-C Coil Resistance				X			X								
Operate and Release Time				X			X7				X4			X	
Contact Bounce				X			X7	X8			X4				
Sensitivity							X8								
Break Time							X8								
Bias Distortion							X8								
Minimum Current								X7				X			
Vibration	X					X		X8	X				X		X12
Contact Overload and Input Overdrive								X8					X		
Operating Speed								X8							
High Temperature Operation		X		X		X		X8							
Low Temperature Operation		X		X		X		X8							
Shock						X		X8		X					X12
Moisture Resistance						X		X8							
Coil Current				X											
Vibration Scan				X							X4	X			
Centrifugal Acceleration	X		X	X		X									X12
Life		X			X										X13
Thermal Shock		X				X									X
Random Drop (when specified)															
Overload															X
Salt Spray (Corrosion)	X												X		
Terminal Strength	X							X8							X
Coil Life															
Contact Drop											X				
Operational Reliability											X3				
Temperature Shock												X			
Endurance Tests												X6			
Motor Load												X			
Resistive Load												X	X		
Inductive Load												X			
Lamp Load												X			
Mechanical Life												X			
Humidity													X		
Sand and Dust (unsealed relays only)													X		
Radio Interference													X		
Timing Characteristics														X	
Solderability															X11
Overvoltage															X12
Mounting Stud Strength	X														
Mechanical Shock		X													
Heating															
Inclination															

1. Omit 30-minute conditioning period except for samples to be further tested under Sampling Plan B.

2. 2-5 second sea level test specified in Table IV may be used.

3. When specified.

4. For Type I ER or Type II ER relays or when specified on the detail specification sheet.

5. Sealing test may be performed as a final assembly operation prior to performing Plan A tests on Types I, II and III provided this test is performed on all of the relays. Types I ER and II ER sealing tests shall be performed after vibration scan.

6. Each time Sampling Plan B is run on two relays, only one type of endurance test shall be run. Sequence of testing on subsequent groups of two relays shall be in the order shown in accordance with 4.5.2. MIL-R-6106F.

7. Tests are not applicable to telegraph relays.

8. Tests are applicable to telegraph relays only.

9. Performed prior to final seal.

10. One additional sample unit (unsealed) for internal examination. No testing required for the unsealed sample unit.

11. Two sample units only.

12. For operate time tolerance, see 3.1 and 3.6.2.1.2. MIL-R-19648B.

13. Two sample units per load rating but not less than three total.

and random vibration are in accordance with MIL-STD-105. Water and *not* Silicone is used for gross leak test. Dielectric test voltage is 1000/500 (1250 for 115 VAC). Contact bounce is specified. Case grounding is required. Minimum current testing is not required.

9.7 *Comparative Tables*

The following comparative tables are for quick reference and should not be used as a substitute for the actual documents.

Table 9-5. Comparison of Government Environmental Test Documents

TEST	MIL-STD-202C NOTICE 4, 20 JAN. 1967	MIL-STD-810B[1] 15 JUNE 1967	MIL-E-5272C AMENDMENT 1, 20 JAN. 1960
Salt Spray (Corrosion)	Method 101C	Method 509	Paragraph 4.6
Temperature Cycling	Method 102A		
Humidity (Steady State)	Method 103B	Method 507	Paragraph 4.3
Immersion (Leakage)	Method 104A	Method 512	Paragraph 4.12
Barometric Pressure (Reduced)	Method 105C		
Moisture Resistance	Method 106B		
Thermal Shock/Temp. Shock	Method 107B	Method 503	Paragraph 4.3
Life (at Elevated Ambient Temp.)	Method 108A		
Explosion (Atmosphere)	Method 109A	Method 511	Paragraph 4.13
Sand and Dust	Method 110		Paragraph 4.11
Flammability (External Flame)	Method 111		
Seal	Method 112A		
High Temperature		Method 501	Paragraph 4.1
Low Temperature		Method 502	Paragraph 4.2
Temperature Altitude		Method 504	Paragraph 4.14
Sunshine		Method 505	Paragraph 4.9
Rain		Method 506	Paragraph 4.10
Fungus		Method 508	Paragraph 4.8
Vibration	Method 201A	Method 514	Paragraph 4.7
Shock (Weight of Specimen Less than 4 lb)	Method 202B	Method 516	Paragraph 4.15
Random Drop	Method 203A		
Vibration, High Frequency	Method 204A	Method 514	Paragraph 4.7
Shock, Medium Impact	Method 205C	Method 516	Paragraph 4.15
Life (Rotational)	Method 206		
Shock, High Impact	Method 207A	Method 516	Paragraph 4.15
Solderability	Method 208B		
Radiographic Inspection	Method 209		
Resistance to Soldering Heat	Method 210		
Terminal Strength	Method 211		
Acceleration	Method 212	Method 513	Paragraph 4.16
Shock (Specified Pulse)	Method 213		
Random Vibration	Method 214	Method 514	
Resistance to Solvents	Method 215		
Acoustical Noise		Method 515	
Space Simulation		Method 517	
Temperature–Humidity–Altitude		Method 518	Paragraph 4.5
Dielectric With Standing Voltage	Method 301		
Insulation Resistance	Method 302		
D–C Resistance	Method 303		
Resistance–Temp. Characteristics	Method 304		
Capacitance	Method 305		
Quality Factor (Q)	Method 306		
Current–Noise Test for Fixed Resistors	Method 308		
Voltage Coefficient of Resistance Determination Procedure	Method 309		
Contact–Chatter Monitoring	Method 310		

[1] MIL-STD-810 is applicable only to completed systems, not components such as relays.

10
Electro-Mechanical Relays and Solid State Devices, and Hybrid Combinations

Introduction

In 1967, a NARM committee[1] studied hybrid combinations of electro-mechanical relays and solid state devices, evaluating each hybrid device to assist circuit designers in planning for their use. It was found that the hybrid combination can perform some functions better and more economically than the individual components.

The hybrids have become so commonplace, it is often not realized that they are formed by combining these two components. Examples are the rectified coil d-c relay used in a-c systems and the electronic time delay relay with conventional output contacts. Two other well-known hybrids, although technically not relays, are the speed control switch in portable drills and the wall dimmer-switch for light intensity control.

The proven reliability and ruggedness of electro-mechanical relays coupled with the flexibility and adaptability of solid state devices hold a promise of increased future use of their hybrid combinations.

This section compares the general characteristics of the individual components and hybrid devices. In most instances each component or device stands on its own because each accomplishes its switching function uniquely. Meaningful comparisons are possible for specific applications only if suitable implementation is provided and if all trade-offs, functional and economic, have been considered. The most salient feature of one device is often the shortcoming of the other. In general, each characteristic of a device is described in a qualitative rather than quantitative manner, although in some cases an order of magnitude is given while realizing that a meaningful measurement is not possible using the same type of measurement for both categories as would be possible in a directly interchangeable situation.

10.1 Characteristics of Relays and Solid State Components as Switching Devices

Table 10-1 compares relays and solid state components used as switching devices. Important applications and electrical characteristics of the devices are compared on a point-by-point basis.

10.2 Typical Hybrid Applications

In the following paragraphs relays are shown in hybrid combinations with solid-state components. Sensors, light-sensitive devices, thermistors and other devices are illustrated as circuit elements functioning with relays and other solid-state devices. In previous sections, examples of hybrid combinations in circuits providing for such things as accelerated operation of a relay (Fig. 5-41), pulse stretching (Fig. 5-43), and time delay using the thermistor cooling effect (Fig. 5-47).

Time Delay (Pull In). Figure 10-1 is a circuit designed to delay a relay on pull in. Upon application of power, capacitor Cl be-

[1]The NARM committee was formed following the Fifteenth Annual Relay Conference.

Table 10-1 Characteristics of Relays and Solid State Components
as Switching Devices

CHARACTERISTIC	DEVICE	
Life	Relay	Solid State
Cyclic	The normal mechanical life of relays (expressed in number of operations) may vary from less than one million operations to hundreds of millions, with some (such as mercury wetted contact relays) capable of many billions of operations, depending on type and design. The electrical life rating is normally a function of the particular electrical loads being switched.	Theoretically, correctly applied semiconductors do not have known wearout modes, since they are essentially mechanically static devices. Cyclic limitations may be encountered which are dependent upon the design, fabrication, construction, or application of the semiconductor. (Life is normally expressed in number of hours rather than operations. A good transistor switch can make one million or more operations in one second without impairing its useful life.)
Static	The static life of electrically functioning relays may be limited by physical or chemical deterioration of their components. The nature of the conventional relay is such that its contact forms can function in a prescribed manner (blocking or conducting) with or without coil power, depending on type and design. In their blocking condition, relay contacts are inherently immune to transients. Relay contacts dissipate very little power while conducting, because of their normal condition of low contact resistance. In some cases, excessive contact resistance may be encountered due to contamination, corrosion, or oxidation. Other possible limitations may be coil deterioration (seldom, if ever, encountered in the absence of electrical stresses) and galvanic action between certain dissimilar metals. The design, materials, and manufacturing processes of the relay — along with the application and environmental surroundings — are the ultimate factors that determine static life, and are normally chosen to minimize or effectively eliminate these problems.	The static life for electrically functioning semiconductors may be limited by chemical or physical changes affecting the intended function of their junctions. Semiconductors usually require a continuous external driving source, except for latching types, which are internally driven by their output. The maximum junction temperature for semiconductors limits the power dissipated. This internally dissipated power is caused by the forward voltage drop across the device and by the requirements of the device drive. Above-rated voltage transients can destroy or cause a device to go into an unwanted condition. The environmental surroundings, application, design, and fabrication of the semiconductor are the ultimate factors that determine static life.
Shelf	With proper storage, shelf life is normally not a problem. Hermetically sealed units have a potentially longer shelf life than open units.	Generally nonapplicable.
Failure Modes	Failure modes may be: contacts sticking, transferring, or welding; high contact resistance; mechanical failure; coil opening or shorting. Contact sticking and high contact resistance may be intermittent and regarded as misses instead of failures for some applications. Coil failures are usually attributable to excessive voltage, electrolysis or other chemical reactions, or harsh environments. Excessive temperature, especially if prolonged, may deteriorate the insulation, causing the coil to become defective. Most relay failures are fairly easily detected because of visual evidence of failure.	Failure modes may be: permanent shorts (although opens do occur), inability to block voltage, or leakage current reaching failure proportions. General failure factors related to semiconductors are: exceeding of maximum voltage ratings, e.g., transients; thermo-mechanical fatigue caused by cyclic temperature surges; chemical reactions, such as channeling; physical changes, such as crystallization of materials; and other associated packaging problems which generally cause greater than intended power dissipation within the device. Most failures are hastened with prolonged temperature increases. Specific failures for semiconductor devices are secondary breakdown found in bipolar transistors, and di/dt and dv/dt found in thyristors. If the commutating dv/dt of a thyristor is exceeded, it will not turn off; and if the static dv/dt of the device is exceeded, it may go into unwanted conduction. Semiconductor failure detection can become quite involved depending on the knowledge, experience, and equipment required. In many instances there is no visual evidence of failure unless it is heat discoloration.
Environment	Relay	Solid State
General	Commercial atmospheres are reasonably well tolerated by most relays in either an unenclosed ("open") condition or, if conditions warrant it, in an enclosure. Extreme problems of atmosphere, moisture, particles, etc. may require hermetic sealing. Relays may be designed with radiation hardened materials.	The types of packaging and small mass of semiconductors make them inherently immune to most environments, particularly shock and vibration. For radiation applications, shielding must be provided.
Temperature	Generally, the ability to withstand heat is ultimately limited by the type of insulating materials employed. Maximum or temperatures above maximum rating, if sustained, will produce a faster deterioration and decomposition of most insulating materials. Above-rated, elevated ambient temperatures for reasonably short durations can usually be tolerated by most relay designs without causing irreversible changes to the unit. Relay designs are available that can operate in maximum ambients of 125°C, with specials good to 200°C. In general, the contact rating applies over its	Essentially, the ability to withstand heat (internal losses plus ambient temperature) is ultimately limited by junction temperature considerations. Above-rated, elevated ambient temperature surges usually have sufficient inertia to cause irreversible changes in the semiconductor if it is functioning near its maximum capacity. Generally, semiconductors can withstand junction temperature overshoots caused by current surges of several millisec. The cumulative effects of the internally dissipated power, combined with the ambient temperature, must not exceed the maximum per-

Table 10-1 Characteristics of Relays and Solid State Components
as Switching Devices (Cont'd)

CHARACTERISTIC	DEVICE	
Environment	Relay	Solid State
Temperature (Cont.)	specified operating temperature range without derating. Coil resistance varies directly with its temperature, according to the temperature coefficient of the coil wire material (copper is used almost exclusively).	missible junction temperature. As the internal power dissipation increases, the maximum allowable ambient temperature decreases. The type of heat sink employed substantially affects semiconductor performance. The proper design for this heat sink may become quite involved, depending upon application and if electrical isolation is required. Prolonged heat exposure hastens chemical and other types of failure. Depending on type, many semiconductors can operate in ambients of 125°C or above if properly applied. Gate sensitivity and gain usually fall off with low temperatures, particularly below −20°C.
Contamination	Contamination is of most concern with contacts. Where contact contamination is encountered, the result may vary from slightly increased contact resistance to an electrically open condition. Relay coils, depending on insulation, may be susceptible to certain contaminants which will chemically deteriorate the coil and may result in electrical breakdown and shorting.	Contamination is mostly of concern when it is an internal type on a semiconductor element. Where semiconductor pellet contamination is encountered, a decrease in blocking voltage and an increase in leakage current normally results.
External Contamination	Unenclosed relays may be affected by undesirable gases and other contaminants, which may require either hermetic or non-hermetic enclosures. Contaminants, such as oxides, on connecting terminals may present difficulties.	Semiconductors are essentially immune to external contamination except when encapsulation flaws permit atmospheric impurities to reach the sealed semiconductor junction. Contamination on leads may offer connecting problems.
Internal Contamination	Internal contamination is generally a result of outgassing of various insulation materials (e.g., in hermetically sealed units). Electrical switching of contacts, at levels producing sparking or arcing, in the presence of outgassing from various organic volatiles may form contaminants and may promote contact erosion. Internal outgassing and contamination are normally controlled by proper choice of materials, design, and manufacturing methods.	Internal contamination consists of entrapment or inclusion of ionizable material inside the sealed package, which may lead to failures. Manufacturing techniques and processes have been developed that provide a high degree of freedom from contamination within the sealed package.
Reliability	Relay	Solid State
Rating Method	Failure rate is generally expressed in percent per 10,000 operations.	Failure rate is usually expressed in percent per 1,000 hours.
Degree	Relays have demonstrated high component reliability using the above rating method; however, this depends greatly on relay type and use.	Under reasonably ideal conditions, extreme reliability can be obtained from semiconductors with the above rating method.
Failure Rate	The failure rate tends to follow a "bathtub" distribution curve, i.e., it decreases after each consecutive, successful operation, levels off, and does not appreciably increase until mechanical wearout begins.	It is generally assumed that the failure rate ranges from constant to slightly decreasing with time, once the infant mortality period is passed. There is no upturn in failure rate with life.
Run-in or burn-in	In some instances where added reliability or stability is desired, relays are given a number of prelife operations (run-in) under predetermined conditions, related to intended use. This tends to minimize early failures. However, extensive run-in will only use up a portion of the useful life.	The initial "burn-in" for semiconductors tends to eliminate devices which would normally fail during the first few hours of operation. It is effective for semiconductor devices having a high initial failure rate followed by a decreasing failure rate. The extent of such testing is usually limited by economic considerations.
System	System reliability is reduced according to the cumulative failures of all the components used. Where the choice of relay or solid state system is considered, the complexity required for each may be a greater factor in system reliability than is the reliability of the individual component.	
Hybrid	The greatest reliability is achieved when the strong points of a certain component offset the weak points of another, as is done in many hybrid devices using both relays and semiconductors.	
Electrical Isolation	Relay	Solid State
Output/Input	Relays have inherently high isolation between output circuits, between output and control (input) circuits, and between control circuits. (Insulation resistance of ≥ 1,000 megohms and dielectric withstanding voltage of the order of 500 to 1,000 VAC are typical.)	Generally, a high degree of electrical isolation between control and output circuits cannot be achieved with junction type semiconductors. In a limited area of application, a high degree of isolation can be achieved with FET's.
High Voltage	Isolation is very little affected by voltages which are relatively high compared with nominal system voltages. The loss of dielectric due to momentary exposure to excessively high voltage is usually temporary. The degree of recovery depends on the type of insulating material used.	If maximum rated voltage values as given by the manufacturer (usually at 25°C) are exceeded even momentarily, many semiconductor devices will be permanently damaged.
Variation	Relay contact isolation normally does not vary substantially with time, temperature, radiation, voltage, etc., unless	Semiconductor leakage current is a variable of temperature, time, radiation, and voltage. If device limitations are not

Table 10-1. Characteristics of Relays and Solid State Components as Switching Devices (Cont'd)

CHARACTERISTIC	DEVICE	
Electrical Isolation (Cont.)	Relay	Solid State
Variation (Cont.)	there is a complete failure under extreme conditions.	exceeded, the variation is reversible, except where due to time (aging).
Electrical Noise and Magnetic Fields	Relays, because of the power and time required for operation, are essentially insensitive to electrical noise. Sensitive relays can be subject to false operation in high magnetic fields unless shielded. RFI, produced by relay contacts during opening and closing but not while carrying current, is difficult to control. EMI, produced by coils and magnetic circuits, may be suppressed to some extent.	In many applications, shielding and signal conditioning are required to prevent false operation caused by electrical noise and electromagnetically induced currents. They do not normally show sensitivity to static magnetic fields (except Hall devices). Semiconductors generate RFI during turn-on and turn-off while switching ac if they are not turned on at zero current. Thyristors using phase control techniques may be a serious RFI source because of turning on during each half cycle (or alternate half cycles). Various techniques for RFI suppression are possible for some applications.
Off/On Characteristics	Relay	Solid State
Off/On Impedance Ratio	The off/on impedance ratio is extremely high.	The off/on impedance ratio is moderately high. (FET's may provide significantly higher ratios.)
Power Loss	Relays have the ability to handle power with extremely low loss because of low resistance of their closed contact circuitry. The coil power must also be considered to obtain the complete power consumption picture.	Semiconductor ability to handle power is limited by inherent "on" voltage drop, dependency on heat sinks, and ambient temperature. The base or gate drive power is small compared to the output. However, for some transistors, as output current increases, input current must be disproportionately increased (beta decreases) to obtain desired output saturation.
On Voltage	The voltage drop across a closed relay contact is the IR product (generally less than 100 millivolts).	The semiconductor usually has a forward voltage drop from 0.3 to 2.5 volts. The voltage drop per junction is approximately 0.3 volts for germanium and 0.6 volts for silicon, in addition to the voltage drop due to bulk resistivity.
On Resistance	The on (closed contact) resistance of the relays may vary slightly from cycle to cycle with life in terms of operations and load. Under adverse conditions, misses may occur because contacts do not close electrically (particles, film, welds on opposite sets of contacts, etc.) or resistance exceeds some predetermined value. The on resistance remains essentially constant with clean contacts. It can increase slightly because of heating of the contact circuitry, and increases with current.	Forward voltage drop across a semiconductor is consistent from cycle to cycle. This drop varies with junction temperature. The on resistance generally decreases as current increases, and for some devices such as transistors can be varied with base drive.
Off Resistance	The off resistance (open contacts) is affected very little by temperature, voltage, etc.	The off resistance varies with time, temperature, voltage, and radiation. Leakage current increases exponentially with temperature (e.g., may double with every 8 to 10°C increase).
Input Considerations	Relay	Solid State
Operating Power	Relays are available with operating power from milliwatts to watts, and specials operate on microwatts. Duration of power pulse required for latching relays may vary from less than one millisecond to several milliseconds. Relays having ferrite magnetic circuits can be made to operate from pulses of less than 5 microsecond duration. Latching relays are normally reset with a power pulse equal to (in some cases less than) the value required to latch. Proper polarity coil voltage must be observed for devices designed to latch magnetically. In special cases, manual reset features may be provided. Relays do not normally require regulated power supplies.	Different semiconductor devices are available with operating power from microwatts to milliwatts. Latching semiconductors, such as thyristors, generally require a 2 microsecond pulse or greater for latching (conduction turn-on). Latch is lost when conducting current is reduced below holding value. Semiconductors require well-regulated, transient-free, d-c power supplies.
Operating Voltage	Relays operate in response to a wide range of a-c or d-c coil input voltages as determined by design. Relay coils are generally designed to operate within a ± tolerance of a specified nominal voltage. While insufficient voltage will not permit the relay to operate properly, if at all, greater than maximum specified coil voltage may cause coil deterioration depending on duration and magnitude. Conventional, nonlatching, relays will drop out (return to unenergized condition) when coil voltage is removed or reduced to a value which may be varied widely by design and/or adjustment. Latching relays require an input voltage of a specified magnitude and duration for latch and reset. (Proper polarity must also be observed for magnetically latched relays.)	Semiconductors easily adapt to a wide range of input voltages via appropriate circuitry. The absolute maximum voltage ratings for the input (and output) of semiconductors were well specified by the manufacturer and are not to be exceeded without risk of permanent damage. The range of operating voltages is predetermined by design.

Table 10-1. Characteristics of Relays and Solid State Components as Switching Devices (Cont'd)

CHARACTERISTIC	DEVICE	
Input Considerations (Cont.)	Relay	Solid State
Operating Current	Relays operate over a wide range of predetermined current levels. Even when voltage levels are specified, the electro-magnetic relay is essentially a current operating device whose operation is accomplished when its inherent ampere-turn requirements are met. Again, those comments made in the section "Operating Voltage" apply to current operated relays.	Semiconductors are current operated devices. Transistors are essentially current amplifiers, i.e., a given input current determines a given output current for a set of conditions. Thyristors require minimum gate-current drive to ensure latching, if load conditions permit. Generally, gate drive can be removed after thyristor turn-on. Semiconductors usually turn off within a matter of microseconds following removal of drive current, whether supplied externally or internally.
Transients	Relay coils are generally insensitive to transient voltages.	High voltage, short duration transients can be particularly damaging.
Duty Cycle	Generally nonapplicable. In some cases, coils may be rated for intermittent duty because of temperature considerations.	As the per cent duty (conduction time) decreases, the drive-current rating usually increases as long as maximum junction temperature is not exceeded. Large drive currents may be required in power transistors to obtain saturation, and in thyristors to minimize di/dt stresses.
Output Considerations	Relay	Solid State
Multipole Switching	Relays are available with various types and numbers of contact forms which can be operated by a single input. For most, the choice of circuits switched by each contact form may be of a widely different voltage and frequency from that switched by the others; this choice requires little if any predetermination in the design of the relay.	Solid-state systems feasibly can perform any switching function. However, switching more than one circuit simultaneously using discrete semiconductor components requires proper combination into a workable assembly. The complication, cost, and size of this assembly will increase substantially with the number of poles, magnitude of current, and degree of electrical isolation. (Where the level of switching permits integrated circuits to be used, considerable economic and size advantages may be realized.)
Switching Range	Contacts are generally adaptable to a wide current, voltage, and frequency range, since they simply physically connect electrical conductors. However, relay families are usually designed for dry, low, intermediate, or high level switching. The upper frequency range which they are capable of switching also varies greatly with design.	Semiconductors and their assemblies are usually designed for a specific voltage, current, and frequency range. The operating current ratio (output to input) for many semiconductors is extremely high. The frequency range depends greatly on the design of the semiconductor.
Voltage	Relay contacts can generally tolerate an exceptionally wide operating range of load voltages without design changes, and they usually recover from short breakdowns or excessive overvoltages. Special designs may be required for high voltages or extreme environmental conditions.	Maximum output voltage ratings are particularly well specified, and it is essential that semiconductors be operated within these ratings to avoid permanent damage.
Current	Relays can generally tolerate overload currents of various degrees. As overload current increases, contact sticking or contact welding during break and make will increase. An empirical determination is usually necessary to find out if the relay will function reliably under given overload current conditions.	While most switching type semiconductors can handle surge currents many times their steady-state ratings, overload currents of relatively sustained duration cannot be tolerated. The junction temperature of the semiconductor is ordinarily the limiting factor in determining the magnitude and duration of its surge current rating.
Transients	The inherent design of relays is such that they are essentially immune to transients.	High voltage, short duration transients can be particularly damaging to semiconductors. Special protective devices and means are frequently required.
Duty Cycle	Generally output is independent of conduction duty; however, the maximum permissible cyclic rate of switching is limited by the magnitude of the load being switched.	As percent duty (conduction time) decreases, current rating usually increases as long as the maximum junction temperature is not exceeded.
Contact Bounce	Contact bounce is usually present to some degree during contact make and, in a few designs, during break. (Duration may be from fraction of a millisecond to several milliseconds, and may consist of several closures and openings per contact operation.) Mercury wetted relays are an exception, since their contacts have essentially no bounce due to the masking effect of the mercury.	No contact bounce exists in semiconductors.
Amplification	Amplification is possible only in that small signals may control large ones. Extremely high amplification factors are possible using a single relay.	Semiconductors amplify the input signal. Some devices are used as switches in that small input signals control large output signals.
Logic	Relay	Solid State
Systems	The logic of simple control systems can be used most economically with control relays, particularly since special power supplies and noise suppression techniques are not required.	Solid state devices lead the field where extensive and complex logic systems are involved or very high-speed operation is required.

Table 10-1. Characteristics of Relays and Solid State Components as Switching Devices (Cont'd)

CHARACTERISTIC	DEVICE	
Logic (Cont.)	Relay	Solid State
Speed	Pick-up times range from 0.5 to 5.0 milliseconds for reed and other relatively fast operating types to 5.0 to 50 milliseconds for conventional control relays. Drop-out times for relays are generally somewhat faster with some reeds having drop-out times of 20 microseconds. Use of overdriving coil voltages to achieve a lower pickup time may increase the severity of contact bounce during make.	Operating times for transistors range from nanoseconds for computer types to microseconds for power types. Typical turn-on time for thyristors varies from 0.5 to 5.0 microseconds while commutation requires from 10 to 50 microseconds. If thyristor turn-off is achieved when conducted ac goes through zero, turn-off time can be approximately as long as a half cycle. The above values vary widely with type of semiconductor, circuit, and application.
Memory	Memory functions can be easily achieved by latching or stepping relays. In such cases, memory can generally be retained in spite of power loss.	Memory is normally accomplished with cores, flip-flops, and integrated circuits. Power loss generally means memory loss, except for core logic or where special auxiliary memory circuits are used.
Electrical Noise	Electrical noise is normally not a problem because of relay operating speed and power requirements.	Signal conditioning and filtering for noise, overshoot, and transients are often required.
Fan-Out	Fan-out logic functions per input for conventional relays is generally not a problem. One relay contact can drive many relay coils. Fan-out speeds for relays are usually in milliseconds.	Fan-out limits the number of gates which can be driven by one logic element. One gate can fan-out to about 10 identical gates. Power gates are available with a fan-out of about 20. Switching times, generally in nanoseconds (both rise and fall time), usually increase with fan-out.
Fan-In	Fan-in is the number of inputs to a logic element. Relays are often considered single input, multiple output devices. Multiple inputs may be obtained by using diode drivers, and to a limited extent, by separate windings.	IC's are often considered to be multiple input, single output devices. Rise time is fairly independent of fan-in (fall time increases with fan-in).
Interfacing	Relays can be driven directly by solid state circuitry. Relays requiring low operating power, such as reed relays, are ideal interfacing devices between solid state circuits and relays or motor starters.	Discrete solid-state power gates can interface directly with relays, solenoids, stepping switches, etc. Integrated microcircuits usually use a transistor to interface with relays and other electromagnetic devices.
Maintenance	Relay	Solid State
Installation	While generally not critical in hookup, reasonable care should be exercised in handling of unenclosed relays.	Care should be exercised so that the maximum permissible temperature for the semiconductor is not exceeded during solder hook-up or potting. Handling of devices is not generally critical except where damage to termination must be considered.
Troubleshooting	Technicians are normally able to diagnose failures with reasonable success. (Unenclosed or transparently enclosed relays give visual evidence of operation.)	Specially trained technicians and special test equipment are often needed to analyze problems. Assembly packages consisting of discrete components require module evaluation rather than simple component evaluation.
Size	Relay	Solid State
Intermediate to High Level Switching	In most cases where power or multipole switching are required, the relay is generally smaller and far less complex than the equivalent solid state unit. However, the life of the equivalent solid state unit may be many times greater than that of the corresponding relay. The relay does easily adapt to various contact forms and combinations as the number of pole requirements increases. Although the size of the contact and motor assemblies for the relay are usually larger than the required semiconductor devices, this is often offset by the size of the peripheral components (including heat sink) required for the semiconductor devices. The relatively small power dissipated in the relay is usually accommodated by its own radiating surfaces. By contrast, the power dissipated in the semiconductor device, because of its forward voltage drop, generally imposes special heat sink requirements which will often substantially increase size.	
Low to Intermediate Level Switching	Low level switching applications that permit extreme reductions in heat sink requirements, especially where extensive logic is performed, favor semiconductors because of savings in weight and size. This is particularly true with microelectronics. For very low level switching applications, however, difficulties may be encountered with semiconductors where direct device operation is necessary, especially if voltage and current requirements are below that of device operation. Special relays often directly fulfill this application. While semiconductors can also work in this region, appropriate supporting circuitry, power supplies and peripheral considerations may become increasingly complex and expensive as the switching level becomes extremely low. How critical these considerations are cannot be sharply defined, but applications in the microamperes — millivolts region should be examined to see which method, or combination of methods, of switching is best suited.	
Cost	Relay	Solid State
Switching Levels	Relays are generally economical devices where heavy-load, high voltage, dry circuit, or multipole switching is desired.	Semiconductors are desirable and economical where low-level, multiple input switching is used or for applications requiring unusually long life or high speed. Where extensive complex logic switching is required, IC systems are the only practical choice.
Application	Worst case condition studies are only moderately difficult and often done by the relay manufacturer.	In general, when solid state switching circuits are to be mass produced, particularly from discrete components, comprehensive and thorough worst case studies usually become quite involved.
General	In many cases, depending upon the application, a comprehensive cost study should be made to determine the most economical route to go; relay, solid state, or a combination of both.	

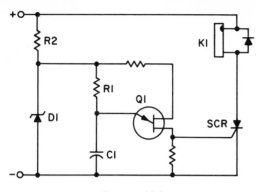

FIGURE 10-1

gins charging through R1 until it reaches the firing point of unijunction transistor Q1. The unijunction transistor triggers the SCR, which energizes the relay K1. Resistor R2 and zener diode D1 form a voltage regulator to allow for a wide range of voltage inputs.

Time Delay. The circuit of Fig. 10-2 simply and accurately delays the dropout of a relay after it is energized. In the quiescent state, no power is applied to the operating components. When S is momentarily closed, transistor Q1 turns on and relay K1 pulls in. Voltage to the circuit is then maintained through the relay contact so that the relay remains energized when S is opened. After a time interval determined by the values of R1, R4, and C1, unijunction transistor Q2 triggers and the discharge of C1 turns off Q1, allowing the relay to drop out. If S is open, voltage to the circuit is removed and the circuit reverts to its quiescent state.

An output voltage can be obained from the relay contacts, as shown, or extra contacts on the relay may be used.

Depending on the supply voltage and the relay used, R2 provides sufficient base current to Q1 to allow the relay to pull in. The size of the capacitor provides sufficient off time for Q1 to allow the relay to drop out. R1 provides the

time delay required and the maximum peak-point current of the unijunction transistor. R3 provides the required overall temperature compensation.

Time Delay (Drop-Out). The circuit of Fig. 10-3 provides a time delay on drop-out using an auxiliary voltage. A control voltage is applied to Q1, causing it to turn on and essentially short cut C1. The auxiliary voltage causes Q3 to turn on and allows relay K1 to pull in. When the control voltage is removed, Q1 turns off, allowing C1 to charge through R3 and R5. When the unijunction transistor Q2 fires, the SCR is triggered, turning off Q3 and de-energizing the relay. R3 and zener diode D1 allow for a wide range of voltage inputs.

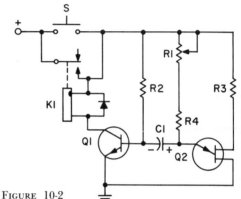

FIGURE 10-2

Time Delay — No Recovery Time. The circuit of Fig. 10-4 provides a drop-out time delay without requiring recovery time. When a positive pulse is applied to the input terminal, the silicon controlled rectifier (SCR) is turned on and current flows through it to turn on Q1 and charge capacitor C1. When C1 is sufficiently charged, current through the SCR drops below its required holding current level. The SCR then turns off and C1 begins discharging through R1 into the base of Q1. Meanwhile, Q1, having been turned on, has

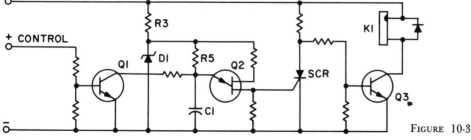

FIGURE 10-3

pulled in relay K1 providing the output connection. As C1 discharges, current in the collector of Q1 and in the relay decreases until it drops below the relay drop-out level. Then the relay opens, breaking the output connection. The circuit may be retriggered at any time after SCR shutoff, provided the trigger amplitude is sufficiently greater than the charge on C1 at that time.

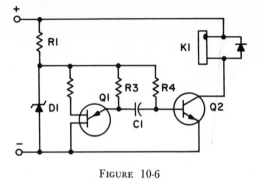

FIGURE 10-6

firing point of unijunction transistor Q1 is reached, C1 discharges, causing a negative shift in the voltage on the base of Q2, turning it off and de-energizing the relay. C1 continues to discharge through R4 until the base voltage of Q2 is positive enough to turn on Q2, thus re-energizing the relay. This cycle repeats itself.

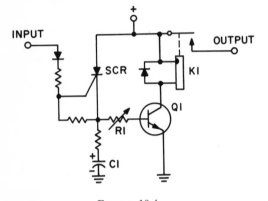

FIGURE 10-4

Time Delay (Pull-In) for Two-Coil Relay. A circuit for the time delay of a two-coil relay is shown in Fig. 10-5. The two coils of relay K1 are so wound that when power is applied, the resultant magnetomotive force is approximately zero. This does not allow the relay to pull in.

Capacitor C2 is charged through the relay coils and R2. When unijunction transistor Q1 fires, it triggers the SCR into conduction. This essentially shorts out one coil of the relay, allowing a magnetomotive force to develop and pull in the relay.

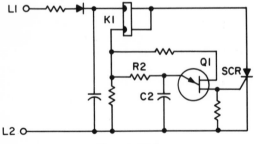

FIGURE 10-5

Repeat Cycle Timer. The circuit of Fig. 10-6 allows the repeat cycling of a relay at a predetermined frequency. Upon application of power, capacitor C1 charges through R3. R4 provides base current to transistor Q2, turning it on and energizing relay K1. The on time of the relay is determined by R3C1. When the

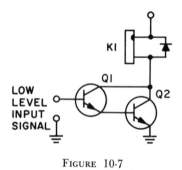

FIGURE 10-7

Amplifier Relay. In the circuit of Fig. 10-7, power required of the controlling source can be greatly reduced by combining a relay with an amplifier-driver. This allows use of a low-level input while retaining the inherent ability of a relay to control power circuits of various voltages and currents.

A Darlington amplifier-driver is shown in Fig. 10-7. Application of a positive input to the base of Q1 produces an amplified drive to Q2, causing relay K1 to operate.

Triac Relay Driver. The triac relay driver, Fig. 10-8, is ideally suited to control a-c operated relays with small input signals. The presence of an input signal causes triac T1 to conduct and in turn operate relay K1. Absence of an input signal causes the triac to assume a blocking state and the relay de-energizes.

Relay Driver. In the circuit of Fig. 10-9,

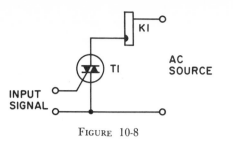

AC
SOURCE

INPUT
SIGNAL

FIGURE 10-8

a bistable polar relay is controlled by a one-polarity low-level input to the amplifier-driver circuit.

Application of a positive input to Q1 causes it to conduct, lowering the voltage at the R1C1 junction. C1 discharges through Q1, the base-emitter junction of Q3, and R3, turning Q3 on for a period determined by the time constant of the circuit. The short duration pulse in direction A through K1 causes the relay to assume one of its stable positions. At the termination

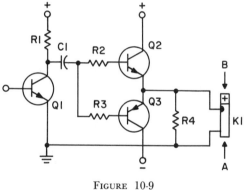

FIGURE 10-9

of the positive input to Q1, Q1 ceases to conduct, the voltage at the R1C1 junction rises, and C1 charges through R1, R2, and the base-emitter junction of Q2. Q2 conducts for a period determined by the circuit time constant, producing a pulse of current in direction B in K1, causing K1 to assume the other of its stable positions.

Fast Operation. Figure 10-10 shows a circuit that decreases the operating time of relays. When S1 is closed and the contacts of K1 transfer, K2 is operated by the sum of source voltage and the charge on capacitor C1. Diode D and resistor R provide a holding circuit which conducts when the voltage across C1 assumes a polarity opposite to that shown and a magnitude adequate to cause diode "turn-on." Momentarily the voltage is doubled. Diode D1 does not conduct until the voltage across capacitor C1 falls to the voltage equal to the drop

across resistor R1 resulting from the holding current for K2.

Voltage Sensor. Figure 10-11 shows a basic d-c voltage sensor. It may be used to sense a-c voltage or current. The ac is rectified and filtered to provide a d-c level. For a-c sensing, a current transformer is used, with the output

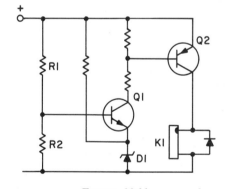

FIGURE 10-10

rectified and filtered. The zener diode D1 establishes a reference voltage at the emitter of transistor Q1. The voltage divider R1R2 is set so that when the desired input voltage is reached, Q1 turns on. This allows transistor Q2 to conduct and causes relay K1 to pull in.

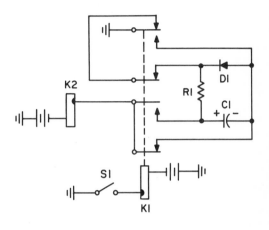

FIGURE 10-11

Voltage Limits Sensor. The circuit of Fig. 10-12 can be in one of two states: if the input voltage is within the specified limits, the contacts are closed; if it is either higher or lower, the contacts are open. The desired voltage limits are determined by the zener diodes, D1 and D2.

When the voltage at the input is within the specified limits, Q2 conducts and relay K1 contacts are closed. If the voltage rises, Q1 also begins to conduct, effectively shorting out the relay coil. Consequently, the contacts open. If the voltage goes down, both transistors cut off and the contacts again open.

Three-Phase, Four-Wire Overvoltage Sensor. The circuit of Fig. 10-13 senses the highest voltage of the three-phase input. The time constant of R1 and C1 is such that a phase voltage after rectification that is higher than the predetermined level as set up by R1 and R2

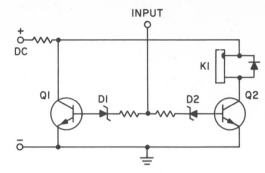

FIGURE 10-12

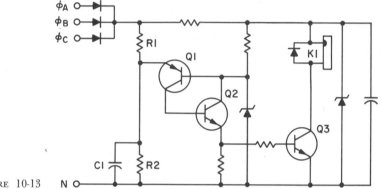

FIGURE 10-13

causes regenerative transistor switch Q1 and Q2 to turn on. This in turn allows transistor Q3 to conduct and to pull in relay K1. When all three phases are below this predetermined point, K1 drops out.

Four-Wire Undervoltage Sensor. The detection of voltage below a reference is provided by the circuit Fig. 10-14. Zener diode D4 establishes a voltage reference level to the emitter of transistor Q1. As long as the average d-c level of L1, L2, and L3 through diodes D1, D2, and D3 and voltage divider R1 and R3 remains higher

than this reference voltage, Q1 remains "off." This in turn allows transistor Q3 to turn on and pull in relay K1. When the average level of the line voltage drops below the predetermined level, Q1 conducts and turns on Q2, causing Q3 to turn off since the base and emitter now are essentially at the same voltage level. This causes K1 to drop out.

Current Sensor. The circuit of Fig. 10-15 monitors the level of an alternating current. The output is a relay and SPDT contacts may be used to determine over-current or under-current.

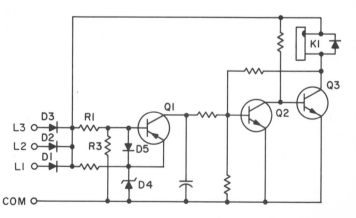

FIGURE 10-14

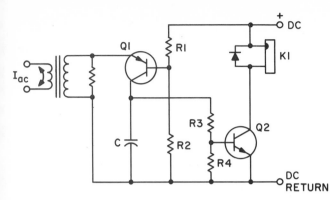

FIGURE 10-15

When dc is applied in absence of any ac, transistor Q1 is biased "off" by R1 and R2. The relative values of R1 and R2 determine this back bias, which is the set point. Q2 is also "off" and relay K1 remains de-energized.

As the a-c level increases, the half-cycle peaks reach a value to forward bias Q1 and cause conduction. These pulses charge C1 and cause current flow in R3 and R4. When this current becomes great enough, Q2 is turned on, causing K1 to pull in.

Synchronous Photoelectric Switch. Synchronous switching is turning "on" only at the instant the a-c supply voltage passes through zero and turning "off" only when current passes through zero. The circuit of Fig. 10-16 theoretically provides this function in response to either a mechanical switch or a variable resistance, such as a cadmium sulfide photocell. Use with caution as there may be erratic behavior caused by too long an operate time of the relay used, and coil inductance may cause a current lag producing too long a time on "turn-off."

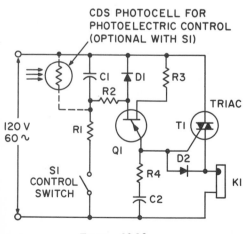

FIGURE 10-16

Current Sensor. The circuit of Fig. 10-17 can detect current level. When d-c voltage is applied, relay K1 pulls in through Q2. Q1 is in the cut-off mode. As long as the current remains below a predetermined value, tunnel diode D1 maintains a very small differential voltage between base and emitter of Q1. When the current increases above the desired value, the tunnel diode acts to increase this differential voltage, causing Q1 to conduct. This in turn effectively shorts out the relay coil, causing it to drop out.

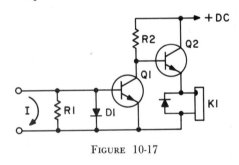

FIGURE 10-17

Low Current Detection. The circuit of Fig. 10-18 is a discriminator that detects 1 microampere currents with a 1 percent accuracy. This is made possible by driving field effect transistor Q1 with the output from backward diode D1. When the input signal exceeds a preset threshold, the sum of the currents through the backward diode switches the diode to its highest voltage stage. This voltage is then amplified by the FET output stage.

The detection threshhold may be varied over a broad range by adjusting resistor R1.

Over Frequency Sensor. The circuit of Fig. 10-19 detects frequencies in excess of a predetermined frequency. This circuit will cause relay K1 to be operated if input frequency exceeds a preset value determined by the time constant of R1C1.

On each half cycle, Q1 is turned on and discharges C1. During alternate half cycles, C1 charges, and at frequencies below the preset limit, will attain the firing voltage of Q2. Firing of Q2 turns on Q3 which discharges C2.

C2 and R2 establish a time constant long enough so that a period exceeding one cycle is required for the charge on C2 to reach the firing voltage of Q4. If the frequency exceeds the preset limit, Q2 and Q3 will not be turned on. C2 can then charge to the firing point of Q4, which will turn on the SCR and K1.

Under Frequency Sensor. The circuit of Fig. 10-20 detects frequencies below a predetermined frequency. This circuit will cause K1 to be energized if the input frequency falls

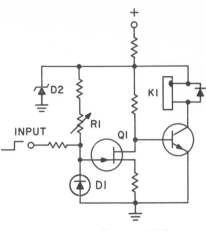

FIGURE 10-18

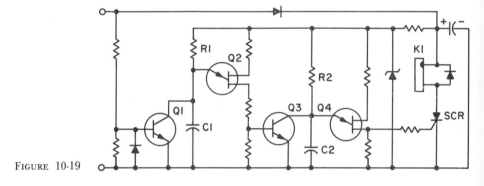

FIGURE 10-19

below a preset value determined by the time constant R1C1.

When the line frequency is above the set trip point, Q1 discharges C1 on each positive half cycle of the line voltage before the charge voltage on C1 reaches the intrinsic level of the unijunction transistor (UJT). Thus the UJT never fires when line frequency is above the sense point.

If the line frequency should drop below the set trip point, C1 is allowed to charge to the

firing level of Q2. This pulses the SCR and fault detecting relay K1 is energized. R1 can be variable to allow for an adjustable trip point.

Thermistors. Thermistors may be used with a relay to provide a time delay or present a constant impedance to a source supply. For many designs the preferred thermistor-type provides a resistance that decreases over a wide temperature range (NTC). Simplified circuits

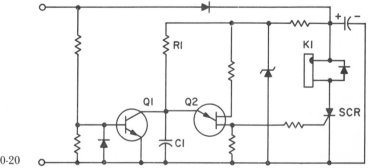

FIGURE 10-20

are shown in Fig. 10-21 and normally are not used in a-c relay applications.

Three-Wire Phase Sequence Sensor. The proper phase sequence of the three-phase system is determined by synchronization of the three squared signals developed from the phase A and B line voltage relative to phase C.

D-c operating voltage for the active circuits is established by rectification between phase A and C.

For the circuit of Fig. 10-22, the sinusoidal line voltages of phase A and B are squared by

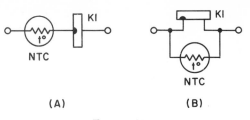

FIGURE 10-21

An advantage of this binary method of phase sequence sensing over some tuned-type sequence sensors is that high harmonics present in the power line and/or small line frequency changes will not affect the operation.

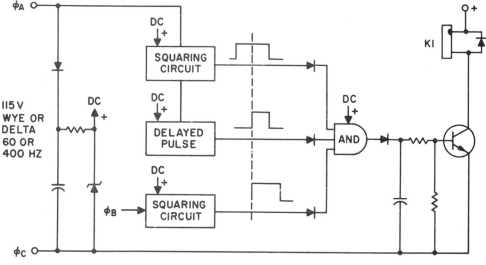

FIGURE 10-22

a Schmidt trigger or equivalent circuit. A short pulse, delayed by a time equal to 120° of the period of the line frequency, is initiated by each positive excursion of the phase A squared pulse. If the system phase relation is proper (A, B, C), the waveforms shown will result and the "And" circuit will transfer a short pulse to the output once in each cycle of the input frequency. A pulse detecting circuit then establishes a forward bias for the relay driver transistor which keeps relay K1 energized.

If any two lines should be reversed (i.e., phase relation becomes A, C, B) the "And" circuit will not transfer the short pulse due to the absence of simultaneous positive inputs through the three summing diodes.

If any of the three input voltages should be lost, the d-c operating voltage is lost and/or the three "And" inputs will be lost, resulting in a de-energized relay.

Four-Wire Phase Sequence Sensor. The circuit of Fig. 10-23 determines proper phase sequence. Inputs from phase A, B, and C are half wave rectified by D2, D4, and D6 to provide polarized operating voltage to relay K1 when transistor Q5 conducts.

Phase C is also rectified, filtered, and regulated by D5, R1, C1, and D7, respectively, to provide d-c voltage to bias Q5 "on" during normal phase sequence.

During the positive half cycle of phase A, Q2 conducts and the positive half cycle of phase B is coupled through D3 to a phase leading network of 60° or more (R2, C2 and R5). When the phase rotation is proper, Q1 and Q2 are simultaneously "on" for more than 120° of a half cycle, which causes Q3 and Q4 to conduct and turn "on." C3 charges during the conduction of Q3 to maintain Q4 and Q5 "on" during the remainder of each cycle.

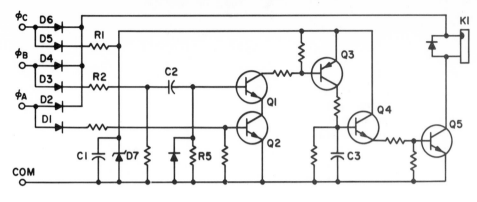

FIGURE 10-23

If the phase sequence should reverse (A, C, B), the positive portions of phase A and B, 60° phase lead shifted, will not coincide so that Q3 is not forward biased due to nonsynchronous conduction of Q1 and Q2. Thus C3 discharges and Q4 and Q5 stop conduction. The relay then drops out to indicate failure.

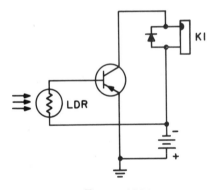

FIGURE 10-24

Photoconductive Driver.   The circuit, Fig. 10-24, for relay operation uses a photoconductive type cell. Here the light-dependent resistor (LDR) is in series with the forward bias for the base-emitter circuit. As shown, the emitter obtains the necessary positive potential from the voltage source, while the negative potential to the base is applied through the photoconductive unit. With low light levels, the resistance of the photocell is high, and insufficient forward bias is present to cause transistor conduction. As incident light levels increase, photocell conduction also increases, and sufficient forward bias is produced to permit current flow and the tripping of collector relay K1. As the resistance of the photocell decreases, increased base-emitter current flows, and the transistor amplifies this current change in the col-

lector-emitter side. When less sensitive relays (requiring higher current to trip) are used, an additional transistor amplifying stage is employed.

Photoconductive Driver.   The circuit of Fig. 10-25 operates a relay with a gated unilateral or bilateral solid state switch. It is fired by a change in the photoresistors to pull in relay K1.

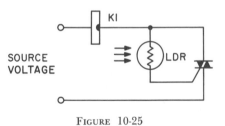

FIGURE 10-25

Photovoltaic Driver.   The circuit of Fig. 10-26 is a photovoltaic relay system using a transistor amplifier to increase current changes to operate a relay. A normally open or a normally closed relay may be used. The voltage produced by the cell is of proper polarity to furnish the necessary forward bias for the PNP transistor. With a more intense light striking the cell, a higher forward bias potential is

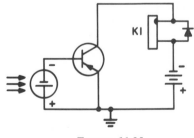

FIGURE 10-26

produced, causing the greater current to flow in the collector-emitter side. When sufficient current flows, relay K1 closes. It will open again when the light intensity falls below a given level.

Ignition Spark Detector. The circuit of Fig. 10-27 determines whether an ignition spark is present in a large combustion chamber be-before starting fuel flow. If no spark is initially present, an explosive mixture could accumulate

control point. The detector uses the high frequency characteristics of an ignition spark circuit E1 and an R.F. choke L1, connected in series with both the ignition transformer T1 secondary and the spark gap. At the instant of spark initiation with ionization, rapid changes of current occur in R.F. choke L1. The extremely fast rise time of the current pulses through the choke results in large, high frequency voltages across the choke which far exceed the firing potential (65 volts peak-to-peak,

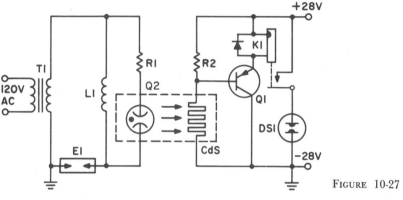

FIGURE 10-27

in the chamber, which, if ignited, could damage the equipment. The spark detector can be used in large and small chambers.

The circuit detects the presence of a spark and uses this information to trigger relay K1, providing power to light a signal lamp at the

minimum) of the neon lamp in Raysistor Q2, causing it to conduct. R1 is a ballast resistor that limits current flow in the Q2 glow tube. Light from the glow tube causes a reduction in resistance of the CdS photoresistor, which in turn decreases the bias on transistor Q1. This

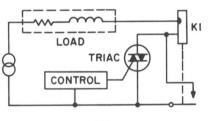

(A)

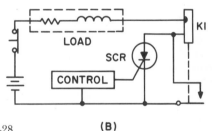

(B)

FIGURE 10-28

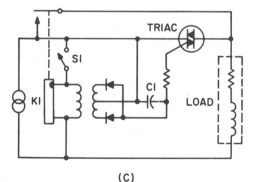

(C)

allows current to flow in the collector-emitter circuit and operate relay K1. Closing of relay K1 provides power to the indicator lamp DS1, which can be located at any convenient position.

Triac — Relay Contact Marriage. Relay contacts and triacs or SCR's may be combined to provide switching capabilities beyond those of either component used independently. See Figs. 10-28A and B. Steady state current han-

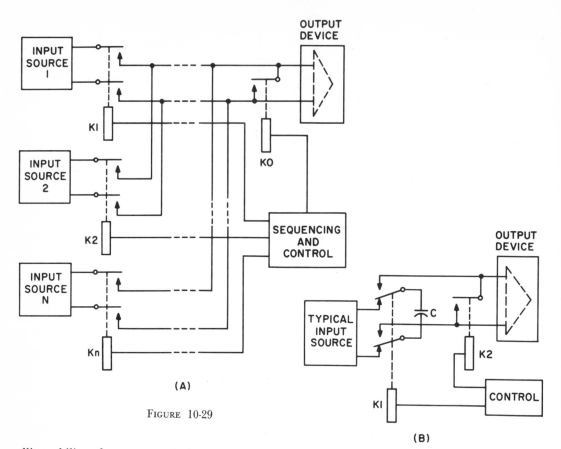

FIGURE 10-29

dling ability of contacts and the bounce-free switching characteristics of solid state devices are used.

When current through the load exceeds the pickup current of the relay K1, the contacts close, shunting the semiconductor and eliminating power dissipation in it. Turn on is accomplished by the semiconductor, which also keeps the circuit closed during any bounce of the relay contacts.

In Fig. 10-28C, when S1 is closed, the triac is turned on and the relay K1 is energized. Turn on time of the triac circuit is less than the operate time of the relay. When the contact closes, conduction shifts from the triac to the contact, eliminating power dissipation in the triac.

When S1 is opened, the relay contacts open, with conduction transferring to the triac which is held "on" by the charge on C1. Triac conduction ends when the current passes through zero and the charge on C1 is below "firing" potential.

Analog Input Switching. Unique requirements of process control and similar systems

make relay contacts the logical interface between signal sources and the solid state amplifiers used. See Fig.10-29.

Switching devices for these applications must meet some or all of these requirements:

1. D-c "offset" voltage introduced by the switch must be a minimum.

2. A-c noise introduced by the switch must be of an acceptable level at the time the signal is sampled.

3. The switch must withstand potential differences as high as several hundred volts. Ground potential at transducer and amplifier locations may be quite different, or signal lines may be subject to induced voltages.

4. The switch must exhibit a high ratio of "off" to "on" impedance.

5. "On" impedance must be low and consistent.

6. Switching speed must be adequate.

Decoding with Relays. Relays in a matrix driven by solid state circuitry provide a simple method of handling multiple outputs, including lamps, without special drivers. See Fig. 10-30. Energizing one "X" and one "Y" selects a particular relay. Flexibility in relay contacts permits many separated outputs at low cost. Diodes eliminate sneak circuits which could cause false operation.

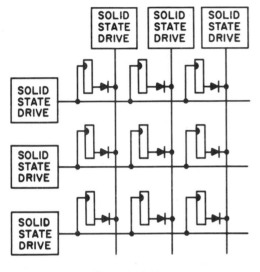

FIGURE 10-30

Pushbutton Interface. Pushbutton inputs to solid state systems can be repeated into the electronic circuitry via relays. See Fig. 10-31. These are potential advantages:

1. Noise and voltage drops associated with long lead lengths can be eliminated.
2. The pushbutton can be a single contact, with the relay supplying the number of circuits required. This also permits a reduction in cabling.
3. Bounce inherent in pushbuttons—and objectionable in some electronic systems—can be

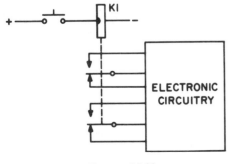

FIGURE 10-31

eliminated by interfacing with a mercury-wetted relay.

Variable Rate Driver for Stepping Switches. Spring driven stepping switches can be driven at controlled rates of less than one step per minute to 20 steps per second by the circuit of Fig. 10-32. Coil "on" time is the minimum necessary, keeping power dissipation at a minimum. The circuit may also be used to drive a relay to produce pulses at a controlled rate.

With voltage applied to the circuit, C1 charges at a rate determined by its value and the setting of R1. When its voltage reaches the level at which Q1 conducts, C1 discharges through Q1 and the gate circuit of the SCR. The SCR turns "on" and energizes the switch drive coil. As the switch cocks, the interrupter contact opens, turning the SCR "off." The switch steps, recloses its interrupter contact, and the solid state circuit repeats its cycle.

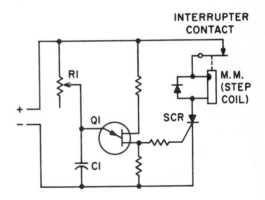

FIGURE 10-32

Reset Control for Direct Drive Stepping Switch. Two coil direct drive (minor) switches may be reliably and economically reset by solid state control of the rotary magnet (reset) coil. See Fig. 10-33. Closing S1 applies voltage to the rotary (step) coil, advancing the switch wiper arm one step, and also applies a positive bias to Q1, holding it "off." When the switch is advanced to position N, positive voltage gates the SCR, but Q1 remains "off" until S1 is opened. With S1 opened, Q1 and the SCR conduct, energizing the release magnet (reset) coil. As the wiper arm reaches O position, positive bias is applied to Q1, stopping conduction through the release magnet coil.

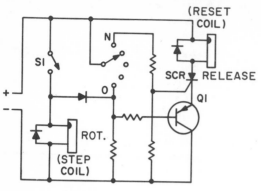

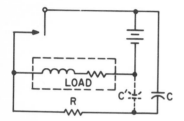

FIGURE 10-33

10.3 Devices and techniques used for arc suppression and relay contact protection

The following methods eliminate or minimize the harmful effects of arcing on contacts which interrupt inductive loads. In both military and commercial applications useful contact life can be extended considerably by the reduction or elimination of contact arcing. As relays, or hybrid relays, work in conjunction with or alongside sensitive logic circuitry, it becomes very important that the devices neither

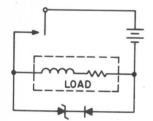

(A) RESISTOR CAPACITOR NETWORK (USE C OR C' AS PREFERRED)

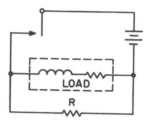

(B) RESISTOR

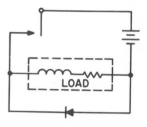

(C) DIODE

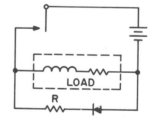

(D) DIODE & ZENER

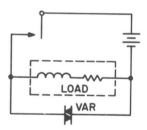

(E) DIODE & RESISTOR

(F) VARISTOR

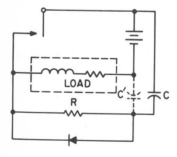

(G) RESISTOR-CAPACITOR-DIODE NETWORK

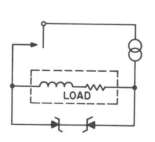

(H) BACK TO BACK DIODE (ZENER OR AVALANCHE)

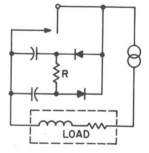

(I) CAPACITOR-DIODE-RESISTOR NETWORK FOR AC SUPPRESSION

FIGURE 10-34

radiate nor conduct transient voltages at radio frequencies of sufficient magnitude to either damage or cause false triggering of sensitive logic circuitry. The following schemes should be useful in combating these problems.

When the circuit to an inductive load is opened, much of the energy stored in the load must be dissipated through arcing of the contacts unless some alternative means is provided. Various "energy absorbers" are employed for this purpose, and the type used is dependent upon the nature of the load, the nature of the applied voltage, the kind of power supplied (ac or dc), the kind of contacts being protected, the environment, etc. In most cases, some testing should be done to determine which kind of contact protection is best.

Figure 10-34(A), the resistor-capacitor network, is the most common solid-state device for contact protection. This network also protects resistive circuits where the rate of rise of voltage across opening contacts must be controlled. (Paragraph 4-11 has a more complete discussion.)

A basic form of protection is a resistor connected across the inductive load as shown in Fig. 10-34(B). Peak transient voltage developed upon opening the contact is dependent on the resistance used. Power dissipated in the resistor while the load is energized may be a disadvantage.

In Fig. 10-34(C), a single semiconductor diode is connected across the load so that it blocks the applied voltage at contact closure, but permits dissipation of the energy stored in the load upon contact opening.

Figure 10-34(D) shows the use of a semiconductor diode with a zener diode in series, both connected across the load. The zener diode reduces the time to dissipate the stored energy. A similar effect is achieved by using a resistor in series with the diode as shown in Fig. 10-34(E). These circuits, too, are described in Par 4-11.

Another simple semiconductor circuit, shown in 10-34(F), has a varistor used as the energy absorber. The resistance of the varistor is very high at nominal applied voltage but decreases to a small value at the higher voltage occurring when the circuit is opened. This makes it very effective in suppressing the voltage generated when the circuit is opened, with a minimum effect while the circuit is closed.

Figure 10-34(G) shows a combination of an RC and a semiconductor diode for contact protection purposes. This circuit is also further described in Par. 4-11.

One of the earliest applications of semiconductor diodes for contact protection was in the form of diodes (zener or avalanche) connected back-to-back across the load as in Fig. 10-34(H). This arrangement has only limited advantages over the use of a non-inductive resistor in the same location but remains in somewhat common usage.

In Fig. 10-34(J) a capacitor-diode net is shunted across the contacts to be protected. This arrangement is particularly effective when the power source is alternating current. (See Par. 4-12 for a more detailed discussion).

10.4 Rectification of ac to provide d-c relay operation

The true a-c operated relay has long been a sought after goal by relay designers particularly for use on 400 Hz a-c circuits. (True 60 Hz a-c relays have been available for many years.) It is generally conceded by relay engineers that a rectified d-c operated relay is preferred on 400 Hz electrical power and in many instances on lower frequencies also. Accordingly, the following paragraphs present various schemes for providing hybrid relays with a variety of rectification circuits for permitting the use of the relay directly on an a-c line.

Figure 10-35(A) shows a full-wave bridge rectifier circuit using semiconductor diodes as the rectifying elements. To improve the quality of the output, a suitable filter is sometimes placed at position C.

Figure 10-35(B) represents a more common arrangement for producing satisfactory d-c power for relays. Capacitor C is a large electrolytic (at 115 volts a-c applied power, a commonly employed capacitor is 40 mf, 230 volts test with a protective resistor in series with the diode of approximately 30-40 ohms). The economy of this arrangement is apparent.

Figure 10-35(C) shows a circuit requiring a relay with two equal windings, one of which functions on one half cycle, the other on the other half cycle. The diodes alternately block and conduct with respect to each other in order to maintain unidirectional flux.

A modification of this circuit is shown in Fig.

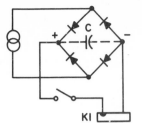

(A) FULL WAVE BRIDGE

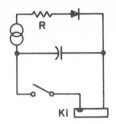

(B) HALF WAVE RECTIFIER
WITH FILTER
CAPACITOR

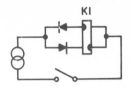

(C) DUAL DIODE-DUAL
WINDING COIL

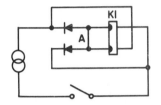

(D) DUAL DIODE-DUAL
WINDING COIL

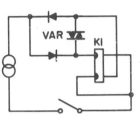

(E) DUAL DIODE-DUAL
WINDING COIL, DIODES
VARISTOR PROTECTED

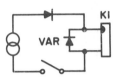

(F) HALF WAVE,
FREE WHEELING

FIGURE 10-35

10-35(D). Here connection A ties a diode direct-ly across each winding, providing a low im-pedance path for circulating current.

Figure 10-35(E) is essentially the same as Fig. 10-35(C) except that a varistor has been em-ployed to protect the diodes from line surges,

a very necessary precaution in some cases.

A half wave circuit satisfactory for many relays is shown in Fig. 10-35(F). Current estab-lished in the coil during one half cycle can continue to circulate cr "free-wheel" during the other half cycle.

11
Reed Switches and Reed Relays

11.1   Introduction

Reeds, as switches and as relays, both dry and mercury wetted, are dealt with generally in Section 3. Because of their many peculiarities, as well as their increasing importance, this section is devoted to them exclusively, something not done elsewhere for other types of relays. This detail is essential to a common understanding of how to best employ them.

Reed relays are those having either the dry or mercury wetted switching elements defined on pages 67-70. Because these switches share many characteristics, the discussion is primarily in terms of dry reeds, with distinguishing aspects of mercury wetted devices presented later.

Though reed switches are relatively new, a number of designs have been developed to take advantage of their unique characteristics:

(1) A high degree of reliability stemming from their controlled contact environment.

(2) Consistency of performance resulting from a minimization of parts, which permits controlled (or automated) production.

(3) Long operational life.

(4) Ease of packaging as a relay.

(5) Relatively high speed operation.

(6) Small size.

(7) Low cost.

Reed switch designs embrace several variations in mechanical configuration and a range of physical sizes. While any generalization is dangerous, for purposes of discussion it is convenient to roughly categorize the switches in terms of size. These terms will be used:

Standard — Switches similar to the early Bell Laboratories design; approximately 2 in. long (glass length) and 0.2 in. in diameter.

Miniature — Switches having a glass length of about 0.8 in. and a diameter of 0.1 in.

Micro-miniature — Switches having a maximum glass length of 0.5 in. and a diameter less than 0.1 in.

These classifications are valid only for this discussion and do not have universal acceptance. For example, the "miniature" category has frequently been referred to as "micro."

11.2   Contact forms

Switches used in dry reed relays provide form A, B, or C contact action. The form A corresponds with the basic switch capsule design. The form B results from the combination of the form A switch and a permanent magnet strong enough to close it. Form C action may be provided by a three-element switch capsule similar in concept to the basic switch, but can also be achieved by joining a form A with an appropriately adjusted form B.

In the typical "true" form C switch design, the armature is mechanically tensioned against the normally closed contact, and is moved to the normally open contact upon application of a magnetic field. In another version, the armature is mechanically centered and the normally closed contact force is derived from a permanent magnet. In application, the primary difference is that the latter device is polarity sensitive, as are any of the assemblies incorporating permanent magnets.

Form B action may be obtained by using the normally closed half of the form C switch, but the magnetically biased form A version is more frequently employed.

Latching contacts, defined as contacts which remain in the position to which they were last driven although coil power is removed, are also frequently provided in dry reed relays. Using the form A switch, this is accomplished by biasing with a permanent magnet similar to that used for form B action. The difference is that the magnet is weaker—strong enough to hold the contact closed, but not strong enough to close it when open. In a variation of this approach, magnet position in relation to the switch capsule is adjusted to obtain the desired response. The ferreed and other devices utilizing magnetic remanence also provide latching contact action.

Latching action is also possible with the "true" form C switches. In those which derive normally closed contact force from armature tension, the approach is essentially the same as with the form A switch. In the mechanically-centered, magnetically-biased version, all that is required is appropriate adjustment of the magnet.

11.3   Relay Configuration

The simplicity of adding a coil to a dry reed switch to create a relay, coupled with the small size of some of the switches, has led to a proliferation of relay package designs. Comment here must therefore be limited to only their general characteristics.

Designs for use on printed circuit boards have proved most popular, followed by plug-in relays and those for "wire-in" usage. Special purpose devices, such as those fitted with co-axial type connectors, are available as standard packages. Many other designs have been created to match the mechanical and electrical requirements of specific applications.

Printed circuit relays. Relays for printed circuit board use are, in general, of a "flat pack" configuration. Where multiple reeds or reeds and magnets are included in the package, they are set in a row and enclosed in an oval coil. Terminals are usually on a 0.1-in. grid pattern, though switch diameters of slightly over 0.2 and 0.1 in. have led to some notable exceptions.

A summary of dimensions from a review of several manufacturers' data is shown. Other manufacturers may have a product differing greatly. The user must be aware of the lack of standards, and must specify dimensions. The information here is to remind him of this necessity.

Some typical dimensions:

Relays using "standard" switches:
    Length — $2\frac{1}{4}$ to 3 in.
    Height — $\frac{1}{2}$ to $\frac{3}{4}$ in.
    Width — Determined by number of
        switches; $\frac{1}{2}$ in. minimum.

Terminal patterns:
    2.50 in. $\times$ 0.200 in.
    2.40 in. $\times$ 0.200 in.
    1.90 in. $\times$ 0.200 in.
    2.40 in. and 2.20 in. $\times$ 0.200 in.
    2.40 in. and 2.00 in. $\times$ 0.200 in.
    2.50 in. $\times$ 0.218 in.

Relays using "miniature" switches:
    Length — $\frac{3}{4}$ to $1\frac{3}{4}$ in.
    Height — $\frac{3}{16}$ to $\frac{5}{8}$ in.
    Width — Determined by number of
        switches; $\frac{3}{16}$ in. minimum.

Terminal patterns:
    1.20 in. $\times$ 0.100 in.
    1.00 in. $\times$ 0.100 in.
    0.70 in. $\times$ 0.100 in.
    1.35 in. $\times$ 0.150 in.
    1.00 in. $\times$ 0.150 in.
    1.10 in. and 0.90 in. $\times$ 0.100 in.
    1.00 in. and 0.90 in. $\times$ 0.100 in.
    1.20 in. and 1.05 in. $\times$ 0.150 in.
    1.60 in. and 1.20 in. $\times$ 0.200 in.
    1.50 in. and 1.30 in. $\times$ 0.200 in.

Relays using "micro-miniature" switches:
    Length — $\frac{5}{8}$ in. to $\frac{3}{4}$ in.
    Height — $\frac{3}{16}$ in. to $\frac{1}{2}$ in.
    Width — Determined by number of
        switches; $\frac{3}{16}$ in. minimum.

Terminal patterns:
    0.60 in. $\times$ 0.100 in.
    0.50 in. $\times$ 0.100 in.

Heights of printed board relays have been dictated, in part, by center-to-center board spacing in users' assemblies. Spacings frequently employed are 1.0, 0.8, 0.75, 0.625, 0.5, and 0.375 in. Maximum acceptable relay height is usually 0.150 in. less than board spacing.

Plug-in relays. Assemblies similar in form to plug-in general-purpose and telephone type relays or to octal base and miniature vacuum tubes have been used to package reed relays. Most mate with the standard octal socket or the similar 9-, 11- or 12-pin socket, although some have been made for the 7- and 9-pin miniature sockets and the 14-pin relay socket.

Wire-in relays. A number of configurations fall in the "wire-in" category. Of these the axial lead variety is one of the more popular. It is also used in printed board assemblies. Other configurations provide lugs for soldered connections, terminals compatible with solderless wrap, screw terminals, or quick connect terminals such as Taper Tab, Faston, etc.

11.4 General package characteristics

Number of switches. There is no limit to the number of switches which can be actuated by a common coil. However, as the number increases, coil efficiency decreases and power input increases. This can lead to a practical limitation. On the other hand, the increase in power required to operate one more switch is usually less than the total required if the assembly were split in two. Most frequently used is the relay with a single switch, but even relays with a dozen or more switches in a single coil are quite common.

Assemblies. Dry reed relay structures can be categorized as open assemblies, enclosed assemblies, potted or molded assemblies, and hermetically sealed asemblies.

Among printed board relays, the open assembly is frequently used. The basic structure, typically molded of an electrical grade plastic, functions as a coil bobbin and provides a means of supporting the reed switches and relay terminals. In many cases, the switch terminals are formed so that they will insert directly into the printed board.

This same structure is often placed in a metal or plastic box, which is then filled with a potting material. In some instances, the box provides terminal support, further simplifying the internal structure or permitting use of a self-supporting coil. These assemblies may offer improved resistance to environmental or handling stresses.

Molded relays are similar to the potted relays, but differ in materials used. In these assemblies, the molding material provides the primary mechanical support for the switches and coil and also produces the finished external surfaces.

Assemblies similar to the potted relays can be hermetically sealed, using a metal cover and a base with terminals mounted in glass-to-metal seals.

Plug-in and wire-in relay assemblies follow the general patterns described for printed board relays. Plug-in relays usually use a potting material to support the coil-switch structure within the enclosure carrying the plug. Wire-in relays follow both the open and potted patterns.

In all assemblies, materials are carefully chosen to offer proper support and protection to the reed switches and to minimize external or internal stresses which could cause fracture of the glass enclosures of the switches. Changes in both temperature and relative humidity can cause dimensional shifts in the supporting structure not compatible with switch characteristics. Similar effects can result from shrinkage of potting or molding materials as they set. Materials are also selected to withstand the effects of solvents used in cleaning the electrical assemblies in which the relays are used.

In general, dry reed devices can be characterized as quite susceptible to the influences of external magnetic fields. For this reason, and to improve magnetic coupling of the coil to the switches, many relays incorporate some form of magnetic shielding. Metal cases serve this function, as do internal wraps or plates affixed to the coil. In some instances, the magnetic shield is connected to a terminal which may be grounded to provide electrostatic shielding, but in most cases the electrostatic shield is nonferrous and separate from the magnetic shield.

11.5 Specialized applications

High voltage. Typical dry reed switches are rather limited in their ability to withstand high voltages across their open contacts, with the standard switch rated at 500 volts rms. For special applications, switches which can withstand voltages as high as 10,000 volts can be incorporated in assemblies similar to those described earlier. Terminal spacing is modified as required to withstand the voltages.

While modifications for higher voltage typically incorporate special versions of the standard dry reed capsule, similar versions of the miniature switches are also available. They are limited to about 2,000 volts.

Power.   Reed switches capable of handling power in excess of the typical 15-VA rating of the standard switch capsule are available. Relays incorporating these switches, rated at 50 to 350 VA, are defined "power relays."

High insulation resistance.   Reed switches manufactured under carefully controlled processes provide an insulation resistance between contacts of in excess of 10^{12} ohms. While most standard relay assemblies provide shunting paths which appreciably lower insulation resistance, special structures using appropriate materials and processes can preserve the basic high insulation resistance capability of the switch.

Low thermal voltage.   Relays typically produce a voltage between contact terminals as a result of differing temperatures between the junctions of materials in the assembly. Changing ambient temperatures or heat produced by the relay coil cause temperature gradients within the relay. Relays incorporating materials and assembly techniques which minimize these effects are available.

Low noise.   The cantilever reed members in a switch continue to move for a few milliseconds following contact closure. This motion can produce a variation in contact resistance, and it does cause a voltage to be generated between switch terminals. Relays using reeds and structural techniques which minimize the latter effect are called "low noise" relays.

Low capacitance.   Since the contact overlap area of most reed switches is small, capacitance between contacts is small. When the switch is installed in a coil, this capacitance is paralleled by the comparatively large capacitance of individual reed blades to the coil. The resulting increased capacitance across contacts and the capacitive coupling from coil to reeds can be objectionable in some applications.

By interposing an electrostatic shield between the reed switch and the coil, the paralleling capacitances can be greatly reduced, with capacitance across contacts approaching basic switch capacitance. In multipole relays, the electrostatic shield can be interposed between the switch group and the coil, or can also be interposed between individual switches.

Cross point.   Relays used in matrix applications are called cross point relays. Reed relays adapt readily to the various schemes of "no response to one input—response to two inputs" and have been used extensively in matrices.

Logic devices.   Reed relays readily adapt to the performance of logic functions through the addition or subtraction of magnetic fluxes produced by multiple coils. If "one flux unit" is defined as the level required to actuate a reed switch, the manner in which "And," "Or," "Exclusive Or," and "Nor" functions can be accomplished will be readily understood from Fig. 11-1.

A characteristic of the standard reed which has made it especially effective as an "And" device is the differential in operate ampere-turns attainable with appropriate coil configuration. If each of the two sections of the coil is located so that it is closely coupled to only one reed in a "centered-gap" switch, input to one coil to cause closure is many times that required if both coils are energized. See Fig. 11-2.

Memory devices.   The ferreed is a memory or latching adaptation of the basic reed switch. Other designs using a remanent structure external to the switch also exist, as do switch designs in which the reeds themselves are of a remanent material. The more commonly used combination of a permanent magnet and a form A reed switch described earlier also fulfills the memory function.

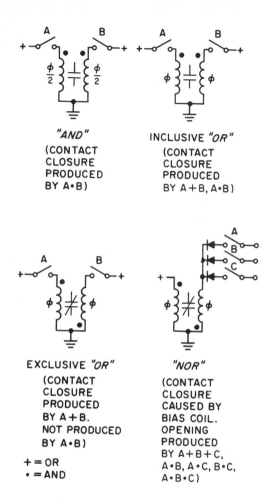

FIG. 11-1. REED RELAY LOGIC FUNCTIONS

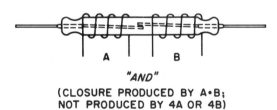

"AND"

(CLOSURE PRODUCED BY A•B;
NOT PRODUCED BY 4A OR 4B)

FIG. 11-2. DRY REED WITH TWO WINDINGS LOCATED
FOR "AND" FUNCTION

11.6 Electrical characteristics

Contact ratings. Ratings of typical dry reed switches are presented in some detail in Paragraph 11.10.

Sensitivity. Power input required to operate dry reed relays is determined by the sensitivity of the particular reed switch used, by the number of reeds operated by the coil, by the permanent magnet biasing used, and by the efficiency of the coil and the effectiveness of its coupling to the reeds. Minimum input required to effect closure ranges from the very low milliwatt level for a single capsule "sensitive" unit to several watts for a standard multipole relay.

Operate time. Coil time constant, overdrive, and the characteristics of the reed switch determine operate time. With maximum overdrive, standard reed switches will operate in just under one millisecond; miniature reeds in 500 microseconds, and micro-miniature reeds in less than 200 microseconds. At normal drive levels, operate times will be two to three times these values.

The other end of the operate time spectrum is less definable, since coil time constant and drive level are the primary determinants. However, with the low inductance typical of reed relay coils, operate times of even the standard reeds rarely exceed 10 milliseconds.

Release time. With the relay coil unsuppressed, dry reed switch contacts release in a fraction of a millisecond. Miniature and microminiature form A contacts open in as little as 10 to 20 microseconds. Standard switches open in 100 microseconds. Magnetically biased form B contacts and normally closed contacts of form C switches reclose in from 100 microseconds to one millisecond.

If the relay coil is suppressed, release times are increased. Resistor-capacitor suppression usually has the least effect. Zener diode suppression stretches release time somewhat more. Diode suppression can delay release for several milliseconds, depending on coil characteristics, drive level, and reed release characteristics.

Bounce. As with other hard contact switches, dry reed contacts bounce on closure. The duration of bounce is typically quite short, and is in part dependent on drive level. In some of the faster devices, the sum of operate time and bounce is relatively constant as drive is increased, operate time decreasing and bounce increasing.

While normally closed contacts—those that are mechanically biased — bounce more than normally open contacts, magnetically biased form B contacts exhibit essentially the same bounce as form A's.

Typical bounce times (mechanically biased normally closed contacts) are:

    Standard:
        Normally Open   — 0.50 millisecond
        Normally Closed   — 2.5   millisecond
    Miniature:
        Normally Open   — 0.25 millisecond
        Normally Closed   — 2.0   millisecond
    Micro-miniature:
        Normally Open   — 0.25 millisecond

Contact resistance.   Because the reeds in a dry reed switch are made of a magnetic material which has a high volume resistivity, terminal-to-terminal resistance is somewhat higher than in some other types of relays. Typical specification limits for initial resistance of form A reed switches and of relays incorporating them are

	Switch	Relay
Standard	0.040 – 0.075 ohm	0.050 – 0.100 ohm
Miniature	0.100 – 0.200 ohm	0.100 – 0.200 ohm
Micro-miniature	0.150 – 0.200 ohm	0.200 – 0.250 ohm

Insulation resistance.   A well-cleaned, dry reed switch made with a properly controlled internal atmosphere will have an insulation resistance of 10^{12} to 10^{13} ohms or greater. When it is assembled into a relay, parallel insulation paths reduce this to typical values of 10^{10} or 10^{11} ohms. Depending on the particular manner of relay construction, exposure to high humidity or contaminating environments can appreciably lower final insulation resistance. Typical procurement specifications call for 10^9 or 10^{10} ohms.

With special care in assembly and with proper choice of materials, the basic insulation resistance capability of the switch capsule can be preserved. Relays having an insulation resistance of 10^{13} (and even 10^{14}) ohms have been produced.

Capacitance.   Reed capsules typically have low terminal-to-terminal capacitance (see Table 11-3). However, in the usual relay structure where the switch is surrounded by a coil,

capacitances from each reed to the coil act to increase basic capacitance many times. If the increased capacitance is objectionable, it can be reduced by placing a grounded electrostatic shield between the switch and coil.

Typical capacitance values for relays using form A switches are:

	Unshielded		Shielded	
	Across Contacts	Closed Switch to Coil	Across Contacts	Closed Switch to Shield
Standard	1.0 pF	4.0 pF	0.2 pF	5.0 pF
Miniature	0.7 pF	3.0 pF	0.1 pF	3.5 pF
Micro-miniature	0.4 pF	2.0 pF	0.08 pF	2.5 pF

Where the capacitance from contact to shield is objectionable, greater spacing or unique methods of coupling the coil to the contacts may be employed.

Dielectric strength.   With the exception of the high-voltage dry reed switches (those which are pressurized or evacuated), the dielectric strength limitation of relays is determined by the capabilities of the switches.

Typical limits are

Standard	— 500 vac.	Not applicable for low NI switches
Miniature	— 250 vac.	
Micro-miniature	— 200 vac.	

Dielectric strength between switch and coil terminals is usually 750 to 1000 volts ac.

When high voltage reeds are employed, relay structures must be modified to withstand the requirements of the application.

Thermal emf.   Since thermally generated voltages result from thermal gradients within the relay assembly, relays built to minimize this effect often use sensitive switches to reduce required coil power and thermally conductive materials to reduce temperature gradients. Latching relays, which may be operated by short duration pulses, are often used if the operational rate is such that the potential benefit of reduced duty cycle can be realized.

Measurements of thermal emf are specified in a number of ways, each suited to a particular application. One of the more standard, and the one documented in MIL-R-5757E, is measurement at maximum ambient with continuous coil input for a time sufficient to ensure temperature stability. Measured in this manner, relays can be supplied to specifications with limits as low as 10 microvolts.

Noise.   In reed relays, noise is defined as a voltage appearing between terminals of a switch for a few milliseconds following closure. It occurs because the reeds are moving in a magnetic field and because voltages are produced within them by magnetostrictive effects. From an application standpoint, noise is important if the signal switched by the reed is to be used in the few milliseconds immediately following closure, if the level of noise compares unfavorably with the signal level, or if the frequencies constituting the noise cannot be filtered conveniently.

When noise is critical in an application, a peak-to-peak limit is established, with measurement made a specified number of milliseconds following application of coil power. Measurement techniques, including filters which are to be used, are also specified. MIL-R-5757E, for example, sets a peak-to-peak limit of 50 microvolts at 10 milliseconds with frequencies below 600 Hz and above 100 kHz attenuated.

11.7   Environmental characteristics

Reed relays are used in essentially the same environments as other types of relays. Factors influencing their ability to function in these environments and construction techniques employed to enhance their capabilities are similar to those used elsewhere. However, the cantilever reed structure and the glass envelope do influence certain characteristics sufficiently to warrant discussion.

Vibration.   The reed switch structure, with so few elements free to move, has a better defined response to vibration than other relay types. Assuming no particular influences from the relay assembly (a fairly valid assumption in most cases), the frequencies which will produce a response in the reeds are well defined.

With vibratory inputs reasonably separated from the resonant frequency, the relay will withstand relatively high inputs, 20 g's or more. At resonance of the reeds, the typical device will fail at very low level inputs.

Typical resonant frequencies are
Standard   —   800 Hz
Miniature   — 2,500 Hz
Microminiature   — 5,000 Hz

Shock.   Dry reed relays withstand relatively high levels of shock. Form A contacts are usually rated as able to pass 30 to 50 g's, 11 msec, half sine wave shock, without false operation of contacts. Switches exposed to a magnetic field tending to close them, such as in the biased latching form, demonstrate somewhat lower resistance to shock. Normally closed contacts of mechanically biased form C switches may also fail at somewhat lower levels.

Temperature.   Differential expansion or contraction of reed switches and materials used in relay assemblies can lead to fracture of the switches. Proper choices of materials and of assembly methods minimize these effects. While reed relays are capable of withstanding temperature cycling or temperature shock over a range of at least $-55°C$ to $+125°C$, limits of each application should be defined to ensure compliance.

Moisture.   The primary effect of exposure to moisture is a probability of reduced insulation resistance, but distortion or expansion of relay structures which could damage switches is also a possibility. Here, as in comprehending the effects of temperature, proper selection of materials and assembly methods provides very satisfactory results.

Radiation.   The basic reed switch is quite resistant to radiation and has been used to perform control functions in "hot" environments. Coils and supporting structures utilizing appropriate materials permit the construction of reed relays resistant to radiation.

11.8   Application notes

In general, the application of dry reed relays follows the pattern of other relay types, and therefore the discussion in Sec. 5 is most pertinent. In particular, reference to page 115 is suggested. A few additional notes are presented here.

Magnetically biased relays. Any of the reed relays incorporating permanent magnets is polarity sensitive. This includes:

(1) The typical form B made by adding a magnet to a form A switch.

(2) The latching form similar to the form B.

(3) A form A or a mechanically biased form C combined with a magnet for adjustment of switch sensitivity.

(4) The mechanically-centered, magnetically-biased form C.

If driven by the wrong polarity, the form B does not operate. The latching form and the mechanically-centered, magnetically-biased form C transfer to the contact appropriate for the applied polarity. The switch, combined with a magnet for sensitivity adjustment, will function, but sensitivity will not be as anticipated because the magnet produces an effect opposite to that intended.

Some of the biased relays yield false operation if subjected to a strong overdrive. The form B is an example. It responds to the sum of the fields produced by the permanent magnet and the coil. With the proper drive, the sum is below the "hold" level for the switch and it opens. With an overdrive, the sum can be above the switch's "operate" level, and although the polarity is opposite to that produced by the permanent magnet, the switch will close. Under dynamic conditions, overdrive which produces a net field only slightly above "hold" level can result in false operation. This is caused by "flagging" of the reeds, which will be discussed later.

The latching form, when driven by the polarity which causes switch opening, is also subject to false operation if overdriven. The mechanically-centered, magnetically-biased form C and the switches combined with a magnet for sensitivity adjustment are not.

Flagging. When form A switches are released or when form B switches are operated, the reeds do not immediately assume their static position. Rather, they oscillate about their static position for a few milliseconds. In some applications, this action can cause unexpected effects.

If a relay is operated at a rate such that the switch open time is not sufficient for the flagging of the reeds to cease, variation in reclosure time will probably be observed. This occurs because reed motion either aids or opposes the effect of the applied field. If open time is varied while observing contact action on an oscilloscope, this variation will be observed to maximize and minimize at a frequency determined by the "beat" between reed oscillation and coil drive. Some, in observing the variation in closure time, have misinterpreted the oscilloscope presentation as bounce.

Flagging in a latching reed (a form A reed combined with a magnet) can lead to false closure. If the coil input which causes the switch contact to open is terminated while flagging is above a given level, the field produced by the permanent magnet will cause the reeds to re-latch when they approach each other. A similar effect can occur in a relay combining magnetically biased form B's and form A's if the permanent magnet field at the A is above hold level, or can occur with form B's if they are subjected to an overdrive.

In some applications, a normally open contact will be observed to reclose momentarily when it is released, with the action interpreted as bounce. This also results from flagging. As the reeds move, they cause changes in coil inductance with resultant changes in coil current (diode suppression assumed). If, as two reeds approach each other, they are given additional energy by an increase in coil current, they may reclose for a few microseconds. In multipole relays, the probability of reclosure of a given switch is increased by the effects of the other switches on coil inductance and on flux paths in the assembly.

Some reed switch manufacturers have largely overcome the effects of flagging by incorporating means of limiting reed motion. However, the techniques are not applicable to all switch designs.

Ladder effect. In multipole relays, operate times are observed to be spread over a broader range than might be expected. This is attributed to the effect of switch closures on coil inductance described above. As each switch closes, it increases inductance, causing a reduction in coil current and in flux available to close other switches. A similar effect is observed on release times if the relay coil is diode suppressed.

11.9   Switch construction

In its simplest form, the dry reed switch is composed of two reeds sealed in a glass envelope. This simplicity of design is based on the unique characterization which develops the magnetic circuit, electrical contacts, and terminal leads in the two-reed elements. The glass acts as the supporting mechanism while its hermetic sealing provides a contamination-free contact set.

Reed materials.   The reed elements are formed from a 52 per cent nickel-iron alloy which when annealed displays high intrinsic induction, high permeability, and low losses. The expansion of this alloy is closely matched to that of the glass from at least the melting temperature of the glass through approximately −55°C. This ensures a virtually stress free expansion seal. The reed design is such that rigidity is maintained through the seal and the flexure all takes place within the envelope. Plastic deformation of the reeds within the stresses imposed by the as-manufactured reed switch and their respective contact gaps is non-existent. Moreover the refined grain structure of the annealed reeds makes them free from fatigue regardless of the number of flexures.

Contacts.   The contact is typically a precious metal—gold, rhodium, silver, etc.—or a combination of precious metals electroplated on the reed elements at their mating points. In addition to providing a low resistance contact, the plating provides corrosion resistance and functions as a residual.

Other metals including the refractory metals — tungsten, rhenium, molybdenum — have been used as contacts where high melting temperatures due to relatively heavy load switching are dictated. Similarly, common metals such as nickel and copper have been alloyed with or used as is under plates for other metals. In addition to electrodeposition, contacts are welded, vacuum deposited, sputtered, clad and inlayed. Furthermore, hybrid switches with one wetted and one dry member have been used for specific applications where stable contact resistance and relatively high load switching characteristics are required.

In addition to the obvious load switching and wear considerations, contact selection should be based on the stability of contact resistance, resistance to cold welding, and inertness of the contact material to formation of damaging oxides, sulfides, etc. Some general properties are given in Table 11-1. It must be noted that in the actual application, the available contact and retractile forces are important factors in any ultimate selection.

Mechanical wear presents no problem. The contact forces are low, ranging from a few grams on the smaller size capsules to over 50 grams on the larger sizes. Coining has not been noted on any of the common plating materials. Galling is excluded because there is no wiping action.

Oxides attack the basic metal of the reed and can attack the contact. Organic film growth or the formation of oxides, sulfides, etc. is a function of the contact metal selection. Gold is the most noble of the precious metals and is, therefore, least subject to the formation of inorganic films. The refractory metals are the poorest, and extreme care must be taken with tungsten for this reason. The corrosion resistance of the gold and gold silver alloy systems is lower when diffused. (The diffusion process is the mechanism which transports the gold into the base metal and the nickel and iron to the surface, and it is often carried out at the time when the magnetic annealing is performed.) The diffusion process does yield a harder surface which is free from cold weld tendencies. Other contamination, such as inclusions and organics in the plating solution, contamination in gaseous or particulate form at the time of sealing, foreign material in the reeds or glass, etc., contributes to the variation of resistance with operation of the switch. The non-wiping action which typifies the dry reed does not allow interfacial "cleaning" upon actuation.

Load ratings vary widely and are very dependent upon the size of the reed, the available contact force, the contact material, and the tolerable contact resistance in a specific application. At low level loads, the limitations are typically those imposed as a maximum tolerable contact resistance in the applicable circuit or a cold weld (sticking) phenomenon. The former is due chiefly to contamination, whereas the latter can in most instances be eliminated in the material selection. At high level loads the transfer of material from electrodes (contact erosion) is aptly described by F. L. Jones (Reference 1). The localized boiling is affected by the material selection in the specified load.

Herein tungsten, melting point 6,170°F, is far superior to silver and gold with 1,761°F and 1,945°F melting points, respectively. Moreover, the thermal conductivity and density of the ions transported versus the field strength must be considered. Pit and cone formation with a lack of contact wipe will destroy the contact unless the pit is mechanically broken by the energy associated with the vibrations of reed closure. For these reasons a-c load switching typically extends life, whereas inductive switching (e.g., when there is a high localized voltage after "heating" the contacts) imposes a severe limitation to the contact life.

Cold welding occurs when a noble metal within a relatively inert atmosphere is mated to a similar metal, or to one with a high diffusion coefficient. A "weld" penetration is formed which can usually be broken by a mechanical shock. The phenomenon bears a time-temperature relationship (typical of most diffusion processes). Selection of a material and/or a reed with sufficient rectractile force can usually eliminate this phenomenon.

Switch manufacture. Operate and release are controlled by the geometry of the reeds, the contact gap, contact thickness, gap position relative to the defining coil, the overlap of the reeds, the proximity of the reeds to the coil, and the alignment of the reeds relative to each other. These considerations, with the addition of contamination control, represent the design and manufacturing criteria relevant to a given switch design.

Switch manufacture is often done on automatic machinery in a controlled environment. The two most common sealing techniques are infra-red absorption by chemically controlled tinted glass and heat from resistance coils surrounding a clear glass tube. Subsequent annealing of the glass to reduce stress is used in some manufacturing processes.

Internal atmospheres are somewhat variable between manufacturers. Commonly they are reducing dry atmospheres using controlled amounts of nitrogen, helium, and hydrogen. Typically, the sealing is done at atmospheric pressure so that upon cooling a slight vacuum is created. For increased dielectric standoff properties, special pressurized and high vacuum switches are available. The dielectric standoff voltage can be increased from 2 to 20 times by various pressurization or evacuation techniques.

Specialized modifications. The aforementioned construction techniques are common to all reed switches. However, special adaptations have been made to fill certain circuit requirements.

The form C switch is the most common modification. Herein, a normally closed and normally open set is defined by the addition of a break contact within the glass envelope. This member is typically nonmagnetic for larger size capsules, although in the smaller capsules the all-magnetic form C capsule is quite popular. In the former case, the make and break reeds terminate axially 180° from the armature reed, whereas the break and armature reed terminate as a pair 180° from the make contact in the all-magnetic member design. In the latter case, the field induces a repulsion between the break and armature since they have the same magnetic sense.

Hinging techniques are employed to achieve special performances. These often take the form of a multi-part assembly, such as in the nonbiased latching remanent reed capsule and in reeds capable of switching power loads. Alternately, special reed stamping or twisting of the reeds is employed to offer some contact wiping action.

11.10 Switch characteristics

Contact ratings. Typical ratings as offered by the manufacturer are given in Table 11-2 and Fig. 11-3. Higher ratings would be anticipated at lower life expectancies. The termination, or end of life, figure represents the point where approximately 80 per cent of the switches are functionally useable in all but highly critical circuitry.

At intermediate levels, the life expectancy is 2.5 to 5 times that of the full rated level, whereas the low level life is generally taken to be a minimum of 10^8 operations. At these levels, the limitation is often a circuit limitation rather than the wear out of a reed switch. Some contact erosion is seen at the intermediate loads, but in all cases the low level load will have no erosion and no mechanical wear-out. Here the failure is normally that of erratic contact resistance. Thus, circuits which can tolerate contact resistance variations may see over 10^{10} operations without failure. Since this variation is erratic, the existence of an increasing contact resistance often will not predict

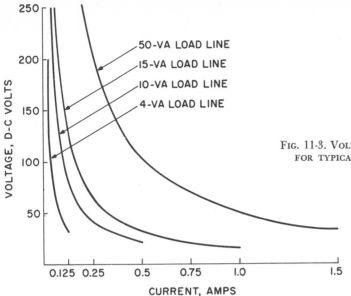

FIG. 11-3. VOLT-AMP MAXIMUM OPERATING CURVES
FOR TYPICAL DRY REED RATINGS

its ultimate failure point. Only in the instance where the hermeticity has been broken, will the increase in contact resistance predict a failure. When variation of resistance is not tolerable, a suitable contact material should be chosen for the switch. Table 11-1 gives a broad reference. Alternate selection may dictate the use of mercury wetted capsules.

The contact resistance defined above is the loop resistance as measured at the terminal points of the reed switch. The bulk of the initial resistance is due to the nickel-iron, which is a relatively high resistance alloy. The precious metal contact (constriction resistance) presents at best a few milliohms resistance. In operation, it is the increase in this constriction resistance which is of primary concern. Initial values of loop resistance range from about 0.030 ohm on the larger switches through approximately 0.150 ohm on the micro-miniature sizes. The nondiffused contacts typically have a lower resistance value due to the shunting effect of the plating, and this can be affected by the axial length of plating.

Electrical characteristics. The electrical parameters given in Table 11-3 are typical of those anticipated of various switches sizes.

Environmental characteristics. The environmental characteristics are usually limited by the relay package more than by the switch itself. The reeds as cantilever beams have discrete resonant points from 0.8 to 5 kHz. The energy resistance to chatter or bridging at these frequencies is highly dependent upon the mounting (packaging). Similarly the high temperature resistance of the capsule far exceeds any of the coil wire insulation temperatures. At the lower temperatures, however, the mismatch between the glass and reeds may be great enough to yield a brittle seal. Moreover, icing may be noted if the internal atmosphere is not dry. Thus, the lower temperature limit is dependent upon the size of seal, the thickness of the lead, etc. Usually little problem is noted to −40°C (−40°F).

11.11   Reliability

Physics of failure. The closure contact forces of the larger capsules are typically 10 times that of the smaller capsules and will generate up to 20 times that of the smaller capsules at 100 per cent overdrive conditions. This increase in contact force is an asset in load switching since it yields larger low resistance mating areas, increased film breakdown forces, etc. There is likewise an associated larger contact gap and a higher retractile force which can retard sticking and welding.

There has not been, however, any successful comparison between the switch size and its reliability. Reliable switches have been made with as low as 0.5 gram of contact force and as small as 0.001 in. gap.

Sensitivity and contact force influence con-

Table 11-1. Contact Material Selection

Contact Material	Resistance to Corrosion (Oxidation & Film Growth)	Resistance to Cold-Weld Tendency	Contact Resistance Stability	Load Rating & Mechanical Wear	Relative Typical Switch Cost	Switch Size[1]
Gold 24K	Excellent	Poor	Excellent	Low-Poor	Low	S
Hard Gold	Excellent	Good-Fair	Excellent	Average-Good	Low	A
Gold Diffused	Good-Fair	Excellent	Good-Fair	Average-Excellent	Low	L
Silver	Good-Fair	Poor	Excellent	Average-Fair	Low	L
Palladium	Good-Fair	Good	Good	Low-Excellent	Low	L
Rhodium	Excellent-Good	Excellent-Good	Excellent-Good	High-Excellent	Average	A
Rhodium Diffused	Good-Fair	Excellent	Fair	High-Excellent	Average	A
Tungsten	Poor	Excellent	Poor	Very High-Excellent	High	L
Rhenium	Fair-Poor	Excellent	Poor-Fair	High-Excellent	High	L
Molybdenum	Fair	Excellent	Poor	Very High-Excellent	High	L
Nickel Gold Alloy	Fair	Excellent	Fair	Average-Excellent	Low	L

[1] Best applicability switch size = A – all sizes; L – for larger (e.g. 2-in.) size; and S – for smaller (e.g. 1 in.) size.

Table 11-2. Typical Contact Ratings (Form A)

Approx. Capsule Size	Plating	Max Volts	Max Switching Current	Max VA Rating	Max Carry Current	Life Expectancy Full Rated X 10^6	Life Expectancy Low Level X 10^6
Standard							
2.0 in.	Au	250	1 A	15	5 A	20	500
2.0 in.	Rh	250	1.5 A	50	5 A	10	500
Miniature							
1.1 in.	Au	250	0.5 A	10	1 A	10	500
0.8 in.	Au	200	0.3 A	4	1 A	10	500
0.8 in.	Rh	200	0.5 A	10	1.5 A	10	500
0.625 in.	Au	100	0.25 A	3	0.5 A	10	500
0.625 in.	Rh	150	0.5A	10	1 A	5	500
Microminiature							
0.500 in.		100	0.25 A	2	0.5 A		
0.375 in.	Rh	28	0.01 A	0.3			

Table 11-3. Typical Switch Characteristics (Form A)

Characteristic	Large	Miniature	Microminiature
Operate Sensitivity	40-120 NI	20-70 NI	20-70 NI
Release Sensitivity	20-50 NI	10-40 NI	10-60 NI
Operate Bounce	0.5 msec	0.25 msec	0.5 msec
Release Bounce	None	None	None
Contact Resistance	0.050-0.100 ohm	0.100-0.200 ohm	0.200 ohm
Capacitance	0.35 pf	0.15 pf	0.15 pf

Table 11-4. Physical Properties of Common Reed Contact Materials

Metal	Density (lb/cu in.)	Melting Point (°F)	Thermal Conductivity (Btu/ hr/sq ft/ °F/ft)	Hardness as Deposited	Electrical Resistance (Microhm-cm)	Electrical Softening Voltage[1]	Observed Rupture Voltage of Bridge[2]	Primary Ionization Potential	Minimum Arcing Voltage[1]	Minimum Arcing Current[1]
Ag	0.379	1761	242	50-150 Knp	1.6	0.09	0.70	7.54	13	0.8
Au	0.698	1945	172	65-125 Knp 150-325 Knp[3]	2.4	0.08	0.82	9.18	16	0.38
Pd	0.434	2826	41	260 Knp	11		1.32	8.3		
Rh	0.447	3560	50	400-1000	4.7			7.7	14	0.35
Pt	0.775	3217	42	285 Knp	10	0.25	1.50	8.88	17.5	0.9
Cu	0.323	1981	226	41-220 DPH	3-8	0.12		7.68	14	0.6
Ni	0.321	2651	36.3	140-500 DPH	7.4-10.8	0.22		7.61	14	0.5
Mo	0.37	4730	84.5	C 38 Rockwell	5.7		1.20	7.35	17	0.75
W	0.70	6170	96.6	27-30 Rockwell	5.5	0.4	1.59	8.1	16	0.9

[1] Source — Holm[2]
[2] Source — Jones[1]
[3] Gold with 1% nickel in solution

tact resistance. The greatest effect is noted near the release of the reeds and results in an increase in contact resistance. This increase, when coupled with the heating and inductive component of the contact loading, often aggravates the metal transport mechanism. Coil and contact suppression networks are often dictated to minimize these effects.

The studies of both the cold cathode arcing (on closure) and field emission phenomenon (on opening) by Holm (Reference 2) and Jones (Reference 1) have given some quantitative measure for contact metal selection (see Table 11-4). The instantaneous heating effects and microsecond plasma production, and effects of the coil suppression or instantaneous acceleration on opening of the reeds make most quantitative measurements complex. Under highly controlled laboratory conditions, Gomez (Reference 3) has investigated the behavior of reeds under varying conditions within the arcing voltage and current energies investigated by Jones and Germer (see Fig. 11-4). The tests were performed on a miniature size switch. Variations of this phenomenon would be anticipated on all sizes. The currents indicate the shortcoming of strict volt-ampere rating techniques.

Erosion is non-existent at voltages below the electrical softening point of the metals. Here contamination is the primary failure mechanism. These contaminants may be organic or inorganic in nature, and particulate, developed film growth, or condensate in structure. The mode of failure is invariably high contact resistance, which at these low puncture voltages might represent a virtual open circuit to the monitoring system. The choice of noncorrosive contacts, controlled atmosphere, and controlled manufacturing processes can lessen these effects or eliminate them entirely. Furthermore, the choice will typically be made within the material limitation of cold-welding (see Par. 11.9 and Table 11-1).

Influence of applications. Load switching is typically optimized when the potential is sinusoidal ac rather than dc. This is reflected by the material transport phenomenon which is polarity sensitive as the plasma is formed. Alternate electrode polarities not only transfer randomly the material from reed to reed, but further have a redistribution effect which repairs small surface irregularities. Because of the increase in contact resistance just prior to open-

ing and the consequential heating, inductive loads tend to be very destructive to reed contacts. For similar reasons, within their ratings, capacitive and lamp load reliability have often surpassed the typical ratings of the manufacturer. Suppression of inductive components is advised.

Deterioration of the contact due to shelf life is nonexistent provided the hermetic seal is maintained.

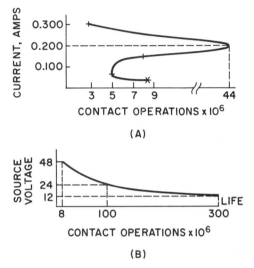

Fig. 11-4. (A) Life vs. current at 48-V resistive load. (B) Life vs. voltage at 100-mA resistive load

Most switches will reliably follow a frequency which is about 10 per cent of their natural resonance. Thus the standard size switches will reliably follow signals up to 80 Hz, the miniature will follow up to 200 Hz, and the microminiature may follow signals as high as 500 Hz. Higher rates are possible and in some instances require overdriving the coil. At high repetition rates, dynamic limitations such as contact bounce and contact noise on closure and coil suppression, release sensitivity, and reclosure on opening must be considered and the necessary stabilization period allowed. Multiswitch operation often limits the drive frequency as well. For the very low duty cycle requirements, the most serious considerations would be icing of the contacts at low temperature if moisture were present and cold welding of the contacts at high temperature and prolonged closure times.

Most reed switches are not permanently affected by shock, vibration, or linear acceleration if proper precautions are taken to ensure support for the terminals. Shocks which do not equally disturb all elements of the switch and shocks on form C switches can yield margin changes. Generally the miniature and micro-miniature capsules with less mass and higher resonant frequencies are less affected by these forces.

Temperature can affect the contact reliability. High temperature accelerates oxidation in contacts which are oxide prone. This includes the refractory metals and all common precious metals except gold and platinum, although the effects are minute in both rhodium and ruthenium. Thus, for most high temperature requirements (above 100°C), gold or gold diffused is advised. At low temperatures, the icing condition can affect reliability. Since this moisture film is external to the reeds, contact material selection is not a factor. Precious metal contacts, not diffused, have been most successful at these temperatures.

Because the primary mode of failure in most applications (excluding very high voltage or current application) is high contact resistance, the reliability of a switch in a circuit is highly dependent upon the maximum permissible contact resistance. The circuit designer or specification engineer should allow as high a resistance as possible to obtain the longest life. The ultimate selection — choice of the lowest resistance contact — might dictate a metal which is less than ideal for the application and thus limit the overall system life. A relatively high resistance contact is not necessarily a bad one, for within limits this contact has a self-reparative nature. By nature the cumulative resistance of a large sample of switches (see Fig. 11-5) typically goes through an increase in resistance before stabilization is reached. This occurs after some number of operations usually in the millions. For this reason "run-in" is sometimes employed. If the criterion for failure was specified as a maximum resistance not to exceed a value below the peak of Fig. 11-5, switches would be rejected before stabilization was reached.

Of further interest to the circuit designer is the dynamic characteristic of this contact resistance. In all applications where the sampling is performed in less than 100 milliseconds after contact closure, the correlation between statically measured and dynamically measured resistance must be reviewed. Since the reeds

are seeking stability upon closure as well as opening and since there is no slide and wipe, the constriction resistance is a function of the damping time as well as the magnetic holding force, both of which depend upon the switch size and design.

For low energy circuits where no wetting or at least no potential capable of puncturing films is present (less than a few hundred millivolts), the nature of the contact resistance is often an insulating contaminating film growth which presents itself more as a voltage barrier than as a true resistance, and as such a puncture potential must be applied to break through it.

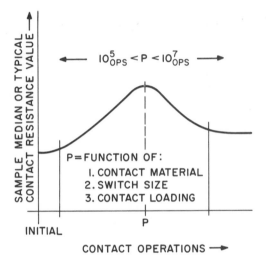

Fig. 11-5. Typical contact resistance variations

For this reason, a more meaningful definition of the failure criterion would be a maximum allowable voltage drop rather than contact resistance.

Mathematical reliability of dry reeds. The maximum life of the dry reed is highly dependent upon the contact loading and the number of closures and openings of a given load. Studies have indicated that the primary limitation to switch life is the opening of a circuit wherein the energy content is sufficient to effect material transfer. Thus life is independent of shelf life, or wear, and bears a secondary relationship to the load closed (cold-cathode erosion), load carried, or duty cycle. For these reasons "strobing" is common. Table 11-2 gives general life expectancy under full ratings. The most common usage is in multimillion and even billion cycle applications at far less than these rated loads. Most ratings at low level are in excess of 10^8 cycles. Failures here are sporadic and are less defined. There is no theoretical maximum limitation to life at these levels.

Verification of the contact switching reliability is typically performed by accelerated load tests at d-c levels. MIL-S-55433A offers a comprehensive test definition. It allows four misses in 100,000 switch operations where a miss is defined as sticking or welding on opening or a contact resistance over 2 ohms on closure. This gives a broad definition which might be too restrictive in many applications and not restrictive enough in others. In any testing of this nature the maximum allowed dynamic resistance, cycle rate, response time of the monitoring equipment, ability to integrate dynamic resistance, differentiation of contact noise and thermal voltages, etc., must be considered.

The results of these tests are reduced by the statistical methods of Sec. 6 or by use of the Weibull Distribution. The systems approach of MOTF statements is commonly used. This MOTF approach has added significance in reed relays where multiswitch relay designs can be considered as small systems. Thus a four-switch relay in essence is a four-point system (neglecting the secondary modes of failure due to interrelationships between capsules and coil failures).

Caution: Reed contacts may fail in a circuit application where load current and voltage ratings are not being exceeded, or even approached, due to accumulated capacitance of the wiring developing enough electrical charge to weld the reed contacts on closure (e.g., as in a large cross point matrix, or a very long cable.)

Mercury Wetted Contact Relays

11.12 Introduction

Mercury wetted switches are a distinct segment of the reed switch family, differentiated from the dry reeds by the fact that contact between switch elements is made via a thin film of mercury rather than by hard metallic contacts.

Two of the most frequently used mercury wetted switches are described and illustrated on pages 68–70. Others which have come into use are:

(1) Modifications of the dry reeds described

earlier in this section in which one reed member and its contact are wetted.

(2) Modifications of the dry reeds wherein all contacts are wetted.

(3) A smaller diameter version of the switch shown in Fig. 3-10.

(4) Switches similar to Fig. 3-10, but with armatures modified for higher speed operation.

Special characteristics. All switches classified as mercury wetted do not demonstrate the same unique capabilities. To simplify the discussion, characteristics of the units shown on page 69 will be presented first.

(1) Contact resistance is esentially constant from operation to operation throughout life. Since the actual contact is mercury-to-mercury and is of relatively large cross section, its resistance is very low when compared with the resistance of the switch members.

(2) Contacts do not bounce. The amount of mercury at the contacts is great enough to both cushion the impact of the underlying members and to electrically bridge any mechanical bounce that remains.

(3) Life is measured in billions of operations. With the contacts constantly renewed, the principal factor limiting the life of the dry reed is overcome.

(4) Contacts are versatile. The same contacts, properly applied, can handle relatively high power and low level signals.

(5) Electrical parameters are constant. With contact wear eliminated, operating characteristics remain the same through billions of operations.

To preserve the characteristics described, rate of change of voltage across contacts as they open must be limited to preclude damage to the contact surface under the mercury. For this reason, resistor-capacitor suppression should be specified for all but low level applications. Optimum values are:

$$C = I^2/10 \text{ microfarads}$$
$$C_{min} = 0.001 \text{ microfarad}$$
$$R = \frac{E}{10I^{(1+50/E)}} \text{ ohms}$$
$$R_{min} = 0.5 \text{ ohm}$$

in which:

I = current immediately prior to contact opening

E = source voltage

In a-c applications, peak values are used.

Mercury wetted switches, other than those discussed, may or may not share all the virtues listed. The primary determining factor is the degree to which contacts retain their initial "wettability."

As an example, the switches in which only one reed member is wetted do not demonstrate the low and consistent contact resistance described. On the other hand, they are not subject to very high contact resistance or actual "opens" as are hard contact reed switches. The action of the mercury may be less consistent, but it does overcome the effects of typical contact contaminants. A greater problem with this type of switch is the eventual wetting of the unwetted contact. Electrical effects or just the mechanical effect of many millions of operations may cause it to wet. The result is a shorted contact, because these devices typically lack the gap necessary to rupture the bridge formed by the mercury.

Other modifications with all contacts wetted may be capable of extended life if the contacts are not subject to the electrical and mechanical effects described. Use of contact suppression, as discussed earlier, may be a factor in preserving contact characteristics. However, not all manufacturers specify its use as mandatory.

11.13   Contact forms

Mercury wetted devices provide form A, B, and C contact action in much the same way dry reeds do. To this, the mercury switches add form D action, which is achieved by shaping and spacing the contacts so that a bridge of mercury joins all members momentarily during transfer.

11.14   Relay Packages

The mercury wetted switches bearing mechanical similarity to dry reed switches are packaged in much the same manner. There is one restriction. All switches are oriented in one direction in a package so that they can be operated in a vertical position.

The larger physical size of the switches shown on page 69 (they are $\frac{5}{16}$-in. diameter) and the fact that the Fig. 3-10 switch is always magnetically biased have led to some differences in packaging. They are much more frequently used in the one-switch-per-coil configuration than are dry reeds. The biased switch is seldom used in assemblies comprising more than two switches. The larger switch, Fig. 3-9, has not been employed with any frequency in assemblies exceeding six switches.

Because these devices were marketed before printed circuit boards came into wide use, there is also some difference in package styles. Compared with dry reeds, a far greater percentage of these switches, in particular the larger switch, appear in cylindrical can plug-in and wire-in configurations.

11.15   Electrical characteristics

While dry reed and mercury wetted contact switches share many electrical characteristics, there are some notable differences. Only those parameters where the difference is worthy of comment are discussed here.

Contact ratings.   Mercury wetted switches, because of their unique self-replenishing contacts, are rated at higher levels than their dry counterparts. With resistor-capacitor contact protection used where specified by the supplier, these ratings are applicable:

Switch shown in Fig. 3-9:
    250 VA; 500 volts maximum; 5 amps maximum; multi-billion operation life.

Switch shown in Fig. 3-10:
    100 VA; 500 volts maximum; 2 amps maximum; multi-billion operation life.

Standard size form C or form D:
    50 VA; 400 volts maximum; 2.0 amps maximum; 25×10^6 operation life.

Standard size form A:
    50 VA; 400 volts maximum; 3.0 amps maximum; 25×10^6 operation life.

Miniature size form A:
    28 VA; 100 volts maximum; 1.0 amps; 25×10^6 operation life.

Operate and release time.   The large mercury wetted switch, Fig. 3-9, is slightly slower to operate than the standard dry reed switch. At maximum drive its operate time is about three milliseconds and at nominal drive, about five milliseconds. The magnetically biased switch, Fig. 3-10, compares with the standard reed in operate time, and the mercury wetted versions of the dry reeds match with their counterparts.

All the mercury wetted devices are slower to release than the dry reeds. This is explained by the fact that the armature has to move some distance to cause the mercury to separate from the mating contact. Release time of the Fig. 3-9 switch in a typical relay is about 3.5 milliseconds, while for the Fig. 3-10 switch it is about 1.5 milliseconds. Release time of other switches will vary with the degree of wetting and ranges from 0.3 to about 1.0 millisecond.

Insulation resistance. The more complicated structure of some of the mercury wetted switches and the internal atmosphere, which is typically hydrogen, combine to produce effects which result in insulation resistance lower than that available in dry reeds. Therefore, specification limits for these devices usually range from 100 to 10,000 megohms.

Capacitance. Capacitance between contacts of mercury wetted contact relays tends to be higher than in dry reed relays. Several factors contribute to this. In the simpler forms of mercury wetted switches, the mercury pool effectively adds area and diameter to one of the reeds. This increases capacitance to the coil, which quite directly affects capacitance across contacts. The more complicated switches are form C or form D, which inherently have higher capacitance between contacts. Their larger elements have greater capacitance to the coil. Biasing magnets, required with the Fig. 3-10 switch, further add to capacitance.

Electrostatic shielding is effective in reducing capacitance between contacts and between contacts and the relay coil. Resulting values for the wetted versions of the dry reeds will be comparable with those cited in Paragraph 11-6, with capacitance of closed contacts to shield increased somewhat by the effect of the mercury pool. In some units, those having all contacts wetted, the greater contact spacing incorporated in the design will yield very low capacitance between contacts when shielded.

Typical values for the switches illustrated on page 69 when incorporated in relays are:

| | Unshielded | | Shielded | |
	Across Contacts	Closed Contacts to Coil	Across Contacts	Closed Contacts to Coil
Fig. 3-9	4 pF	10 pF	1.8 pF	0.5 pF
Fig. 3-10	3 pF	8 pF	1.5 pF	1.0 pF

Dielectric strength. Most mercury wetted contact switches will withstand appreciably higher voltages without breakdown than will the dry reed switches. Many have greater contact gaps, and all have a higher internal pressure. The switch shown in Fig. 3-9 will withstand at least 3,000 volts ac; the one in Fig. 3-10 well over 2,000 volts ac; and the standard size dry reed modified to have a wetted contact will withstand from 1,000–3,000 volts ac, depending on the degree of pressurization.

11.16 Environmental characteristics

Shock and vibration. Since mercury wetted switch and relay structures are so similar to their dry reed counterparts, their basic ability to withstand shock and vibration is not radically different. However, from an operational standpoint they have very limited capability due to the presence of the mercury pool.

These devices have been shown to withstand normal shipping exposure to shock and vibration, usually stated as 30 g's, 11 msec, and 0.06 in. double amplitude or 10 g's, 10–500 Hz.

Temperature. A limitation shared by all mercury wetted switches is the freezing point of mercury, −38.8°C. This is an operational limit only, and the relays are not adversely affected if stored at lower temperatures. Where operation at temperatures below the freezing point is required, a heater coil can be incorporated in the relay assembly.

11.17 Application notes

The comments of Paragraph 11.8 and of Paragraphs 5.22 through 5.27 apply, at least in part, to the mercury wetted relays discussed. A few additional notes are presented here.

Servicing. Mercury wetted relays are occasionally damaged or cause damage to other components when equipment is serviced with power on. If a unit carrying these relays is inverted, shorting of the contacts can produce effects never envisioned in circuit design.

Mounting position. To ensure that distribution of mercury to the relay contacts is proper, relays should be mounted with switches oriented vertically. It is generally agreed that deviation from vertical by as much as 30° will have only a limited effect on performance, and even at 45° operation will generally be satisfactory if the switch armature is in a vertical plane.

Bounce. Mercury wetted relays do not bounce if operated within appropriate limits. However, if drive rates are increased, resonance effects in the switch armature may cause rebound from contacts to exceed the level which can be bridged by the mercury and electrical bounce will result. Altered distribution of mercury to the contacts caused by the high rate of operation may contribute to this effect.

Contact protection. Worthy of stress because it is so essential to realization of the full capabilities of mercury wetted contact relays is use of resistor-capacitor suppression where it is specified by the manufacturer. Other methods of suppression may be used in conjunction with the RC to accomplish certain objectives (clamping of a transient by a diode or zener diode), but the RC is still required to control the rate of rise of voltage as the contacts open.

REFERENCES

(1) Jones, F. Llewellyn, "Matter Transfer in Contacts and Microscopic Molten Metal Bridge", *Proceedings 12th Annual National Relay Conference.*

(2) Holm, Ragnar, *Electric Contacts,* Hugo Gerbers, Stockholm, 1946.

(3) Gomez, Richard S., "Contact Protection for Miniature Reed Switch", *Proceedings 13th Annual National Relay Conference.*

12

NARM Standard Specification: Electro-Magnetic Relays for Industrial and/or Commercial Application

Introduction

To assist users of relays, the National Association of Relay Manufacturers has provided this specification for non-military type relays pertaining to industrial and commercial applications. It reflects the NARM attitude of continual improvement in the communication between manufacturer and user and the desire to provide greater services in the non-military area.

This standard was written to encompass all of the pertinent information pertaining to functional requirements and excludes superfluous items. The result should be a concise statement which will have a common basis understood by all users and manufacturers.

12.1 Scope

12.1.1 This standard covers General Purpose Electro-Mechanical Relays for industrial and/or commercial applications.

12.1.2 It is not intended to cover contactors, specific purpose types of relays, circuit breakers, choppers, timers or smaller allied devices.

12.2 Reference Documents

12.2.1 *Engineers' Relay Handbook* sponsored by NARM, dated 1966.

12.3 Environmental Section

12.3.1 **Altitude**
12.3.1.1 Altitude will not exceed 10,000 ft, above sea level.

12.3.2 **Ambient**
12.3.2.1 Operating Temperature Range—Enclosed Relays: —20°C to +40°C (Refer to Par. 12.4.1.1)

Open Relays: —20°C to +40°C
12.3.2.2 Storage Temperature Range—Enclosed and Open Relays: —55°C to +70°C

12.3.3 **Humidity**
12.3.3.1 Relative humidity up to 50% will be considered standard.

12.3.4 **Shock and Vibration**
12.3.4.1 Only normal shock and vibration conditions encountered in handling and shipping are considered applicable.

12.3.5 **Unusual Service Conditions**

12.3.5.1 The use of relays at altitudes, ambients, humidity, shock or vibration other than that specified in Par. 12.3.1, 12.3.2, 12.3.3 and 12.3.4 shall be considered as a special application. Other unusual service conditions where they exist will be called out to the manufacturer, such as:
(a) Excessive dust
(b) Excessive fumes
(c) Excessive sprays
(d) Excessive corrosion
(e) Excessive oil and oil vapor
(f) Excessive dampness

12.4 Mechanical and Physical Requirements Section

12.4.1 **Physical**
12.4.1.1 Enclosure: The relay enclosure refers to a protective enclosure which is fastened to the relay as an integral part at the place of manufacture and not an enclosure into which the complete relay is mounted with or without other components. The following enclosures shall be considered standard:
(a) Dust cover
(b) Gasket sealed
(c) Hermetically sealed

12.4.1.2 Terminals: The following terminals shall be considered standard:
(a) Screw type

(b) Threaded stud with nut and hardware
(c) Solder lug
(d) Plug-in for socket mounting
(e) Printed circuit board mounting
(f) Quick connect (dis-connect)
(g) Clamp or crimp type terminals
(h) Solderless wrap

12.4.1.3 Coils: Construction: Coil winding may be untreated, molded, vacuum impregnated, varnish dipped or brushed.

12.5   *Electrical Requirements*

12.5.1 **Voltages:** The following nominal voltage ratings shall be considered standard:

12.5.1.1 A-C Voltage: 6 volts; 12 volts; 24 volts; 48 volts; 120 volts; 208 volts; 240 volts; 480 volts; 600 volts.

12.5.1.2 D-C Voltage: 6 volts; 12 volts; 24 volts; 48 volts; 120 volts; 240 volts.

12.5.2 **Coils:**

12.5.2.1 Range of Operation: Relays are to operate satisfactorily over a range of voltage from 85% to 110% of rated nominal voltage on a-c coils, and 80% of rated nominal voltage to 110% of rated voltage on d-c coils. Relays will be required to pick-up and seal at the minimum voltage with the coil at ultimate operating temperature due to the nominal coil voltage. The coil shall be able to withstand 10% above rated nominal voltage without injury. The above tests to be conducted at 25°C.

12.5.2.2 Duty Cycle: Continuous duty coils will be considered standard except pulse operated coils as used in latching, stepping, etc., may be considered standard when operated within their specified duty cycle.

12.5.2.3 Temperature Rise: The temperature rise of the coil or coils shall be limited to the allowable rise for the insulation used. An optional method to determine coil temperature rise is that specified in UL Standard 508.

12.5.2.4 Winding Tolerance: If relay coil resistance is rated or specified, the standard winding tolerance at 25°C shall be ±10%.

12.5.3 **Contacts:**

12.5.3.1 Unless specified otherwise, contacts are rated on basis that:

(1) Each pole is capable of controlling the rated load.
(2) All circuits controlled by a given pole are of the same polarity.

12.5.3.2 Contacts may be rated in these terms for the following types of loads as specified by the user:

(1) Resistive — in terms of continuous current and nominal voltage.
(2) Motor Load —
    (a) Horsepower — in terms of horsepower and voltage.

(b) Continuous current and in-rush current at nominal voltage.
(3) Lamp — in terms of type, watts and volts.
(4) Inductive —
    (a) DC — D-c inductive rating shall call out the amount of inductance by specifying either maximum number of henries or a maximum L/R ratio.
    (b) AC — A-c inductive rating is specified by indicating minimum power factor.

12.5.3.3 Contact must be able to control rated load (service rating). An optional method to determine performance is that specified in UL Standard 508.

12.5.3.4 Life — Ratings must be determined by application requirement. Relay life varies with the application and is not directly related to ratings. For a complete discussion of the factors affecting life, refer to Sec. 8. When life is specified, the following levels are preferred or should be used as a guideline for actual application requirements:

No. of Operations (Electrical)

(1)	10,000
(2)	25,000
(3)	50,000
(4)	100,000
(5)	250,000
(6)	500,000
(7)	1,000,000
(8)	3,000,000
(9)	5,000,000
(10)	10,000,000
(11)	100,000,000 and over.

12.6   *Test Section*

The performance for relays meeting this standard shall be tests performed on units in accordance with the requirements listed below. All tests shall be performed at room temperature with the relay in its normal mounting position. Performance tests shall include:

12.6.1 **Visual Inspection** to ensure compliance with outline drawings and standards of good workmanship.

12.6.2 **Pick-up Voltage** — All relays are to pick up at 85% of rated nominal a-c voltage and at 80% of rated nominal d-c voltage.

12.6.3 **Contact and Coil Continuity** — Check coil continuity "and/or" resistance. Check contact continuity with the relay energized and de-energized.

12.6.4 **Dielectric Strength** — Test dielectric strength to values as specified by the manufacturer.

12.6.5 **Life Testing** — All relays shall meet manufacturer's standard and/or special ratings when applicable and tested as specified by the manufacturer.

12.7 *Marking*

12.7.1 Relays manufactured to satisfy this standard will include as visible minimum marking:

(a) Manufacturer's name or trademark
(b) Manufacturer's part number

(c) Coil rating (voltage and frequency when applicable)

12.7.1.1 The following would be considered optional marking requirements:

(a) Contact rating (voltage and current)
(b) Customer's designation
(c) Circuit connection diagram

Appendix A

MAGNET WIRE

Magnet wire is any coated conductor used to wind an electromagnetic coil and maintain a magnetic field under prescribed conditions. This section deals with the physical and insulation characteristics of many different types of magnet wire used in winding relay coils.

A.1   Requirements

The thermal, mechanical, and chemical environments to be encountered as well as the electrical requirements must be determined before an insulation can be selected by the relay manufacturer. Since these requirements have a varying effect on such things as number of turns per square inch of winding cross section, ohms per cubic inch of winding volume, and the like, some study on the part of the user is worthwhile. He will then appreciate why specific application data are needed by the relay manufacturer if the latter is to meet his requirements.

Table A-1. Copper Magnet Wire Conversion Factors

(1) Density, weight, and space factors	
Density of copper	8.89 gm/cu cm (0.32117 lb/cu in.)
Weight of copper wire per 1000 ft	Multiply square mil area by 0.003854
Feet of copper wire per pound	1000 divided by lb per 1000 ft
Pounds per cubic inch of round wire	No. of wires per sq in. of bundle cross-section times lb per 1000 ft divided by 12,000
Number of wires per linear inch of cross lay	1/Nominal wire diameter

(2) General units of measure
1 mil = 0.001 in.
1 sq mil = area of a square, 1 mil on a side
1 circular mil = area of a circle, 1 mil in diameter
1 circular mil = 1 sq mil x 0.7854
1 square mil = 1 circ mil x 1.2732

(3) Resistivity values of copper wire	
Resistivity of annealed copper wire	1.743 microhm/cu cm
100 per cent conductivity at 20°C	10.371 ohm/circ mil-ft
Resistance in ohms per cubic inch	(No. of wires per sq in.)(ohms/1000 ft) / 12,000
Resistance in ohms per pound	Ohms per 1000 ft/Pounds per 1000 ft
Temperature coefficient of resistance at 20°C	0.00393/deg C annealed / 0.00382/deg C hard drawn

Round copper wires are made to comply (where applicable) with the latest issue of American Standards Specification C7.1-1953 for soft annealed copper wire and C9.1-1953 for enameled wire. The thermal classifications follow the nomenclature of AIEE (now the IEEE) Standard No. 1, dated December 1962, except for Class 200, which is defined only in military specification MIL-W-583C. Conversion factors for copper magnet wire are given in Table A-1.

A.2   Effect of temperature on resistance

The wire tables in this section give the resistance at a temperature of 20°C. If it is desired to find the resistance at some other temperature, the following formula may be used:

$$R_t = R_{20} [1 + K (T - 20)]$$

in which:

R_t = resistance at the new temperature

R_{20} = resistance at 20°C

K = temperature coefficient (0.00393 for copper at 20°C)

T = new temperature in deg C

Since the temperature coefficients given are for an initial temperature of 20°C, they will not be correct for other initial temperatures.

To convert a known resistance at 20°C to a resistance at a different temperature in degrees Centigrade, multiply by the temperature correction factors given in Table A-2 for the different temperature. To obtain the resistance of copper at 20°C when the resistance at some other temperature is known, divide by the factors given in the table.

Table A-2. Temperature-Resistance Correction Factors for Copper

To obtain resistance of copper at 20°C, divide resistance at any other temperature by factor given below:

Deg C	Factor	Deg F	Deg C	Factor	Deg F
15	0.9804	59.0	28	1.0315	82.4
16	0.9842	60.8	29	1.0354	84.2
17	0.9882	62.6	30	1.0393	86.0
18	0.9922	64.4	31	1.0433	87.8
19	0.9961	66.2	32	1.0471	89.6
20	1.0000	68.0	33	1.0511	91.4
21	1.0039	69.8	34	1.0551	93.2
22	1.0079	71.6	35	1.0590	95.0
23	1.0118	73.4	36	1.0630	96.8
24	1.0157	75.2	37	1.0668	98.6
25	1.0197	77.0	38	1.0709	100.4
26	1.0235	78.8	39	1.0747	102.2
27	1.0275	80.6	40	1.0786	104.0

A.3 Maximum continuous wattage for relay coils

When electrical current is passed through a coil, the temperature of the coil will rise until the rate of heat dissipation is equal to the rate of heat generation. The deterioration of the insulation of the windings due to the temperature attained is generally the current limiting factor. A "self-protecting coil" is one in which the maximum temperature reached (with normal confinement and maximum expected ambient temperature) when the specified current is passed continuously through the coil is below the point causing injury to the coil insulation at its hottest spot. The *mean temperature* of a coil winding in degrees Centigrade can be calculated as follows:

$$T = (234.5 + T_c)\left(\frac{R_t}{R_c}\right) - 234.5$$

in which:

R_c = resistance at "cold," or pre-energized, temperature

T_c = temperature of the coil prior to energization

R_t = measured resistance at the elevated temperature

A.4 Winding space factors

The space required for the various types of magnet wires is an important factor in the design of electrical equipment. Small differences in builds of the individual wires in a winding become important when multiplied by the total number of turns in a winding. Obviously, the smaller the coil, the shorter the mean length of turn in the complete coil. A small coil means not only a smaller quantity of wire used but also increased efficiency and a reduction of over-all size with savings in other component parts.

Various methods of showing coil space factor relationships have been used. Table A-3 shows the possible number of turns of wire per linear inch and per square inch for two weights of magnet wire insulating films. These values have been determined for random-wound coils by squaring the nominal wire outer diameters and dividing into 1 square inch. Assuming a square lay consisting of wires wound on top of each other, a base space factor for bare wire of 78.5 per cent of the available space consumed by the wire is then applied. A perfect lay, consisting of wires in subsequent layers wound between adjacent wires, gives a space factor of 90.7 per cent for bare wire. The actual lay of a random-wound coil (no insulating film between layers) will be somewhere in between these two figures.

Fundamental tables are given here to provide a quick and easy way of determining the relationships of the space consumed in a winding by the various types of wire. Tables A-4 to A-9 give the nominal outside diameter of the general types of wire coatings most commonly used. This information is useful for getting a quick picture of insulation build and can also be used by inspectors, winding supervisors, and others to identify a wire grade. The relationship of the coil winding space factor to the wire type, size, and insulation is given in Fig. A-1.

Economic factors.   The economics of coil winding is usually a factor not only in the choice of winding resistance but also in the number and placement of windings on the coil spool. For best economy of first cost, a value of resistance just high enough to prevent overheating of the coil on full and sustained voltage, but not overburdensome of winding time, is usually chosen. On some relays the power consumed over a period of time may dictate the choice of a higher resistance than would otherwise be made in order to keep the current (power) drain low.

A.5 Choice of coil winding details

The choice of coil winding details to be used must be left to the relay manufacturer. The buyer needs only to specify the requirements to be met, leaving the manufacturer a free hand to engineer for best results. However, a knowledge of wire size and effect of insulation characteristics will assist the user in an understanding of the choice made by the manufacturer for any specific case.

Basis for standardization of wire sizes.   The following data are for copper magnet wire in accordance with American Wire Gauge (abbreviated AWG; also referred to as B & S) sizes. An understanding of the relationship of resistance to nominal wire diameter is helpful in making coil winding choices. For example, No. 10 AWG copper wire has a resistance of 1 ohm per 1000 ft, and for every third size smaller wire (larger gauge number by three) the resistance doubles, so that the resistance for 1000 ft of No. 13 is 2 ohms; for 1000 ft of No. 16, 4 ohms; for 1000 ft of No. 19, 8 ohms, etc. The effect of gauge tolerances on resistance should also be understood.

Figure A-2 shows that for a coil wound to a consistent fullness, the changes in coil resistance and number of coil turns with respect to changes in wire size are predictable. For example, an increase in wire size of 3 numbers gives double the number of turns and four times the resistance; an increase of six numbers gives four times as many turns and 16 times as much resistance.

Winding arrangements.   In the use of multiple wound coils the "concentrically wound" coil is usually the least expensive, and since for such a coil both windings are equally effective on the relay armature (from the electromagnetic viewpoint), the concentrically wound coil is preferred to the sectional coil, other factors permitting. If possible, the larger wire is placed on the bottom (next to the coil core) and the smaller (finer) wire on top. This helps to prevent wire breakage.

A.6 Magnet wire insulating coatings

The following is a list of the most common magnet conductor film insulations:

(1) Plain enamel
(2) "Formvar" (vinyl-acetal)
(3) Nylon
(4) Polyurethane
(5) "Formvar nylon" (vinyl-acetal with nylon overcoat)
(6) "Pyre-ML" polymer[1]
(7) Polyurethane nylon (polyurethane with nylon overcoat)
(8) Solderable acrylic
(9) Solderable acrylic nylon (solderable acrylic nylon with nylon overcoat)
(10) Epoxy
(11) "Teflon"
(12) Polyester
(13) Polyester-linear (polyester overcoat)
(14) Anodic film (aluminum)

[1] Pyre-ML is a trade name for a Du Pont material for coating magnet wire.

Table A-3. Space Factors For Random-Wound Coils Based on Average Commercial Practice

AWG gauge	Turns possible per linear inch			Turns possible per square inch			Ohms possible per cubic inch	
	Single	Heavy		Single	Heavy		Single	Heavy
10	9	8		86	75		0.00714	0.00624
11	10	9		108	95		0.01135	0.01075
12	11	11		133	130		0.01760	0.01715
13	12	12		162	159		0.02710	0.0266
14	14	13		212	193	100% Build	0.0446	0.0406
15	15	15		255	248		0.0676	0.0657
16	17	17	90% Lay	324	316		0.1082	0.1048
17	19	19		405	394		0.1705	0.166
18	22	21		525	487		0.279	0.259
19	24	23		641	596		0.429	0.399
20	27	26		850	792		0.718	0.668
21	30	29		1055	982		1.120	1.044
22	34	32		1340	1210	95% Build	1.820	1.635
23	31	30		1370	1260		2.320	2.130
24	35	33		1730	1550		3.70	3.320
25	39	37		2150	1940		5.78	5.23
26	44	42		2990	2700	85% Build	10.22	9.25
27	49	47		3700	3550		15.85	15.20
28	55	52		4680	4180	84% Build	25.45	22.75
29	62	58		5900	5160		39.90	34.90
30	69	65		7500	6560	83% Build	64.50	54.60
31	77	72	75% Lay	9270	8090		101.10	97.00
32	85	80		11400	10000	82% Build	154.4	135.0
33	96	89		14500	12500		248.5	214.5
34	109	101		18800	16250	81% Build	409.0	340.5
35	123	114		24000	20600		662.5	586.0
36	136	125		29650	25000	80% Build	1022.	862.0
37	153	139		37400	30900		1595.	1320.
38	170	156		40670	39300	79% Build	2190.	2125.
39	197	179		62700	51500		4425.	3635.
40	250	224		89600	72000	78% Build	8060.	6450.
41	274	250		107800	89800		11880.	9890.
42	304	284	85% Lay	133500	116500	77% Build	18450.	16100.
43	340	314		167000	143000		29850.	25550.
44	386	340		217000	168500	76% Build	46800.	33450.

(Courtesy, Phelps Dodge Copper Products Corp.)

B = linear inches of winding space
B x F = square inches of winding space
0.7854B = factor for conversion of circular mils to square mils
$\left[D^2 - (E + 2G)^2 \right] \times 0.7854B$ = cubic inches of winding space

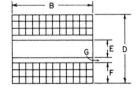

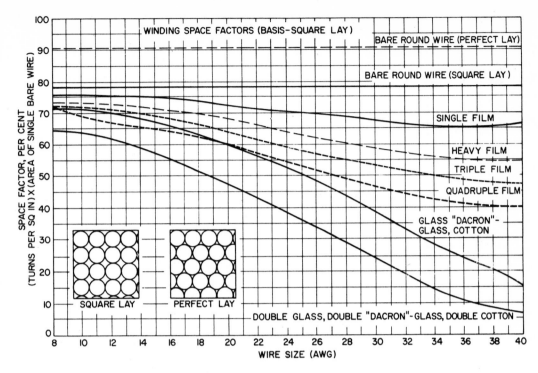

FIG. A-1. RELATIONSHIP OF COIL WINDING SPACE FACTOR TO WIRE TYPE, SIZE, AND INSULATION (EDN, MAY 1963)

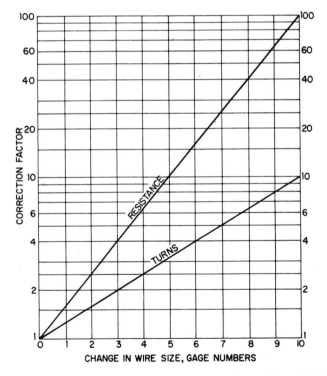

FIG. A-2 RELATIONSHIP OF WIRE SIZE TO RESISTANCE AND THE NUMBER OF TURNS FOR A FULL-COIL BOBBIN

For increase in resistance and turns, add to wire size and multiply by correction factor. For decrease in *resistance and turns, subtract from wire size and divide by correction factor.*

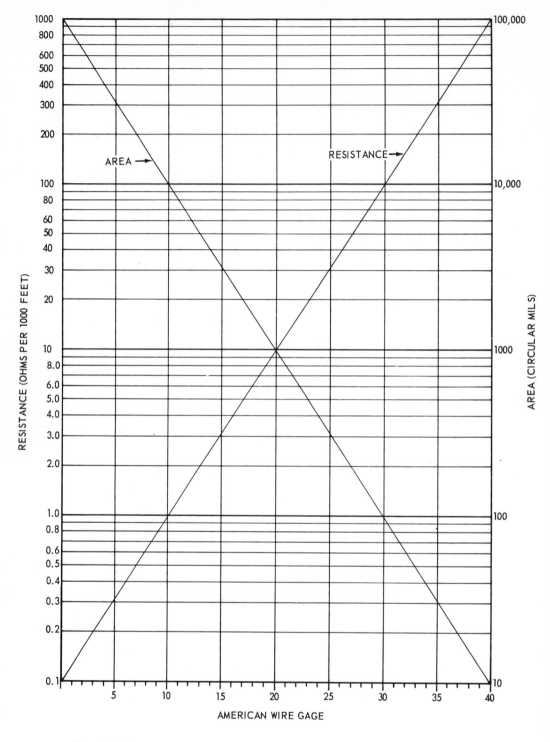

FIG. A-3. RELATIONSHIP OF COPPER WIRE SIZE TO ELECTRICAL RESISTANCE

(Source: Electronic Design News, *Jan. 1996)*

Table A-4. Engineering Data on Round Annealed Bare Copper

AWG size	Diameter (in.)			Area (cir mils)			(sq mils)	Weight (lb/1000 ft)	(ft/lb)	Resistance @ 20 C or 68 F (ohms/1000 ft)			(ft/ohm)	(ohms/lb)	AWG size
	Min	Nom	Max	Min	Nom	Max	Nom	Nom	Nom	Min dia	Nom dia	Max dia	Nom	Nom	
8	0.1272	0.1285	0.1292	16,180	16,512	16,693	12,969	49.98	20.01	.6410	.6281	.6213	1,592	.0126	8
9	0.1133	0.1144	0.1150	12,837	13,087	13,225	10,279	39.62	25.24	.8079	.7925	.7842	1,262	.0200	9
10	0.1009	0.1019	0.1024	10,180	10,384	10,486	8,156	31.43	31.82	1.019	.9988	.9892	1,001	.0318	10
11	0.0898	0.0907	0.0912	8,064	8,226	8,317	6,461	24.90	40.16	1.286	1.261	1.247	793.0	.0506	11
12	0.0800	0.0808	0.0812	6,400	6,529	6,593	5,128	19.76	50.61	1.620	1.588	1.573	629.7	.0804	12
13	0.0713	0.0720	0.0724	5,084	5,184	5,241	4,072	15.69	63.73	2.040	2.001	1.979	499.7	.1275	13
14	0.0635	0.0641	0.0644	4,032	4,109	4,147	3,227	12.44	80.39	2.572	2.524	2.501	396.2	.2029	14
15	0.0565	0.0571	0.0574	3,192	3,260	3,295	2,560	9.869	101.3	3.249	3.181	3.147	314.4	.3223	15
16	0.0503	0.0508	0.0511	2,530	2,581	2,611	2,027	7.812	128.0	4.099	4.018	3.972	248.9	.5143	16
17	0.0448	0.0453	0.0455	2,007	2,052	2,070	1,612	6.213	161.0	5.167	5.054	5.010	197.9	.8135	17
18	0.0399	0.0403	0.0405	1,592	1,624	1,640	1,275	4.914	203.5	6.514	6.386	6.324	156.6	1.300	18
19	0.0355	0.0359	0.0361	1,260	1,289	1,303	1,012	3.900	256.4	8.231	8.046	7.959	124.3	2.063	19
20	0.0317	0.0320	0.0322	1,005	1,024	1,037	804.4	3.099	322.7	10.32	10.13	10.00	98.70	3.268	20
21	0.0282	0.0285	0.0286	795.2	812.3	818.0	638.0	2.459	406.7	13.05	12.77	12.68	78.32	5.193	21
22	0.0250	0.0253	0.0254	625.0	640.1	645.2	502.7	1.937	516.3	16.59	16.20	16.07	61.74	8.363	22
23	0.0224	0.0226	0.0227	501.8	510.8	515.3	401.2	1.546	646.8	20.66	20.30	20.12	49.26	13.13	23
24	0.0199	0.0201	0.0202	396.0	404.0	408.0	317.3	1.223	817.7	26.19	25.67	25.42	38.96	20.99	24
25	0.0177	0.0179	0.0180	313.3	320.4	324.0	251.6	.9699	1,031	33.13	32.37	32.01	30.89	33.37	25
26	0.0157	0.0159	0.0160	246.5	252.8	256.0	198.5	.7653	1,307	42.07	41.02	40.51	24.38	53.62	26
27	0.0141	0.0142	0.0143	198.8	201.6	204.5	158.3	.6101	1,639	52.17	51.44	50.71	19.44	84.31	27
28	0.0125	0.0126	0.0127	156.3	158.8	161.3	124.7	.4806	2,081	66.37	65.31	64.30	15.31	135.9	28
29	0.0112	0.0113	0.0114	125.4	127.7	130.0	100.3	.3866	2,587	82.68	81.21	79.78	12.32	210.1	29
30	0.0099	0.0100	0.0101	98.01	100.0	102.0	78.55	.3025	3,306	105.8	103.7	101.7	9.643	342.8	30
31	0.0088	0.0089	0.0090	77.44	79.21	81.00	62.21	.2398	4,170	133.9	130.9	128.0	7.639	545.9	31
32	0.0079	0.0080	0.0081	62.41	64.00	65.61	50.27	.1937	5,163	166.2	162.0	158.1	6.174	836.3	32
33	0.0070	0.0071	0.0072	49.00	50.41	51.84	39.59	.1526	6,553	211.7	205.7	200.1	4.861	1,348	33
34	0.0062	0.0063	0.0064	38.44	39.69	40.96	31.17	.1201	8,326	269.8	261.3	253.2	3.827	2,176	34
35	0.0055	0.0056	0.0057	30.25	31.36	32.49	24.63	.0949	10,537	342.8	330.7	319.2	3.024	3,485	35
36	0.0049	0.0050	0.0051	24.01	25.00	26.01	19.64	.07569	13,212	431.9	414.8	398.7	2.411	5,480	36
37	0.0044	0.0045	0.0046	19.36	20.25	21.16	15.90	.06128	16,319	535.7	512.1	490.1	1.953	8,357	37
38	0.0039	0.0040	0.0041	15.21	16.00	16.81	12.57	.04844	20,644	681.9	648.2	617.0	1.543	13,381	38
39	0.0034	0.0035	0.0036	11.56	12.25	12.96	9.622	.03708	26,969	897.1	846.6	800.2	1.181	22,832	39
40	0.0030	0.0031	0.0032	9.000	9.610	10.24	7.549	.02910	34,364	1,152	1,079	1,013	.9270	37,086	40
41	0.0027	0.0028	0.0029	7.290	7.840	8.410	6.158	.02374	42,123	1,423	1,323	1,233	.7559	55,729	41
42	0.0024	0.0025	0.0026	5.760	6.250	6.760	4.909	.01892	52,854	1,801	1,659	1,534	.6028	87,685	42
43	0.0021	0.0022	0.0023	4.410	4.840	5.290	3.802	.01465	68,259	2,352	2,143	1,960	.4666	146,280	43
44	0.0019	0.0020	0.0021	3.610	4.000	4.410	3.142	.01210	82,645	2,873	2,593	2,352	.3857	214,298	44

(Source: REA Magnet Wire Co.)

Table A-4A. Engineering Data on Round Annealed Bare Aluminum

AWG size	Diameter (in.)			Area (cir mils)			(sq mils)	Weight (lb/1000 ft)	(ft/lb)	Resistance @ 20 C or 68 F (ohms/1000 ft)			(ft/ohm)	(ohms/lb)	AWG size
	Min	Nom	Max	Min	Nom	Max	Nom	Nom	Nom	Min dia	Nom dia	Max dia	Nom	Nom	
8	0.1272	0.1285	0.1292	16,180	16,512	16,693	12,969	15.20	65.79	1.034	1.013	1.002	987.2	.0666	8
9	0.1133	0.1144	0.1150	12,837	13,087	13,225	10,279	12.05	82.99	1.303	1.278	1.265	782.5	.1061	9
10	0.1009	0.1019	0.1024	10,180	10,384	10,486	8,156	9.559	104.6	1.643	1.611	1.595	620.7	.1685	10
11	0.0898	0.0907	0.0912	8,064	8,226	8,317	6,461	7.572	132.1	2.074	2.034	2.011	491.6	.2687	11
12	0.0800	0.0808	0.0812	6,400	6,529	6,593	5,128	6.010	166.4	2.614	2.562	2.537	390.3	.4263	12
13	0.0713	0.0720	0.0724	5,084	5,184	5,241	4,072	4.772	209.6	3.290	3.227	3.192	309.9	.6764	13
14	0.0635	0.0641	0.0644	4,032	4,109	4,147	3,227	3.782	264.4	4.149	4.071	4.034	245.6	1.076	14
15	0.0565	0.0571	0.0574	3,192	3,260	3,295	2,560	3.000	333.3	5.241	5.131	5.077	194.9	1.710	15
16	0.0503	0.0508	0.0511	2,530	2,581	2,611	2,027	2.376	420.9	6.612	6.481	6.407	154.3	2.728	16
17	0.0448	0.0453	0.0455	2,007	2,052	2,070	1,612	1.889	529.4	8.335	8.152	8.081	122.7	4.316	17
18	0.0399	0.0403	0.0405	1,592	1,624	1,640	1,275	1.494	669.3	10.51	10.30	10.20	97.09	6.894	18
19	0.0355	0.0359	0.0361	1,260	1,289	1,303	1,012	1.186	843.2	13.28	12.98	12.84	77.04	10.94	19
20	0.0317	0.0320	0.0322	1,005	1,024	1,037	804.4	.9423	1,061	16.64	16.34	16.13	61.20	17.34	20
21	0.0282	0.0285	0.0286	795.2	812.3	818.0	638.0	.7477	1,337	21.04	20.59	20.45	48.57	27.53	21
22	0.0250	0.0253	0.0254	625.0	640.1	645.2	502.7	.5892	1,697	26.76	26.13	25.93	38.27	44.34	22
23	0.0224	0.0226	0.0227	501.8	510.8	515.3	401.2	.4702	2,127	33.33	32.75	32.46	30.53	69.66	23
24	0.0199	0.0201	0.0202	396.0	404.0	408.0	317.3	.3719	2,689	42.24	41.41	41.00	24.15	111.4	24
25	0.0177	0.0179	0.0180	313.3	320.4	324.0	251.6	.2949	3,391	53.39	52.21	51.63	19.15	177.0	25
26	0.0157	0.0159	0.0160	246.5	252.8	256.0	198.5	.2326	4,299	67.86	66.17	65.34	15.11	284.5	26
27	0.0141	0.0142	0.0143	198.8	201.6	204.5	158.3	.1855	5,391	84.14	83.02	81.80	12.05	447.6	27
28	0.0125	0.0126	0.0127	156.3	158.8	161.3	124.7	.1461	6,845	107.0	105.3	103.7	9.497	720.8	28
29	0.0112	0.0113	0.0114	125.4	127.7	130.0	100.3	.1176	8,503	133.4	131.0	128.7	7.634	1,114	29
30	0.0099	0.0100	0.0101	98.01	100.0	102.0	78.55	.0920	10,870	170.7	167.3	164.0	5.977	1,819	30
31*	0.0088	0.0089	0.0090	77.44	79.21	81.00	62.21	.0729	13,717	216.0	211.2	206.5	4.735	2,897	31*
32*	0.0079	0.0080	0.0081	62.41	64.00	65.61	50.27	.0589	16,978	268.0	261.4	255.0	3.826	4,438	32*
33*	0.0070	0.0071	0.0072	49.00	50.41	51.84	39.59	.0464	21,552	341.4	331.8	322.7	3.014	7,151	33*
34*	0.0062	0.0063	0.0064	38.44	39.69	40.96	31.17	.0365	27,397	435.2	421.5	408.4	2.372	11,548	34*
35*	0.0055	0.0056	0.0057	30.25	31.36	32.49	24.63	.0289	34,602	553.0	533.4	514.9	1.875	18,457	35*
36*	0.0049	0.0050	0.0051	24.01	25.00	26.01	19.64	.0230	43,478	696.7	669.1	643.1	1.495	29,091	36*
37*	0.0044	0.0045	0.0046	19.36	20.25	21.16	15.90	.0186	53,763	864.0	826.1	790.5	1.211	44,414	37*
38*	0.0039	0.0040	0.0041	15.21	16.00	16.81	12.57	.0147	68,027	1,100	1,046	995.1	.9560	71,156	38*
39*	0.0034	0.0035	0.0036	11.56	12.25	12.96	9.62	.0113	88,496	1,447	1,366	1,291	.7321	120,886	39*
40*	0.0030	0.0031	0.0032	9.000	9.610	10.24	7.549	.0088	113,636	1,859	1,741	1,634	.5744	197,840	40*
41*	0.0027	0.0028	0.0029	7.290	7.840	8.410	6.158	.0072	138,889	2,295	2,134	1,989	.4686	296,389	41*
42*	0.0024	0.0025	0.0026	5.760	6.250	6.760	4.909	.0058	172,414	2,904	2,676	2,475	.3737	461,380	42*
43*	0.0021	0.0022	0.0023	4.410	4.840	5.290	3.802	.0045	222,222	3,793	3,456	3,162	.2894	767,999	43*
44*	0.0019	0.0020	0.0021	3.610	4.000	4.410	3.142	.0037	270,270	4,634	4,182	3,793	.2391	1,130,269	44*

*Orders for gauges 31 and finer are subject to mill approval.

(*Source: REA Magnet Wire Co.*)

Table A-5. Engineering Data on Single-Build Copper

AWG size	Bare wire diameter (in.) Nom	Minimum insulation increase (in.)	Diameter (in.)			Weight		Resistance		Wires per sq in.	AWG size
			Min	Nom	Max	(lb/ 1000 ft)	(ft/lb)	(ohms/ 1000 ft)	(ohms/lb)		
14	0.0641	0.0016	0.0651	0.0659	0.0666	12.51	79.94	2.524	.2016	230	14
15	0.0571	0.0015	0.0580	0.0587	0.0594	9.962	100.4	3.181	.3193	290	15
16	0.0508	0.0014	0.0517	0.0524	0.0531	7.888	126.8	4.018	.5101	365	16
17	0.0453	0.0014	0.0462	0.0469	0.0475	6.275	159.4	5.054	.8050	455	17
18	0.0403	0.0013	0.0412	0.0418	0.0424	4.974	201.1	6.386	1.285	572	18
19	0.0359	0.0012	0.0367	0.0373	0.0379	3.949	253.2	8.046	2.038	715	19
20	0.0320	0.0012	0.0329	0.0334	0.0339	3.141	318.4	10.13	3.225	896	20
21	0.0285	0.0011	0.0293	0.0298	0.0303	2.496	400.6	12.77	5.116	1,126	21
22	0.0253	0.0011	0.0261	0.0266	0.0270	1.972	507.1	16.20	8.215	1,413	22
23	0.0226	0.0010	0.0234	0.0239	0.0243	1.576	634.5	20.30	12.88	1,751	23
24	0.0201	0.0010	0.0209	0.0213	0.0217	1.242	805.2	25.67	20.67	2,204	24
25	0.0179	0.0009	0.0186	0.0190	0.0194	.9896	1,010	32.37	32.69	2,770	25
26	0.0159	0.0009	0.0166	0.0170	0.0173	.7810	1,280	41.02	52.74	3,460	26
27	0.0142	0.0008	0.0149	0.0153	0.0156	.6244	1,603	51.44	82.46	4,272	27
28	0.0126	0.0008	0.0133	0.0137	0.0140	.4922	2,028	65.31	132.5	5,328	28
29	0.0113	0.0007	0.0119	0.0123	0.0126	.3971	2,519	81.21	204.6	6,610	29
30	0.0100	0.0007	0.0106	0.0109	0.0112	.3108	3,215	103.7	333.4	8,417	30
31	0.0089	0.0006	0.0094	0.0097	0.0100	.2464	4,049	130.9	530.0	10,628	31
32	0.0080	0.0006	0.0085	0.0088	0.0091	.1997	5,000	162.0	810.0	12,913	32
33	0.0071	0.0005	0.0075	0.0078	0.0081	.1576	6,345	205.7	1,305	16,437	33
34	0.0063	0.0005	0.0067	0.0070	0.0072	.1241	8,058	261.3	2,106	20,408	34
35	0.0056	0.0004	0.0059	0.0062	0.0064	.0980	10,204	330.7	3,375	26,015	35
36	0.0050	0.0004	0.0053	0.0056	0.0058	.0785	12,739	414.8	5,284	31,888	36
37	0.0045	0.0003	0.0047	0.0050	0.0052	.0634	15,773	512.1	8,077	40,000	37
38	0.0040	0.0003	0.0042	0.0045	0.0047	.0503	19,881	648.2	12,887	49,383	38
39	0.0035	0.0002	0.0036	0.0039	0.0041	.0384	26,042	846.6	22,047	65,746	39
40	0.0031	0.0002	0.0032	0.0035	0.0037	.0303	33,003	1,079	35,610	81,633	40
41	0.0028	0.0002	0.0029	0.0031	0.0033	.02448	40,850	1,323	54,045	104,058	41
42	0.0025	0.0002	0.0026	0.0028	0.0030	.01960	51,020	1,659	84,642	127,551	42
43	0.0022	0.0002	0.0023	0.0025	0.0026	.01532	65,274	2,143	139,882	160,000	43
44	0.0020	0.0001	0.0020	0.0022	0.0024	.01247	80,192	2,593	207,938	206,611	44

(Source: REA Magnet Wire Co.)

Table A-5A. Engineering Data on Single-Build Copper Aluminum

AWG size	Bare wire diameter (in.) Nom	Minimum insulation increase (in.)	Diameter (in.)			Weight		Resistance		Wires per sq in.	AWG size
			Min	Nom	Max	(lb/1000 ft)	(ft/lb)	(ohms/1000 ft)	(ohms/lb)		
14	0.0641	0.0016	0.0651	0.0659	0.0666	3.891	257.0	4.071	1.046	230	14
15	0.0571	0.0015	0.0580	0.0587	0.0594	3.092	323.4	5.131	1.659	290	15
16	0.0508	0.0014	0.0517	0.0524	0.0531	2.454	407.5	6.481	2.641	365	16
17	0.0453	0.0014	0.0462	0.0469	0.0475	1.954	511.8	8.152	4.172	455	17
18	0.0403	0.0013	0.0412	0.0418	0.0424	1.548	646.0	10.30	6.654	572	18
19	0.0359	0.0012	0.0367	0.0373	0.0379	1.235	809.7	12.98	10.51	715	19
20	0.0320	0.0012	0.0329	0.0334	0.0339	.9829	1,017	16.34	16.62	896	20
21	0.0285	0.0011	0.0293	0.0298	0.0303	.7838	1,276	20.59	26.27	1,126	21
22	0.0253	0.0011	0.0261	0.0266	0.0270	.6214	1,609	26.13	42.04	1,413	22
23	0.0226	0.0010	0.0234	0.0239	0.0243	.4970	2,012	32.75	65.89	1,751	23
24	0.0201	0.0010	0.0209	0.0213	0.0217	.3939	2,539	41.41	105.1	2,204	24
25	0.0179	0.0009	0.0186	0.0190	0.0194	.3145	3,180	52.21	166.0	2,770	25
26	0.0159	0.0009	0.0166	0.0170	0.0173	.2486	4,023	66.17	266.2	3,460	26
27	0.0142	0.0008	0.0149	0.0153	0.0156	.1998	5,005	83.02	415.5	4,272	27
28	0.0126	0.0008	0.0133	0.0137	0.0140	.1577	6,341	105.3	667.7	5,328	28
29	0.0113	0.0007	0.0119	0.0123	0.0126	.1281	7,806	131.0	1,023	6,610	29
30	0.0100	0.0007	0.0106	0.0109	0.0112	.1003	9,970	167.3	1,668	8,417	30
31	0.0089	0.0006	0.0094	0.0097	0.0100	.0795	12,579	211.2	2,657	10,628	31
32	0.0080	0.0006	0.0085	0.0088	0.0091	.0649	15,408	261.4	4,028	12,913	32
33	0.0071	0.0005	0.0075	0.0078	0.0081	.0510	19,608	331.8	6,506	16,437	33
34	0.0063	0.0005	0.0067	0.0070	0.0072	.0406	24,631	421.5	10,382	20,408	34
35	0.0056	0.0004	0.0059	0.0062	0.0064	.0320	31,250	533.4	16,669	26,015	35
36	0.0050	0.0004	0.0053	0.0056	0.0058	.0258	38,670	669.1	25,934	31,888	36
37	0.0045	0.0003	0.0047	0.0050	0.0052	.0207	48,309	826.1	39,908	40,000	37
38	0.0040	0.0003	0.0042	0.0045	0.0047	.0166	60,241	1,046	63,012	49,383	38
39	0.0035	0.0002	0.0036	0.0039	0.0041	.0126	79,365	1,366	108,413	65,746	39
40	0.0031	0.0002	0.0032	0.0035	0.0037	.0100	100,000	1,741	174,010	81,633	40
41	0.0028	0.0002	0.0029	0.0031	0.0033	.0080	125,000	2,134	266,750	104,058	41
42	0.0025	0.0002	0.0026	0.0028	0.0030	.0064	156,250	2,676	418,125	127,551	42
43	0.0022	0.0002	0.0023	0.0025	0.0026	.0051	196,078	3,456	677,646	160,000	43
44	0.0020	0.0001	0.0020	0.0022	0.0024	.0041	243,902	4,182	1,020,000	206,611	44

(*Source: REA Magnet Wire Co.*)

Table A-6. Engineering Data on Heavy-Build Copper

AWG size	Bare wire diameter (in.) Nom	Minimum insulation increase (in.)	Diameter (in.)			Weight		Resistance		Wires per sq in.	AWG size
			Min	Nom	Max	(lb/ 1000 ft)	(ft/lb)	(ohms/ 1000 ft)	(ohms/lb)		
8	0.1285	0.0033	0.1305	0.1319	0.1332	50.43	19.83	.6281	.0125	57	8
9	0.1144	0.0032	0.1165	0.1177	0.1189	40.01	25.00	.7925	.0198	72	9
10	0.1019	0.0031	0.1040	0.1051	0.1061	31.77	31.48	.9988	.0315	91	10
11	0.0907	0.0030	0.0928	0.0938	0.0948	25.20	39.68	1.261	.0500	113	11
12	0.0808	0.0029	0.0829	0.0838	0.0847	20.01	49.98	1.588	.0794	142	12
13	0.0720	0.0028	0.0741	0.0749	0.0757	15.91	62.85	2.001	.1258	178	13
14	0.0641	0.0032	0.0667	0.0675	0.0682	12.63	79.18	2.524	.1999	219	14
15	0.0571	0.0030	0.0595	0.0602	0.0609	10.03	99.70	3.181	.3171	276	15
16	0.0508	0.0029	0.0532	0.0539	0.0545	7.956	125.6	4.018	.5047	344	16
17	0.0453	0.0028	0.0476	0.0482	0.0488	6.337	157.7	5.054	.7970	430	17
18	0.0403	0.0026	0.0425	0.0431	0.0437	5.021	199.2	6.386	1.272	538	18
19	0.0359	0.0025	0.0380	0.0386	0.0391	3.992	250.6	8.046	2.016	671	19
20	0.0320	0.0023	0.0340	0.0346	0.0351	3.176	314.5	10.13	3.185	835	20
21	0.0285	0.0022	0.0304	0.0309	0.0314	2.525	395.3	12.77	5.048	1,047	21
22	0.0253	0.0021	0.0271	0.0276	0.0281	1.993	502.5	16.20	8.141	1,313	22
23	0.0226	0.0020	0.0244	0.0249	0.0253	1.594	628.9	20.30	12.77	1,613	23
24	0.0201	0.0019	0.0218	0.0223	0.0227	1.266	787.4	25.67	20.21	2,011	24
25	0.0179	0.0018	0.0195	0.0199	0.0203	1.007	990.1	32.37	32.05	2,525	25
26	0.0159	0.0017	0.0174	0.0178	0.0182	.7965	1,256	41.02	51.52	3,156	26
27	0.0142	0.0016	0.0157	0.0161	0.0164	.6356	1,575	51.44	81.02	3,858	27
28	0.0126	0.0016	0.0141	0.0144	0.0147	.5021	1,992	65.31	130.1	4,822	28
29	0.0113	0.0015	0.0127	0.0130	0.0133	.4049	2,469	81.21	200.5	5,917	29
30	0.0100	0.0014	0.0113	0.0116	0.0119	.3178	3,145	103.7	326.2	7,431	30
31	0.0089	0.0013	0.0101	0.0105	0.0108	.2536	3,937	130.9	515.4	9,070	31
32	0.0080	0.0012	0.0091	0.0095	0.0098	.2053	4,878	162.0	790.2	11,080	32
33	0.0071	0.0011	0.0081	0.0085	0.0088	.1623	6,173	205.7	1,270	13,834	33
34	0.0063	0.0010	0.0072	0.0075	0.0078	.1274	7,874	261.3	2,058	17,777	34
35	0.0056	0.0009	0.0064	0.0067	0.0070	.1009	9,901	330.7	3,274	22,276	35
36	0.0050	0.0008	0.0057	0.0060	0.0063	.0806	12,407	414.8	5,146	27,776	36
37	0.0045	0.0008	0.0052	0.0055	0.0057	.0657	15,221	512.1	7,795	33,055	37
38	0.0040	0.0007	0.0046	0.0049	0.0051	.0520	19,230	648.2	12,465	41,649	38
39	0.0035	0.0006	0.0040	0.0043	0.0045	.0399	25,063	846.6	21,218	54,080	39
40	0.0031	0.0006	0.0036	0.0038	0.0040	.0312	32,051	1,079	34,589	69,248	40
41	0.0028	0.0005	0.0032	0.0034	0.0036	.0254	39,370	1,323	52,087	86,501	41
42	0.0025	0.0004	0.0028	0.0030	0.0032	.0201	49,751	1,659	82,537	111,109	42
43	0.0022	0.0004	0.0025	0.0027	0.0029	.0157	63,694	2,143	136,496	137,174	43
44	0.0020	0.0004	0.0023	0.0025	0.0027	.0131	76,336	2,593	197,939	160,000	44

(*Source: REA Magnet Wire Co.*)

Table A-7. Engineering Data on Heavy-Build Aluminum

AWG size	Bare wire diameter (in.) Nom	Minimum insulation increase (in.)	Diameter (in.)			Weight		Resistance		Wires per sq in.	AWG size
			Min	Nom	Max	(lb/ 1000 ft)	(ft/lb)	(ohms/ 1000 ft)	(ohms/lb)		
8	0.1285	0.0033	0.1305	0.1319	0.1332	15.65	63.90	1.013	.0647	57	8
9	0.1144	0.0032	0.1165	0.1177	0.1189	12.44	80.39	1.278	.1027	72	9
10	0.1019	0.0031	0.1040	0.1051	0.1061	9.899	101.0	1.611	.1627	91	10
11	0.0907	0.0030	0.0928	0.0938	0.0948	7.867	127.1	2.034	.2585	113	11
12	0.0808	0.0029	0.0829	0.0838	0.0847	6.258	159.8	2.562	.4094	142	12
13	0.0720	0.0028	0.0741	0.0749	0.0757	4.988	200.5	3.227	.6470	178	13
14	0.0641	0.0032	0.0667	0.0675	0.0682	3.968	252.0	4.071	1.026	219	14
15	0.0571	0.0030	0.0595	0.0602	0.0609	3.161	316.4	5.131	1.623	276	15
16	0.0508	0.0029	0.0532	0.0539	0.0545	2.520	396.8	6.481	2.572	344	16
17	0.0453	0.0028	0.0476	0.0482	0.0488	2.013	496.8	8.152	4.050	430	17
18	0.0403	0.0026	0.0425	0.0431	0.0437	1.601	624.6	10.30	6.433	538	18
19	0.0359	0.0025	0.0380	0.0386	0.0391	1.278	782.5	12.98	10.16	671	19
20	0.0320	0.0023	0.0340	0.0346	0.0351	1.019	981.4	16.34	16.04	835	20
21	0.0285	0.0022	0.0304	0.0309	0.0314	.8136	1,229	20.59	25.31	1,047	21
22	0.0253	0.0021	0.0271	0.0276	0.0281	.6455	1,549	26.13	40.48	1,313	22
23	0.0226	0.0020	0.0244	0.0249	0.0253	.5186	1,928	32.75	63.14	1,613	23
24	0.0201	0.0019	0.0218	0.0223	0.0227	.4152	2,408	41.41	99.72	2,011	24
25	0.0179	0.0018	0.0195	0.0199	0.0203	.3320	3,012	52.21	157.3	2,525	25
26	0.0159	0.0017	0.0174	0.0178	0.0182	.2641	3,786	66.17	250.5	3,156	26
27	0.0142	0.0016	0.0157	0.0161	0.0164	.2110	4,739	83.02	393.4	3,858	27
28	0.0126	0.0016	0.0141	0.0144	0.0147	.1676	5,967	105.3	628.3	4,822	28
29	0.0113	0.0015	0.0127	0.0130	0.0133	.1359	7,358	131.0	963.9	5,917	29
30	0.0100	0.0014	0.0113	0.0116	0.0119	.1073	9,320	167.3	1,559	7,431	30
31	0.0089	0.0013	0.0101	0.0105	0.0108	.0867	11,534	211.2	2,436	9,070	31
32	0.0080	0.0012	0.0091	0.0095	0.0098	.0705	14,184	261.4	3,708	11,080	32
33	0.0071	0.0011	0.0081	0.0085	0.0088	.0561	17,825	331.8	5,914	13,839	33
34	0.0063	0.0010	0.0072	0.0075	0.0078	.0438	22,831	421.5	9,623	17,777	34
35	0.0056	0.0009	0.0064	0.0067	0.0070	.0349	28,653	533.4	15,284	22,276	35
36	0.0050	0.0008	0.0057	0.0060	0.0063	.0279	35,842	669.1	23,982	27,776	36
37	0.0045	0.0008	0.0052	0.0055	0.0057	.0230	43,478	826.1	35,917	33,055	37
38	0.0040	0.0007	0.0046	0.0049	0.0051	.0182	54,945	1,046	57,472	41,649	38
39	0.0035	0.0006	0.0040	0.0043	0.0045	.0141	70,922	1,366	96,879	54,080	39
40	0.0031	0.0006	0.0036	0.0038	0.0040	.0109	91,743	1,741	159,725	69,248	40
41	0.0028	0.0005	0.0032	0.0034	0.0036	.0089	112,359	2,134	239,774	86,501	41
42	0.0025	0.0004	0.0028	0.0030	0.0032	.0070	142,857	2,676	382,285	111,109	42
43	0.0022	0.0004	0.0025	0.0027	0.0029	.0056	178,571	3,456	617,141	137,174	43
44	0.0020	0.0004	0.0023	0.0025	0.0027	.0047	212,765	4,182	889,783	160,000	44

(Source: REA Magnet Wire Co.)

Table A-8. Engineering Data on Ultrafine Wire

AWG size	Theoretical insulated wire diameter (in.)			(ohms/ft @ 20 C)	(lb/ 1000 ft)	(ft/lb)	(ohms/lb)	(gm/ 1000 ft)	(ft/gm)	(ohms/gm)	AWG size
	Min dia	Nom dia	Max dia	Nom dia	Nom dia	Nom dia	Nom dia	Nom dia	Nom dia	Nom dia	
Single insulation											
45	.00179	.00192	.00205	3.348	.00965	103,600	346,850	4.38	228.3	764.3	45
46	.00161	.00173	.00185	4.207	.00768	130,200	547,200	3.48	287.4	1,210	46
47	.00145	.00158	.00170	5.291	.00604	165,600	876,200	2.74	365.0	1,930	47
48	.00129	.00140	.00150	6.745	.00487	205,300	1,384,750	2.21	452.5	3,050	48
49	.00117	.00124	.00130	8.417	.00385	259,700	2,185,900	1.75	571.4	4,810	49
50	.00105	.00113	.00120	10.58	.00308	324,700	3,435,300	1.40	714.3	7,560	50
51	.00095	.00103	.00110	13.39	.00246	406,500	5,443,000	1.12	892.9	11,960	51
52	.00085	.00093	.00100	17.05	.00196	510,200	8,698,900	.889	1,125	19,180	52
53	.00072	.00079	.00085	21.17	.00153	653,600	13,836,700	.694	1,441	30,510	53
54	.00065	.00070	.00075	26.98	.00121	826,400	22,296,300	.549	1,821	49,130	54
55	.00058	.00064	.00070	34.28	.000969	1,032,000	35,377,000	.440	2,273	77,920	55
56	.00052	.00059	.00065	43.19	.000779	1,283,700	55,443,000	.353	2,833	122,360	56
57	.000461	.000509	.000557	54.06	.000611	1,636,700	88,480,000	.277	3,610	195,160	57
58	.000416	.000462	.000507	68.01	.000490	2,040,800	138,796,850	.222	4,505	306,390	58
59	.000374	.000408	.000442	85.93	.000382	2,617,800	224,955,400	.173	5,780	496,680	59
60	.000328	.000365	.000402	108.41	.000307	3,257,300	353,123,900	.139	7,194	779,900	60
Heavy insulation											
45	.00199	.00215	.00230	3.348	.01006	99,400	332,800	4.56	219.3	734.2	45
46	.00181	.00196	.00210	4.207	.00805	124,200	522,500	3.65	274.0	1,153	46
47	.00165	.00178	.00190	5.291	.00645	155,000	820,100	2.93	341.3	1,806	47
48	.00139	.00155	.00170	6.745	.00507	197,200	1,330,100	2.30	434.8	2,933	48
49	.00127	.00139	.00150	8.417	.00402	248,800	2,094,150	1.82	549.5	4,625	49
50	.00115	.00128	.00140	10.58	.00324	308,600	3,265,000	1.47	680.1	7,195	50
51	.00105	.00117	.00129	13.39	.00260	384,600	5,149,800	1.18	947.5	11,350	51
52	.00095	.00107	.00115	17.05	.00209	478,500	8,158,450	.948	1,055	17,990	52
53	.00080	.00090	.00103	21.17	.00161	621,100	13,148,700	.730	1,370	29,000	53
54	.00073	.00082	.00095	26.98	.00129	775,200	20,914,900	.585	1,709	46,110	54
55	.00066	.00075	.00087	34.28	.00104	961,500	32,960,200	.472	2,119	72,640	55
56	.00060	.00069	.00081	43.19	.000836	1,196,200	51,663,900	.379	2,639	113,980	56

(Source: REA Magnet Wire Co.)

Table A-9. Engineering Data on Ultrafine Wire

AWG size	Recommended winding tension* (gm) Copper	Turns per linear inch†		Turns per square inch†		AWG size
		(single insulation)	(heavy insulation)	(single insulation)	(heavy insulation)	
45	18.2	521	465	271,441	216,225	45
46	14.5	578	510	334,084	260,100	46
47	11.5	633	562	400,689	315,844	47
48	9.05	714	645	509,796	416,025	48
49	7.30	806	719	649,636	516,961	49
50	5.75	885	781	783,225	609,961	50
51	4.55	971	855	942,841	731,025	51
52	3.58	1,075	935	1,155,625	874,225	52
53	2.87	1,266	1,111	1,602,756	1,234,321	53
54	2.26	1,429	1,220	2,042,041	1,488,400	54
55	1.78	1,562	1,333	2,439,844	1,776,889	55
56	1.40	1,695	1,449	2,873,025	2,099,601	56
57	1.14	2,000	–	4,000,000	–	57
58	.90	2,174	–	4,726,276	–	58
59	.72	2,500	–	6,250,000	–	59
60	.56	2,703	–	7,306,209	–	60

*Winding tension is based on 33,000 lb per sq in. for copper and nominal bare dimensions. If the recommended values are exceeded, the conductor may be permanently damaged.
†Calculations are based on square lay, one wire directly above the other.

(*Source: REA Magnet Wire Co.*)

Magnet Wire Standards and Specifications

The statement has often been made that there is no central authority for the assignment of a temperature class to any magnet wire. Although this is still true, it is possible that the new edition of military specification MIL-W-583C and the proposed new edition of MIL-E-917 combined with IEEE Standard No. 1 (*see* Table A-10) may serve as a suitable reference authority. These documents contain much that is sound. The effect of military purchasing practices involving magnet wires will tend to establish a sort of published authority.

The temperature classifications that follow are for use of the wire in free air. Higher temperatures may be used in compatible gases, liquids, and solids. The publication number of the applicable NEMA standard is given. If the specification has been accepted by the American Standards Association, the number and year of issue are also stated.

The military specification data are taken from MIL-W-583C, which requires that all enameled wires intended for Classes 130, 155, 180, 200, and 220 be approved before production and delivery to the military agencies. Approval is conveyed by letter. The wire makers can supply copies of their approval letters.

The most commonly used types of magnet wire insulation are as follows:

(1) *Oleoresinous ("plain") enamel:* Lowest cost and highest space factor. Insulating properties good enough for the average job.

(2) *Polyvinyl formal ("Formvar") film:* Excellent windability, good insulating properties, and over-all properties good enough for most service conditions.

(3) *Polyvinyl formal with nylon overcoat:* Unexcelled windability with excellent solvent resistance.

(4) *Solderable acrylic:* For solderability and low cost.

(5) *Epoxy:* For compatibility with liquid insulating materials and encapsulants.

(6) *Polyesters:* Windability with a theoretical improvement in resistance to heat and solvent shock.

(7) *Pyre-ML:* For exceptional thermal stability and superior cut-through resistance.

These and other types of magnet wire insulation are described in detail below. The descriptions have been taken from data in various trade publications. The thermal ratings have not been verified by tests performed by the relay manufacturers, nor are any recommendations by NARM member companies implied as to a particular type of coating.

A.7   Oleoresinous ("plain") enamel

The oleoresinous enamel wire is the oldest of the enamel magnet wires. The film is basically a cured varnish made with a natural resin and a drying oil, for example, with rosin and

Table A-10. Thermal Classification of Insulation

Classification	Definition of insulating materials
Class 90 (also called Class O)	Unimpregnated materials shown to be capable by experience or tests of operating at 90°C. Magnet wires: cotton, silk, paper, and similar organic materials when neither impregnated nor immersed in a liquid dielectric.
Class 105 (also called Class A)	Materials or combinations of materials such as cotton, silk, and paper when suitably impregnated or coated, or when immersed in the dielectric liquid. Magnet wires: plain enamel, Formvar, nylon, nylon-Formvar, polyurethane, epoxies, and polyesters with and without varnish treatments suitable for operation at 105°C.
Class 130 (also called Class B)	Materials or combinations of materials such as mica, glass fiber, asbestos, etc., with suitable bonding substances. Magnet wires: Epoxies and polyesters with suitable impregnating varnish or bonding materials for operation at 130°C.
Class 155 (also called Class F)	Materials or combinations of materials such as mica, glass fiber, asbestos, etc., with suitable bonding substances. Magnet wires: Polyesters, polyimides, and glass fiber covered with suitable bonding materials for operation at 155°C.
Class 180 (also called Class H)	Materials or combinations of materials such as silicone elastomer, mica, glass fiber, asbestos, etc., with suitable bonding substances such as appropriate silicone resin. Magnet wires: Polythermaleze 200, polyimides, and glass fiber covered with suitable bonding material for operation at 180°C.
Class 200	"Isonel 200." Trade name used since it is available to all wire makers. This is a polycarboxylic acid isocyanurate polyester.
Class 220 (also called Class C)	Materials or combinations of materials which by experience or accepted tests can be shown to have the required thermal life at 220°C. Magnet wires: Polyimides with suitable bonding substances for operation at 220°C.
Over Class 220	Materials consisting entirely of mica, porcelain, glass, quartz, and similar materials which are capable of operation at temperatures over 220°C.

Source: Institute of Electrical & Electronic Engineers Standard No. 1, revised December 1962. Class 200 is defined only in MIL-W-583C.

tung oil. Other common resins are oil modified phenolic resin, coumarone-indene resins, and certain hydrocarbon resins.

The enamel is cured by the oxidation of the oils. Although a desirable cure is obtained during the initial bake cycle, the enamel will continue to cure (oxidize) during the total life of the equipment but at a progressively slower rate. Pertinent data includes:

(1) Thermal classification: 105
(2) NEMA Standard: MW-1 (ASA C9.1 — '1953)
(3) Military specification: MIL - W - 583C. Class 105. Types E and E2.
(4) Availability: Round sizes 8 to 56 AWG for the grade known as plain enamel. Sizes 10 to 44 AWG for the grade known as heavy plain enamel.

Plain enamel has been used for many years and is still preferred where the best utilization of space is desired and the hazards encountered in winding are not severe. It is easy to wind at high speeds. For paper-filled coils it is the preferred choice.

Associated by common practice with the plain enamels, and having the same virtues as plain enamel, but also with some added ones of their own, are the synthetic resins, or condensation polymers known as "Formvar" and nylon.

A.8 "Formvar"

"Formvar" is a trade name for the resin developed by Shawinigan Resins, now Monsanto Plastic Products and Resins Division. It is formed in place from a solution of two principal resins, polyvinyl formal and phenol formaldehyde. In some cases one or more other resins may be added. The resin present in the larger proportion is polyvinyl formal. The resin present in smaller proportion is an alkyl phenol-formaldehyde condensation reaction product. Other resins that may be present are polyisocyanante and butylated melamine formaldehyde.

"Formvar" is often called polyvinyl acetal. The NEMA Standard MW-15 uses this term. "Acetal" is used as the family name for a group of resins that include the polyvinyl formal, actually the specific resin used. Pertinent data includes:

(1) Thermal classification: 105
(2) NEMA Standard: MW-15
(3) Military specification: MIL - W - 583C. Class 105. Types T, T2, T3, and T4.
(4) Availability: Round sizes 4 to 56 AWG. Single and heavy grades only for sizes 45 to 56 AWG. Other sizes in single, heavy, triple, and quadruple grades.

"Formvar" wire has been used in very large quantities since its introduction about 20 years ago. It is still the most widely used wire. Its characteristics are such that it is suitable for use in most electrical apparatus designed for operation as "Class A" devices. It has excellent windability and is compatible with most insulations, varnishes, and compounds.

A.9 Nylon

The nylon fiber used in making nylon enamel is made by mixing adipic acid and hexamethylene diamine and is commonly referred to as a "polyamide." The fiber is put into solution and placed on the magnet wire by conventional methods. Nylon resins are thermoplastic and hygroscopic.

Nylon enamel consists entirely of Nylon 66 (hexamethylene adipamide). Some brands may be colored for identification purposes. Pertinent data includes:

(1) Thermal classification: 105
(2) NEMA Standard: MW-6 (ASA C9.8 — 1958)
(3) Military specification: MIL - W - 583C.

Class 105. Types T, T2, T3, and T4. Note: T3 and T4 may be special items.

(4) Availability: Round wires, sizes 14 AWG to 44 AWG. Grades, both single and heavy.

This wire has excellent windability, partly as a result of its smooth coating, which resists rubbing abrasion. It is compatible with most other insulation compounds. Impregnating varnishes containing strong solvents can be used on it. It can be soldered through by using rosin alcohol flux and tin-lead solders. Because of the good windability, it has replaced plain enamel in some small relays and other miniature coils. The major use for the film is over other types of coating where it imparts strength and windability without degrading the desirable properties of the underlying film. Nylon coatings are not recommended for use in oil-filled or hermetic devices because of their tendency to hydrolyze in sealed systems.

A.10   Polyester

Class F (155°F) polyester enamels are made from terephthalic acid, while Class A (105°F) polyesters (used in polyurethane enamels) are made from orthophthalic acid. Polyester has excellent thermal endurance, mechanical and electrical properties comparable to "Formvar," high cut-through strength, and good chemical resistance.

With so many compounds and combinations available, it is difficult for a user to make a sound selection. The choice would be very easy if there were improvements in all characteristics of a polyester enameled wire to parallel the improvements in the thermal classification of the coating. However, this is not necessarily the case. There are indications that some sacrifices in other characteristics may be exacted as the price for increased thermal endurance.

None of these wires are intended to be solderable without prior removal of the insulation. If optimum performance and thermal endurance are to be attained, all the members of the insulation system must be selected with care. Being polyesters, they will hydrolyze under conditions where moisture is entrapped in contact with them. They are not compatible with chlorine-containing insulations. They differ in degree of sensitivity to these exposures.

Resistances to heat shock and to solvent shock are prominent in the discussions of the characteristics of these wires. The overcoated wires exhibit higher resistance to these hazards, insofar as is presently known, than those without overcoats. It should be noted that this is a matter of relative degree of resistance to heat or solvent shock. It is possible to cause cracking of any of them if the test conditions are made sufficiently severe. The problem is to balance what is acceptable in this respect against all the other characteristics. Developments in this area may be expected.

Pertinent data includes:

(1) Thermal classification: 155 or 180, depending on wire type

(2) NEMA Standard: MW-5 and MW-13

(3) Military specification: MIL-W-583C. Classes 155, 180, and 200, depending on type and overcoat (preproduction approval required). Types L, L2, L3, L4-H, H2, H3, H4-K, K2, K3, K4. Note that Isonel 200 is presently the basis of approval for class 200. This class does not appear in IEEE Standard No. 1.

(4) Availability: All sizes and grades of round, square, and rectangular wires.

A.11   Polyurethane

Polyurethane resin is made by combining polyester resins and isocyanate compounds, often with the addition of polyvinyl formal and epoxy. Polyurethane has a 105C thermal rating (Class A), dielectric strength, chemical stability, moisture resistance, and heat shock resistance similar to "Formvar." It has less solvent resistance, however, and does not have sufficient abrasion resistance to withstand high-speed winding on all types of automatic equipment. Pertinent data includes:

(1) Thermal classification: 105

(2) NEMA Standard: MW-2

(3) Military specification: None (not specifically covered in MIL-W-583C)

(4) Availability: Round wires, sizes 10 AWG and smaller. Very small wires are made to size 56 AWG. The four grades — single, heavy, triple, and quadruple — are available except in sizes 45 AWG and smaller, for which only single and heavy grades are made.

These wires can be soldered without prior removal of the film by one of the following methods: (1) dipping in molten tin-lead solder; (2) using soldering irons or soldering guns; or (3) any other suitable means of applying heat and solder. A flux of rosin-alcohol solution assists the soldering operation. The temperature of the solder bath can be maintained at a level that will prevent damage to the solder.

A.12   Anodic film

Aluminum oxide is built up on the surface of an aluminum conductor by an electrochemical process. The aluminum is made the anode in an electrolytic cell in which the aqueous electrolyte is capable of yielding nascent oxygen when current is passed. The oxygen reacts with the aluminum and forms a hard, porous oxide film. When the oxide has built up to the desired thickness, the anodic film is sealed with boiling water, and a wash coat of silicone is then applied to the strip and cured. This provides additional dielectric strength and lubrication while the coils are being wound. The silicone coating is also additional protection against the entry of moisture.

A.13 Polyvinyl formal with nylon overcoat

The insulating film next to the conductor is that described in the heading for polyvinyl formal ("Formvar") wires. The overcoat is Nylon 66. Pertinent data includes:

(1) Thermal classification: 105
(2) NEMA Standard: MW-17
(3) Military specification: MIL - W - 583C. Class 105. Types T, T2, T3, and T4
(4) Availability: Round sizes 8 AWG to 46 AWG. Single, heavy, and triple grades.

This composite enameled wire combines the characteristics of the two resins. The nylon improves the windability and the choice of impregnating varnishes.

A.14 Polyvinyl formal with polyvinyl butyral overcoat (self-bonding)

These are composite enamel magnet wires having a polyvinyl formal film next to the conductor and a polyvinyl butyral overcoat. Pertinent data includes:

(1) Thermal classification: 105
(2) NEMA Standard: MW-19
(3) Military specification: None
(4) Availability: Round sizes, 10 to 44 AWG. Grades 1, 2, and 3. The single, heavy, and triple undercoats have a single overcoat making the total film thickness equal to heavy, triple, and quadruple.

The overcoat is a thermoplastic resin used to cement or bond the turns in a winding together. Bonding is accomplished by heating the coil after it is wound by passing current through the coil. The wire can be wet with a solvent while being wound to activate the overcoat. The solvent escape can be improved by heating the coil.

This wire is used in complicated coils that must be self-supporting as well as to eliminate bobbins in encapsulated coils.

A.15 "Pyre-ML"

This insulating film is a polyimide developed by Du Pont and identified by them as "Pyre-ML." Colored films for identification purposes are made by dispersing suitable pigments in the enamel or by the use of thermally stable dyes. Pertinent data includes:

(1) Thermal classification: 220
(2) NEMA Standard: None
(3) Military specification: MIL - W - 583C. Class 220. Types M, M2, M3, and M4. Preproduction approval required.
(4) Availability: All sizes and grades of round, square, and rectangular wires, as well as strip.

Pyre-ML magnet wire has outstanding thermal stability and resistance to overload and cutthrough. Full utilization of its characteristics is now possible since other insulation forms based on this or related polymers are commercially available. Glass fabrics can be coated with such polymers.

Recently, Pyre-ML wire has demonstrated thermal, nuclear radiation, and cryogenic endurance not previously available in an organic enamel. Use of this wire in an oil-filled enclosure where paper is present should be approached with caution.

A.16 Polyvinyl formal with Pyre-ML undercoat

This composite film wire has a Pyre-ML coating next to the conductor. The outer coating is of polyvinyl formal. The film thickness proportions are about 25 per cent Pyre-ML and 75 per cent polyvinyl formal. The polyvinyl formal coatings may be any of those in previous listings. Pertinent data includes:

(1) Thermal classification: 180
(2) NEMA Standard: None
(3) Military specification: None
(4) Availability: Generally the same as for standard polyvinyl formal ("Formvar") wires, that is, all shapes — round, square, and rectangular — and all grades and sizes. This wire is a very recent development, so specific statements of what can be secured cannot be made at this time.

This wire combines the good properties of both kinds of coating to present a unique magnet wire of high thermal stability. It has excellent heat and solvent shock resistance, a high thermoplastic flow point, outstanding resistance to burnout, and high resistance to hydrolysis. The polyvinyl formal on the outside contributes the excellent windability for which this wire is well known. The Pyre-ML undercoat contributes the thermal stability.

A.17 Polyurethane-nylon

A solderable film that has sufficient abrasion resistance to withstand automatic winding. The nylon overcoat imparts the same advantages and disadvantages to polyurethane as it does to "Formvar" without impairing the solderability. Polyurethane-nylon is used on high-speed winding equipment where the conductor is subject to severe stresses and abrasion.

In this wire the film next to the conductor is polyurethane as defined and described under polyurethane wires. An overcoat of Nylon 66 (hexamethylene adipamide) is applied. Pertinent data includes:

(1) Thermal classification: 130 (Class B)
(2) NEMA Standard: None
(3) Military specification: None. Not specifically covered by MIL-W-583C, but may be considered as meeting Class 130 (Type B, B2, B3, and B4) requirements. Requires preproduction approval. If used as Class 105 (Types T, T2, T3, or T4) preproduction approval not required.
(4) Availability: Round wires, sizes 8 AWG to 46 AWG. Single, heavy, triple, and quadruple grades.

This wire can be soldered without prior removal of the film.

A.18   Solderable acrylic

The insulation is a copolymer of acrylonitrile and an acrylic ester and may be soldered without prior removal of the film. Pertinent data includes:

(1) Thermal classification: 105
(2) NEMA Standard: None
(3) Military specification: Not specifically covered in MIL-W-583C
(4) Availability: Round sizes AWG 9 through 44. Single and heavy grades.

This wire is offered as a replacement in all applications for oleoresinous enameled wires, and in many applications for polyurethane and "Formvar" wires. It is intended for operations at 105°C. It has better winding resistance and is generally mechanically stronger and more chemically resistant than other wires. It solders readily at 850°F by melting of the film. It is not recommended for use where overload resistance is required.

A.19   Solderable acrylic with nylon overcoat

The characteristics of this wire are similar to those of the solderable acrylic except that it offers improved resistance to winding abuse. Pertinent data includes:

(1) Thermal classification: 105
(2) NEMA Standard: None
(3) Military specification: Not specifically covered in MIL-W-583C.

A.20   Epoxy

This is an enamel in which the basic resin is an epoxy of high epoxide equivalent with urea formaldehyde modifying resins. Other resins may be present as modifiers in some enamels. Pertinent data includes:

(1) Thermal classification: 130
(2) NEMA Standard: MW-14
(3) Military specification: MIL - W - 583C. Class 130. Types B, B2, B3, and B4. Preproduction approval required.
(4) Availability: All sizes of round wires in single, heavy, triple, and quadruple grades. All sizes of square and rectangular wires in single, heavy, and quadruple grades.

This wire has a broad field of application and is of particular value in oil immersion. It is compatible with the large majority of other insulations and strongly resists the effects of moisture.

A.21   Epoxy with self-bonding epoxy overcoat

The film insulation next to the conductor is the epoxy and urea formaldehyde combination. The overcoat is a combination of epoxy and polyvinyl formal resins. Other resins are present in both undercoats and overcoats. Pertinent data includes:

(1) Thermal classification: 130
(2) NEMA Standard: None
(3) Military specification: None. Not specifically recognized by MIL-W-583C.
(4) Availability: All sizes, round, square, and rectangular. The over-all diameters are equal to heavy, triple, and quadruple grades.

The overcoat is hard and smooth and has good windability. The bonding or cementing overcoat can be activated by heating. Passing electric current through the wire is one convenient source of heat. Solvents can be used to wet the outer surface to activate the overcoat, but the wire can be used, if desired, without this activation. The solvent escape can be assisted by heating the coil.

The bond strength at the rated temperatures and above is very good. Baking or heating at relatively higher temperatures or for longer times increases the bond strength.

This wire is used to make coils that are self-supporting and where bonding the turns together is desirable.

A.22   Polytetrafluoroethylene ("Teflon")

A recent multi-coat polymer is available with a thermal rating of 180°C (Class H). The film is polytetrafluoroethylene, or "Teflon" (Du Pont). This is usually formed by suspending the polymer in water and then baking the multiple coats until the particles fuse into a film. Some use may be made of an undercoat or overcoat of silicone varnish. The conductor may be copper, nickel-coated copper, or silver-coated copper. Pertinent data includes:

(1) Thermal classification: 180
(2) NEMA Standard: MW-10
(3) Military specification: MIL - W - 583C. Class 200. Types K, K2, K3, and K4. Preproduction approval required.
(4) Availability: Round wires, sizes 12 to 50 AWG. Single, heavy, triple, and quadruple grades.

This wire is used in electrical devices intended for service at high temperatures. The coating is smooth and wax-like to the touch. The scrape abrasion resistance is low compared with that of other enameled wires such as "Formvar."

A.23   Ultra fine enameled wires

The previous listings mention the availability of some enameled wires in a size as small as No. 56. Examples are polyurethane and polyvinyl formal ("Formvar"). The smallest size in other listings vary; generally it is the smallest size shown in the NEMA Standard for the listed wire.

The development of very small devices wound of ultra fine magnet wires has created a demand for wire as fine as No. 60 of copper and No. 52 of aluminum. These wires are now available with six insulations.

The smallest size shown in the wire tables of the different standards and specifications varies from No. 40 in ASTM B3-63 to No. 56 in B258-61 and NEMA MW-2 and MW-15. Size No. 50 is the smallest that appears in Circular No. 31 of the National Bureau of Standards and in MIL-W-583C. Data on all sizes from No. 45 to No. 60 is given in the catalogs of the makers of these wires.

Ultra fine enameled wires of copper are now available in single and heavy grades in sizes Nos. 45 to 60 (inclusive) and of aluminum in sizes Nos. 45 to 52 (inclusive).

The insulations available for ultra fine magnet wires are oleoresinous, polyesters (including "Isonel" 200), polyurethane, polyvinyl formal ("Formvar"), "Pyre-ML," and polyurethane with polyvinyl butyral overcoat.

The successful use of ultra fine magnet wires requires specialized techniques in storage, handling, winding, and treating. The use of "white rooms," which are dust-free and of controlled temperature and humidity, is considered essential in working with these wires.

A.24 Ultra fine glass-coated wires (also known as microwire)

Various publications and papers have reported on the development and availability of wires having a copper core in a glass envelope. A minimum outside diameter of 0.01 mm with a copper core of 0.001 mm has been described. Developments continue in this field, and additional information may be available as papers are given in future engineering association and society meetings.

A.25 Ceramic

The coating of this wire is a fully cured ceramic insulation. The conductor may be nickel-clad copper, nickel-clad silver, or any other oxidation resistant metal or alloy. The insulation thickness may be 0.00015 to 0.0005 in. (0.15 to 0.5 mil). A protective lubricating covering may be present, which is burned off after winding. Some wires do not use this covering. Pertinent data includes:

(1) Thermal classification: As high as 650°C, depending on the construction of the wire
(2) NEMA Standard: None
(3) Military specification: None
(4) Availability: Round sizes 17 to 45 AWG (inclusive).

Ceramic wire may be used over a wide range of temperatures, from low values to as high as 650°C. Depending on construction, materials, and end use, this wire tolerates nuclear radiation. It is currently not in much use but may become increasingly important.

A.26 Ceramic-conversion type

The insulating film is an organic enamel with ceramic or glass materials dispersed throughout.

Smooth and glossy, it generally resembles the familiar enamels. The conductor is copper or silver with an oxidation-resistant metal cladding. Pertinent data includes:

(1) Thermal classification: Over 220. Class, 650°C
(2) NEMA Standard: None
(3) Military specification: None
(4) Availability: Round sizes 18 to 40 AWG (inclusive).

Windings are made of this wire in the usual manner. The bobbins or other parts of the insulating system must be inorganic. Supporting insulations and encapsulants are available that have characteristics matching the enamel after firing.

After the winding operation, the complete coil is fired at 700°C until the enamel is completely converted to the total ceramic or glass state.

These wires can be used in any device where temperatures of 650°C, vacuum or corrosive atmospheres, intense radiation, or severe overloads occur. Operations may combine temperature, radiation, and vacuum conditions. These wires may also be used to produce coils having marked rigidity and resistance to thermal shock.

A.27 Asbestos fiber

Insulation for this wire consists of a layer of resin impregnated asbestos fibers. The outer surface may be varnish treated or coated with an adhesive. Saturants for 130°C (Class 130) are phenolic or asphaltic. Saturants for 180°C (Class 180) are silicone.

The felted asbestos insulation is applied to the conductor by employing adhesives, a card, and sizing dies. Pertinent data includes:

(1) Thermal classification: 130 with phenolic or asphaltic varnish; 180 with silicone varnish
(2) NEMA Standard: None
(3) Military specification: MIL-W-583C. Class 130. Type AV. Note: this specification may require special handling by the wire maker.
(4) Availability: Round sizes 2 to 25 AWG. Rectangular and square, 2400 to 166,000 square mils.

This wire is used primarily in apparatus subjected to overload. The coating is tough and withstands high pressures. The space factor is similar to that for double cotton. The dielectric strength is comparable to that for served or wrapped insulation but is generally somewhat lower.

A.28 Cotton yarn

The insulating covering for this wire is made of one or more servings of cotton yarn. Pertinent data includes:

(1) Thermal classification: 90 if not impregnated; 105 if impregnated.

(2) NEMA Standard: MW-11 for round wires; MW-12 for rectangular wires.

(3) Military specification: MIL - W - 583C. Class 90. Types C and C2.

(4) Availability: Round wire, sizes 4/0 to 36 AWG. Square and rectangular wire, all sizes. Single and double served.

This, the oldest magnet wire, is used where space separation of the conductors is required and where complete penetration of insulating varnishes, compounds, or oils is desired.

A.29 Magnet wire insulation specification cross references

All magnet wire for government use is included in military specification, MIL-W-583C.

A revised MIL-W-583C is in process. Table A-11 cross references the NEMA and ASA specifications for the various magnet wire types.

Detailed magnet wire specifications may be obtained from the following sources:

(1) NEMA "MW" Series: National Electrical Manufacturers Association, 155 E. 44 St., New York, N. Y. 10017.

(2) United States of America Standards Institute (USASI), 1430 Broadway, New York, N. Y. 10018.

(3) American Society for Testing & Materials (ASTM), 1916 Race St., Philadelphia 3, Pa.

(4) MIL-W-583: Business Service Center, General Services Administration, Washington, D. C.

Table A-11. NEMA and USASI Specifications Cross-Referenced

Type of insulated magnet wire	NEMA	USASI	Type of insulated magnet wire	NEMA	USASI
Plain enamel	MW-1 (1953)	C9.1 (1953)	Silk covered	MW-21 (1953)	C9.3 (1953; revised 1961)
Single and heavy polyurethane	MW-2 (1961)	C9.14 (1963)	Nylon fiber covered	MW-22 (1953)	C9.4 (1953; revised 1961)
Heavy and triple acrylic	MW-4 (1961)	C9.15 (1963)	Single, heavy, and triple Class 180 polyester	MW-25 (Proposed)	....
Single, heavy, and triple polyester	MW-5 (1961)	C9.16 (1963)	Heavy and quadruple Class 180 polyester, rectangular and square	MW-26 (Proposed)	....
Single and heavy nylon	MW-6 (1957)	C9.8 (1958)			
Single, heavy, and triple epoxy	MW-9 (1963)	....	Heavy and triple polyvinyl-formal urethane, round	MW-27	....
Single, heavy, triple, and quadruple "Teflon"	MW-10 (1961)	C9.17 (1963)	Single and heavy nylon and polyurethane	MW-28 (1964)	....
Cotton covered	MW-11 (1953)	C9.2 (1953; reaffirm. '61)	Single paper covered	MW-31 (1956)	C9.9 (1958)
Heavy and quadruple polyester, rectangular and square	MW-13 (1964)	....	Double paper single cotton covered, rectangular and square	MW-32 (1955)	C9.7 (1955; revised 1961)
Heavy and quadruple epoxy, rectangular and square	MW-14 (1964)	....	Paper covered, rectangular and square	MW-33 (1957)	C9.10 (1958)
Single and heavy "Formvar"	MW-15 (1959)	C9.5 (1961)	Glass fiber covered	MW-41 (1963)	....
Single, heavy, and triple polyimide	MW-16 (1963)	....	Glass fiber covered, rectangular and square	MW-42 (1964)	C9.11 (1958)
Single and heavy nylon "Formvar"	MW-17 (1959)	C9.12 (1961)	Glass fiber covered, silicone treated, rectangular and square	MW-43 (1963)	....
Heavy and quadruple "Formvar," rectangular and square	MW-18 (1964)	C9.6 (1955; revised 1961)	Glass fiber covered, silicone treated	MW-44 (1963)	....
"Formvar" with bonding	MW-19 (1959)	C9.13 (1961)	Polyester glass fiber covered	MW-45 (1962)	....
Heavy and quadruple polyimide, rectangular and square	MW-20 (Proposed)	....	Polyester glass fiber covered, rectangular and square	MW-46 (1964)	....

Table A-11A. Index of Magnet Wire Trade Names (Part I)

	Plain Enamel (Oleo-Resinous)	Polyvinyl Formal ("Formvar"; "Synthetic Enamel")	Polyvinyl Formal Modified	Polyvinyl Formal with Nylon Overcoat	Polyvinyl Formal with Butyral Overcoat	Polyamide	Acrylic	Epoxy	Fiber Coated and Varnished	Teflon	Polyurethane
Thermal Class	105 C	105 C	105 C	105 C	105 C	105 C	105 C	130 C	130 C	200 C	105 C
NEMA Standard	MW 1	MW 15	MW 27	MW 17	MW 19	MW 6	MW 4	MW 9		MW 10	MW 2
American Supertemp Wires			Hermetic Formvar							Teflon	
Anaconda Wire and Cable	Plain Enamel	Formvar		Nyform	Cement Coated Formvar			Epoxy, Epoxy/Cement Coated	Vitrotex		Analac
Asco Wire & Cable	Enamel	Formvar		Nyform	Formbond	Nylon	Acrylic	Epoxy			Poly
Belden Mfg. Co.	Belden-amel[1]	Formvar		Nyclad				Epoxy	Dacron-Glass		Beldure
Bridgeport Insulated Wire Co.		Formvar			Quick Bond	Quicksol					Polyure-thane
Chicago Magnet Wire Corp.	Plain Enamel	Formvar		Nyform	Bondable Formvar	Nylon	Acrylic	Epoxy			Soder-brite
Essex Wire Corp.	Plain Enamel	Formvar	Formtex	Nyform	Bondex		Ensolex/ESX	Epoxy	Glass, Dacron/Glass		Solderex
General Cable Corp.	Gen-enamel	Genvar	Genvar H	Genvar N	SB Genvar		Gensol (Solderable Acrylic)	Genex	Dacron/Glass, Glass Fiber	Teflon	Gendure
Haveg Supertemp Div.										Teflon	
Hitemp Wires Co., Div., Simplex Wire & Cable										Temprite	
Hudson Wire Co.	Plain Enamel	Formvar		Nyform	Formvar AVC	Ezsol					Hudsol
New Haven Wire and Cable, Inc.	Plain Enamel										Impsol
Phelps Dodge Magnet Wire Co., Inc.	Enamel	Formvar	Hermeteze	Nyform	Bondeze						Sodereze
REA Magnet Wire Co., Inc.	Plain Enamel	Formvar	Hermetic Formvar Special	Nyform	Koilset	Nylon		Epoxy			Solvar
Viking Wire Co. Inc.	Enamel	Formvar		Nyform	F-Bondall	Nylon					Polyure-thane

[1] Also manufactures "Celenamel", a solderable cellulose acetate film for 105°C

Table A-11B. Index of Magnet Wire Trade Names (Part II)

	Polyurethane with Friction Surface	Polyurethane with Nylon Overcoat	Polyurethane with Butyral Overcoat	Polyurethane with Nylon and Butyral Overcoat	Glass Fiber Covered	Glass Fiber Coated and Varnished	Silicone Film	Polyester (155°C or higher)	Polyester Polyimide (180°C or higher)	Polyester with Overcoat (155° or higher)	Polyimide	Polyester Polyimide	Ceramic Ceramic/Teflon Ceramic Silicon
Thermal Class	105 C	.130 C	105 C	130 C	155 C	180 C	180 C	155 C			220 C	155 C	180 C+
NEMA Standard		MW 28	MW3 (Prop.)	MW29 (Prop.)	MW 41	MW 44		MW 5			MW 16	MW 24	MW 7
American Super-temp Wires							Silicone	Isonel					
Anaconda Wire & Cable		Nylac	Cement Coated Analac	Cement Coated Nylac	Vitro-tex	Silotex				Anatherm D, Anatherm 200	Al 220 ML		
Asco Wire & Cable		Nypol	Asco-bond P	Asco-bond				Asco-therm	Ascomid	Isotherm 200	ML		
Belden Mfg. Co.		Beldsol			Dacron/ Glass	Glass	Silicone	Isonel		Polytherm-aleze	ML		
Bridgeport Insulated Wire Co.	Uni-wind	Poly-nylon	Poly-bond		Glass/ Daglass	Glass Fiber		Isonel 200					
Chicago Magnet Wire Corp.		Nysod	Bondable Polyure-thane					Polyester 155					
Essex Wire Corp.		Soderon	Soder-bond	Soder-bond N	Dacron/ Glass			Therma-lex F		Polythermaleze PTX 200	Allex	Nytherm	Cerami-cite
General Cable Corp.		Gendur N			Dacron/ Glass	Dacron Glass Silicone Bonded			Gentherm		Gen Ml	Gentherm N	Cerami-cite
Haveg Supertemp Div.								Isonel					
Hitemp Wires Co., Div., Simplex Wire & Cable							Ther-malon						Cerama-temp
Hudson Wire Co.	Gripon	Nypoly	Hudsol AVC	Nypoly AVC				Isonel 200	Isomid	Isonel 200A	ML		
New Haven Wire & Cable, Inc.		Impolson								IMP-200			
Phelps Dodge Magnet Wire Co., Inc.	Gripeze	Nyleze		S-Y Bondeze	Daglass	Daglass Silicone				Poly-therm-aleze 200	ML	Therm-aleze N	
REA Magnet Wire Co., Inc.		Nylon Solvar	Solvar Koilset					Isonel 200	Isomid	Polythermaleze 200	Pyre-ML[1]		Ceroc, Ceroc T & S
Viking Wire Co., Inc.		Poly-nylon	P-Bondall					Isonel 200	Isomid, Isomid-P	Isopoly	ML		

[1] DuPont trademark.

Table A-12. Summation of Magnet Wire Properties

Plain Enamel (Oleoresinous)

Advantages

1. High space factor, resulting in maximum number of turns for a given space.
2. High dielectric strength and excellent continuity.
3. Outstanding moisture resistance for good performance under humid conditions.
4. Resistance to oils and varnishes containing aliphatic solvents.

Precautions

1. Cannot be used with some of the newer synthetic varnishes which contain strong solvents and/or require high baking temperatures.
2. Low solvent resistance to toluol, xylol, alcohol, and acetone.
3. Has to be stripped as preparation for soldering.
4. Does not stand up well in high speed winding because of poor resistance to mechanical abrasion.

Synthetic Enamel ("Formvar")

1. Coil production costs reduced — eliminates mechanical or chemical stripping of insulation, although these standard methods can be used if desired.
2. Solvar decomposes at the temperature of molten solder (680-750°F); therefore, clean tinning of the wire without the use of flux is possible.
3. Improved dimensional tolerances available through REA customized production techniques, especially important in fine wire sizes; superior film continuity and dielectric strength.
4. Low moisture sensitivity results in superior "Q" characteristics at high frequencies and high humidities.
5. Superior film adhesion and flexibility; good heat-shock resistance.

1. Not recommended for use in applications where severe overloads may occur since Solvar decomposes at higher temperatures.
2. High soldering temperatures should be avoided; damage to solder composition and oxidation of bare conductor may occur.
3. Susceptible to softening through prolonged exposure to alcohol, acetone, and methylethylketone.
4. For encapsulated systems, certain catalysts and hardeners may cause softening of Solvar and eventual compatibility difficulties; consult your REA representative for further details and assistance.

Class H (200°C)

1. High continuous operating temperature up to 200°C.
2. Can be used in class A (105°C), class B (130°C), and class F (155°C) systems, and up to a maximum temperature of 200°C continuously; in class H service, other components should be selected to match the thermal capabilities of Isonel; for example, use of class A varnish with Isonel may not result in a class H system.
3. Excellent cut-through resistance.
4. Flexibility and adhesion comparable to Formvar.
5. Excellent wet and dry dielectric characteristics.
6. Excellent moisture resistance in open constructions, i.e., those allowing a free flow of air; Isonel can also give good performance in enclosed constructions when coils and components have been dried thoroughly by preheating, coated with a moisture-resistant varnish, and thoroughly cured; and when no materials are present which contain or generate moisture.

1. Polyesters are vulnerable to heat-shock failure. Stretching, together with rapid temperature rise, should be kept to a minimum. Units wound with Isonel should be gradually pre-heated before varnishing or encapsulating.
2. Insulating materials containing chlorine, such as polyvinyl chloride, neoprene, chloroprene, chlorowaxes, and many others should be avoided in enclosed or sealed systems containing Isonel. Hydrogen chloride is released at temperatures above 105°C, and creates an atmosphere harmful to magnet wire insulation.
3. Isonel will hydrolyze and therefore is not recommended for sealed units, oil- or askarel-filled transformers. These systems may contain other moisture-retaining or acid-producing insulating materials harmful to Isonel.
4. Certain epoxy hardeners and encapsulating materials are not compatible with Isonel. Consult your REA Magnet Wire representative for full details and assistance.
5. Isonel is not solderable.

Class H + (200°C (+))

1. High continuous operating temperature up to 200°C.
2. Can be used in class A (105°C) and class B (130°C) applications as well as class H+(200°C) — simplifies stocking and production procedures; in class H service, other components should be selected to match the thermal capabilities of Isomid; for example, use of class A varnish with Isomid may not result in a class H system.
3. Excellent cut-through resistance.
4. Flexibility and adhesion comparable to Formvar.
5. Excellent wet and dry dielectric characteristics.
6. Can be used in automated winding equipment with proper tension adjustments.
7. Excellent moisture resistance in open constructions, i.e., those allowing a free flow of air; Isomid also gives excellent performance in both open and enclosed constructions when coils and components have been dried thoroughly by preheating, coated with a moisture-resistant varnish, and thoroughly cured; Isomid may also be used in hermetic applications with proper handling.
8. Very good solvent-shock resistance.

1. Although Isomid has an improved heat shock, excessive stretching with rapid temperature rise should be avoided.
2. Units wound with Isomid should be gradually preheated before varnishing or encapsulating.
3. Isomid requires mechanical or chemical stripping as preparation for soldering.
4. Insulating materials containing chlorine, such as polyvinyl chloride, chloroprene, neoprene, chlorowaxes, and many others should be avoided in enclosed or sealed systems containing polyesters; HCl is released at temperatures above 105°C and creates an atmosphere harmful to the magnet wire insulation.

Table A-12. Summation of Magnet Wire Properties (Cont'd)

Pyre ML (220°C)	
Advantages	**Precautions**
1. Exceptional resistance to heat shock and chemical attack with space factor equal to other film-insulated wires. Pyre-ML makes possible a reduction in the size and weight of wound units by replacing bulky glass-served and fused insulations.	1. Abrasion resistance not as high as some film-insulated wires; therefore, adjustment of winding tensions, particularly in fully automated operations, is suggested.
2. Retains high dielectric values at operating temperatures of 220°C (class C).	2. Pyre-ML is subject to hydrolysis in sealed systems containing moisture. Thorough drying is needed before sealing units.
3. Most resistant to burnout conditions of temporary overloads; extremely high cut-through resistance and thermal stability make this possible.	3. Pyre-ML will solvent craze unless winding stresses are relieved by preheating one-half to one hour at 150°C to 170°C. All insulating materials used in final assembly should be class H (180°C) or better to take full advantage of the outstanding characteristics of REA Pyre-ML insulated magnet wire.
4. Highest resistance to radiation.	
5. Replaces Teflon[1] where high cut-through plus high thermal stability is required.	4. Highly corrosive chemical strippers are needed to remove Pyre-ML insulation. Complete neutralization of these stripping liquids is necessary.
6. Lowest weight loss factor, minimum outgassing – an absolute necessity for space-age applications.	
7. Windability properties suitable for automatic operations.	
8. Chemically compatible with a wide range of varnishes and encapsulating materials.	

[1] Registered trademark, E. I. duPont de Nemours & Co., Inc.

A.30 Magnet wire testing

The literature is full of descriptions of test methods, test results, and claims for some particular kind or brand of magnet wire based upon the results of one or more tests. The prospective relay user cannot be blamed if he finds it difficult to evaluate a proposed wire. The relay manufacturers can furnish additional information, if required. The user need only specify the conditions to be met, leaving the choice of wire to the relay maker.

Tables A-11A and A-11B present an index of magnet wire trade names.

A.31 Magnet wire temperature classification

A widely accepted temperature classification system is the IEEE thermal classification shown in Fig. A-4. A material properly rated into one of these classifications can be expected to operate continuously and reliably up to the maximum operating temperature of its classification for a predetermined period (usually 20,000 hours but sometimes up to 100,000 hours). This implies performance only as electrical insulation but does not necessarily cover satisfactory mechanical performance.

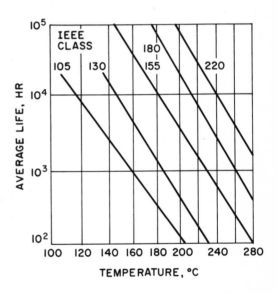

FIG. A-4. TYPICAL LIFE CURVES FOR IEEE THERMAL CLASSES OF INSULATED MAGNET WIRE

(*Source:* Elecronic Design, *12, June 7, 1969*)

A.32 Summary of magnet wire properties

A summation of some of the strong points for using each type of magnet wire, and some disadvantages for each is shown in Table A-12.

Appendix B

LEAD WIRE

B.1 Lead wire insulation

If the application under consideration is within the Class A (105°C) temperature maximum, chlorinated compounds, such as polyvinyl chloride or neoprene, are acceptable for lead wire insulation. However, where an unavoidable or unintentional overload can be foreseen or where thermal requirements are Class B or higher, silicone glass, "Teflon," or polyester impregnated glass lead wire insulation or sleeving is recommended.

B.2 Lead wire current capabilities

Relays are designed to operate on specified coil currents derived from an indicated voltage. A factor of safety is normally provided to allow for some drop in voltage in the conductor between power source and relay coil. Relays have been known to fail in service because the user neglected to take this drop into account in an adequate fashion. The voltage drop due to lead resistance is easily calculated, or read from a chart, for static conditions. Under pulsing (dynamic) conditions, coil inductance may account for a larger share of the circuit voltage appearing across the coil than its proportion of the total circuit resistance would seem to indicate. Ohms law and the nomograph of Fig. B-1 are therefore not applicable to other than static conditions.

The nomograph design is based on the following equation for direct current:

$$A = \frac{21.6 \, I \, d}{E}$$

in which:

A = cross-sectional area of lead wire, in circular mils
I = current, in amperes
d = distance from source to load, in feet
E = maximum allowable line drop, in volts

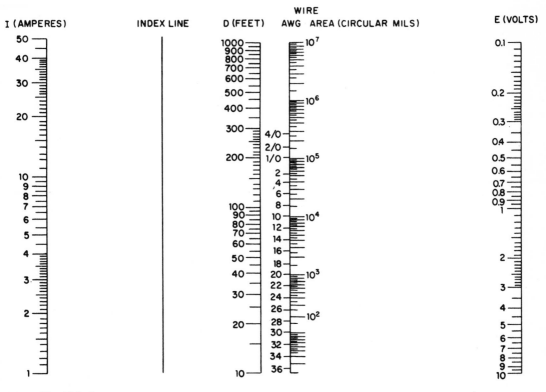

FIG. B-1. SELECTION OF WIRE SIZE FOR VOLTAGE DROP ON A GIVEN LEAD WIRE LENGTH (AFTER S. J. SALVA AND L. J. CRULL, EDN, MAY, 1964)

Table B-1. Suggested Maximum Current-Carrying Capacity of Lead Wire

All values are based on an ambient temperature of 30°C (86°F).

AWG	Current carrying capacity in free air, amperes			
	Rubber	Neoprene	Hypalon	Silicone
24	1	1.5	2	3
22	2	3	4	6
20	4	5	6	9
18	8	9	10	18
16	13	14	15	29
14	20	21	22	45
12	25	27	29	55
10	40	43	47	75
8	65	70	75	100
6	95	100	105	135
4	125	135	150	180
3	145	155	174	210
2	170	180	205	240
1	195	210	235	280
0	230	245	275	325

Courtesy, C. F. Sudds, Belden Mfg. Co.

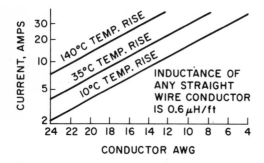

FIG. B-2. CURRENT CARRYING CAPACITY OF COPPER WIRE IN STILL AIR AT 25°C

Example: 20 amperes in No. 12 AWG gives slightly less than 35°C rise over 25°C ambient or 60°C total. The sum of ambient plus rise must not exceed temperature rating of insulation. Values shown are approximate — actual temperature rise depends on heat transfer characteristics in the installation.

When there is doubt as to which wire size to use, the larger-sized wire generally is chosen.

Example: Some equipment is to be installed 20 ft from its source of power. The current required by the equipment is 15 amps and the allowable voltage drop is 2 volts. Determine the necessary wire size.

Solution: Extend a straight line from 15 amps on the I scale to 20 ft on the d scale. From the intersection of the line with the index line, extend another line to 2v on the E scale. Where this line intersects the wire scale, read the answer as 3100 cm (No. 14 AWG probably would be used).

Tables B-1, B-2 and Fig. B-2 provide data on current carrying capacities of various gauges of copper and aluminum lead wire and cable and the fusing currents of several more types of wire.

Table B-2. Current-Carrying Capacity of Wires and Cables

Wire and cable size designation	Continuous-duty current, amperes	
	Single wire in free air	Wires and cables in conduit or bundles
Copper		
AN-22		5
AN-20	11	7.5
AN-18	16	10
AN-16	22	13
AN-14	32	17
AN-12	41	23
AN-10	55	33
AN-8	73	46
AN-6	101	60
AN-4	135	80
AN-2	181	100
AN-1	211	125
AN-0	245	150
AN-00	283	175
AN-000	328	200
AN-0000	380	225
Aluminum		
AL-8	60	36
AL-6	83	50
AL-4	108	66
AL-2	152	82
AL-1	174	105
AL-0	202	123
AL-00	235	145
AL-000	266	162
AL-0000	303	190

Source: MIL-W-5088A(ASG)

Appendix C

REFERENCE TABLES, CHARTS, AND GRAPHS

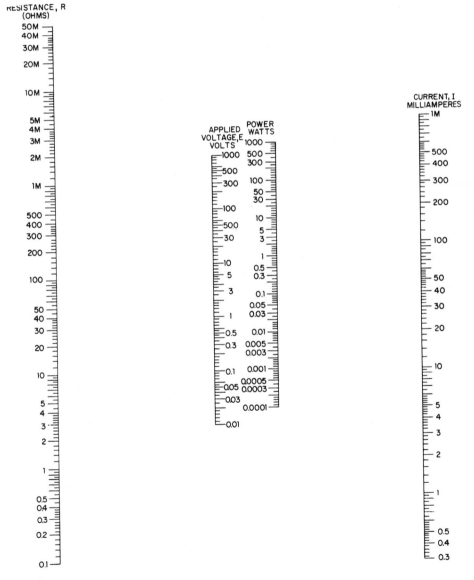

Fig. C-1. Ohms Law power relationships

Example: *For a 100 ohm coil operating at 1.0 watts, the coil will draw 100 milliamperes at 10 volts.*

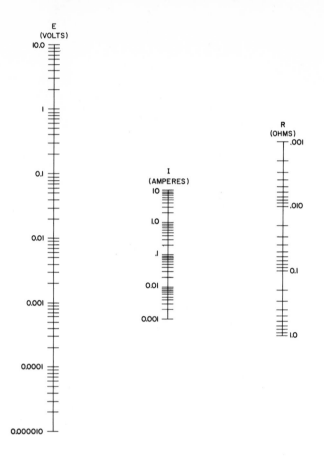

FIG. C-2. OHMS LAW RELATIONSHIP FOR $E = IR$ IN NORMAL RELAY CONTACT RESISTANCE RANGE
Example: *If* E = 0.1 *volts and* I = 1.0 *amps, the resistance will be 0.1 ohms.*

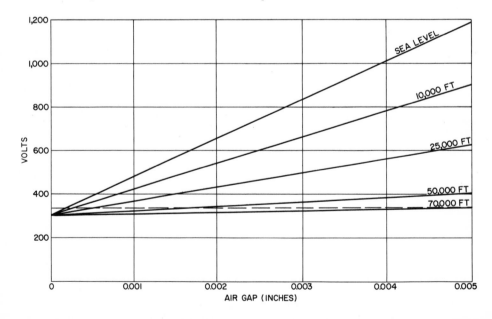

FIG. C-3. HIGH POTENTIAL VOLTAGE BREAKDOWN IN RELATION TO AIR GAP AT VARIOUS ALTITUDES

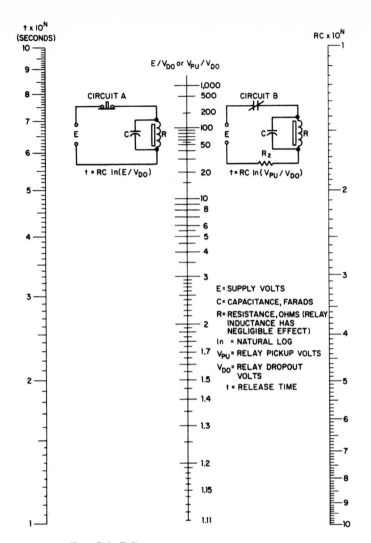

FIG. C-4. RC EFFECT ON RELAY RELEASE TIME

E/V_{DO} = *ratio of supply to dropout volts (circuit A)*
V_{PU}/V_{DO} = *ratio of pickup to dropout volts (circuit B)*

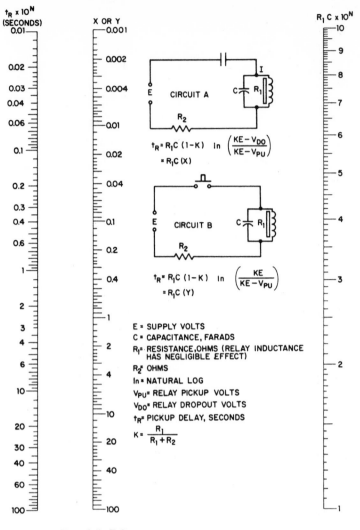

FIG. C-5. RC EFFECT ON RELAY OPERATE TIME

$$X = (1 - K) \left(ln \ \frac{KE - V_{DO}}{KE - V_{PU}} \right) \ in \ circuit \ A.$$

$$Y = (1 - K) \left(ln \ \frac{KE}{KE - V_{PU}} \right) \ in \ circuit \ B.$$

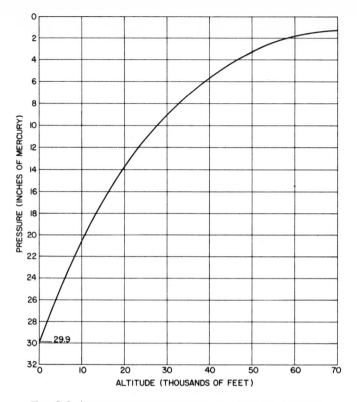

FIG. C-6. ATMOSPHERIC PRESSURE IN RELATION TO ALTITUDE

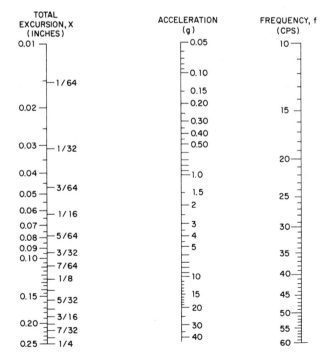

FIG. C-7. ACCELERATION WITH SIMPLE HARMONIC MOTION $(g = 0.0511f^2X)$
Example: *The total excursion required to produce 10 g at 55 cycles is 0.065 in.*

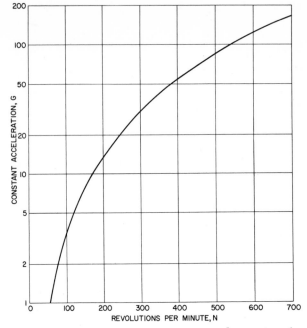

FIG. C-8. ACCELERATION IN RELATION TO ROTATIONAL SPEED AT 1-FT RADIUS $(g = 3.40 \times 10^{-4}N^2)$
For radii other than 1 ft, multiply value of g obtained by radius in feet.

OHM'S LAW FOR DIRECT CURRENT   **OHM'S LAW FOR ALTERNATING CURRENT**

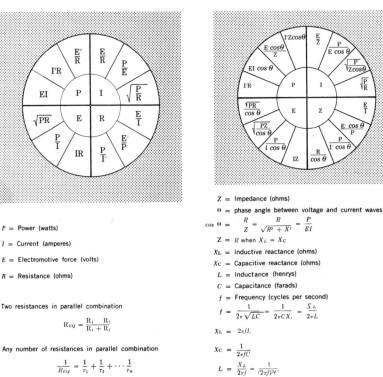

P = Power (watts)

I = Current (amperes)

E = Electromotive force (volts)

R = Resistance (ohms)

Two resistances in parallel combination

$$R_{EQ} = \frac{R_1 \; R_2}{R_1 + R_2}$$

Any number of resistances in parallel combination

$$\frac{1}{R_{EQ}} = \frac{1}{r_1} + \frac{1}{r_2} + \cdots \frac{1}{r_n}$$

For calculating capacitances in series combinations substitute C for R in the above formulae.

Z = Impedance (ohms)

θ = phase angle between voltage and current waves

$$\cos \theta = \frac{R}{Z} = \frac{R}{\sqrt{R^2 + X^2}} = \frac{P}{EI}$$

Z = R when $X_L = X_C$

X_L = Inductive reactance (ohms)

X_C = Capacitive reactance (ohms)

L = Inductance (henrys)

C = Capacitance (farads)

f = Frequency (cycles per second)

$$f = \frac{1}{2\pi \sqrt{LC}} = \frac{1}{2\pi C X_c} = \frac{X_L}{2\pi L}$$

$X_L = 2\pi fl.$

$X_C = \dfrac{1}{2\pi fC}$

$L = \dfrac{X_L}{2\pi f} = \dfrac{1}{(2\pi f)^2 C}$

$C = \dfrac{1}{2\pi f X_c} = \dfrac{1}{(2\pi f)^2 L}$

$Z = \sqrt{R^2 + X^2} = \sqrt{R^2 + (X_L - X_C)^2}$

$2\pi f \cong 377$ for 60 cycles / sec

FIG. C-9. OHM'S LAW WHEELS

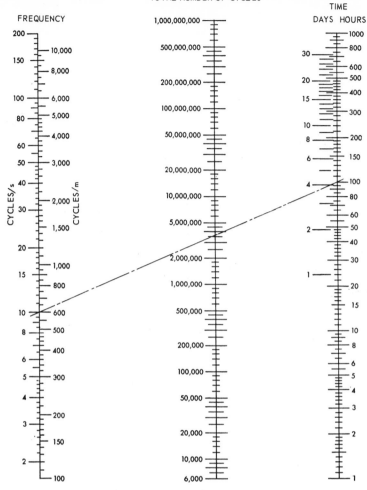

TOTAL NUMBER OF CYCLES

FIG. C-10. FREQUENCY IN RELATION TO TOTAL CYCLES AND TOTAL TIME

MILLIONS OF CYCLES									
Hours	Cycles per minute				Hours				
	1000	1500	2000	2500	3000		3500	4000	4500	5000
1	.06	.09	.12	.15	.18	1	.21	.24	.27	.30
25	1.5	2.25	3.0	3.75	4.5	25	5.25	6.0	6.75	7.5
50	3.0	4.5	6.0	7.5	9.0	50	10.5	12	13.5	15
100	6	9	12	15	18	100	21	24	27	30
150	9	13.5	18	22.5	27	150	31.5	36	40.5	45
200	12	18	24	30	36	200	42	48	54	60
250	15	22.5	30	37.5	45	250	52.5	60	67.5	75
300	18	27	36	45	54	300	63	72	81	90
400	24	36	48	60	72	400	84	96	108	120
500	30	45	60	75	90	500	105	120	135	150
600	36	54	72	90	108	600	126	144	162	180
700	42	63	84	105	126	700	147	168	189	210
800	48	72	96	120	144	800	168	192	216	240
900	54	81	108	135	162	900	189	216	243	270
1000	60	90	120	150	180	1000	210	240	270	300

When testing repetitive functions to determine probable life, it is often necessary to convert from frequency in cycles per unit time to time units or total cycles. The nomograph expands on the table to provide quick conversion from cycles per second or per minute to total cycles or time in hours or days.

Example: A relay operating at a repetitive rate of 10 cycles per second that has lasted 100 h on test has a life of 3,600,000 cycles. Conversely, a unit operating at 600 cycles per minute through 3,600,000 cycles will last 100 h. The frequency scale also can be used for easy conversion from cycles per second to cycles per minute.

Table C-1. Low Temperature Conversion Table (Celsius to Fahrenheit and Kelvin)

0°C taken as + 273.15 °K

°C	°F	°K	°C	°F	°K	°C	°F	°K	°C	°F	°K	°C	°F	°K	°C	°F	°K
−273.15	−459.67	0	−229	−380.2	44.15	−184	−299.2	89.15	−139	−218.2	134.15	−94	−137.2	179.15	−49	−56.2	224.15
−273	−459.4	0.15	−228	−378.4	45.15	−183	−297.4	90.15	−138	−216.4	135.15	−93	−135.4	180.15	−48	−54.4	225.15
−272	−457.6	1.15	−227	−376.6	46.15	−182	−295.6	91.15	−137	−214.6	136.15	−92	−133.6	181.15	−47	−52.6	226.15
−271	−455.8	2.15	−226	−374.8	47.15	−181	−293.8	92.15	−136	−212.8	137.15	−91	−131.8	182.15	−46	−50.8	227.15
−270	−454.0	3.15	−225	−373.0	48.15	−180	−292.0	93.15	−135	−211.0	138.15	−90	−130.0	183.15	−45	−49.0	228.15
−269	−452.2	4.15	−224	−371.2	49.15	−179	−290.2	94.15	−134	−209.2	139.15	−89	−128.2	184.15	−44	−47.2	229.15
−268	−450.4	5.15	−223	−369.4	50.15	−178	−288.4	95.15	−133	−207.4	140.15	−88	−126.4	185.15	−43	−45.4	230.15
−267	−448.6	6.15	−222	−367.6	51.15	−177	−286.6	96.15	−132	−205.6	141.15	−87	−124.6	186.15	−42	−43.6	231.15
−266	−446.8	7.15	−221	−365.8	52.15	−176	−284.8	97.15	−131	−203.8	142.15	−86	−122.8	187.15	−41	−41.8	232.15
−265	−445.0	8.15	−220	−364.0	53.15	−175	−283.0	98.15	−130	−202.0	143.15	−85	−121.0	188.15	−40	−40.0	233.15
−264	−443.2	9.15	−219	−362.2	54.15	−174	−281.2	99.15	−129	−200.2	144.15	−84	−119.2	189.15	−39	−38.2	234.15
−263	−441.4	10.15	−218	−360.4	55.15	−173	−279.4	100.15	−128	−198.4	145.15	−83	−117.4	190.15	−38	−36.4	235.15
−262	−439.6	11.15	−217	−358.6	56.15	−172	−277.6	101.15	−127	−196.6	146.15	−82	−115.6	191.15	−37	−34.6	236.15
−261	−437.8	12.15	−216	−356.8	57.15	−171	−275.8	102.15	−126	−194.8	147.15	−81	−113.8	192.15	−36	−32.8	237.15
−260	−436.0	13.15	−215	−355.0	58.15	−170	−274.0	103.15	−125	−193.0	148.15	−80	−112.0	193.15	−35	−31.0	238.15
−259	−434.2	14.15	−214	−353.2	59.15	−169	−272.2	104.15	−124	−191.2	149.15	−79	−110.2	194.15	−34	−29.2	239.15
−258	−432.4	15.15	−213	−351.4	60.15	−168	−270.4	105.15	−123	−189.4	150.15	−78	−108.4	195.15	−33	−27.4	240.15
−257	−430.6	16.15	−212	−349.6	61.15	−167	−268.6	406.15	−122	−187.6	151.15	−77	−106.6	196.15	−32	−25.6	241.15
−256	−428.8	17.15	−211	−347.8	62.15	−166	−266.8	107.15	−121	−185.8	152.15	−76	−104.8	197.15	−31	−23.8	242.15
−255	−427.0	18.15	−210	−346.0	63.15	−165	−265.0	108.15	−120	−184.0	153.15	−75	−103.0	198.15	−30	−22.0	243.15
−254	−425.2	19.15	−209	−344.2	64.15	−164	−263.2	109.15	−119	−182.2	154.15	−74	−101.2	199.15	−29	−20.2	244.15
−253	−423.4	20.15	−208	−342.4	65.15	−163	−261.4	110.15	−118	−180.4	155.15	−73	−99.4	200.15	−28	−18.4	245.15
−252	−421.6	21.15	−207	−340.6	66.15	−162	−259.6	111.15	−117	−178.6	156.15	−72	−97.6	201.15	−27	−16.6	246.15
−251	−419.8	22.15	−206	−338.8	67.15	−161	−257.8	112.15	−116	−176.8	157.15	−71	−95.8	202.15	−26	−14.8	247.15
−250	−418.0	23.15	−205	−337.0	68.15	−160	−256.0	113.15	−115	−175.0	158.15	−70	−94.0	203.15	−25	−13.0	248.15
−249	−416.2	24.15	−204	−335.2	69.15	−159	−254.2	114.15	−114	−173.2	159.15	−69	−92.2	204.15	−24	−11.2	249.15
−248	−414.4	25.15	−203	−333.4	70.15	−158	−252.4	115.15	−113	−171.4	160.15	−68	−90.4	205.15	−23	−9.4	250.15
−247	−412.6	26.15	−202	−331.6	71.15	−157	−250.6	116.15	−112	−169.6	161.15	−67	−88.6	206.15	−22	−7.6	251.15
−246	−410.8	27.15	−201	−329.8	72.15	−156	−248.8	117.15	−111	−167.8	162.15	−66	−86.8	207.15	−21	−5.8	252.15
−245	−409.0	28.15	−200	−328.0	73.15	−155	−247.0	118.15	−110	−166.0	163.15	−65	−85.0	208.15	−20	−4.0	253.15
−244	−407.2	29.15	−199	−326.2	74.15	−154	−245.2	119.15	−109	−164.2	164.15	−64	−83.2	209.15	−19	−2.2	254.15
−243	−405.4	30.15	−198	−324.4	75.15	−153	−243.4	120.15	−108	−162.4	165.15	−63	−81.4	210.15	−18	−0.4	255.15
−242	−403.6	31.15	−197	−322.6	76.15	−152	−241.6	121.15	−107	−160.6	166.15	−62	−79.6	211.15	−17	1.4	256.15
−241	−401.8	32.15	−196	−320.8	77.15	−151	−239.8	122.15	−106	−158.8	167.15	−61	−77.8	212.15	−16	3.2	257.15
−240	−400.0	33.15	−195	−319.0	78.15	−150	−238.0	123.15	−105	−157.0	168.15	−60	−76.0	213.15	−15	5.0	258.15
−239	−398.2	34.15	−194	−317.2	79.15	−149	−236.2	124.15	−104	−155.2	169.15	−59	−74.2	214.15	−14	6.8	259.15
−238	−396.4	35.15	−193	−315.4	80.15	−148	−234.4	125.15	−103	−153.4	170.15	−58	−72.4	215.15	−13	8.6	260.15
−237	−394.6	36.15	−192	−313.6	81.15	−147	−232.6	126.15	−102	−151.6	171.15	−57	−70.6	216.15	−12	10.4	261.15
−236	−392.8	37.15	−191	−311.8	82.15	−146	−230.8	127.15	−101	−149.8	172.15	−56	−68.8	217.15	−11	12.2	262.15
−235	−391.0	38.15	−190	−310.0	83.15	−145	−229.0	128.15	−100	−148.0	173.15	−55	−67.0	218.15	−10	14.0	263.15
−234	−389.2	39.15	−189	−308.2	84.15	−144	−227.2	129.15	−99	−146.2	174.15	−54	−65.2	219.15	−9	15.8	264.15
−233	−387.4	40.15	−188	−306.4	85.15	−143	−225.4	130.15	−98	−144.4	175.15	−53	−63.4	220.15	−8	17.6	265.15
−232	−385.6	41.15	−187	−304.6	86.15	−142	−223.6	131.15	−97	−142.6	176.15	−52	−61.6	221.15	−7	19.4	266.15
−231	−383.8	42.15	−186	−302.8	87.15	−141	−221.8	132.15	−96	−140.8	177.15	−51	−59.8	222.15	−6	21.2	267.15
−230	−382.0	43.15	−185	−301.0	88.15	−140	−220.0	133.15	−95	−139.0	178.15	−50	−58.0	223.15	−5	23.0	268.15
															−4	24.8	269.15
															−3	26.6	270.15
															−2	28.4	271.15
															−1	30.2	272.15
															0	32.0	273.15

Table C-2. Celsius and Fahrenheit Conversion Table

Numbers in the center column (between those marked **C** and **F**) refer to temperature, either Centigrade or Fahrenheit, which it is desired to convert into the other scale. To convert from Fahrenheit to Centigrade find equivalent temperature in left hand column

°C.		°F.	°C.		°F.	°C.		°F.	°C		°F	°C		°F	°C		°F
−40.0	−40	−40.0	− 6.7	20	68.0	15.6	60	140.0	37.8	100	212.0	82.2	180	356.0	137.8	280	536.0
−38.9	−38	−36.4	− 6.1	21	69.8	16.1	61	141.8	38.9	102	215.6	83.3	182	359.6	140.6	285	545.0
−37.8	−36	−32.8	− 5.6	22	71.6	16.7	62	143.6	40.0	104	219.2	84.4	184	363.2	143.3	290	554.0
−36.7	−34	−29.2	− 5.0	23	73.4	17.2	63	145.4	41.1	106	222.8	85.6	186	366.8	146.1	295	563.0
−35.6	−32	−25.6	− 4.4	24	75.2	17.8	64	147.2	42.2	108	226.4	86.7	188	370.4	148.9	300	572.0
−34.4	−30	−22.0	− 3.9	25	77.0	18.3	65	149.0	43.3	110	230.0	87.8	190	374.0	151.7	305	581.0
−33.3	−28	−18.4	− 3.3	26	78.8	18.9	66	150.8	44.4	112	233.6	88.9	192	377.6	154.4	310	590.0
−32.2	−26	−14.8	− 2.8	27	80.6	19.4	67	152.6	45.6	114	237.2	90.0	194	381.2	157.2	315	599.0
−31.1	−24	−11.2	− 2.2	28	82.4	20.0	68	154.4	46.7	116	240.8	91.1	196	384.8	160.0	320	608.0
−30.0	−22	− 7.6	− 1.7	29	84.2	20.6	69	156.2	47.8	118	244.4	92.2	198	388.4	162.8	325	617.0
−28.9	−20	− 4.0	− 1.1	30	86.0	21.1	70	158.0	48.9	120	248.0	93.3	200	392.0	165.6	330	626.0
−27.8	−18	− 0.4	− 0.6	31	87.8	21.7	71	159.8	50.0	122	251.6	94.4	202	395.6	168.3	335	635.0
−26.7	−16	3.2	0.0	32	89.6	22.2	72	161.6	51.1	124	255.2	95.6	204	399.2	171.1	340	644.0
−25.6	−14	6.8	+ 0.6	33	91.4	22.8	73	163.4	52.2	126	258.8	96.7	206	402.8	173.9	345	653.0
−24.4	−12	10.4	1.1	34	93.2	23.3	74	165.2	53.3	128	262.4	97.8	208	406.4	176.7	350	662.0
−23.3	−10	14.0	1.7	35	95.0	23.9	75	167.0	54.4	130	266.0	98.9	210	410.0	179.4	355	671.0
−22.2	− 8	17.6	2.2	36	96.8	24.4	76	168.8	55.6	132	269.6	100.0	212	413.6	182.2	360	680.0
−21.1	− 6	21.2	2.8	37	98.6	25.0	77	170.6	56.7	134	273.2	101.1	214	417.2	185.0	365	689.9
−20.0	− 4	24.8	3.3	38	100.4	25.6	78	172.4	57.8	136	276.8	102.2	216	420.8	188.2	370	698.0
−18.9	− 2	28.4	3.9	39	102.2	26.1	79	174.2	58.9	138	280.4	103.3	218	424.4	190.6	375	707.0
−17.8	0	32.0	4.4	40	104.0	26.7	80	176.0	60.0	140	284.0	104.4	220	428.0	193.3	380	716.0
−17.2	1	33.8	5.0	41	105.8	27.2	81	177.8	61.1	142	287.6	105.6	222	431.6	196.1	385	725.0
−16.7	2	35.6	5.6	42	107.6	27.8	82	179.6	62.2	144	291.2	106.7	224	435.2	198.9	390	734.0
−16.1	3	37.4	6.1	43	109.4	28.3	83	181.4	63.3	146	294.8	107.8	226	438.8	201.7	395	743.0
−15.6	4	39.2	6.7	44	·111.2	28.9	84	183.2	64.4	148	298.4	108.9	228	442.4	204.4	400	752.0
−15.0	5	41.0	7.2	45	113.0	29.4	85	185.0	65.6	150	302.0	110.0	230	446.0	210.0	410	770.0
−14.4	6	42.8	7.8	46	114.8	30.0	86	186.8	66.7	152	305.6	111.1	232	449.6	215.6	420	788.0
−13.9	7	44.6	8.3	47	116.6	30.6	87	188.6	67.8	154	309.2	112.2	234	453.2	221.1	430	806.0
−13.3	8	46.4	8.9	48	118.4	31.1	88	190.4	68.9	156	312.8	113.3	236	456.8	226.7	440	824.0
−12.8	9	48.2	9.4	49	120.2	31.7	89	192.2	70.0	158	316.4	114.4	238	460.4	232.2	450	842.0
−12.2	10	50.0	10.0	50	122.0	32.2	90	194.0	71.1	160	320.0	115.6	240	464.0	237.8	460	860.0
−11.7	11	51.8	10.6	51	123.8	32.8	91	195.8	72.2	162	323.6	116.7	242	467.6	243.3	470	878.8
−11.1	12	53.6	11.1	52	125.6	33.3	92	197.6	73.3	164	327.2	117.8	244	471.2	248.9	480	896.0
−10.6	13	55.4	11.7	53	127.4	33.9	93	199.4	74.4	166	330.8	118.3	245	473.0	254.4	490	914.0
−10.0	14	57.2	12.2	54	129.2	34.4	94	201.2	75.6	168	334.4	121.1	250	482.0	260.0	500	932.0
− 9.4	15	59.0	12.8	55	131.0	35.0	95	203.0									
− 8.9	16	60.8	13.3	56	132.8	35.6	96	204.8	76.7	170	338.0	123.9	255	491.0	265.6	510	950.0
− 8.3	17	62.6	13.9	57	134.6	36.1	97	206.6	77.8	172	341.6	126.7	260	500.0	271.1	520	968.0
− 7.8	18	64.4	14.4	58	136.4	36.7	98	208.4	78.9	174	345.2	129.4	265	509.0	276.7	530	986.0
− 7.2	19	66.2	15.0	59	138.2	37.2	99	210.2	80.0	176	348.8	132.2	270	518.0	282.3	540	1004.0
									81.1	178	352.4	135.0	275	527.0	287.8	550	1022.0

Table C-3. Numerical Values of Metric Unit Prefixes with Conversion Table

The National Bureau of Standards scientists decided to follow the recommendations of the International Committee on Weights and Measures to use prefixes for denoting multiples and submultiples of metric units. The International Committee adopted the prefixes at its meeting in Paris in the fall of 1958. Prefixes used by the Bureau of Standards are listed in the October, 1959, issue of NBS's Technical News Bulletin. In addition to the numerical prefixes already in common use, the Committee expanded the list by adding the four prefixes marked with an asterisk. Thus, for example, 10^{-12} farads is to be called 1 picofarad, replacing the designation "1 micromicrofarad," which some engineers have been using.

Multiples	Prefixes	Multiples	Prefixes
10^{12}	*tera- (tēr'a)	10^{-1}	deci-
10^{9}	*giga- (jǐ'ga)	10^{-2}	centi-
10^{6}	mega-	10^{-3}	milli-
10^{4}	myria-	10^{-6}	micro-
10^{3}	kilo-	10^{-9}	*nano- (nā'no)
10^{2}	hekto-	10^{-12}	*pico- (pī'co)
10	deka-		

The following table provides a fast and easy means of conversion from one metric notation to another, including the units mentioned above. The value labeled "Unit" represents the basic units of measurement, such as ohms, watts, amperes, grams, etc. First, locate the original or given value in the left-hand column. Follow this line horizontally to the vertical column headed by the prefix of the desired value. The figure and arrow at this intersection represent the direction in which the decimal point should be moved and the number of places to move it.

Example: Convert 0.15 kilowatts to watts. Starting at the "Kilo-" box in the left-hand column, move horizontally to the column headed by "Unit" (since a *watt* is a basic unit of measurement), and read 3⟶ . Thus 0.15 kilowatts is the equivalent of 150 watts.

Example: Convert 4,500 kilocycles to megacycles, read in the box horizontal to "Kilo-" and under "Mega-" the notation ⟵3, which means a shift of the decimal point three places to the left. Thus 4,500 kilocycles is the equivalent of 4.5 megacycles.

ORIGINAL VALUE	Tera-	Giga-	Mega-	Myria-	Kilo-	Hekto-	Deka-	Units	Deci-	Centi-	Milli-	Micro-	Nano-	Pico-
Tera-		3→	6→	8→	9→	10→	11→	12→	13→	14→	15→	18→	21→	24→
Giga-	←3		3→	5→	6→	7→	8→	9→	10→	11→	12→	15→	18→	21→
Mega-	←6	←3		2→	3→	4→	5-→	6→	7→	8→	9→	12→	15→	18→
Myria-	←8	←5	←2		1→	2→	3→	4→	5→	6→	7→	10→	13→	16→
Kilo-	←9	←6	←3	←1		1→	2→	3→	4→	5→	6→	9→	12→	15→
Hekto-	←10	←7	←4	←2	←1		1→	2→	3→	4→	5→	8→	11→	14→
Deka-	←11	←8	←5	←3	←2	←1		1→	2→	3→	4→	7→	10→	13→
Units	←12	←9	←6	←4	←3	←2	←1		1→	2→	3→	6→	9→	12→
Deci-	←13	←10	←7	←5	←4	←3	←2	←1		1→	2→	5→	8→	11→
Centi-	←14	←11	←8	←6	←5	←4	←3	←2	←1		1→	4→	7→	10→
Milli-	←15	←12	←9	←7	←6	←5	←4	←3	←2	←1		3→	6→	9→
Micro-	←18	←15	←12	←10	←9	←8	←7	←6	←5	←4	←3		3→	6→
Nano-	←21	←18	←15	←13	←12	←11	←10	←9	←8	←7	←6	←3		3→
Pico-	←24	←21	←18	←16	←15	←14	←13	←12	←11	←10	←9	←6	←3	

Appendix D

POLARIZED RELAYS

Note: This subject was defined in Sec. 1, Definitions. Some Government preferences are shown below.

"The proper poling for a polarized relay shall be shown by the use of + and − designations applied to the winding leads. The interpretation of this shall be that current in the direction indicated shall move or tend to move the armature toward the contact shown nearest the coil on the diagram. If the relay is equipped with numbered terminals, the proper terminal numbers shall also be shown." (Y32.2)

Monostable +(P), or Single side stable or Single biased +(NP), two-position polarized relays—(a) Magnetically biased: A polarized relay that is held in the unoperated position by a permanent magnet or magnets and that will

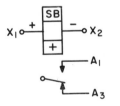

FIG. D-1. SINGLE BIASED POLARIZED MONOSTABLE (SIDE STABLE) RELAY

move to its operated position when energized by the correct polarity. Commonly called single biased, side stable. (b) Electromagnetically biased: A relay that is held in the unoperated position with current flowing in one winding and that moves to its operated position when reverse polarity is applied to this or another winding. (c) Mechanically biased: A polarized relay that is held in the unoperated position by means of mechanical bias, such as a spring, but that will move to the operated position when energized by the correct polarity. A large residual gap in the operated position aided by

the mechanical bias causes restoration on de-energization.

Bistable +(P), or *Double biased +(NP),* two-position polarized relay—A polarized relay that is held in either of two operated positions by a permanent magnet or magnets, or remanent flux, when power is removed and that will operate to the opposite position when energized with the correct polarity. Commonly called double biased, bistable. Also called magnetic latch.

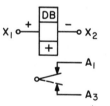

FIG. D-2. POLARIZED BISTABLE (DOUBLE BIASED) RELAY

Center-off, three-position polarized relay — A polarized relay having a de-energized mechanically stressed neutral position and two energized positions either side of neutral. The polarity of the coil current determines which of the two energized positions is taken. Also called a three-position center stable relay and a null-seeking relay. (NB = No Bias Relay)

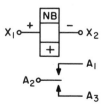

FIG. D-3. POLARIZED THREE POSITION (NO BIAS; CENTER-OFF) RELAY

313

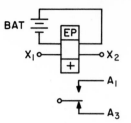

FIG. D-4. ELECTRICALLY POLARIZED RELAY

Electrically — An electrically polarized relay is a neutral relay with multiple windings, one of which is normally continuously energized by a d-c source, thereby polarizing the relay so that operation depends upon the algebraic sum of the fluxes of all the windings. In effect, relay is monostable, — i.e., single biased — see note.

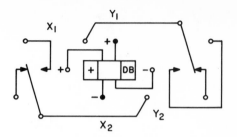

FIG. D-5. SYMMETRICALLY OPERATING RELAY BUT WITH NONSYMMETRICAL CONTACTS

Crystal can *polarized double biased* (magnetic latch) relay type. (Note that both lower contacts are made and not diagonally opposite as in crystal can neutral relay of MIL-5757/21.)

Bibliography

Bibliography

A meaningful bibliography must be as complete as practicable, with a large listing of reference articles such as is presented here. The arrangement of this listing is designed to help the reader find articles of interest in a minimum of time. The Table of Contents indicates the categories into which the bibliography is separated. Each category lists the reference articles in chronological order, the oldest articles appearing first. It is hoped this bibliography will provide a real service to the reader who wishes to pursue a subject to the fullest extent.

Table of Contents

Applications

1 General

"New Fields for Magnetic Contact Relays," A. H. LAMB, *Electronics,* Dec. 1940, vol. 13, pp 35-38.

"Telephone Type Relays," V. E. JAMES, *Product Engineering,* Oct. 1950, vol. 21, pp. 130-133, and Nov. 1950, Feb. 1951, March 1951.

"Your Next Switch Selection Problem," A. L. RICHE, *Product Engineering,* June 1951, vol. 22, pp. 162-167.

"The Equipment Manufacturer's Problem Concerning Relay Selection, J. G. CROCKETT, Relay Conference, 1953.

"Relay Requirements for the Equipment Manufacturer," V. R. HUDEK, Relay Conference, 1953.

"Performance Characteristics and the Application of Relays," C. A. PACKARD, Relay Conference, 1953.

"Equipment Manufacturer's Problem Concerning Relay Selection," J. G. CROCKETT, *Machine Design,* April 1954, vol. 26, pp. 341-342.

"The Mutual Responsibility in the Selection, Specification and Design of Relays," P. H. BERRIEN, Relay Conference, 1954.

"Relay Requirements for Business Machines," R. E. MARKLE, Relay Conference, 1954.

"The User's Viewpoint," G. D. CURTISS, Relay Conference, 1954.

"The Use and Abuse of Sensitive Relays," W. H. HOLCOMBE, Relay Conference, 1954.

"Special-Purpose Relays Gain New Uses," F. ROCKETT, *Electronics,* Feb. 1955, vol. 28, pp. 150-156.

"Relay Characteristics and Uses," C. F. CAMERON, *Tele-Tech and Electronic Industries,* April 1955, vol. 14, pp. 97, 173-174.

"Efficient Application of Relays," E. H. LOCKWOOD, Relay Conference, 1955.

"Selling Relays vs. Helping the Customer Buy Relays," F. O. STRATTON, Relay Conference, 1955.

"Picking Right Relay," E. H. LOCKWOOD, *Machine Design,* Sept. 1955, pp. 219-222.

"Relay Applications — Closing the Gap!," Z. R. SMITH, Relay Conference, 1956.

"Some Hints on Relay Operation," L. B. STEIN, JR., *QST,* June 1956, pp. 40:21-25.

"Rectifiers and Circuits for D. C. Relays," F. W. PARRISH, *Electronic Design,* Nov. 15, 1956.

"Advanced Data System in the Power Industry," G. M. KEYSER and J. R. LESLIE, AIEE: *Communication and Electronics,* May 1957, pp. 206-210.

"Automatic Checkout Equipment," KLIVANS, *Electronic Industries,* April 1958.

"High-Speed Relay Self-Rectifying Circuit for Conductivity Measurements," D. M. G. ARMSTRONG, *Journal of Scientific Instruments,* Oct. 1958, p. 381.

"This Money-Saving Guide Tells How to Size Up Electromagnetic Relays," R. PRO-

BERT, *Product Engineering,* Nov. 24, 1958, pp. 66-69.

"Compiling a Complete Relay Directory," R. N. AUGER, Relay Conference, 1959.

"How to Adjust Relays for Smooth Operation," J. V. FOSTER, *Industrial Laboratories,* May 1959, pp. 93-98.

"The Correct Choice-Relay or Transistor," H. H. BREWER, Relay Conference, 1960.

"The Optimization of Relay Application Data," W. T. WEIR and J. S. YOUTCHEFF, Relay Conference, 1960.

"Novel Roles for Relays," R. N. AUGER, *Automatic Control,* Jan. 1960, pp. 15-18.

"The Relay — A Versatile, Dependable Tool," R. H. WILLIAMS, JR., Relay Conference, 1960.

"An Adaptation of a Telephone Type Relay for Power Switching," E. J. PISKORZ, Relay Conference, 1961.

"Radio Noise Suppression of A-C Operated Relays," J. K. MURAVEZ, Relay Conference, 1961.

"The Design Engineer's Most Reliable Piece of Hardware — The General Purpose Relay," C. W. DERRICKSON and C. P. WEGENKA, Relay Conference, 1961.

"How to Get the Most Out of a Relay — And Its Manufacturer," P. GARNICK, Relay Conference, 1961.

"Relay Designers and Users Meet" (Summary Report of 9th National Conference on Electromagnetic Relays at Oklahoma State University), M. M. MYERS, *Electro-Technology,* July 1961, p. 74.

"How Relays Work," T. JASKI, *Radio-Electronics,* 1961 (Series), June p. 43, July pp. 54-55, Aug. pp. 47-49, Oct. p. 96, Nov. pp. 56-58, Dec. pp. 33-35.

"Increasing Relay Operate Speed by Circuit Design," (Nomograph) F. F. YANIKOSKI, *Electro-Technology,* Jan. 1962, p. 96.

"Relays and Switches," A. C. KELLER, *IRE Proceedings,* vol. 50, May 1962, pp. 932-934.

"Selection and Application of Electromagnetic Relays," (Survey of literature for past 30 years), J. A. CSEPELY, *Electromechanical Components and Systems Design,* Nov. 1962, pp. 52-80.

"The Design Engineer's Most Reliable Piece of Hardware, The General Purpose Relay — Phase II," C. W. DERRICKSON and C. P. WEGENKA, Relay Conference, 1963.

"Progress in the Relay Field," C. F. CAMERON, *Electronic Industries,* June 1963, pp. 25-27.

"Relays — Least Understood, Least Standardized, Most Abused," M. M. PERUGINI, *Electronic Equipment Engineering,* June 1963, pp. 44-53.

"The Use of Trade Off Parameters for the Application and Manufacturing of Relays," J. S. JORDAN, Relay Conference, 1964.

"Are Relays Going the Way of the Dodo Bird?," W. A. MURRAY, Relay Conference, 1964.

"Choosing Relays or Solid-State Switching," J. A. PFINGSTEN, *Electronic Industries,* June 1964, p. 99.

"Relay Circuit Symbols," (First of a series on telephone relays), L. B. MITCHELL, *Automation,* May 1965, p. 103.

"Relays in Action," *Electronic Design,* Nov. 29 1965, pp. 70-81 (collection of short case histories of relay functional circuits).

2   Aerospace and military applications

"Aircraft Contactors," F. J. RUSSELL and A. P. CHARBONNEAU, *Transactions of the AIEE,* 1943, vol. 62, pp. 563-566.

"A Polarized Relay as an Aircraft Control Element," R. E. JOHNSON and G. A. GLASGOW, *Electrical Engineering,* Nov. 1948, vol. 67, p. 1059.

"Special Problems of the Naval Air Service," R. F. SCHARMANN, Relay Conference, 1953.

"The Air Force Looks at Relays," F. C. WENGER, Relay Conference, 1953.

"Relays in Bumblebee Guided Missiles," H. W. BISHOP and D. D. ZIMMERMAN, Relay Conference, 1954.

"Requirements of A.C. Operated Relays for Military Applications," R. J. COPPOLA, Relay Conference, 1954.

"Guided Missile Relays — Performance Limits and Proposed Designs," A. P. BOYLAN, Relay Conference, 1955.

"What's Wrong with Today's Missile Relays?," J. D. LESLIE, Relay Conference, 1955.

"The Navy Reports on Relays," S. G. OSTERLUND and M. SHUCK, Relay Conference, 1955.

"The Guided Missile Relay Working Group, Its Operation and Objectives," B. J. WILSON, Relay Conference, 1955.

"Fuel Cut-Off Control for Guided Missiles," G. L. ZOMBER and D. MAC MILLAN, *Electronics,* Jan. 1956, pp. 29:126-127.

"Engineering Information for Missile Relays," J. D. LESLIE, Relay Conference, 1957.

"Organizing and Interpreting the Requirements for Electronic Components in Advanced Weapons Systems," S. G. OSTERLUND and A. E. GUTHRIE, Relay Conference, 1957.

"Problems Encountered in Obtaining Satisfactory Electro-Magnetic Relays for Use in Douglas DC-8 Jet Transport," B. B. STUART and D. ROELANDS, Relay Conference, 1957.

"Relay Application Problems in a Production Missile," M. E. THOMPSON, Relay Conference, 1957.

"Investigating Requirements of Missile Relays," B. J. WILSON, Relay Conference, 1957.

"Evaluating Relays for Guided Missiles," D. D. ZIMMERMAN, *Military Electronics,* Oct. 1957, pp. 40-42.

"In-Line Relay Cuts (Missile) Launching Delays," R. M. NOLAN, *Missile Electronics* (Supplement to *Missiles and Rockets*), May 1958, p. 219.

"Simplified Aircraft Electrical Diagrams," H. L. YARBROUGH, *Electrical Manufacturing,* Sept. 1958, pp. 95-99, 313-314.

"Design Considerations for Aircraft Relays," L. E. MASSIE and E. F. KOTNIK, *AIEE Transactions — Applications and Industry,* vol. 77, pt. 2, No. 39, Nov. 1958, pp. 305-307.

"Magnetic Amplifier Operated Relays for Aircraft and Missiles," A. O. ADAMS, *Electronic Industries,* Dec. 1958, pp. 72-74.

"Relay Coil Surge Voltage Effects at High Altitudes," K. B. AUSTIN, Relay Conference, 1959.

"Large Bomber Aircraft Requirements for Relays," F. M. KINNEY, Relay Conference, 1959.

"Static vs. Relay Logic for Aircraft Protective Panels," W. O. HANSEN and J. PAPA, *Electrical Engineering,* Nov. 1960, pp. 899-902 (AIEE CP 60-1045).

"Relays in Space Systems," W. T. WEIR, Relay Conference, 1961.

"An Integrated Parts Model for Space Systems Development," W. T. WEIR, E. KARMIOL, and J. YOUTCHEFF, Relay Conference, 1962.

"Choosing Airborne Relays," E. U. THOMAS and J. V. IVERSON, *Space/Aeronautics,* May 1962, p. 91.

"Some Considerations of Power Switching with Sealed Relays in Spacecraft Systems," S. D. MARKS and D. R. SAEWERT, Relay Conference, 1963.

"Status Report on Manned Space Flight," J. T. GILSTRAP, Relay Conference, 1964.

"Relay Coil Temperature Rise at Simulated Outer Space Pressure Levels," RICHARD J. BACKE, Relay Conference, 1969.

"Requirements for Relays in Spacecraft Having Magnetic Field Constraints," JAMES L. SWYLER, Relay Conference, 1969.

3   Arc suppression systems

"Spark Quenching at Relay Contacts Interrupting DC Circuits," A. HAMILTON and R. W. SILLARS, *Proceedings, Institution of Electrical Engineers,* March 1949, vol. 96, pt. I, pp. 64-76.

"Telephone Type Relays: Arc Suppression and Contacts," V. E. JAMES, *Product Engineering,* Feb. 1951, vol. 22, pp. 136-140.

"Arc Suppression with Semiconductor Devices," F. W. PARRISH, *Electrical Manufacturing,* June 1956, pp. 127-131.

"P-N Junction Arc Suppressor," W. MILLER, Relay Conference, 1957.

"Arc Suppression for Relay Contacts in DC Service," W. J. GODSEY, *IRE Transactions on Component Parts,* CP 4 No. 2, June 1957, pp. 36-42.

"Relay Contact Protection for DC Application," L. W. HILL, Relay Conference, 1958.

"Arc Suppression Techniques," R. B. Taylor, *Automatic Control,* April 1958.

"Small Lightweight R-F Interference Suppressors Using Transistors," W. PECOTA, *IRE National Convention Record,* vol. 6, pt. 8, 1958.

"Report on Arc Suppression for Relay Contacts," R. GREEN and A. P. BOYLAN, *ASTIA Report 227716,* Aug. 1959.

"Determination of RC Type Spark Quenchers for Different Load Conditions," O. DE-MAYER, Relay Conference, 1960.

"Evaluation of Arc and Electro-Interference Suppression in DC Relays in the Datico Mark 3 System," *ASTIA Report 282570,* Nov. 1960.

"Using Varistors to Suppress Relay Sparking," R. DE PROOST and R. SERVANCKX, *Electronics,* Jan. 20, 1961, pp. 68:70, 72.

"R-C Networks for Relay Contact Protection," *Military Systems Design,* July-Aug. 1961.

"Suppression of Inductive Loaded Contact Interference with Zener Diodes," W. JARVA, *TM-1103-1,* Filtron Co. Inc., Aug. 8, 1961.

"For Relay Circuits — How to Suppress the Arc," *Electronic Industries,* June 1962, pp. 12-13.

"Voltage Suppression with PTC Thermistors," A. HEMEL, *Electronic Design,* Aug. 2, 1962.

"Transistor Switch Cuts Arcing, Increases Relay Sensitivity," P. CUTLER, *Electronic Design,* March 1, 1963.

"Some Considerations of the Design Criteria of the Spark Quenching Circuits," S. MITANI and Y. ARAKI, Relay Conference, 1964.

"Miniaturized Suppression Components for Relay Interference Reduction," E. BUSCH and A. L. ALBIN, 1965 National Relay Conference.

"Contact Protection for Miniature Reed Switch," R. S. GOMEZ, 1965 National Relay Conference.

"Curing (RF) Interference in Relay Systems: Look to the Source, Then Suppress," S. J. BURRUANO, *Electronic Design,* Nov. 29, 1965, pp. 37-43.

4 Communication (telephone, telegraph, radio) applications

"The Principles of Relay Timing in Connection with Automatic Telephone Circuits," T. H. TURNEY, *Journal of the IEEE,* 1928, vol. 66, pp. 341-384.

"Control of Release Time of Relays in Automatic Telephone Systems," R. ST. G. TERRY, *Electrical Communication,* July 1929, vol. 8, pp. 9-15.

"Anti-Electrolysis Relay," DAVIS and WAINWRIGHT, *Electronics,* March 1942, p. 72.

"Relay Preference Lockout Circuits in Telephone Switching," A. E. JOEL, JR., *Transactions of the AIEE,* vol. 67, pp. 1720-1725, 1948.

"The 'Director' for Automatic Telephone Switching Systems," A. B. SMITH, *AIEE Transactions,* June 1948, p. 539.

"Ground Relay Protection," G. R. MC DONALD, *Mechanical and Electrical Engineering,* Sept. 1952, vol. 126, pp. 70-74.

"Versatile Phase - Comparison Carrier - Current Relaying System," N. O. RICE and J. S. SMITH, *Radio Communication,* Sept. 1952, vol. 12, pp. 27-28.

"Microwave Protective Relaying," H. W. LENSNER, *Radio Communication,* Dec. 1952.

"Selection of a Relaying System," R. C. CHEEK and J. L. BLACKBURN, *Communication Engineering,* Jan. 1953, pp. 13:30-33.

"Pulse-Operated Relays for the Ham Transmitter," C. H. ERICSON, *QST,* June 1953, pp. 34:44-45.

"Conelrad Switcher for Sequential Mode, Time-Delay Relay Circuits," N. J. THOMPSON, *Electronics,* Dec. 1953, vol. 26, pp. 158-159.

"Economics of Telephone Relay Applications," H. N. WAGAR, *Bell System Technical Journal,* Jan. 1954, vol. 33, pp. 218-256.

"Broadcasting Transmitter Switching System Uses Antenna - Change-over Relay," F. KNAACK, *Electronics,* March 1954, vol. 27, p. 192.

"Conelrad Monitor," L. D. OLIPHANT, *Radio and TV,* Jan. 1955, vol. 99, p. 100.

"Telephone Switching Network and Its Electronic Controls," S. T. BREWER and G. HECHT, *Bell System Technical Journal,* March 1955, vol. 34, pp. 361-402.

"The Full Stature of the Cross-bar Tandem Switching System," J. MESZAR, *AIEE: Communication and Electronics,* Sept. 1956, pp. 486-496.

"Electronics in Telephone Switching Systems," A. E. JOEL, *AIEE: Communication and Electronics,* Jan. 1957, pp. 701-710.

"Inverse-Time Underfrequency Relay," R. G. HOFT, *AIEE: Communication and Electronics,* Jan. 1957, pp. 625-629.

"Coaxial Relays for Antenna Switching in 2-Way Mobile Radio," H. LAUFFENBERGER, Relay Conference, 1958.

"Comparison of Various Types of Receiving Relays for Carrier Telegraph and Carrier Telephone System," H. HAMMANO, Y. HOSOKAWA, and H. KIKUCHI, Relay Conference, 1959.

"Relays for Telegraph and Signaling Equipment," D. MURMANO, *Siemens Reviews,* vol. 28, No. 8, 1961, pp. 255-260.

"Comparator Relays Reduce Data Link Cabling," N. ANNIS, *Control Engineering,* Aug. 1963, p. 98.

"Analysis of Faults in Automatic Switching Equipment," T. WATANABE, 1965 National Relay Conference (Second International Conference on Electromagnetic Relays).

"Dial Impulse Receiving Circuit Utilizing Mercury Contact Relay," J. TASHIRO, 1965 National Relay Conference (Second International Conference on Electromechanical Relays).

"Mechanical Latching Crossbar Switch," SHOJI MITSUISHI, MASAD TAKAMURA, ICHIZO NAKANO, YUICHI SHIMIZU, YUJI OTSUKA, Relay Conference, 1969.

5. Computers, encoders, memories

"Use of Relay Digital Computer," E. G. ANDREWS and H. W. BODE, *Electrical Engineering,* vol. 69, Feb. 1950, pp. 158-163.

"A Relay Computer for General Application," S. B. WILLIAMS, *Bell Laboratories Record,* Feb. 1947, vol. 25, pp. 49-54.

"Use of High Speed Relays in Electric Analog Computers," R. R. BENNETT and A. S. FULTON, *Electrical Engineering,* Dec. 1951, vol. 70, p. 1083.

"Computer Switching with Semiconductors and Relays," G. L. LA PORTE and R. A. MARCOTLE, *Electronics,* Aug. 14, 1959, pp. 64-65.

"A Method for Evaluating Relays for Analog Computer Integrating Networks," R. A. NEWELL and J. KEELY, Relay Conference, 1960.

"Voltage-to-Digits Conversion With Relays," T. L. GREENWOOD, *Electronics,* Jan. 13, 1961, pp. 96-98.

"Simple Decimal to Binary Encoder, Using Relays," D. NAIRN, *Electronic Engineering* (London), April 1963, pp. 232-235.

"Economical Magnetic Memory Device," W. CHOW and A. R. LUCAS, Relay Conference, 1963.

"Don't Dismiss the Relay for Data Processing Systems," G. SILVERMAN, *Electronic Design,* Nov. 29, 1965, pp. 24-29.

6 Control systems

"Applying Magnetic Relays for Sensitive Control," A. H. LAMB, *Electronics,* Feb. 1941, vol. 14, pp. 31-33.

"Experience with Relays in Heater Circuits," O. S. GIBBS, *Science,* May 1947, vol. 105, pp. 574-575.

"R-F Operated Remote Control Relay," D. G. FINK, *Electronics,* Sept. 1947, vol. 20, pp. 114-116.

"How to Select and Maintain Definite-Time-Control Relays," R. B. TAYLOR, *Factory Management and Maintenance,* Dec. 1947, vol. 105, pp. 102-106.

"Relay Control Circuits for Stepping Switches," C. J. DORR and H. W. WEST, *Electronics,* Jan. 1948, vol. 21, p. 158.

"The Design of Contactors with Regard to Their Industrial Application," B. FELDBAUVER, *AIEE Transactions, 1948,* vol. 95, pt. II, pp. 439-451.

"Stepping Relays," J. P. LAIRD, *Machine Design,* April 1949, vol. 21, pp. 133-138.

"Sequential Aspects of Relay Circuits," A. E. RITCHIE, *Transactions of the AIEE,* 1949, vol. 68, pp. 577-581.

"Selecting Magnetic Relays for Industrial Control Circuits," H. F. LITTLEJOHN, JR., *Product Engineering,* Sept. 1949, vol. 20, pp. 89-93, Oct. 1949, pp. 140-145.

"Relay Circuit Ideas Taken from Telephone Practice," L. F. CRABTREE, *Electrical Manufacturing,* May 1950, vol. 45, pp. 112-116, 188.

"Relay Servomechanisms," T. A. ROGERS and W. C. HURTY, *Transactions of the ASME,* Nov. 1950, vol. 72, pp. 1163-1172.

"Design and Application of Electric Switching Relays for Industrial Control Systems," E. B. SHECKER, *Instrumentation,* Fourth Quarter 1950, vol. 5, pp. 31-33.

"Performance of Magnetic Control Devices," M. MORGAN, *Electrical Manufacturing,* Dec. 1950, vol. 46, pp. 100-104.

"Application of Industrial Control Relays," B. H. CARLISLE, *Iron and Steel Engineer,* Nov. 1950, vol. 27, pp. 119-125.

"Carrier-Controlled Relay Servos," J. C. LOZIER, *Electronic Engineering,* Dec. 1950, vol. 69, pp. 1052-1056.

"Making Electrical Contacts Stand up in Control Service," F. E. REEVES, *Electrical Manufacturing,* Jan. 1951, vol. 47, p. 102.

"Relay Circuit Ideas From Miniature Train Control," W. K. WALTERS, *Electrical Manufacturing,* March 1951, vol. 47, pp. 68-69.

"Sensitive Relays in Process Control," R. T. PIERCE, *Electrical Engineering,* July 1951, vol. 70, pp. 625-626.

"L-V Relays Cinch Lamp Switching," J. SPARKS, *Power,* Feb. 1952, vol. 96, pp. 124-125.

"Relay Circuits for Operating Oil Burner Controls," W. G. HOLZBACK, *Heating and Ventilating,* Aug. 1952, vol. 49, pp. 71-77.

"Speed-Sensing Relay," J. H. PORTER, *Electronics,* Nov. 1952, pp. 25:174.

"Contactor Amplifiers for Automatic Control," S. DAVIS, *Product Engineering,* March 1953, pp. 24:186-194.

"Automatic Relay Control," E. BROOKE, *Machine Design,* April 1953, pp. 25:154-158.

"Circuits and Applications of Contactor Control Devices," S. DAVIS and A. GRONNER, *Product Engineering,* April 1953, pp. 24:204-213.

"Qualification Testing of Control Relays," R. H. SCHUMANN, *Electrical Manufacturing,* June 1953, p. 113.

"Relay for Automatic Power Factor Correction," CHAMBERLAIN and HOOKHAN, *Engineer,* Nov. 13 and Nov. 20, 1953, vol. 196, pp. 625-626 and 671.

"Phase Transducer Uses High-Speed Relay," D. E. S. ISLE, *Electronics,* Jan. 1954, vol. 27, p. 234.

"Capacitor Control Relay," FERRANTE, *Engineer,* Feb. 12, 1954, vol. 197, p. 245.

"Dual Voltage Operation of Relays and Crossbar Switches," A. C. WEHRING and E. L. IRWIN, *Bell System Technical Journal,* Nov. 1955, pp. 34:1225-1240.

"Stabilized D-C Crane Hoist Control," K. S. KUKA, *Iron and Steel Engineer,* Feb. 1956, pp. 86-95.

"Simplification of Control Circuits," W. H. T. HOLDEN, *Electrical Manufacturing,* April 1956, p. 828.

"Application of Small Relays to Industrial Process Control," R. H. LEE, Relay Conference, 1956.

"Relay Matrices Analyze Tape Data in Automatic Lathe," Staff Report, *Electrical Manufacturing,* Oct. 1956, p. 140.

"Relays and Contactors," A. E. MORRIS, *Applied Hydraulics,* March 1957.

"Relay Memory Directs Automatic Interfloor Conveyor," Staff Report, *Electrical Manufacturing,* April 1957, p. 110.

"Practical Aspects of Relay or Pulse Servomechanisms," H. ADKINS, ASME Paper No. 57, IRD-5, April 1957.

"Magnetic Amplifier Operated Relays," A. O. ADAMS, Relay Conference, 1957.

"Stepping Relays for Automatic Operations Formerly Assigned to People," V. E. JAMES, *Product Engineering,* Nov. 11, 1957, pp. 101-105.

"Crossbar Switch Applications," (Industrial), K. ENSLEIN, *Electrical Manufacturing,* April 1958, p. 86.

"Meter Relay Control of Ball Grinding Process," *Automation,* Nov. 1958, pp. 67-68.

"Copying Lathe Programmed by Stepping Switches," R. T. FENN, *Electrical Manufacturing,* March 1959, p. 86.

"Effects of Shunting Circuits on Relay Operation," L. D. DE LALIO, Relay Conference, 1959.

"Single-Pulse Operation of DC Relays," L. B. STEIN, Relay Conference, 1959.

"Relays Keep the Bettors Happy : Totalizator System," L. H. YOUNG, *Control Engineering,* Sept. 1959, pp. 36-39.

"Dual-Mode Relay Servos," R. H. BULAND and N. FURUMOTO, *AIEE Applications and Industry,* Jan. 1960, pp. 405-411.

"Basic Relay Circuits," L. B. MITCHELL, *Automation,* 1960 Series, Jan. pp. 57-60, Feb. pp. 93-96, March pp. 87-90.

"Optimum Response Relay Servos," J. B. LEWIS, *Control Engineering,* 1960 Series, May pp. 125-129, July pp. 77-84, Oct. pp. 129-132.

"Using Relay Control Effectively," Z. SMITH, *Automation,* Oct. 1960, pp. 101-106.

"Applying Electrical Controls: Relay Circuits and Limit Switches," D. FITZPATRICK, *Hydraulics and Pneumatics,* Nov. 1960, p. 88.

"Photoreed: A New Versatile Frequency Sensitive Control Element," H. W. INDERWIESEN, *Electronics,* Sept. 8, 1961, p. 88.

"D-C Differential Relay," G. L. MARTHINRISS, *Iron and Steel Engineer,* Nov. 1961, pp. 164-167.

"Precision Positioning Employing Relay Philosophy and Relay Techniques," H. C. ROBERTS, Relay Conference, 1962.

"Considerations in Pulse Operation of Micro-Miniature Latching Relays," H. O. WELLS, Relay Conference, 1962.

"Time-Delay Relay Helps Spinner Match Stub

Lengths," *Textile Industries,* May 1962, p. 163.

"Voltage-Sensitive Relay Circuit with Adjustable Operating Parameters," P. C. CARINGELLA, *Review of Scientific Instruments,* Sept. 1963, pp. 66-68.

"Electrical Controls: Relays," *Machine Design,* Dec. 31, 1964, pp. 57-90.

"Low-Voltage Lighting Control: Relay Switching," D. F. KLINGENHAGEN and R. K. KOESTNER, *Electrical Construction and Maintenance,* Jan. 1965, pp. 82-85.

7 Counting functions

"Predetermined Counter for Process Control," R. J. BLUME, *Electronics,* Feb. 1948, vol. 21, pp. 88-93.

"Counting with Relays," G. R. FROST, *Transactions of the AIEE,* vol. 68, pt. I, pp. 587-591, 1949.

"Relays Used in Counters and Recording Cup-anemometers," J. L. FRENCH and G. M. LANE, *Journal of Scientific Instruments,* May 1949, vol. 26, p. 160.

"Electrical Count Control Devices," F. E. REEVES, *Electrical Manufacturing,* Nov. 1949, vol. 44, pp. 71-75.

"Counting Devices with Control Functions," *Electrical Manufacturing,* Jan. 1950, p. 102.

"Floating Zero Matrix Established by 'Unipulser' Circuits," K. STEINER, Relay Conference, 1966.

8 Low level (dry circuit) applications

"The Effects of Temperature, A.C. and D.C. Loads on Relays in Dry Circuit Applications," L. TARTAKOWSKY, Relay Conference, 1956.

"Evaluation of Relays for Low-Level Switching," V. F. ARGENTO, *Sperry Engineering Review, July-Aug.* 1956, pp. 18-22.

"Investigations in Low Energy Level Circuits," S. T. EAST, Relay Conference, 1957.

"Technique to Validate Relays Switching Low Energy," L. L. MONTAGUE, Relay Conference, 1957.

"Behind the Dry Circuit Curtain," J. SCHMIDT, Relay Conference, 1957.

"The Dry Circuit Problem," W. A. SCISM, JR., *Electrical Manufacturing,* Jan. 1957, p. 111.

"An Evaluation of Relays for Dry Circuit Switching," V. F. ARGENTO, Relay Conference, 1957.

"Dry Circuit Test Procedures," W. B. LURIE, Relay Conference, 1958.

"Dry Circuit Test Procedures and Equipment Proposed for Air Force Consideration," E. R. DUBAS, Relay Conference, 1961.

"A New DC Dry Circuit Testing Technique," E. G. TUTLE, Relay Conference, 1962.

"Relays That Challenge Semiconductors," W.

HOLCOMBE, *Electronics,* March 23, 1964.

"Projections in Control Equipment: Low Level Switching," *Control Engineering,* Jan. 1965, pp. 106-107.

9   Electronic circuits

"Relays for Tube Circuits," B. DUDLEY, *Electronics,* May 1938, p. 18.

"Telephone-Type Relays in Electronic Circuits," DORR and GALTON, *Electronic Industries,* March 1943, p. 68.

"Relays in Industrial Tube Circuits," U. R. FURST, *Electronics,* Dec. 1944, vol. 17, pp. 134-137, and Jan. 1945, vol. 18, pp. 136-138.

"Telephone Relays and Their Use in Electronic Circuits," A. A. CHUBB, *Electronic Engineering,* June and July 1947, vol. 19, pp. 172-177, 211-213.

"Counter Circuits for Television," A. EASTON and P. H. ODESSAY, *Electronics,* 1949, vol. 21, pp. 120-123.

"Photo-electric Relays," S. A. MORRIS, *Mechanical World,* Aug. 1950, vol. 128, pp. 177-181, and Sept. 1950, pp. 205-207, 215-216.

"Transistor-Operated Photocell Relay," L. E. GARNER, JR., *Radio and TV News,* March 1953, pp. 49:64-65.

"Using a Transistor to Increase Relay Sensitivity," L. E. GARNER, JR., *Radio and TV News,* June 1953, pp. 49:39.

"Relay Unit for Time Signal Receiver," J. HERS, *Journal of Scientific Instruments,* April 1954, vol. 31, pp. 146-147.

"Signal Overload Relay for Television Receivers," C. MASUCCI and OTHERS, *Electronics,* April 1954, vol. 27, pp. 153-155.

"TV Outage Alarm," G. WASLO, *Radio and TV News,* July 1954, vol. 52, p. 12.

"Cold-Cathode Electronic Relay," F. A. LEISEY, *Analytical Chemistry,* Sept. 1954, p. 1527.

"Relays in Electron Tube Circuits," A. LEEN, *Electrical Manufacturing,* July 1955, pp. 114-119.

"Photoelectric Relays and Circuits," G. F. BALL, *Product Engineering,* mid Oct. 1955, pp. 26:1, 29:31.

"Detecting Infra-red Radiation; Sensitive Electronics Relays," *Engineer,* Nov. 1955.

"Transistor Amplifier Operates Relay on 20 Ma Current," C. F. KEZER and M. H. ARONSON, *Instruments and Control Systems,* April 1959, p. 553.

"Small Photoconductive Cell Controls Relay," W. GRABOWSIC and OTHERS, *Instruments and Control Systems,* Jan. 1960, pp. 108-109.

"Miniature Relays for Use in Electronic Equipment," N. E. HYDE, *Research,* March 1960.

"Transistor-Relay Hybrids for Close Differential Switching," A. N. DESAUTELS, *Control Engineering,* April 1960, pp. 151-153.

"Electromechanical Devices and Systems for Electronics" (contact capsules for switching), M. F. TOMANIO and G. J. FLYNN, *Electronics,* Sept. 30, 1960, pp. 62-64.

"Proximity Relay," L. J. D'AIRO, *Radio Electronics,* Sept. 1960, pp. 48-49.

"Zener Diodes as Coupling Elements in Relay Circuits," F. NIBLER, *Review of Scientific Instruments,* Oct. 1961, p. 1143.

"Minimizing Residual Current in Transistor Relay Circuits," I. M. GOTTLEIB, *Electronic Industries,* June 1962, p. F14-15.

"Use of D-C Relays in Home Audio Systems," F. F. CHEN, *Audio,* Sept. 1962, pp. 27-28.

"Transistorized RC Time Delay Relays," W. PECOTA, Relay Conference, 1963.

10   Instrument and meter relay applications

"Ultra-Sensitive Control Relays of Instrument Type," A. H. LAMB, *Electrical Manufacturing,* Dec. 1947, vol. 4, pp. 74-78.

"Differential and Ratio Applications of Weston Relays," E. G. DE MOTT, *Weston Engineering Notes,* Nov. 1950, vol. 5, p. 4.

"Instruments with Control Functions," B. THOMPSON, *Electrical Manufacturing,* April 1951, p. 132.

"The Functioning and Utilization of Contact-Meter-Relays with Electro-Magnetically Locking Contacts," P. M. SAINT-AMOUR, Relay Conference, 1953.

"Construction and Application of a Moving Magnet Instrument Type Relay," J. A. GARRATT, Relay Conference, 1954.

"Applying Meter Relays," P. M. SAINT-AMOUR, *Machine Design,* Jan. 10, 1957.

"Contact-Making Meters as Controllers," S. W. ECKETT, *Automation Progress* (London), Feb. 1959, pp. 66-69.

"Continuous Reading Meter Relays," *Electronic Industries,* Dec. 1959, p. 102.

"Choosing the Right Type of Meter Relay," J. F. SCHMIDHEINI, *Control Engineering,* July 1962, pp. 77-81.

11   Mercury plunger relay applications

"Application of the Plunger Type Relay," R. S. WARREN, Relay Conference, 1953.

"Mercury Plunger Relays," K. D. FLAMM, *Product Engineering,* March 1956, pp. 182-187.

"Try Mercury Plunger Relays," J. J. BERNSTEIN, *Electrical Manufacturing,* Nov. 1957, p. 152.

"Mercury Plunger Relays," *Electric Controls Book, Machine Design,* June 14, 1962, pp. 88-94.

12   Motor control and protection

"Sequenced Motor Controls," R. H. MECKLENBORG, *Electrical Manufacturing,* Sept. 1948, vol. 42, pp. 120-124.

"Overload Relays for Motor Protection," L. E. DAEHLER, *Product Engineering,* Aug. 1952, vol. 23, pp. 130-137.

"Direct-Current Relays and Devices for Industrial Motor Controllers," R. B. IMMEL, *Product Engineering,* Dec. 1952, pp. 23:181-193.

"Motor Overload Relays," J. SHEETS, *Product Engineering,* Jan. 1955, vol. 26, pp. 177-181.

"Overload Relays for Hermetic Motors," R. S. KURTZ, *Electrical Manufacturing,* Feb. 1955, p. 76.

"Safety in D-C Motor Controls," T. C. BEEMAN and R. H. KANTNER, *Product Engineering,* pp. 26:193-198, Dec. 1955.

"AC Motor Protection," D. T. BLIZZARD, *IEEE Transactions on Aerospace,* vol. AS-1, Aug. 1963, pp. 1137-1144.

"Survey of Electric Motor Protection," *Machine Design,* Aug. 13, 1964, pp. 143-158.

13   Protective circuits

"Thermionic Delay Relays for Cathode Protection," L. D. MILES and M. M. MORBACK, *Electronics,* April 1935, pp. 124-125.

"Ultra High-Speed Relays in the Fields of Protection and Measurement," W. CASSON and F. H. LAST, *Proceedings of the IEEE,* Feb. 1949, pp. 50-56.

"Matching Fully Magnetic Circuit Breakers to the Application," N. J. SCHWARTZ, *Electrical Manufacturing,* June 1952, p. 118.

"Thermal Relay Gives Overload Indication," J. F. BRUBAKER and E. A. THOMPSON, *Electrical World,* Oct. 20, 1952, vol. 138, p. 132.

"Circuit Breakers for Electronic Circuits," F. M. BALLOU, *Electrical Manufacturing,* Jan. 1953, p. 90.

"Protective Time Delay Circuit for a Thyratron Relay," S. H. GROSS, *Journal of Scientific Instruments,* Nov. 1953, vol. 30, pp. 434-435.

"High-Speed Balanced Current Protective System Using Biased and Unbiased Relays," J. RUSHTON, *Electrical Journal,* Nov. 1953, vol. 151, pp. 1660-1665.

"Check Your Overload Relays and Avoid Costly Shutdowns," D. POLLOCK and D. KIEFER, *Factory Management,* May 1954, vol. 112, p. 118-119.

"Capacitance Relay Serves as Pump-Seal Failure Detector," W. B. JARZEMBSKI, *Oil and Gas Journal,* Jan. 1956, pp. 54167-54168.

"Electronic Over-Current Relay for Electrical Machines," F. S. H. GOODALL and G. S. CHAPMAN, *Inst. E. E. Proceedings,* Aug. 1956, pp. 103:A:375-378.

"Meter Relay Protects Punch Presses," F. C. MARX, *Control Engineering,* July 1959, p. 129.

"How to Select Overcurrent Relay Characteristics," D. V. FAWCETT, *IEEE Transactions — Applications and Industry,* May 1963, pp. 94-99, discussion pp. 99-104.

"How to Field Test Electrical Protective Relays," E. R. REDHAMMER and D. E. GROSS, *Coal Age,* July 1963, pp. 90-94.

"New Current Balance Relays Make Electricity Safer," E. BOYCE, *Factory and Plant,* May 1964, pp. 62-63.

14   Railroad equipment applications

"The Wheatstone Bridge Applied to Train Braking," C. M. HINES, *AIEE Transactions,* April 1948, p. 317.

"Diesel-Electrics; How to Keep'em Rolling; Contactors and Relays," B. L. JUDY and P. W. PELTON, *Railway Mechanical and Electrical Engineer,* Aug. 1952, vol. 126, pp. 89-94.

"Diesel-Electric Locomotive Ground Relays," G. R. MC DONALD, *Electrical Engineering,* Oct. 1953, vol. 72, p. 877.

15   Reed relay applications

"The Dry Reed Logic and Memory Unit," R. TEVONIAN, *Western Electric Engineer,* April 1960, pp. 43-47.

"The Design and Application of Dry Reed Relays to an Electronic Switching System," J. C. DIETZ, Relay Conference, 1961.

"Reed Logic," L. A. BURNETT, *Electro-Technology,* March 1963, p. 120.

"Applications and Characteristics of Dry Reed Relays," D. BALLINGER, Relay Conference, 1963.

"Dry Reed Switches and Switch Modules," L. D. DUMBAULD, *Control Engineering,* July 1963, pp. 75-108.

Bibliography of Reed-Type Contacts and Devices, J. N. PEARSE, *IEEE Transactions on Parts, Materials and Packaging,* vol. PMP-3, No. 3, September 1967. Includes a list of 164 U.S. patents.

16   Thermal relay applications

"Some Notes on the Design and Application of Electro-Thermal Relays," J. J. DIETZ, Relay Conference, 1954.

"How to Apply Thermal Relays," A. LEEN, *Electrical Manufacturing,* Nov. 1954, pp. 103-108.

"Thermal Relays Perform Unique Functions," J. D. MARKS, *Electrical Manufacturing,* Jan. 1958, p. 109.

17   Time delay and timing functions

"Time Delay in Resistance-Capacity Circuits," KELLOGG and PHELPS, *Electronics,* Feb. 1937, p. 22.

"Time-Delay Circuits," C. FELSTED, *Electronics,* March 1938, p. 38.

"Capacitor Relay Timing," C. STANSBURY and T. B. JOCHEM, *AIEE Transactions,* 1940, vol. 59, pp. 65-70.

"Low - Frequency Timing Circuits," C. E. BERRY, *Electronics,* Oct. 1942, p. 84.

"Time-Delay Electronic Relays," F. A. ANNET, *Power,* Sept. 1949, vol. 93, p. 126.

"Electronic Timers," T. W. MACIEJOWSKI, *Microtecnic,* 1951, vol. 5. pp. 208-224.

"Timing Relays; Their Selection and Application in Electrical Control Circuits," J. C. PONSTINGL, *Machine Design,* April 1951, vol. 23, pp. 131-134.

"Condenser Time Delay," J. HOWLE, *Radio and TV News,* Feb. 1952, vol. 47, p. 144.

"Electronic Time Delay Relay Circuit," G. H. BATEMAN, *Tele-Tech,* Oct. 1953, vol. 12, pp. 94-96.

"Simple Time-Delay Relay," E. D. MORGAN, *Electronics,* April 1954, vol. 27, pp. 178-179.

"Relay Time Delay Techniques," J. F. RINKE, Relay Conference, 1955.

"Your Choice of Recycling Timers," E. F. KING, *Product Engineering,* Aug. 8, 1960, pp. 48-49.

"Relay Uses Transistor Timing Circuit for Adjustable Delay," R. S. KURTZ, *Electro-Technology,* Dec. 1960, p. 206.

Circuits and Switching Theory and Analysis

18 General

"A Symbolic Analysis of Relay and Switching Circuits," (Application of Boolean Algebra), C. E. SHANNON, *Transactions of the AIEE,* 1938, vol. 57, p. 713.

"Philosophy of Relaying," E. W. KNAPP and B. C. HICKS, *Electrical Engineering,* Nov. 1946, vol. 65, pp. 735-741.

"Relay Trees and Symmetric Circuits," S. H. WASHBURN, *Transactions of the AIEE,* 1949, vol. 68, pt. I, pp. 582-586, 587-591.

"Logic of Relay Circuits," W. KEISTER, *Transactions of the AIEE,* 1949, vol. 68, pp. 571-576.

"A Contribution to the Algebra of Relay and Switch Contacts," G. H. BUFFERY, *Proceedings of the IEE,* 1950, vol. 97, pp. 357-363.

"Sketch for Algebra of Relay and Contactor Circuits," G. A. MONTGOMERIE, *Radio and Communication Engineering,* Jan. 1951, No. 51, pp. 75-76.

"A Symbolic Method for the Solution of Some Switching and Relay-Circuit Problems," I. A. D. LEWIS, *Proceedings of the IEEE,* May 1951, vol. 98, pp. 181-191.

"Boolean Matrices and Design of Combinational Relay Switching Circuits," F. E. HOHN and L. R. SCHISSLER, *Bell System Technical Journal,* Jan. 1955, pp. 177-202.

"Switching Systems and Systems Concepts," J. L. WIMPEY, Relay Conference, 1955.

"Analytical Method for the Design of Relay Servomechanisms," J. E. HART, *Electrical Engineering,* Nov. 1955, pp. 74:1009.

"Analyzing Relay Networks," R. E. MARKLE, *Electrical Manufacturing,* Sept. 1956, pp. 124-129.

"Switching Logic Functions," J. SHEETS and R. A. BROWN, *Product Engineering,* Aug. 1957, pp. 196-200.

"Minimizing Partially Developed Relay Tree Circuits," M. P. MARCUS, *Electrical Manufacturing,* Aug. 1957, p. 102.

"Numerical Graphical Method for Synthesizing Switching Circuits," A. H. SCHEINMAN, *AIEE Transactions,* vol. 76, pt. I (Communication and Electronics), No. 34, Jan. 1958, pp. 687-689.

"Solution of Logic Problems by Means of Relays, D. D. LINGELBACH and C. C. FREENY, Relay Conference, 1958.

"Mechanical Method for Designing Switching Circuits," J. H. WALLACE, *Western Electric Engineer,* Oct. 1958, pp. 43-48.

"Ancient Relays to Modern Logic," P. T. MILLUNZI, Relay Conference, 1960.

"A New Concept in Relay Logic Modules," W. L. DEEG, Relay Conference, 1961.

"A New Method for Calculating Circuits for Maximum Relay Speeds," F. F. YANIKOSKI, Relay Conference, 1961.

"Simple Mercury Relay Pulse Generator," J. M. BLAIR, *American Journal of Physics,* Sept. 1961, Suppl. 17.

"Relay Matrix Design for Automatic Checkout Systems," H. CARTER, Relay Conference, 1962.

"Stability-Boundary Approximations for Relay-Control Systems via Steepest-Ascent Construction of Liapunor Functions," S. WEISSENBERGER, 1965 Joint Automatic Control Conference, Troy, N. Y., June 22-25.

"You'd Think They *Invented* Logic," R. E. STOFFELS, Relay Conference, 1966.

"Applying Relays for Reliable and Safe Performance," P. N. MARTIN, Relay Conference, 1967.

Contacts

19 General

"Fundamentals of Blow-Out Structures," L. G. RILEY, *Electrical Journal,* vol. 25, pp. 485-489, 553-554, 1928.

"A Study of Contact Reliability," R. R. FOWLER, *Strowger Technical Journal,* vol. 5, pp. 13-16, 30-32, 1936; vol. 6, pp. 9-16.

"Electrical Contacts—Factors Affecting Their Life and Performance," K. L. EMMERT, J. W. WIGGS and V. E. HEIL, Parts I and II, *Product Engineering,* 1939, vol. 10, Nos. 5 and 6, pp. 194, 249.

"Contacts That Don't Bounce," *Electrical Journal,* vol. 36, p. 12, 1939.

"Before You Specify Electrical Contacts," K. L. EMMERT, J. W. WIGGS, and V. E. HEIL, *Electrical Manufacturing,* Dec. 1939, vol. 24, No. 6, p. 42.

"Design of Heavy Current Contacts, Particularly for Radio-Frequency Use," A. J. MADDOCK, *Institute of Electrical Engineers Proceedings,* Jan. 1947, vol. 94, pt. 3, pp. 52-54.

"Some Design Considerations for Electrical Contact Operation," R. B. IMMEL, *Product Engineering,* Feb. 1947, vol. 18, pp. 107-112.

"Contacts," P. W. SWENSON, *Bell Laboratories Record,* Feb. 1949, vol. 27, pp. 50-53.

"Contact Transients in Simple Electrical Circuits," F. E. MARTIN and H. E. STAUSS, *Electrical Engineer,* Dec. 1951, vol. 70, p. 1039.

"Electric Contacts in Electronic Relay Applications," S. T. EAST, Relay Conference, 1954.

"Microcontacts," A. L. VAN EMDEN; "Historical Variation in Microcontacts," A. H. LAMB; "Configuration in Microcontacts," W. D. KINGSLOVING, 1954 *Proceedings: Engineering Seminar on Electrical Contacts,* Penn. State University, State College, Pa.

"Experience with Relay Contacts in Sealed Enclosures with No Organic Materials," P. N. MARTIN, Relay Conference, 1956.

"An Effort to Promote the Selection of Reliable Contact Systems," H. P. LYNCH, Relay Conference, 1959.

"Electrical Contacts in an Electric Watch," J. A. VAN HORN, Relay Conference, 1959.

"Contact Research Expanded" (Report of Engineering Seminar on Electrical Contacts held at Penn. State University), *Electrical Manufacturing,* Aug. 1959, p. 132.

"Design and Testing of Semi-Permanent Metallic Contacts for Use at Low Voltages," A. FAIRWEATHER and E. J. FROST, *Post Office Electrical Engineers Journal* (London), vol. 53, pt. 1, April 1960, pp. 26-33.

"A Practical Guide to Contact Applications," U. A. POMMERENING, Relay Conference, 1961.

"Fundamentals in the Engineering and Application of Electrical Contacts to Relay Make and Break Service Requirements," C. B. GWYN, JR., Relay Conference, 1961.

"Hazards in the Use of Double-Throw Contacts," P. N. MARTIN, Relay Conference, 1963.

"Multilayer Diffused Contacts," Y. OHKI, 1965 National Relay Conference (Second International Conference on Electromechanical Relays).

"Dynamic Analysis of Contact Separation Phenomenon in Rotary Printed Circuit Boards," H. W. SCHMITT, R. L. LOWERY, Relay Conference, 1967.

"High Production Precious Metal Contact Welding on Relay and Switch Springs," J. S. GELLATLY, Relay Conference, 1967.

20 Arcing and bridge transfer

"Extinction of Short A-C Arcs," T. E. BROWNE, JR., *Transactions AIEE,* vol. 50, pp. 1461-1465, 1931.

"The Formation of Metallic Bridges Between Separated Contacts," G. L. PEARSON, *Physical Review,* Sept. 1939.

"Bridge Erosion in Electrical Contacts and Its Prevention," W. G. PFANN, *Transactions of the AIEE,* 1948, vol. 67, pp. 1528-1533.

"Bridge Erosion of Electrical Contacts," J. J. LANDER and L. H. GERMER, *Journal of Applied Physics,* Oct. 1948, vol. 19, pp. 910-928.

"Contact Bridge Erosion and Its Prevention," W. G. PFANN, *Electrical Engineering,* March 1949, vol. 68, p. 197.

"Erosion of Electrical Contacts on Make," L. H. GERMER, F. E. HAYWORTH, and D. P. LING, *Journal of Applied Physics,* Nov. 1949, vol. 20, pp. 1085-1109.

"Arcing Phenomena at Electrical Contacts as Used in Communication Engineering," F. L. JONES, *Institute of Electrical Engineers Proceedings,* Nov. 1949, vol. 96, pt. I.

"Arcing at Electrical Contacts on Closure, Part I: Dependence Upon Surface Conditions and Surface Parameters," L. H. GERMER, *Journal of Applied Physics,* July 1951, vol. 22, p. 955.

"Arcing at Electrical Contacts on Closure, Part II," L. H. GERMER, *Journal of Applied Physics,* Sept. 1951, vol. 22, No. 9, pp. 1133-1139.

"Heat Dissipation at Electrodes of Short Electric Arc," L. H. GERMER, *Bell System Technical Journal,* Oct. 1951, vol. 30. pt. I, pp. 933-944.

"Arcing at Electrical Contacts on Closure; Development of an Arc," L. H. GERMER and J. L. SMITH, *Journal of Applied Physics,* May 1952, vol. 23, pp. 553-562.

"Electric Arcs," T. B. JONES; "Distribution of Short Arcs at Tungsten Contacts Breaking Inductive Currents," W. B. ITTNER; "Contact Transfer Deterrents," L. A. RICE; "Life of Silver Surfaced Contacts Under Repetitive Arcing Duty," W. R. WILSON; "Wear in Contacts," M. R. SWINEHART, *Proceedings: Engineering Seminar on Electrical Contacts,* July 1954, Penn. State University, State College, Pa.

"Ways and Means of Preventing Contact Welding," L. A. RICE; "Welding in Contacts," F. SPAYTH, *Proceedings: Engineering Seminar on Electrical Contacts,* 1954, Penn. State University, State College, Pa.

"Variation with Current and Inductance of Metal Transfer Between Platinum Contacts," J. RIDDLESTONE, *Institution of Electrical Engineers Proceedings* (London), vol. 102, pt. C, No. 1, March 1955 (Monograph No. 103), pp. 29-34.

"Metal Transfer Between Palladium and Silver Contacts at Low Inductances," J. RIDDLE-STONE, *British Electrical and Allied Industries Research Assn., Technical Report U/T 133,* 1955.

"Oscillographic Observation of Short Duration Arcs between Separating Platinum and Palladium Contacts," J. RIDDLESTONE, *British Electrical and Allied Industries Research Assn., Technical Report U/T 135,* 1956.

"Bridge and Short Arc Erosion of Copper, Silver and Palladium Contacts on Break," W. B. ITTNER, *Journal of Applied Physics,* vol. 27, No. 4, April 1956, pp. 382-388.

"Erosion of Electrical Contacts by Normal Arc," W. B. ITTNER and H. B. ULSH, *Institution of Electrical Engineers Proceedings* (London), vol. 104, pt. B (Radio and Electronic Engineering) No. 13, Jan. 1957, pp. 63-68.

"Varation with Current and Inductance of Metal Transfer Between Contacts of Palladium and Silver," R. I. B. COOPER and J. RIDDLESTONE, *Institution of Electrical Engineers Proceedings* (London), vol. 105, pt. C (Monograph No. 272), March 1958, pp. 212-217.

"Optical Measurement Sampling of Relay Contact Erosion," E. R. LOUREY, *Industrial Quality Control,* Aug. 1959, pp. 5-10.

"Arc Discharge at Electrical Contacts on Break," S. HOH and Y. WANTANABE, *Institute of Electrical Engineers Journal* (Japan), vol. 81, No. 875, Aug. 1961, pp. 1331-1337 (in Japanese with English summary).

"Measurement of Metal Transfer in Electrical Contacts by Radioisotope Methods," F. L. JONES, *British Journal of Applied Physics,* vol. 12, No. 9, Sept. 1961, pp. 485-489.

"Fast Growing Whiskers Near Arcing Contacts," G. R. LAWSON, Relay Conference, 1962.

"The Causes and Effects of Fretting Erosion on Contact Surfaces," H. L. WICKSTROM, Relay Conference, 1963.

"The Use of Radioactive Contact Electrodes in the Measurement of Metal Migration in Electrical Contacts," M. R. HOPKINS and C. H. JONES, *British Journal of Applied Physics,* vol. 14, p. 137, 1963.

"Matter Transfer in Contacts and the Microscopic Molten Metal Bridge, F. LLEWELLYN JONES, Relay Conference, 1964.

"The Physical Phenomena Leading to Metal Transfer Between the Electrodes of Electrical Contacts," M. R. HOPKINS, 1965 National Relay Conference (Second International Conference on Electromechanical Relays).

"Observations on Contact Erosion in Palladium and Copper-Silver Contacts," H. O. KARLSTROM, 1965 National Relay Conference (Second International Conference on Electromechanical Relays).

"The Role of the Microscopic Molten Metal Bridge in the Electrical Erosion of Contacts," M. J. PRICE, 1965 National Relay Conference (Second International Conference on Electromechanical Relays).

"Half-Crystal Can Relays Operating at 1000-Percent Overload — An Analysis of the Arc Power," W. C. MUELLER, Relay Conference, 1966.

21   Bounce and chatter effects

"The Vibration of Electric Contacts," M. N. RUSSELL and S. KEILIEN, *Transactions of the AIEE,* 1944, vol. 63, pp. 153-155.

"Relay Contact-Bounce Measurements," R. JIU, *Electronics,* Aug. 1955, vol. 28, pp. 137-139.

"Methods of Studying Contact Chatter," G. E. MORRIS, Relay Conference, 1957.

"Use of the Optron for Study of Contact Bounce and Noise," G. A. HOTHAM, Relay Conference, 1958.

"Contact Chatter of Switching Relays," M. TAKAMURA, Relay Conference, 1961.

"Contact Bounce Control," N. C. SHAW, Relay Conference, 1962.

"A Contact Bounce Measuring Instrument With Digital Readout," T. ERICKSON, Relay Conference, 1964.

"Contact Chatter Indicator," R. TETZ and R. ROTUNDA, Relay Conference, 1962.

"Measuring Relay Contact-Bounce," T. ERICKSON, *Electronic Industries,* June 1964, pp. 206-207.

"Chatter Characteristics of a Linear Viscous Damped Contact System," A. F. BAKER and R. L. LOWERY, Relay Conference, 1966.

"Contact Chatter in Rotary Printed Circuit Board Relays," H. W. SCHMITT, RICHARD L. LOWERY, Relay Conference, 1967.

"When Contact Bounce Counts," JOHN S. JORDAN, Relay Conference, 1968.

22   Contamination problems

"Relay Contact Contamination," W. D. SELLERS, Relay Conference, 1956.

"Dust on Relay Contacts," H. J. KEFFER, *Bell Laboratories Record,* Jan. 1957.

"Activation of Electrical Contacts by Organic Vapors," L. H. GERMER and J. L. SMITH, *Bell System Technical Journal,* May 1957, vol. 36, pp. 769-812.

"Organic Vapor and Relay Contacts," L. H. GERMER and J. H. SMITH, *Bell Laboratories Record,* April 1958, vol. 36, No. 4, pp. 122-126.

"Organic Deposits on Precious Metal Contacts," HERMANCE and EGAN, *Bell System Technical Journal,* May 1958, vol. 37.

"Contamination on Electrical Contacts," E. FREUDINGER, Relay Conference, 1960.

"The Effects of Contamination on Relay Performance," P. MAHLER, Relay Conference, 1960.

"Creeping Silver Sulfide," T. F. EGAN and A. MENDIZZA, *Electrochemical Society Journal,* vol. 107, No. 4, April 1960, pp. 353-354.

"Relay Contaminants — And How to Identify Them," E. F. LISH, JR., Relay Conference, 1961.

"Reduction of Contact Contamination with Activated Carbon Getters," R. J. WAGNER, A. E. SPRANDO, and J. R. LASKIE, Relay Conference, 1961.

"Mechanics of Electrical Contact Failure Caused by Surface Contamination," S. W. CHAIKIN, *Electro-Technology,* Aug. 1961, p. 70.

"Surface Films on Precious Metal Contacts," H. C. ANGUS, *British Journal of Applied Physics,* vol. 13, No. 2, Feb. 1962, pp. 58-63.

"On Corrosion of Electrical Contacts," H. KONDO, *Institute of Electrical Engineers Journal* (Japan), May 1962, pp. 733-742 (with English summary).

"Control of Contamination, Key to Reliable Relays," *Automation,* May 1962, p. 13.

"Getters Absorb Organic Contaminants," *Electronics,* Sept. 7, 1962, pp. 70-72.

"Some Materials Problems in Electrical Contacts," A. G. KEIL, *Materials Research and Standards,* June 1963, pp. 489-491.

"Effects of Air Pollution on Electrical Contacts," M. ANTLER and J. GILBERT, *Air Pollution Control Association Journal,* Sept. 1963, p. 405.

"Automated Contact Resistance Problem," M. ANTLER, L. V. AULETTA, and J. CONLEY, *Review of Scientific Instruments,* Dec. 1963, pp. 1317-1322.

"Air Pollution Effects on Electric Contact Materials," R. V. CHIARENZELLI, 1965 Seminar on Electric Contact Phenomena, Univ. of Maine, Dept. of Electrical Engrg., Orono, Me.

"Contact Performance, Residual Gases, and Sealed Contact Chambers," CHARLES P. NUNN, Relay Conference, 1967.

"Contamination of Relay Internal Ambients," W. M. CRAWFORD, B. L. WEIGAND (Ph.D) Relay Conference, 1967.

"A New Approach to the Continuity Problem of Commercial Switching Devices," CHARLES KADERBEK, Relay Conference, 1969.

23 Contact material selection

"What Contact Materials to Use and Why," *Electrical Manufacturing,* vol. 17, pp. 36-40, June 1936.

"What Metals for Electrical Contacts?," C. R. UNDERHILL, *Electrical Manufacturing,* Feb. 1942, vol. 29, pp. 52-54, 76-78, 102-108.

"Things You Should Know About Contact Assembly Methods," C. B. GWYN, JR., *Electrical Manufacturing,* Feb. 1943, vol. 31, pp. 89-92, 162-164.

"Electrical Contacts — Pt. I — Possible and Actual Materials," C. B. GWYN, JR., *Metals and Alloys,* May 1945, vol. 21, pp. 1318-1323.

"Electrical Contacts," U. R. EVANS, *Metal Industry,* July 1948, vol. 73, pp. 10-13.

"Powdered Metals in Electrical Contacts," R. K. BEGGS, *Journal of Metals,* Oct. 1951, vol. 3, pp. 860-863.

"Survey of Contact Materials," J. D. KLEIS; "Composite Contact Materials," D. K. WELLS, *Proceedings: Engineering Seminar on Electrical Contacts,* Penn. State University, State College, Pa., 1954.

"Electrical Contact Materials," J. D. KLEIS, *Electrical Manufacturing,* April 1955, pp. 102-107.

"New Developments for the Relay Industry," G. L. MCDERMOTT & JOSEPH A. WILLOUGHBY, Relay Conference, 1966.

"Precious Metal Electrodeposits," RAYMOND F. VINES, Relay Conference, 1966.

"A New Contact Material for Reed Switch and Special Relay Applications," W. JACOBS, R. KOBLER, J. MARLEY, H. R. PIEFFER, Relay Conference, 1969.

"Selecting Materials for Electrical Contacts," *Materials and Methods,* Sept. 1956, pp. 121-140.

"Electrical Contact Materials for Light-Duty Applications," L. B. HUNT, *Platinum Metals Review,* July 1957, pp. 74-81.

"How Relay Application Factors Affect Selection of Contact Materials," Z. R. SMITH, *Machine Design,* March 6, 1958, pp. 129-133.

"Let's Take Some of the Mystery Elements Out of Electrical Contacts," C. B. GWYN, JR., Relay Conference, 1960.

"Design of Light-Duty Electrical Contacts," J. G. WANT, *Platinum Metals Review,* April 1961, pp. 42-50 (see also *Mass Production,* June 1961, pp. 72-79).

"Better Metal Composites for Electrical Contacts by Two New Processes," *Materials in Design Engineering,* Feb. 1962, p. 15.

"Interesting Mechanical Physical Properties for Some Precious Metal Electrical Contact Alloys," C. BARKER, Relay Conference, 1962.

"Selecting Electrical Contacts," R. W. MEADES, *Engineering Materials and Design,* June 1962, pp. 410-416.

"Electrical Contact Materials — Properties and Selection," E. FREUDINGER, *Electro-Technology,* June 1962, p. 72.

"Spring Properties of Some Precious Metal Contact Alloys," C. S. Baker, *Englehard Industries Technical Bulletin,* vol. 4, No. 4, March 1964, pp. 121-130.

"Spring Performance of Electrical Contact Alloys," C. S. BARKER, *Product Engineering,* May 11, 1964, pp. 62-66.

"Electrical Contact Materials in Low Current Technology," W. H. ABBOTT and H. R. OGDEN, *Battelle Technical Review,* March 1965, vol. 14, No. 3, p. 14.

"Contacts Stressed at Relay Conference," F. J. OLIVER, *Electro-Technology,* Aug. 1965, pp. 69-72.

"Advancements in Cadmium Oxide Alloys," K. R. COMEY, JR., and T. SANTALA. 1965

Seminar on Electrical Contact Phenomena, Univ. of Maine, Dept. of Electrical Engrg., Orono, Me.

"Contact Geometry and Action Versus Material," D. R. MORRISON, Relay Conference, 1966.

"Precious Metal Electrodeposits," R. F. VINES, Relay Conference 1966.

"New (Material) Developments for the Relay Industry," G. L. McDERMOTT and J. A. WILLOUGHBY, Relay Conference, 1966.

24   Contact phenomena (other)

"Contact Phenomena in Telephone Switching Circuits," A. M. CURTIS, *Bell System Technical Journal,* Jan. 1940, vol. 19, p. 40.

"Calculation of Electrical Contacts under Ideal Conditions," E. I. SHOBERT, American Society for Testing Materials, Preprint in A3 for Meeting June 24-28, 1946, pp. 155-173 (also in *A.S.T.M. Proceedings,* vol. 46, pp. 1126-1144.)

"Calculation of Temperature Development in Contact Surface, and Application to Problem of Temperature Rise in Sliding Contact," R. HOLM, *Journal of Applied Physics,* April 1948, vol. 19, pp. 361-366.

"Calculation of the Temperature Development in a Contact Heated in the Contact Surface, and Application to the Problem of the Temperature in a Sliding Contact," W. J. OOSTERKAMP, *Journal of Applied Physics,* Dec. 1948, vol. 19, pp. 1180-1181.

"Theory of Thompson Effect in Electrical Contacts," P. M. DAVIDSON, *Proceedings of the Institute of Electrical Engineers,* Nov. 1949, vol. 96, pt. I, pp. 293-295.

"Linear Theory of Fluctuations Arising from Diffusional Mechanism; An Attempt at a Theory of Contact Noise," J. J. RICHARD-SON, *Bell System Technical Journal,* Jan. 1950, vol. 29, pp. 117-131.

"Electric Tunnel Effect Across Thin Insulator Films in Contacts," R. HOLM, *Journal of Applied Physics,* May 1951, vol. 22, No. 5, pp. 569-574.

"The Contribution of Non-uniform Current Flow," W. B. KOVWENHOVEN and W. T. SACKETT, *Transactions of the AIEE,* 1951, vol. 70, pp. 791-795.

"Contribution to the Theory of the Silicon Carbide Contact," R. HOLM, *Journal of Applied Physics,* May 1952, vol. 53, pp. 509-517.

"Application of Basic Research to Low Level Phenomena," F. R. DUBAS, Relay Conference, 1959.

"Single Contact Observations in the Low Level Area," H. ROBERTSHAW, JR., Relay Conference, 1960.

"A Study of Discharge Transients in Relays with Grounded Cases," C. P. NUNN and R. HALBECK, Ninth Annual NARM Relay Symposium, 1961, Oklahoma State University.

"Physics of Electrical Contact Phenomena," F. L. JONES," *British Journal of Applied Physics,* July 1961, pp. 318-322.

"Approach to the Analysis of the Dynamic Phenomena Occurring at Contact Make in a Simply Built Flexure-Operated Relay Spring Assembly," G. WIKELL, 1965 National Relay Conference (Second International Conference on Electromagnetic Relays).

"Contact Geometry and Action Versus Material," D. R. MORRISON, Relay Conference, 1966.

"Low Voltage Contact Resistance Behavior of Relays," F. LOZENBY, D. MARR, Relay Conference, 1966.

"Intermetallic Compounds of Au-Hg System Used for Contact Material in Reed Switch," HIDEO OKAMATO, Relay Conference, 1969.

25   Contact rating factors (loads)

"Rating of Contacts and Switching of Different Circuits," G. WINDRED, *Electrical Engineering,* Sept. 1939, pp. 662, 721.

"Relay Contact Rating," G. O. WAGNER, Relay Conference, 1954.

"DC Inductive Ratings for Electrical Contacts," S. T. EAST, Relay Conference, 1956.

"Contact Loading," A. N. GARDINER, Relay Conference, 1957.

"Current Carrying Capacity of Switch and Relay Contacts," A. WHYS, *Systems Design,* Feb. 1960, vol. 4.

"The DC Inductive Loading of Contacts," L. D. DE LALIO and C. P. NUNN, Relay Conference, 1960.

"AC Contact Ratings, Effect of Power Frequency and Type of Load," P. N. MARTIN, Relay Conference, 1961.

"Half-Crystal Can Relays Operating at 1,000 Per Cent Overload — An Analysis of the Arc Power," WILLIAM C. MUELLER, Relay Conference, 1966.

26 Contact resistance measurement

"The Electrical Resistance of Metal Contacts," J. J. WENT, *Philips Technical Review,* vol. 4, pp. 332-335, November, 1939.

"Contact Resistance," R. HOLM, *Proceedings, Engineering Seminar on Electrical Contacts,* Penn. State University, State College, Pa., 1954.

"Contact Resistance As It Affects Dry Circuit Relays," J. W. SCANNELL, Relay Conference, 1958.

"An Improved Method of Measuring Contact Resistance," A. SCHNIPPER, Relay Conference, 1958.

"Contact Resistance Measurements at Low Loads," D. G. FLOM, *Review of Scientific Instruments,* Nov. 1958, pp. 979-981.

"An Investigation of Relay Contact Resistance by Means of Voltage Current Characteristics," T. B. THOMPSON and R. C. SADLER, Relay Conference, 1959.

"Improved Probe Apparatus for Measuring Contact Resistance," S. D. CHAIKIN, J. R. ANDERSON, and G. J. SANTOS, JR., Review of Scientific Instruments, Dec. 1961, pp. 1294-1296.

"Contact Resistance Testing of Relays at Low Level Switching," N. E. HYDE, Relay Conference, 1962.

"Measurement of Electrical Contacts," E. S. MATHISEN, Instruments and Control Systems, June 1962, pp. 125-127.

"Massacre-Machine for Automatic Surface Sampling and Contact Resistance Evaluation," FAIRWEATHER, JURY, LOZENBY, PARKER, THRIFT, and WRIGHT, Institute of Electrical Engineers Proceedings (London), vol. 109, pt. A (Supplement), No. 3, 1962, pp. 210-219.

"Measurement of Resistance of Light-Duty Electrical Contacts," J. PULLEN, Institute of Electrical Engineers Proceedings (London), vol. 109, pt. A (Supplement), No. 3, 1962, pp. 220-223.

"Load Parameter Effects on Relay Contact Resistance," W. M. CRAWFORD, 1965 National Relay Conference.

"Contact Resistance Studies of Relay for Submarine Cable," C. SCHNEIDER, 1965 National Relay Conference.

"The Effect of Contact Geometry and Surface Finish on Contact Resistance," G. T. WENNING and D. S. CHHABRA. 1965 Seminar on Electric Contact Phenomena, Univ. of Maine, Dept. of Electrical Engrg., Orono, Me.

"Low Voltage Contact Resistance Behaviour of Relays," F. LAZENBY and D. MARR, Relay Conference, 1966.

27 Contact testing procedures (general)

"Electrical Surge Tests on Contact Materials," E. F. HOLT and H. C. GRAVES, JR., A.S.T.M. Standards on Electrical Heating and Resistance Alloys, Oct. 1942, pp. 119-128.

"Use of Phototube to Correlate Contact Separation with Electrical Transients," O. E. BERG and STAUSS, Review of Scientific Instruments, vol. 22, No. 3, pp. 153-155.

"The Closure and Partial Separation of a Metallic Contact," A. FAIRWEATHER, Journal of I.E.E., 1945, vol. 92, pt. I, pp. 301-321.

"Instrumentation for Analysis of Contact Wear," M. R. SWINEHART, Electronic Engineering, May 1951, vol. 70, p. 414.

"Statistical Analysis of Contact Tests," J. C. SOFIANEK, Proceedings: Engineering Seminar on Electrical Contacts, Penn. State University, State College, Pa., 1954.

"Examination of Electric Contacts by Plastic Replica Method," H. W. HERMANCE and T. F. EGAN, Bell Telephone Laboratories Monograph 2952, 1958.

"A System to Monitor Relay Contacts to Determine Reliability in Switching Loads," J. S. SJOSTROM, Relay Conference, 1960.

"Measurement of Electrical Contacts," E. S. MATHISEN, Instruments and Control Systems, June 1962, pp. 125-127.

"Relay Tests Focus on Contact Performance" (Abstracts of papers at Twelfth National Relay Conference, Oklahoma State University), F. J. OLIVER, Electro-Technology, July 1964, p. 91.

"A Stability Criterion for Analyzing Contact Vibration in Electromagnetic Relays," M. C. BURKHURT and R. L. LOWERY, 1965 National Relay Conference.

"Experimental Arc Energy Meter for Relays," A. K. HALDER, G. KARADY, Relay Conference, 1969.

"Magnitude and Stability of Switch Resistance," H. D. INFELD, Relay Conference, 1969.

28 Contact troubleshooting

"Relay Contacts — Their Ailments," A. W. CLEMENT, Electronics, 1938, vol. 11, p. 29.

"How To Make Sure Electrical Contacts Work," W. H. BLOODWORTH, Factory Management and Maintenance, June 1946, vol. 104, pp. 134-136.

"Electrical Contact Troubles — How to Cope with Them," V. E. HEIL, Power Generation, June 1948, vol. 52, pp. 62-63, 128, 130, 132.

"How to Prevent Sticking Contacts and Relays," R. S. KERCHER and L. E. MARKLE, Coal Age, Aug. 1953, pp. 58:112.

"Relay Contact Failures," L. D. CARR, Relay Conference, 1960.

"Contact Headaches — Why Have Them?," C. B. GWYN, JR., Relay Conference, 1964.

Design (General)

29 Analysis and theory of relay design

"A Condensation of the Theory of Relays," A. C. VAN C. WARRINGTON, General Electric Review, vol. 43, pp. 370-373, Sept., 1940.

"Electromagnetic Field Analysis," S. A. SCHELKUNOFF, Bell System Technical Journal, vol. 27, p. 487.

"Factors Affecting Magnetic Quality," R. M. BOZORTH, Bell System Technical Journal, vol. 29, p. 251.

"Bases of Design for the Telephone Relay," E. STUTIUS, Fernmeldetechnische Zeitschrift (FTZ), Oct. 1948, vol. I, p. 16108 (in German).

"Analyzing Relay Characteristics," E. R. MORTON, *Product Engineering*, Feb. 1949, vol. 20, pp. 144-145.

"Relay Armature Rebound Analysis," E. E. SUMNER, *Bell System Technical Journal*, Jan. 1952, vol. 31, pp. 172-200.

"Estimation and Control of the Operate Time of Relays," R. L. PEEK, JR., and M. A. LOGAN, *Bell System Technical Journal*, Jan. 1954, vol. 33, pp. 109-186.

"Magnetic Analysis of a Miniature Time Delay Relay," W. CAMP, Relay Conference, 1956.

"The Differential Equation of the Electromagnetic Relay," C. F. CAMERON and E. F. ALLEN, Relay Conference, 1956.

"Relay Characteristics," C. F. CAMERON and D. D. LINGELBACH, Relay Conference, 1956.

"Transient Characteristics of Electro-Magnetic Relays," C. F. CAMERON and D. D. LINGELBACH, Relay Conference, 1957.

"Evaluation of Relay Transients," C. F. CAMERON and D. D. LINGELBACH, Relay Conference, 1958.

"Transient Analysis of Relays with Slugs and Sleeves," C. F. CAMERON and D. D. LINGELBACH, Relay Conference, 1958.

"Relay Design by Digital Computer," R. DIDIER, Relay Conference, 1958.

"Probability Mathematics as a Relay Design Tool," P. T. MILLUNZI, Relay Conference, 1959.

"Armature Overtravel in Relays," C. F. CAMERON, D. D. LINGELBACH and C. C. FREENY, Relay Conference, 1959.

"Dynamics of Relays," C. F. Cameron and D. D. LINGELBACH, *Electronic Industries*, Sept. 1959, pp. 70-76, Oct. 1959, pp. 86-90, Nov. 1959, pp. 96-102.

"Relay Stability," C. F. CAMERON, D. D. LINGELBACH, and C. C. FREENY, Relay Conference, 1960.

"A Practical Method for the Prediction of Relay Operate Time," R. E. STOFFELS, Relay Conference, 1960.

"Transient Relay Characteristics, Their Contribution to Improved Relay Design and Use," R. C. SADLER, Relay Conference, 1960.

"Dynamics of Relays," C. F. CAMERON and D. D. LINGELBACH, Oklahoma State University Engineering Experiment Station, Publ. No. 113, May 1960.

"A Scientific Approach to Relay Analysis," H. J. CULLIN and J. JORDAN, Relay Conference, 1961.

"Theory of Design," C. F. CAMERON, D. D. LINGELBACH, and C. C. FREENY, Relay Conference, 1961.

"An Application of Theory of Design," C. F. CAMERON, D. D. LINGELBACH, and C. C. FREENY, Relay Conference, 1962.

"The Application of Basic Heat Transfer Principles in Optimizing Relay Design," L. A. RICE, Relay Conference, 1962.

"Let's Re-Define Pick-Up and Drop-Out Values," J. K. SCOOT and J. J. MC GORRAY, Relay Conference, 1962.

"Analysis of Dynamic Performance of Electromagnetic Relays," Y. TOMITO, Relay Conference, 1962.

"Dynamic Analysis of the Relay and its Application to the Improvement of the Impulse Relay," H. KUBOKOYA, Relay Conference, 1963.

"The Relay Signature, A Technique for Characteristics Analysis," E. G. TUTLE, Relay Conference, 1964.

"The Importance of Design Analysis in Relay Engineering," J. M. ALFIERO, 1965 National Relay Conference.

"Digital Computation as a Tool in D.C. Solenoid Design," J. C. EVEN, JR., 1965 National Relay Conference.

"Analysis of Miniature Polarized Relay," Y. FUJINAMI and Y. SUDA, Relay Conference, 1966.

"A General Mathematical Model of D. C. Relay Performance," W. M. GRENGG, Relay Conference, 1966.

"Relay Design by Statistical Methods," E. B. HAUGEN, Relay Conference, 1966.

"A New Method of Limiting Armature Travel on the Release Cycle of Non-Latching Relays," C. B. KNOX, JR., Relay Conference, 1966.

"Analog Computer Simulation of Bifilar Wound Power Relay," D. D. LINGELBACH, Relay Conference, 1966.

"Some Notes on Eddy Currents and the Effect of Slots in Relay Structures," R. M. ROVNYAK, Relay Conference, 1966.

"You'd Think They *Invented* Logic," R. E. STOFFELS, Relay Conference, 1966.

"Dynamic Pull Curve Approximation," G. B. SPELLMAN and J. H. BIGELOW, Relay Conference, 1966.

"Application of 'Available Work' to Relay Design," MASAO HIYANE, Relay Conference, 1967.

"Electromechanical Chopper," CAESAR T. TORIE, Relay Conference, 1967.

"Method for Finding Coercive Force of Relay Piece Parts," P. F. ELARDE, Relay Conference, 1967.

"A Theory for the Dynamic Behavior of an Electromagnetic Relay," CURT AHLBERG, Relay Conference, 1967.

"Utilization of the Magnetic Circuit of an AC Relay to Eliminate Kiss Position," JAMES E. MADISON, Relay Conference, 1967.

"A Computer Program to Design Balanced Transmission for Relays," C. A. BROMBAUGH, Relay Conference, 1968.

"Design for Manufacture of a Small Crossbar Switch," P. R. TILLMAN, Relay Conference, 1968.

"Design of the Vertical Unit of the Minibar Switch," H. J. DESMET, Relay Conference, 1968.

"Influence of the Shorted Coil on the Response

of a Bifilar Wound Power Relay," D. D. LINGELBACH, Relay Conference, 1968.

"A New and Smaller Crossbar Switch," R. P. HOLTFRETER, Relay Conference, 1968.

"The Relay Engineer and the Time-Sharing Computer," LEE O. WOODS, Relay Conference, 1968.

"Reliability Goes In Long Before the Wrapper Goes On," A. O. ADAMS, Relay Conference, 1968.

"Semiconductors Expand the Control Application for General Purpose Relays," ALBERT METZLER, Relay Conference, 1969.

30   Coils and electromagnets

"Design Characteristics of Electromagnets for Telephone Relays," D. D. MILLER, *Bell System Technical Journal*, 1924, pp. 206-231.

"A Method of Designing an Efficient Iron-Clad Electromagnet," H. N. WAGAR, Bell System Monograph B-508, Sept. 1930.

"Magnet Coil Design," G. L. MOSES, *Product Engineering*, 1938, vol. 9, pp. 483-486, 503-504; 1939, vol. 10, pp. 85-86, 129-130, 317-318; 1940, vol.11 , pp. 47-48, 97-98, 132-133.

"Factors Affecting the Design of D-C Magnets," L. T. RADAR, *Transactions of the AIEE*, 1943, vol. 62, pp. 307-310.

"Relay Coils with Improved Longitudinal Balance," C. M. MORRIS, *Bell Laboratories Record*, Jan. 1947, p. 10.

"Matching Solenoid Characteristics to Load," F. E. REEVES, *Electrical Manufacturing*, June 1950, vol. 45, pp. 104-107.

"Internal Temperatures of Relay Windings," R. L. PEEK, JR., *Bell System Technical Journal*, Jan. 1951, vol. 30, pp. 141-148.

"Magnetic Design of Relays," R. L. PEEK, JR., *Bell System Technical Journal*, Jan. 1954, vol. 33, pp. 23-78.

"Coil Temperature Rise and Its Measurement," R. FERRY, Relay Conference, 1956.

"Design of Magnetic Circuits for Miniature Relays," W. RICHERT, Relay Conference, 1957.

"Design of Magnetic Circuits for Miniature Relays," W. RICHERT, *Electronic Industries*, Oct. 1957.

"Electro-Magnet Configuration Having Improved Efficiency and Shock Resistance," C. PACKARD, Relay Conference, 1958.

"Double Coil Relay with Single Working Gap," J. SCHUESSLER, Relay Conference, 1959.

"Another Concept in Coil Shunts for Limiting the Inductive Kick," R. W. COLLEY, Relay Conference, 1961.

"Design of Switching Relay Coil," T. SHINO-HARA, Relay Conference, 1961.

"Coil Constant of the Core in Switching Relay," T. SHINOHARA, Relay Conference, 1961.

"Shading A.C. Electromagnets," J. W. MO-BARRY, Relay Conference, 1962.

"Approximate Power-Temperature Relationships for Copper Wire Coils," B. GIESE, Relay Conference, 1963.

"Coil Winding Tension As It Applies To Wire Spring Relay Coils and Other Filled Type Coils," C. C. POULSON, Relay Conference, 1964.

"Suppressing Relay Coil Transients with Bifilar Winding," R. M. ACKER, 1965 National Relay Conference.

"Suppressing Transients within Relay Coils," F. M. BLATT, 1965 National Relay Conference.

"Steady-State Temperature Rise in Magnet Coils," T. J. PEMBERTON, 1965 National Relay Conference.

"Theoretical Analysis of an A.C. Shading Coil Magnet under the Magnetic Leakage," S. YAMAMOTO, 1965 National Relay Conference (Second International Conference on Electromagnetic Relays).

"Dynamic Pull Curve Approximation," G. B. SPELLMAN and J. H. BIGELOW, Relay Conference, 1966.

"A Design Procedure for Rotary Solenoids," R. C. SADLER, Relay Conference, 1966.

"Relationship of Microstructure and Magnetic Values of Low Carbon Steel," ARTHUR S. WISEMAN, Relay Conference, 1967.

"Utilization of Silicon Steel in the Wire Spring Relay," J. S. LEE, Relay Conference, 1967.

"Coil Current Is Complicated," RICHARD W. COBEAN, Relay Conference, 1969.

"Internal Temperatures of Relay Windings," R. L. PEEK, JR., *Bell System Technical Journal*, Jan. 1951, vol. 30, pp. 141-148.

31   Design considerations

"Appraisal of Relay Design," J. A. CSEPELY and G. K. BORSKI, Relay Conference, 1953.

"Construction and Operational Features of Magnetic Contact Relays," E. M. EADIE, JR., Relay Conference, 1953.

"Design of Relays," A. C. KELLER, *Bell System Technical Journal*, Jan. 1954, vol. 33, pp. 1-2.

"Relay Design," E. HOEL, Relay Conference, 1955.

"Design for Performance vs. Design for Specifications," F. STAUNTON, Relay Conference, 1955.

"Relays," J. F. RINKE, *Machine Design*, Oct. 1955, pp. 27:160-170.

"Temperature and Relay Adjustments," D. F. DIEL, Relay Conference, 1957.

"An Evaluation of Relay and Contactor Design Types," H. LYNCH and P. J. M. CLUTE, Relay Conference, 1957.

"Another Step in Relay Stability." D. F. DIEL and J. COONS, Relay Conference, 1958.

"Recent Relay Developments in the United Kingdom," K. E. V. WILLIS, Relay Conference, 1958.

"Design Considerations for Aircraft Relays," L. E. MASSIE and E. F. KOTNIK, *Transactions of the AIEE — Applications and Industry*, vol. 77, pt. 2, No. 39, Nov. 1958, pp. 305-307.

"Review of UK Joint Service Relay Development," N. L. JEFFERS, Relay Conference, 1960.

"The Electromagnetic Relay," (Review of Trends), M. MEYERS, *Electro-Technology,* Jan. 1962, p. 127.

"A Critical Evaluation of Electrical Control Devices," (Tests by General Motors), S. F. NEWMAN, *Electro-Technology,* April 1962, p. 203.

"Relationship Between Design and Specification," D. D. LINGELBACH, Relay Conference, 1963.

"New Relay Developments," (Report of 1963 Conference on Electromagnetic Relays at Oklahoma State University), H. FALK, *Electro-Technology,* July 1963, p. 143.

"A Comparison of Military and Industrial Relay Design Progress," H. J. CULLIN, 1965 National Relay Conference.

"Some Factors Affecting Design, Construction, and Testing of High Reliability Relays for Dry Circuits and 5-10 Ampere," F. F. YANIKOSKI, 1965 National Relay Conference.

"Designing with Relays is More Subtle Than You Think," F. F. YANIKOSKI, *Electronic Design,* Nov. 29, 1965, pp. 30-34.

"High Performance Contactors — A New Design Approach," A. O. ADAMS, Relay Conference, 1966.

"An Experimental Miniature Crossbar Switch (MXB)," A. C. KELLER, Relay Conference, 1966.

"Military Relay Reliability," C. SCHNEIDER, Relay Conference, 1966.

"Relay Design by Statistical Methods," E. B. HAUGEN, Relay Conference, 1966.

"The Logic of Solid State or Electro Mechanical," WARREN WRIGHT, Relay Conference, 1969.

"Selection of Mounting Means to Maximize Relay Vibration Capability," CARL B. KNOX, JR., Relay Conference, 1969.

32 Design for severe environments

"Preventing Corrosion in Relays," A. E. HERMAN, *Electrical Manufacturing,* May 1949, vol. 43, pp. 116-118.

"Relay Armature Rebound Analysis," diags., E. E. SUMNER, *Bell System Technical Journal,* Jan. 1952, vol. 31, pp. 172-200.

"The Rotary Switch in Extremes of Environment," E. C. COULOMBE, Relay Conference, 1955.

"Effect of Shock and Vibration on Relays," AIEE Committee Report, Abstract, *Electrical Engineering,* June 1955, vol. 74, p. 489.

"Practical Approaches to Vibration Resistant Relay Design," J. SCHMIDT, Relay Conference, 1956.

"Vibration and Shock Resistant Relay Designs," A. P. BOYLAN and J. L. PFEFFER, *IRE National Convention Record,* March 1957, pt. 6, pp. 148-156.

"Mounting Arrangements and Their Influence on Vibration," J. SCHMIDT, Relay Conference, 1958.

"Development of a Relay for 650 Degrees F Ambient," H. J. WISE and C. A. STEWART, Relay Conference, 1962.

"Vibration Control in Relay Design," R. L. LOWERY, B. C. RIDDLE and G. C. STONE, Relay Conference, 1963.

"Chatter Characteristics of a Linear Viscous Damped Contact System," ALVIN F. BAKER and R. L. LOWERY, Relay Conference, 1966.

"High Performance Contactors — A New Design Approach," A. O. ADAMS, Relay Conference, 1966.

"Tomorrow's Relay Today — The Balanced Force Series," J. C. SCHUESSLER and A. O. ADAMS, Relay Conference, 1967.

"The Development of a High Performance Micro Miniature Latching Relay," MAX HURTER, Relay Conference, 1969.

Design (Specific Types)

33 A-C relays

"A-C Magnets and Solenoids," L. T. RADAR, *Electrical Engineering,* 1947, vol. 66, pp. 487-492.

"Development of Alternating Current Operated Power Relays and Contactors for Aircraft Applications," R. J. COPPOLA, Relay Conference, 1956.

"New Relay Forms for A-C Operation," R. J. COPPOLA, *Electrical Manufacturing,* Oct. 1957, p. 156.

"Design of Rectifier-Relay Combination," P. N. MARTIN and T. MC LAUGHLIN, Relay Conference, 1958.

"Design of Relay-Rectifier Combinations," P. N. MARTIN and T. MC LAUGHLIN, *Electronic Equipment Engineering,* Sept. 1958, pp. 28-34.

"Miniature True A.C. Coil Relay," G. A. MARSHALL, Relay Conference, 1961.

"Miniature 'True' A-C Coil Relay," (North American Aviation design), G. A. MARSHALL, *Transactions of the AIEE — Applications and Industry,* vol. 81, pt. 2, No. 60, May 1962, pp. 68-71.

"Considerations in Design of 300-Volt Relay," Z. J. KRUZIC, IEEE Electrical Engineering Problems in Rubber and Plastics Industries, Fifteenth Annual Conference Spec. Publ. T-158, 1963, pp. 124-136.

34 Electronic relays

"Universal Electronic Relay," L. F. BOSS, *Electronics,* May 1942, p. 68.

"Electronic Relay Developments," J. J. LOVING, *Electrical Engineer,* June 1949, p. 478.

"Close-Differential Thyratron Relay," J. J. BARUCH, *Electronics,* Nov. 1951, vol. 24, p. 256.

"Improved Electronic Relay With no Mechanical Moving Parts," S. C. EINHORN, *Journal of Scientific Instruments,* April 1954, vol. 25, pp. 396-397.

"Simple Chatter-proof Electronic Relay," L. A. CRAM, *Journal of Scientific Instruments,* April 1955, vol. 32, pp. 148-149.

"Combining Relay Versatility and Integrated Circuit Technology in High Reliability Digital Equipment," D. R. SAEWERT, Relay Conference, 1966.

35   Hermetically sealed relays

"Glass-Sealed Switches and Relays," C. G. MC CORMICK, *Bell Laboratories Record,* Sept. 1947, pp. 342-345.

"Contamination in Sealed Relays," C. F. JOHNSON, JR., *Electrical Manufacturing,* Aug. 1949, vol. 44, pp. 112-114.

"An Improved Enclosing Relay," L. E. GOFF, *Transactions of the AIEE,* 1950, vol. 69, pt. II, pp. 1480-1487.

"Comparison of Sealed and Unsealed Relays," R. BRUMFIELD, Relay Conference, 1953.

"A New Look at Hermetically Sealed Relays," G. M. HAUSLER, Relay Conference, 1953.

"The Effect of Cracks in Glass-to-Metal Seals on Performance of Hermetically Sealed Relays,' H. N. STAATS, Relay Conference, 1954.

"Aspects of Hermetic Sealing for Gas Filled Relay Enclosures," W. BROWN, Relay Conference, 1955.

"Atomic Energy and Quality Control of Hermetically Sealed Parts," C. W. REED, Relay Conference, 1956.

"Factors Determining the Selection of Gases for Hermetically Sealed Relays," W. BROWN, Relay Conference, 1956.

"Capability of Sealed Contact Relays," O. M. HOVGAARD, *AIEE: Communication and Electronics,* Sept. 1956, pp. 466-468.

"What's Wrong with Plug-In Relays?," I. S. MAYER, *Electrical Manufacturing,* April 1957, p. 148.

"Degassing of Sealed Relays," W. F. JUPTNER, Relay Conference, 1960.

"Unique Seal in Compact Time-Delay Relay," *Electrical Manufacturing,* Nov. 1959, pp. 188-189.

"Considerations in Thermally Rating Small Hermetic Relays," R. A. HOLCOMB, Relay Conference, 1961.

"Miniature Medium-Duty Sealed High Quality Relays," N. E. HYDE, *British Institution of Radio Engineers Journal,* vol. 21, No. 6, June 1961, pp. 557-559.

"Contamination of Sealed Switching Devices for Special Weapons," P. MAHLER, Relay Conference, 1962.

"Thermally Rating Small Hermetic Relays," R. A. HOLCOMB, *Electromechanical Components and Systems Design,* Oct. 1962, pp. 22-27.

"Evaluation and Control of Residual Moisture in Hermetic Relays," R. A. HOLCOMB, Relay Conference, 1964.

"Hermetic Sealing by Electron Beam," M. G. NELSEN and A. O. ADAMS, Relay Conference, 1964.

"Development of High Integrity Seals," J. A. GARRATT, Relay Conference, 1965.

"The Internal Atmosphere of Hermetically Sealed Components," W. E. BERGSTEN and N. L. KNUDSEN and J. F. MCDOWELL, Relay Conference, 1966.

"Change in Relay Atmosphere and Its Effect on Low Temperature Operation," FREDERICK B. FULLER, Relay Conference, 1968.

"Relay Industry Savings Resulting from Polarized Bistable Crystal Can Relay Header Standardization," G. E. FOGLEMAN and E. U. THOMAS, Relay Conference, 1968.

36   Mercury plunger relays

"Spin Out Mercury Plunger Type Load Relays," A. C. JOHNSON, Relay Conference, 1960.

"Mercury Relay Adjustment Techniques," H. D. MARSHALL, Relay Conference, 1963.

"A Mercury-Needle Relay," H. P. SCHULTZ, Relay Conference, 1963.

37   Miniature relays

"Relay Design for Compactness," T. B. HOLLIDAY, *Product Engineering,* Dec. 1947, vol. 18, pp. 118-121.

"Design of Subminiature Electrostatic Relays," E. W. PIKE, *Tele-Tech,* April 1952, vol. 11, pp. 36-37.

"Practical Relay Miniaturization," J. F. RINKE. Relay Conference, 1954.

"Limitations in Miniaturization of Electro-Magnet Relays," P. N. MARTIN, Relay Conference, 1957.

"Design of Magnetic Circuits for Miniature Relays," W. J. RICHERT, *Electronic Industries* and *Tele-Tech,* Oct. 1957, pp. 56-156.

"A New Approach to a 200 Degree C. Reliable Miniature Relay," P. N. BOSSART, Relay Conference, 1958.

"Miniaturization Design Techniques," J. S. ZIMMER, *Electronic Equipment Engineering,* July 1958, pp. 37-38.

"A Miniature Relay for High Reliability," C. SCHNEIDER and C. F. SPAHN, *Proceedings,* 1959 Electronic Components Conference, pp. 109-115 (reprinted in Bell Telephone Technical Publ. Monograph 3307).

"Unimite Relay — Its Characteristics and Statistically Planned Test Program," R. A. HOLCOMB and W. H. LESSER, *Proceedings,* 1962 Electronic Components Conference, pp. 184-189.

"Miniaturization Pro and Con," J. SCHMIDT, JR., Relay Conference, 1962.

"Grounded Case Crystal Can Relay — A Second Look," K. A. WANTUCK, Relay Conference, 1962.

"Design and Manufacture of Type 130 Relay," C. GRAVES and G. W. PAUTNEY, *AEI Engineering* (London), July-Aug. 1962, vol. 2, No. 4, pp. 179-184.

"A Miniature Latch-in Relay for the Telstar Satellite," C. SCHNEIDER, *Bell Laboratories Record,* June 1963, pp. 241-243.

"Development of Miniature, Sealed, Magnetic Circuit Breakers," N. J. SCHWARTZ, *IEEE Transactions on Component Parts,* Sept. 1963, vol. CP-10, No. 3, pp. 123-127.

"Miniature Relays for Key Telephone Systems," W. W. WERRING, *Bell Laboratories Record,* Dec. 1962, pp. 414-417.

"Recent Developments in Bell System Relays (Sealed contact and Miniature)," A. C. KELLER, *Bell Systems Technical Journal,* Jan. 1964, pp. 15-44. Also, IEEE: *Communication and Electronics,* Jan. 1964, pp. 79-87.

"A New Method of Limiting Armature Travel on the Release Cycle Of Non-Latching Relays," C. B. KNOX, JR., Relay Conference, 1966.

38 Polarized and latching relays

"Polarized Telegraph Relay," H. C. A. VAN DUUREN, *Electro-techniek,* Dec. 1946, vol. 24, pp. 304-306; Jan. 1947, vol. 25, pp. 7-9 (in Dutch).

"Magnetic Latching of Relays," F. DIDSZUNS, *Product Engineering,* April 1948, vol. 19, pp. 110-112.

"A Change-Over Relay Operated by Pulses of One Polarity Only," H. F. HINDLEY, *Journal of Scientific Instruments in Industry,* Sept. 1948, vol. 25, p. 322.

"Polarized Relay of Improved Performance," H. A. TURNER and B. SCOTT, *Post Office Electrical Engineers Journal,* July 1950, pp. 85-92, British Post Office.

"Improved Polar Telegraph Relay," W. D. CANNON and T. RYSTEDT, *Electrical Engineering,* Dec. 1951, vol. 70, pp. 1088-1092.

"Centre Stable Electronic Relay," R. BAILEY, *Journal of Scientific Instruments,* April 1953, vol. 30, p. 139.

"Balanced Polar Mercury Contact Relay, J. T. L. BROWN and C. E. POLLARD, *Bell System Technical Journal,* Nov. 1953, vol. 32, pp. 1393-1411.

"Electronic Latching Relay," R. P. TURNER, *Radio and TV News,* July 1956, pp. 56:123.

"Limit of Minimizing the Dimensions of Polarized Relay," I. NUKADA, Y. HOSOKAWA, and H. KIKUCHI, Relay Conference, 1958.

"The Design of a Large Polarized Actuator for an Aircraft Contactor," P. L. EPSTEIN, Relay Conference, 1958.

"Characteristics of 450 Type Polarized Relay," I. NUKADA and Y. HOSOKAWA, Relay Conference, 1958.

"Evolution of a Micro-Miniature Magnetic Latching Relay," W. J. RICHERT, Relay Conference, 1960.

"Permanent Magnet Relay Uses No Springs," *Electro-Technology,* Nov. 1960, p. 188.

"Magnetic Lock, Latch Relay," J. J. CUMMINGS, Relay Conference, 1961.

"Polar Relay Adaptor Corrects Coil Polarity," R. E. PAFENBERG, *Electronics,* July 14, 1961, pp. 74-75.

"Study on Performance of Polar Relays," S. MITSUISHI and I. TAKAHASHI, Institute of Electrical Communication Engineers (Japan), Nov. 1962, pp. 1555-1563 (in Japanese with English summary).

"Polarized Relays," E. U. THOMAS, *Machine Design,* March 28, 1963, pp. 156-161.

"Miniature Latch-In Relay for Telstar Satellite," C. SCHNEIDER, *Bell Laboratories Record,* June 1963, pp. 241-243.

"Subminiature Polar Telegraph Relay," H. OMI, T. OKAMOTO and A. ISHII, *IEEE Transactions on Component Parts,* Dec. 1963, vol. CP-10, No. 4, pp. 132-144.

"A Subminiature Polar Telegraph Relay," H. OMI, A. ISHII, and T. OKAMOTO, Relay Conference, 1964.

"Analysis of the Magnetic Field Distribution of the Magnetic Latching Reed Devices," TAKEO SHINOHARA, HISAEI KIKUCHI, and SADAYUKI MITSUHASHI, Relay Conference, 1967.

"Shunting Type Magnetic Circuit Arrangement for Commercial Latching Relays," WALTER J. RICHERT, Relay Conference, 1968.

"The Design and Application of Magnetic Latching Relays," THOMAS G. GRAN, Relay Conference, 1969.

39 Reed, dry and mercury-wetted contact relays

"Recent Developments in Relays — Glass-Enclosed Reed Relay," W. B. ELLWOOD, *Electrical Engineering,* Nov. 1947, vol. 66, pp. 1104-1109.

"Recent Developments in Relays," W. B. ELLWOOD, J. T. L. BROWN, and C. E. POLLARD, Bell Telephone System, Monograph B-1516.

"Balanced Polar Mercury Contact Relay," J. T. L. BROWN and C. E. POLLARD, *Bell System Technical Journal,* vol. 32, Nov. 1953, pp. 1393-1411.

"Development of Reed Switches and Relays," O. M. HOVGAARD and G. E. PERRAULT, *Bell System Technical Journal,* March 1955, vol. 34, pp. 309-332.

"Mercury Wetted Contact Relays," A. J. KODA, Relay Conference, 1956.

"The Development of Automatic Manufacturing Facilities for Reed Switches," J. A. HOSFORD, *AIEE: Communication and Electronics,* Sept. 1956, pp. 496-500.

"Non-Linear Aspects of Vibrating Reed Design," D. A. ROBINSON, Relay Conference, 1957.

"Sealed Contact Reed Relays," J. BANNOCHIE and R. FURSEY, Automatic Tele. and Elec. Co. Journal, Oct. 1958, vol. 14, No. 4, pp. 262-273.

"Multicoil Reed Relays," O. WUYTS, Relay Conference, 1959.

"Sealed Contact Reed Relays," R. A. E. FURSEY, Electronics, July 31, 1959, p. 79.

"The Mercury Wetted Relay as a Millimicrosecond Pulse- Forming Switch," C. P. WOMACK, Bulletin of Engineering and Architecture, No. 43, University of Kansas, 1959.

"Air Reed, The Driven Reed Relay," H. J. CULLEN, Relay Conference, 1960.

"The Ferreed — A New Switching Device," A. FEINER, C. A. LOVELL, T. N. LOWRY, and P. G. RIDINGER, Bell System Technical Journal, 1960, vol. 39, No. 1.

"Magnetic Latching Relays Using Glass-Sealed Contacts," P. HUSTA and G. E. PERREAULT, Bell System Technical Journal, Nov. 1960, pp. 1553-1571.

"Sealed Contact Relays," J. G. BANNOCHIE and R. A. E. FURSEY, British Institution of Radio Engineers Journal, Feb. 1961, pp. 193-199.

"Magnetization and Pull Characteristics of Mating Magnetic Reeds," R. L. PEEK, JR., Bell System Technical Journal, March 1961, pp. 523-546. Also, AIEE: Communication and Electronics, Sept. 1961, pp. 372-380.

"Some Applications of Mercury Wetted Contact Relays," W. E. SPEAR and OTHERS, Journal of Scientific Instruments, Feb. 1962, pp. 81-83.

"The Frequency-Sensitive Photoreed as a Device for Relaying Without Contacts," C. IACCARINA, Relay Conference, 1962.

"Reed Relays Using Barium Ferrite Magnet," H. KIKUCHI, Relay Conference, 1962.

"Analysis of the Electrical Closure Time of a Mercury Wetted Relay," C. WOMACK, Relay Conference, 1962.

"Taking Bounce Out of Reed Relays," H. CULLIN, Electronics, July 6, 1962, pp. 66.

"Permanent Magnet Biasing and Operation of Dry Reed Switches," F. C. EBERT, Relay Conference, 1963.

"Position Independent Mercury Contacts," C. E. POLLARD, Bell Laboratories Record, Feb. 1963, p. 58.

"Sealed Switches with Reed Contacts," Engineering (London), April 19, 1963, p. 531.

"An Experimental Dry Reed Sealed Transfer Contact," K. F. BRADFORD, Bell Laboratories Record, May 1963 p. 200.

"Development of the Multireed Relay — A Small Company's Approach to Relay Design," N. H. MAGIDA, Relay Conference, 1963.

"Adjustable Glass Encapsulated Reed Relays," B. MISHELEVICH and E. G. TUTTLE, Relay Conference, 1963.

"The Ferreed," A. FEINER and R. L. PEEK, JR., Bell Laboratories Record, Feb. 1964, pp. 71-74.

"Sealed Switches with Reed Contacts," Engineering (London), April 19, 1963, p. 531.

"Development of the Multireed Relay — A Small Company's Approach to Relay Design," N. H. MAGIDA, Relay Conference, 1963.

"Adjustable Glass Encapsulated Reed Relays," B. MISHELEVICH and E. G. TUTTLE, Relay Conference, 1963.

"New Miniaturized Dry Reed Glass Sealed Contacts," I. S. RAFUSE, Bell Laboratories Record, March 1964, pp. 99-100.

"A Mathematical Analysis of the Magnetic Reed Switch," A. R. LE BLANC, Relay Conference, 1964.

"How To Design Sealed Reed Switches," S. TAKASHI, Relay Conference, 1964.

"Fundamentals of Dynamic Noise Generation in Reed Switch Contacts," J. J. VITOLA and J. P. BREICKNER, Relay Conference, 1964.

"Dynamic Noise Generation in Reed Switch Contacts," J. J. VITOLA and J. P. BREICKNER, Electronic Industries, Dec. 1964, pp. 66-69.

"Reed Relay Packaging Design Concepts," S. C. SCHANTZ, Relay Conference, 1966.

"Magnetic Characteristics of Miniature Reed Relays," B. C. STICKLEY, Relay Conference, 1966.

"Magnetic Characteristics of Miniature Reed Relays," B. C. STICKLEY, Relay Conference, 1966.

"Reed Relay Packaging Design Concepts," SPENCER C. SCHANTZ, Relay Conference, 1966.

"Analysis of the Magnetic Field Distribution of the Magnetic Latching Reed Devices," TAKEO SHINOHARA, HISAEI KIKUCHI, and SADAYUKI MITSUHASHI, Relay Conference, 1967.

"Induced Current Operation of Reed Switches," J. T. L. BROWN, Relay Conference, 1967.

"Testing and Packaging for Reed Relay Reliability," JOHN B. BREICKNER, Relay Conference, 1967.

"Experimental Miniature Mercury-Wetted Contact Switch and Relay," YASUSHI ICHIJI, HARUZO SEMBA, and YOSHIO UEMATSU, Relay Conference, 1968.

"A New Concept in Reed Switches," J. A. BONGARD, Relay Conference, 1968.

"A Realistic and Dynamic Life Test for Reed Switches," DEAN B. FOX, Relay Conference, 1968.

"Revamping the Ferreed Switch," N. WASSERMAN, Bell Laboratories Record, Feb. 1969, pp. 53-56.

"A Mercury Relay Which Operates in Any Plane," JOHN P. BREICKNER, Relay Conference, 1969.

"The Reed Switch with a Gold Amalgam Contact," ARIFUMI TOMIKAWA, Relay Conference, 1969.

"A Study on Design of the Reed Switch,"
SAITOB KIOCHI, Relay Conference,
1969.

"Systems Application of Latching Reed Relays
in Scientific Satellite Instrumentation,"
ROBERT S. CUIKAY, Relay Conference,
1969.

40   Sensitive relays

"Adjusting Sensitive Relays," R. T. FISHER,
Electronics, Feb. 1943, p. 70.

"Design Problems Involving Sensitive Relays,"
R. T. FISHER, *Electronics,* Oct. 1943, p.
125.

"High-Capacity Sensitive Relay," R. A. FUL-
TON, *Science,* Oct. 18, 1946, vol. 104, pp.
373-374.

"Improving Performance of Millivolt Relays,"
G. HALPERIN, *Electronics,* Nov. 1948, vol.
21, pp. 140-144.

"Design Considerations in Sensitive Relays," E.
M. EADIE, JR., Relay Conference, 1956.

"Sensitive Relay Switch," G. MILLS, *Radio and
TV News,* July 1956, pp. 56:139.

"Sensitive Thyratron Relay Operates on Micro-
Ampere," J. N. HARRIS, *Electronics,* Dec.
1956, pp. 28-172.

"Developments in the Domain of Sensitive Subminiature Relays," U. PIERRE, Relay Conference, 1959.

"Sensitive Relays," (Staff report), *Electromechanical Components and Systems Design,*
April 1959, pp. 45-68.

41   Slow-acting relays

"Slow Acting Relays," A. B. SMITH, *Electrical
Engineering,* Dec. 1946, vol. 65, pp. 557-563.

"Slow Acting Relays," H. N. WAGAR, *Bell
Laboratories Record,* April 1948, vol. 26, pp.
161-164.

"Principles of Slow Release Relay Design," R. L.
PEEK, JR., *Bell System Technical Journal,*
Jan. 1954, vol. 33, pp. 187-217.

42   Stepping relays and switches

"Reversible Stepping Switch," M. H. WINK-
LER, *Review of Scientific Instruments,* May
1955, vol. 26, pp. 517-518.

"Bidirectional Rotary Stepping Switch," H.
YOSHITOSHI and O. YOSHITAMI, Relay Conference, 1960.

"Design Considerations for Optimizing Performance of Electromagnetic Rotary Stepping
Switches," R. M. ROVNYAK, Relay Conference, 1964.

"Design and Construction Parameters of a High-
Performance, Class B-8, Aerospace Miniature Stepping Relay," G. J. MERRICK,
1965 National Relay Conference.

"How to Use Rotary Stepping Switches," V. E.
JAMES, *Electromechanical Design,* Feb.,
March, and June, 1968.

43   Thermal relays

"Designing an Electro-Thermal Relay," J.
J. DIETZ, *Tele-Tech and Electronic Industries,* Sept. 1954, vol. 13, pp. 65-67.

"Development of a Thermal Relay for Missile
Environment," W. C. BROEKHUYSEN,
Relay Conference, 1959.

"Some Recent Developments in Thermal Relays," J. D. MARKS, Relay Conference,
1957.

"Thermal Relay is Voltage Sensitive," *Electro-
Technology,* June 1963, p. 128.

44   Time delay relays

"Thermionic Time-Delay Relay," G. MUCHER,
Electronics, April 1936, p. 38.

"Time-Delay Relays and Their Characteristics,"
R. B. IMMEL, *Product Engineering,* Feb.
1942, vol. 13, pp. 86-88.

"Timing Relays Molded of Phenolic Compound," *Product Engineering,* Sept. 1948,
vol. 19, p. 136.

"Frictionless Bearings in Timer Relays," B. C.
WELLS, *Electrical Manufacturing,* Nov.
1950, vol. 46, pp. 118-119.

"A Novel Time Delay Relay," M. S. SAKATOS,
Relay Conference, 1954.

"Time Delay Relays," B. H. SMITH, Relay Conference, 1954.

"Time-Delay Relay Uses Novel Air Impedance,"
C. W. CALVIN, *Electro-Technology,* Dec.
1962, p. 152.

45   Vacuum relays

"New Developments in Vacuum Relays," H. C.
ROSS, Relay Conference, 1955.

"New Developments in Vacuum Relays," H. C.
ROSS, *Tele-Tech* and *Electronic Industries,*
Jan. 1956, pp. 15:58-60.

"Vacuum Relays and Vacuum as Insulation,"
H. C. ROSS, Relay Conference, 1956.

"High Voltage Switching with Vacuum Relays,"
R. TETZ and R. W. HANSEN, 1965 National Relay Conference.

46   Wire spring relays

"Wire Straightening and Molding for Wire
Spring Relays," A. J. BRUNNER and
others, *Bell System Technical Journal,* July
1954, vol. 33, pp. 859-884.

"Automatic Contact Welding in Wire Spring
Relay Manufacture," A. L. QUINLAN,
Bell System Technical Journal, July 1954,
vol. 33, pp. 897-923.

"Development of a Wire Contact Relay," R. E.
MARKLE, *Product Engineering,* Jan. 1956,
pp. 27:340-341.

"Design Features of Bell System Wire Spring
Relays," H. M. KNAPP, *AIEE: Communication and Electronics,* Sept. 1956, pp. 482-
486.

"Improving the Performance of the IBM Wire Contact Relay," L. HILL, Relay Conference, 1956.

"Dynamic Gauging and Automatic Adjusting of Wire Spring Relays," J. G. WEEKS, *AIEE, Communication and Electronics,* Nov. 1957, p. 520.

"Two-in-One Wire Spring Relay," T. H. GUETTICH, *Bell Laboratories Record,* Dec. 1958, pp. 458-460.

"New Wire Spring Crossbar Switch," H. YOSHITOSHI, T. KUNIKIRO, and J. OSHIBA, Relay Conference, 1960.

"Wire-Spring Relay, Class 'W'," G. S. LYCHYK, Relay Conference, 1961.

"Ruggedizing the Wire Spring Relay," F. P. BALACEK, *Bell Laboratories Record,* Oct. 1963, pp. 363-364.

"Magnetic Latching Wire Spring Relays," T. G. GRAU and A. K. SPIEGLER, *Bell Laboratories Record,* vol. 42, No. 4, April 1964, pp. 139-140.

"Design and Manufacture of a Latching General Purpose Wire Spring Relay," F. S. FORD, 1965 National Relay Conference.

"Mass Production Techniques of Wire Spring Relay Manufacture," R. L. MANN, 1965 National Relay Conference.

"Machine Aided Selection and Specification of Miniature Wire Spring Relays," R. F. MILLS and W. P. SIMON, Relay Conference, 1967.

"Utilization of Silicon Steel in the Wire Spring Relay," J. S. LEE, Relay Conference, 1967.

47 Miscellaneous relays

"Development of Aviation Relays," R. STEINER, Relay Conference, 1957.

"Recent Developments on Ball Armature Relays," F. D. REYNOLDS, Relay Conference, 1956.

"Novel Capacitance Relay," R. GRAHAM, *Radio and TV News,* Dec. 1952, pp. 48:50-51.

"Commutated Relay Combines Solid-State Switching," J. W. VON BRIMER, 1965 National Relay Conference.

"Commutated Relay Spearheads New Switching Technique," J. W. VON BRIMER, *Electronic Design,* Nov. 29, 1959, pp. 18-21.

"An Experimental Sychronous Contactor for Repeated Automatic Operation," H. W. BAXTER, *Journal of Scientific Instruments,* Nov. 1950, vol. 27, pp. 299-300.

"Single-Digit Counting Relay," *Engineer* (London), Oct. 18, 1963, p. 145.

"Design and Application of a Crossbar Switch," L. JOHNSON, Relay Conference, 1959.

"Fundamental Mechanism and Circuitry of the North Crossbar Switch," J. F. LINDEMANN,, Relay Conference, 1960.

"D.C. Relays," N. E. Hyde, *Electronic Engineering,* Jan. 1953, pp. 11-17.

"DDD Relay," A. C. KELLER, *Bell Laboratories Record,* Sept. 1960, pp. 322-327.

"Differential Relay Sensitivity Adjuster," C. L. HEADLY, *Electrical Engineering,* Nov. 1950, vol. 69, p. 967.

"Solid- State Transformer Differential Relay," S. D. T. ROBERTSON, 1965 National Relay Conference (Second International Conference on Electromagnetic Relays).

"The EA Relay," D. D. MILLER, *Bell Laboratories Record,* Aug. 1948, p. 340.

"Flat Type Relays," D. D. MILLER, *Electrical Communications,* Feb. 1923, vol. 1, pp. 41-49.

"A Study of the Ferroresonant Relay, L. L. WEBER, Relay Conference, 1958.

"Simple (Voltage) Sensing Relay Uses Ferroresonant Circuit," L. L. WEBER, *Electrical Manufacturing,* April 1959, p. 143.

"A Subminiature Resonant Reed Selector — A Frequency-Sensitive Relay," T. OKAMATO, 1965 National Relay Conference (Second International Conference on Electromechanical Relays).

"New General-Purpose Relay for Telephone Switching Systems," A. C. KELLER, *Electrical Engineer,* vol. 71, pp. 1007-1012.

"New General Purpose Relay for Telephone Switching Systems," A. C. KELLER, *Bell System Technical Journal,* Nov. 1952, pp. 31:1023-1067.

"A Heavy-Current Relay," A. H. WILLOUGHBY, *Journal of Scientific Instruments and Physics in Industry,* Nov. 1948, vol. 25, pp. 385-386.

"Hingeless Electromagnet Relay," R. STEINER, G. O. NELSON and F. D. SNYDER, Relay Conference, 1961.

"Designing of High Speed Relay," A. F. BISCHOFF, *Tele-Tech and Electronic Industries, Oct.* 1954, vol. 13, pp. 84-86.

"The Small '300 Volt' Relay (Industrial)," J. ZAMBRZYCKI, *Electro-Technology,* May 1962, p. 191.

"A Second Evaluation of the Industrial '300 Volt' Relay," W. KETTERER and W. FRANK, *Electro-Technology,* March 1963, p. 171.

"New Multicontact Relay for Telephone Switching Systems," I. S. RAFUSE, *Bell System Technical Journal,* Sept. 1954, vol. 33, pp. 1111-1132.

"Design of a Non-Adjusted Relay," W. D. MAYNARD, Relay Conference, 1963.

"Research and Development of Novel Electro-Magnetic Relay Design," W. N. BORG, Relay Conference, 1954.

"A Novel Relay Design," H. J. LEBHERZ, JR., Relay Conference, 1960.

"Opto-Electronic Relays-Function and Application," R. F. MC MAHON and V. HUDSON, Relay Conference, 1965.

"Printed Contact Permanent Magnet Relay," *Automation,* Dec. 1960, p. 115.

"Development of Permissive-Make Relay" (for Business Machines), B. J. GREENBLOTT and J. E. WALLACE, *IBM Journal of Research and Development,* July 1957, pp. 198-211.

"The Resonant Reed Relay, A Frequency-Sensitive Switch," H. C. RUMM and H. B. DORREN, Relay Conference, 1962.

"Advancing the Sequence Relay," C. PACKARD, Relay Conference, 1957.

"A New Concept in Solid State Relays," W. KOEFFLER, Relay Conference, 1963.

"Special-Purpose Relays," L. J. NIJS and R. A. H. FAICT, Electrical Communications, Dec. 1952, pp. 29:260-265.

"Speed-Sensing Relay," J. H. PORTER, Electronics, Nov. 1952, vol. 25, p. 174.

"Subminiature Relay (Ugon) Application and Design," R. T. WEST, British Communications and Electronics, June 1962, pp. 434-439.

"New Temperature Relay tor Use with Resistance Temperature Detectors," M. E. HODGES, Electrical Engineering, Nov. 1955, pp. 74:998-1001.

"Improved U, UA, Y Type Relays," W. C. SLAUSON, Bell Laboratories Record, Oct. 1951, p. 466.

"Video Relay," H. HAMANO and Y. HOSOKAWA, Relay Conference, 1959.

"Zero Hysteresis Relays," I. BARDITCH, Electronics, Dec. 1955, pp. 28:202.

"Combining Relay Versatility and Integrated Circuit Technology in High Reliability Digital Equipment," DANIEL R. SAEWERT, Relay Conference, 1966.

"A Design Procedure for Rotary Solenoids," R. C. SODLER, Relay Conference, 1966.

"Optoelectronic Relays as Decoders and Drivers for a Numeric Display," T. P. BELING, Relay Conference, 1968.

"In the Era of Electronic Switching, Why Design a Small Crossbar Switch?" A. JAMROZ, Relay Conference, 1968.

Design (Manufacturing)

48 Procedures

"Relay Manufacturing Procedures," A. N. GARDINER, Relay Conference, 1957.

"Production of a Relay Under Controlled Conditions," K. V. NEWTON, Relay Conference, 1960.

"Quality Control — Small Plants' Philosophy (Relays)," L. KUPFERMAN, Proceedings, Third Annual New York Conference on Electronic Reliability, October 1962 (sponsored by IRE, New York Section).

"A New Twist in Relay Automation," J. SCHMIDT, JR., Relay Conference, 1963.

"An Approach to Manufacturing Development," C. J. STAPP, Relay Conference, 1963.

"Our Approach to Push Button Relay Production," (C. P. Clare), T. C. BURNETTE, JR., 1965 National Conference.

"The Internal Atmosphere of Hermetically Sealed Components," W. E. BERGSTEN, N. L. KNUDSEN, and J. F. McDOWELL, Relay Conference, 1966.

49 Materials

"Thermostatic Bimetals," S. G. ESKIN and J. R. FRITZE, Transactions of the ASME, 1940, vol. 62, 433-442.

"Dielectric Strength and Insulation of Relays," V. C. HUCKABEE, Relay Conference, 1953.

"Engineering Materials for Relay Use," E. H. LOCKWOOD, Relay Conference, 1954.

"Design Requirements for Relay Core Materials," J. P. MARTIN, Electrical Manufacturing, April 1954, p. 138.

"New Relay Materials Improve Performance," F. ROCKETT, Electronics, Jan. 1955, vol. 28, pp. 144-148.

"Basic Raw Materials for Relays," W. LOVE, Relay Conference, 1956.

"Engineering Metals and Alloys," E. H. LOCKWOOD, Relay Conference, 1956.

"Magnetic Materials," J. G. BONNAR, Relay Conference, 1956.

"Milling Silver Inserts in Plastic Relay Bases," R. L. CAMP, Electronics, March 1956, pp. 29:300-301.

"Ceramoplastic Relay Components," J. H. DU BOIS, Relay Conference, 1957.

"Why 13 Different Materials are Used in this Relay," C. A. SCHAEFER, H. C. BELLING, R. F. GOTTSACKER, and D. F. GROBE, Materials in Design Engineering, Sept. 1957.

"The Molded Switch Stack Module," G. O. WAGNER and W. SCHAPIRO, Relay Conference, 1958.

"Modifying The Product Through The Use of Epoxy Resins," A. C. JOHNSON, Relay Conference, 1959.

"Application of Heat Shrinkable Mylar to Relay Manufacture," B. J. GROVES, Relay Conference, 1963.

"Molded Coils and Relays," J. A. FOERSTER, Relay Conference, 1963.

"Developments in the Magnetic Analysis of Relay Materials," E. M. WOODS, Relay Conference, 1964.

"A New Magnetically Stable Core Iron," ROBERT W. EASTON, Relay Conference, 1968.

Reliability Concepts

50 General

"What Makes for 'Reliability' in Relays?," C. F. CAMERON, Electrical Manufacturing, Oct. 1952.

"Important Design Factors Influencing Reliability of Relays," J. R. FRY, Bell System Technical Journal, Sept. 1952, vol. 31, pp. 976-978.

"Relay Reliability Required by the Signal Corps," H. H. HAGENS, Relay Conference, 1953.

"Relay Reliability," D. CROPSEY, Relay Conference, 1955.

"Process Controls for Relay Reliability," D. L. HALL, Relay Conference, 1955.

"Reliability Problems of Airborne Relays and Suggested Solutions," G. D. CURTIS, Relay Conference, 1956.

"A Study of Relay Reliability," T. J. BUROOJY, Relay Conference, 1955.

"Uniform Quality Not Performance — The Prime Requisite of Guided Missile Relays," M. R. SUMMER and B. D. JOHNSTON, Relay Conference, 1956.

"Reliable Circuits Using Less Reliable Relays," E. F. MOORE and C. E. SHANNON, *Franklin Institute Journal,* Sept.-Oct. 1956.

"Reliability Testing of Miniature Relays in Dry Circuits," H. R. WILLIAMS, JR., Relay Conference, 1956.

"Reliability of Relays," J. VETRANO, Relay Conference, 1957.

"Relay Reliability is a Design Problem and Not a Statistical Problem," L. E. MASSIE, Relay Conference, 1958.

"Some Causes and Remedies for Undesirable Variability of Relay Performance Characteristics," J. W. GREAR, Relay Conference, 1958.

"Testing for Relay Reliability," P. GOTTFRIED,, Relay Conference, 1958.

"Improving Reliability of Relays," A. E. SPRANDO, *Electronic Equipment Engineering,* Jan. 1959, pp. 47-49.

"Predicting Relay Reliability," T. R. WELCH, *Electronic Equipment Engineering,* Jan. 1959, pp. 53-55.

"Contact Capsules — Aid to Relay Reliability," A. P. BOYLAN, Relay Conference, 1960.

"A Comparison of the Reliability of Relay and Transistorized Logic Circuits," W. O. HANSEN and J. POPA, Relay Conference, 1960.

"Prerequisite of Relay Reliability," B. G. GEBAUR, Relay Conference, 1960.

"The Status of Relay Reliability," J. SCHMIDT, JR., and E. T. SLIWINSKI, Relay Conference, 1960.

"Reliability Provisions in Specifications for Relays," C. J. BRZEZINSKI, Relay Conference, 1960.

"Hints for Improving Relay System Reliability," B. K. LEDGERWOOD, *Control Engineering,* Dec. 1960, pp. 104-107.

"Eventually, Why Not Now!," J. SCHMIDT, JR., Relay Conference, 1961.

"Specifying Reliability as a Purchase Requirement," H. P. Lynch, Relay Conference, 1961.

"A Means of Improving and Proving Relay Reliability," T. R. WELCH, Relay Conference, 1961.

"Catastrophic Relay Failures," C. P. NUNN and R. HOLBECK, *Electronics,* Aug. 18, 1961, p. 74; Aug. 25, p. 68.

"Reliability, A Design and Production Reality — The MM-22 Military Relay," G. S. LYCHYK and R. E. JUREWICZ, Relay Conference, 1962.

"Reliability Analysis Equipment — Electromagnetic Switching Elements," F. J. SOYCHAK, Relay Conference, 1962.

"Reliability of Production Relays and Its Relation to Operate Phenomena," K. M. MIRACLE, Relay Conference, 1962.

"Determinate Relay Reliability," D. DIEL and L. G. REYNOLDS, Relay Conference, 1962.

"An Inquiry into Reliability and Quality Control," F. SCHLEICHER, Relay Conference, 1962.

"Atmospheric Effects on Relay Reliability," W. M. CRAWFORD, Relay Conference, 1962.

"Basic Operations Research: Its Role In Product Quality," A. H. GREBE, Relay Conference, 1962.

"Operational Reliability of Electrical Controls for Machine Tools" (Relays vs. transistors, contact trouble), *Mass Production,* April 1962, pp. 74-85, 92.

"Component Parts Failure Data Compendium," F. MC GINNIS and B. BERGER, Reliability Subcommittee M-5.2, Engineering Dept., Electronic Industries Assn., N. Y.

"Improving Contact Reliability in Low-Level Circuits," J. J. MC MANUS, *Electro-Technology,* May 1962, p. 98.

"Optimizing Simple Circuitry for Reliability and Performance by Failure Mode," J. R. HANNE, *AIEE: Applications and Industry,* vol. 81, pt. 2, No. 60, May 1962, pp. 78-84.

"Emphasis on Reliability at Relay Conference," (Report of Tenth National Conference on Electromagnetic Relays at Oklahoma State University), J. R. RIGGS, *Electro-Technology,* July 1962, p. 132.

"Reliability Stress and Failure Rate Data for Electronic Equipment," *Military Handbook No. 217,* Aug. 8, 1962.

"Effects of Combined Operating Environments on Reliable Relay Life," A. P. BOYLAN, W. J. FONTANA, and W. H. LESSER, Relay Conference, 1963.

"Relayability Applied to Reliability," J. S. JORDAN, Relay Conference, 1963.

"On Stockpile Electrical Reliability of Sealed Switching Devices for Nuclear Weapons," P. MAHLER, Relay Conference, 1963.

"Relay Degradation — A New Reliability Tool," B. R. SCHWARTZ and A. SIEGEL, Relay Conference, 1963.

"Relay Reliability Stemming from Specifications and Applications," E. U. THOMAS, Relay Conference, 1963.

"Increased Reliability Through Proper Application," B. WINTERS and C. B. RAU, Relay Conference, 1963.

"Spot-Testing Aids Manufacture of High Reliability Relays," E. F. LISH, *Electronics,* April 12, 1963, p. 106.

"Relay Microminiaturization and Its Effect on Reliability," R. M. ADKINS, Relay Conference, 1964.

"Circuits and Relays for Equipment Reliability," H. C. ROBERTS, Relay Conference, 1964.

"Relays-Equipment Expectation Versus Equipment Performance," J. K. SCOTT and J. J. MC GORRAY, Relay Conference, 1964.

"Relay Reliability Through Spring Stability," M. D. SCOTT, Relay Conference, 1964.

"Military Relay Reliability," C. SCHNEIDER, Relay Conference, 1966.

"Relay Failure Analysis Techniques," J. J. LOMBARD, JR., Relay Conference, 1968.

"Reliability Goes In Long Before the Wrapper Goes On," A. O. ADAMS, Relay Conference, 1968.

"Guidelines for Reliable Relay Application and Selection," L. W. WENDLING and E. U. THOMAS, Relay Conference, 1969.

"Reliability vs Cost," ALBERT METZLER, Relay Conference, 1969.

Specifications and Standards

51 General

"When Specifying Relays," R. VRADEN-BURGH, *Electrical Manufacturing*, Sept. 1941, vol. 28, pp. 44-47.

"Intelligent Relay Specification Determines Product Performance," C. R. UNDER-HILL, *Electrical Manufacturing*, Feb. 1945, vol. 35, p. 90.

"Relays Classified by Types to Simplify Their Selection," R. B. IMMEL, *Product Engineering*, Oct.-Nov. 1942.

"Suggested Standards for Telephone-Type Relays," A. W. CLEMENT, *Electronics,* Jan. 1945, vol. 18, p. 150.

"Relay Standards for the Equipment Manufacturer," T. BUROOJY, Relay Conference, 1953.

"Preferred List of Relays," I. S. MAYER, Relay Conference, 1953.

"Preparation of Technical Data Sheets by Relay Purchasers on Their Specific Applicational Requirements," R. D. BEAN, Relay Conference, 1954.

"Standards and What They Mean to the American Economy," G. F. HUSSEY, Relay Conference, 1954.

"A Better Specification for a Better Relay," F. A. PAUL, Relay Conference, 1954.

"Standardization vs. Progress," T. R. WELCH, Relay Conference, 1954.

"Standardization of Headers," A. NEUMANN, Relay Conference, 1954.

"Standardization of Relays," U. L. ALLEN, Relay Conference, 1955.

"Factors to Consider in Specifying Relays," J. F. RINKE, *Machine Design,* Oct. 1955, pp. 160-170.

"Practical Approach to Standardization," T. R. WELCH, Relay Conference, 1956.

"A Proposal for the Standardization of Micro-Miniature Relays," A. H. MASCHMEYER, Relay Conference, 1957.

"JIC Electrical Standards for Industrial Equipment," Joint Industry Conference, *Electrical Manufacturing,* June 1957, p. 127.

"Realistic Relay Specifications," J. SCHMIDT, JR., Relay Conference, 1959.

"Machine Tool Electrical Standards," National Machine Tool Builders Assn., *Electrical Manufacturing,* June 1960, p. 198.

"Relay Field Data Invited for Standards Program," A. E. RUDAHL (Summary report of the Eighth National Association of Relay Manufacturers Relay Conference), *(Electrical Manufacturing,* July 1960, p. 121.

"A System Approach to Relay Specification," E. U. THOMAS and J. V. IVERSON, Relay Conference, 1961.

"Are Our Military Relay Specifications Adequate?," R. J. SOUCEK, Relay Conference, 1961.

"Additional Polar Relay Symbols Are Needed," E. U. THOMAS, National Relay Conference, 1961.

"Effect of Darnell Report Recommendations on Relay Specifications," H. G. ROMIG, Relay Conference, 1962.

"Relay Definitions and Terminology," E. U. THOMAS, Relay Conference, 1963.

"Anatomy of a Relay Specification for Military Application," CARL B. KNOX, JR., Relay Conference, 1967.

Testing Procedures

52 General

"Relay Testing," W. M. GORE, *Electrical Review,* Feb. 22, 1946.

"A Relay Sensitivity Test Set," E. T. BURTON, *Bell Laboratories Record,"* Dec. 1947, p. 454.

"Directional Test of Directional Relays," A. SALZMANN, *Electrician,* March 5, 1948.

"Testing of Relays," K. B. AUSTIN, Relay Conference, 1953.

"Appraisal of Adequacy of Relay Design Through Tests," H. H. HAGENS, Relay Conference, 1953.

"Measuring the Pull of Relays," R. L. PEEK, JR., *Bell Laboratories Record,* June 1953, p. 211.

"Dynamic Measurements on Electromagnetic Devices," M. A. LOGAN, *Bell System Technical Journal,* Nov. 1953, pp. 32:1413.

"Continuously Recorded Relay Measurements," E. G. WALSH, *Bell Laboratories Record,* Jan. 1954, p. 27.

"Surge Voltage Testing of Relay Coils," K. B. AUSTIN, Relay Conference, 1954.

"Test Standards and Techniques," H. H. HAGENS, Relay Conference, 1954.

"Relay Test Methods," K. B. AUSTIN, Relay Conference, 1955.

"Relay Testing," G. O. WAGNER, Relay Conference, 1955.

"Are Your Relay Test Results Valid?," H. R. GROSS, Relay Conference, 1957.

"A Study of the Results of Relay Qualification Tests," E. J. PARNELL-SMITH, Relay Conference, 1958.

"Transient Coil Current As Means of Relay Evaluation," C. F. CAMERON and D. D. LINGELBACH, *Proceedings, Electronics Components Conference,* 1958, pp. 129-137.

"Aircraft Switch and Relay Inductive-Circuit Test Loads," J. P. DALLAS, *AIEE: Applications and Industry,* vol. 77, pt. 2, No. 39, Nov. 1958, pp. 352-355.

"Relay Case Leakage and Radiflo Testing," D. BURNHAM and T. SMITH, Relay Conference, 1959.

"Measurement of Pull-in and Drop-out," T. R. WELCH, Relay Conference, 1959.

"Two Economical Circuits for High-Speed Checking of Contact Closures," K. ENSLEIN, *Transactions on Instrumentation,* Institute of Radio Engineers, vol. I-8, No. 2, Sept. 1959, pp. 51-55.

"Relay Parameters By The Push Method," D. W. HOECK, Relay Conference, 1960.

"Instrumentation Techniques Used to Study Inductive Testing of Aircraft Switching Devices," J. D. SEGREST, Relay Conference, 1960.

"Testing Time-Delay Relays," J. GESSAROLI, *Electronic Industries,* June 1960, pp. 241-243.

"Transients in Relay Dielectric Testing," K. B. AUSTIN, Relay Conference, 1961.

"Standard Test Methods for Relays," V. F. ARGENTO, Relay Conference, 1961.

"A Study of Discharge Transients in Relays with Grounded Cases," C. P. NUNN and R. HALBECK, Relay Conference, 1961.

"A Method for Experimental Study of Relay Stability," C. F. CAMERON, D. D. LINGELBACH, and C. C. FREENY, *Electro-Technology, March* 1961, p. 156.

"Monitoring Densities of Artificial Atmospheres in Hermetically Sealed Equipment," B. A. HICKS, *Electrical Engineering,* vol. 80, No. 10, Oct. 1961, pp. 772-774.

"Acceptance Testing For Reliability Analysis," J. L. FARBO, Relay Conference, 1963.

"Non-Destructive Testing for Parasitic Arc Susceptibility in Relays," T. N. LOCKYER, JR., Relay Conference, 1963.

"Circuits for Testing Reliability of Relays," C. W. LOESEKE, Relay Conference, 1963.

"Study About Impacts and Damping Problems in a Fast Miniature Telegraph Relay," J. PANDELLE and M. TACNET, Relay Conference, 1963.

"Practical Contributions in Testing Relays," F. J. SOYCHAK, Relay Conference, 1963.

"Minimum Current Testing and Studies," C. NUNN, SR., Relay Conference, 1964.

"A Method For Measuring DC Inductive Loads," R. HYINK, Relay Conference, 1964.

"Recommended Measurement Techniques and Specifications for Low Level Switching," J. A. GARRATT, Relay Conference, 1964.

"Remanence Testing Applied to Process Control," L. LYNCH, 1965 National Relay Conference.

"The Application of Control Chart Techniques to the Analysis of Environmental Test Data for Relays," JUNE M. ALFIERO, Relay Conference, 1966.

"Radiographic Screening of Relays to Ameliorate High Reliability Devices," J. E. LANDERS and M. W. TATUM, Relay Conference, 1967.

"Compensation for Capacitance During Dielectric Withstanding, Voltage Testing," GEORGE NEYHOUSE, Relay Conference, 1969.

53   Environmental tests

"An Investigation of the Effects of Vibration on Relay Operation," R. H. JACOBSON and F. MINTZ, Relay Conference, 1954.

"Relays: Vibration Test Methods," R. J. GARON, Relay Conference, 1955.

"Instrumentation for High G Tests," S. BOND, Relay Conference, 1956.

"Evaluating Relays for Missile Vibration Environment," A. H. MASCHMEYER, Relay Conference, 1956.

"Effects of High Intensity Acoustic Excitation on Relays," R. H. JACOBSON, Relay Conference, 1956.

"Vibrational Stability Tests for Magnetic Relays," A. H. MASCHMEYER, *Tele-Tech and Electronic Industries,* Aug. 1956, pp. 15:68-70.

"Vibration Equipment," E. G. ORAVEC, Relay Conference, 1956.

"A Different Approach to Shock Testing," C. PACKARD, Relay Conference, 1956.

"The Protection of Relays Against the Effects of Extreme Mechanical Environment," J. I. MERANDA, Relay Conference, 1957.

"Vibration Testing of Relays," C. T. MORROW, Relay Conference, 1957.

"Shock, Acceleration and Tumbling," L. D. LA FLAMME, Relay Conference, 1959.

"Correlation of Test Procedure Under Various Environments," F. YULE, Relay Conference, 1960.

"Contact Monitoring for Vibration Tests," W. KEAR, *Electronics,* April 8, 1960, p. 78.

"Environmental Testing of Relays at Sandia Corporation," R. W. RUSSELL, Relay Conference, 1962.

"Missile Environments — Their Definitions, Measurements, and Test Criteria," M. W. RALSTEN and H. E. WELCH, Relay Conference, 1964.

"The Application of Control Chart Techniques to the Analysis of Environmental Test Data for Relays," J. M. ALFIERO, Relay Conference, 1966.

"Life Expectancy of a Form C Dry Reed Switch as a Function of Its Operating Environment," WILLIAM J. FONTANA, Relay Conference, 1966.

"Analysis of a Spacecraft Relay Failure," A. J. BABECKI, Relay Conference, 1967.

"New Relay Testing Requirements for the Saturn Programs," W. H. SMITH, Relay Conference, 1967.

"On Random Vibration Testing of Relays," HUGH O. WELLS and CHARLES F. CASSON, Relay Conference, 1967.

"Relay Reliability: A Test and Analysis Program," CHARLES L. BUCKNER, IVAN J. SOPER, Relay Conference, 1967.

54 Life testing

"An Innovation in Life Testing Electromagnetic Relays," T. WEIR, Relay Conference, 1956.

"Why Run Mechanical Life Tests," S. M. DE PUY, Relay Conference, 1959.

"Monitoring Relay Life Tests," H. H. BREWER, Relay Conference, 1959.

"Simplified Monitoring Circuits for Contact Life Tests," N. C. SHAW, Relay Conference, 1959.

"Fallacies in Life Testing," F. F. YANIKOSKI, Relay Conference, 1962.

"Evaluation of Relay Life," C. B. BROWN, Relay Conference, 1963.

"Bureau of Ships Program to Determine the Characteristic Life Profiles of Electromagnetic and Thermal Time Delay Relays," J. BROOKS and D. N. SCHOCHET, Relay Conference, 1963.

"Instrumentation for Mass Relay Life Testing," J. K. SCOTT and C. V. LEACH, Relay Conference, 1963.

"Life Expectancy of a Form C Dry Reed Switch as a Function of its Operating Environment," W. J. FONTANA, Relay Conference, 1966

"An Analysis of Life Limiting Factors for Medium Sized Reed Switches," S. MITANI, G. KAMOSHITA, K. OHO, and T. TANII, Relay Conference, 1968.

"A Realistic and Dynamic Life Test for Reed Switches," DEAN B. FOX, Relay Conference, 1968.

55 Production and automatic testing

"Testing Relays on the Production Line," P. C. TALMADGE, Relay Conference, 1953.

"Stepping Switches Speed Circuit Testing," W. W. HANNAN and C. ESTEP, *Electrical Manufacturing*, March 1955, p. 136.

"Automatic Manufacturing Testing of Relay Switching Circuits," L. D. HANSON, *Bell System Technical Journal*, Sept. 1956, pp. 35:1155-1178.

"The Application of Automatic Testing Techniques for Relay Evaluation," J. J. O'DONNELL, Relay Conference, 1957.

"Relay Production Testing," K. B. AUSTIN and R. FERRY, Relay Conference, 1958.

"Production Line Checker for Relay Contact Chatter," E. H. KOPP, *Electronics,* May 20, 1960, pp. 94-95.

"Automatic Relay Tester Detects Intermittents," F. TRAINOR, *Electronics,* Dec. 9, 1960, pp. 79-81.

"Automation of Relay Acceptance Testing," R. L. BEAVER and W. E. BEST, Relay Conference, 1961.

"Constant-Current Regulator Speeds Relay Testing," D. H. LIEN, *Electronics,* July 27, 1962, pp. 48-49.

"Building-Block Approach to Automation of Relay Test Equipment," K. BOTKER, Relay Conference, 1963.

"Automatic Relay Testing," H. N. MILLER, Relay Conference, 1963.

"Automatic Relay Test Set," *Electronic Industries,* Sept. 1963, p. 102.

"Contamination of Relay Internal Ambients," W. M. CRAWFORD and B. L. WEIGAND (Ph.D.), Relay Conference, 1967.

"A New Life Test Set for Miniature Dry Reed, Sealed Contacts, M. B. PURVIS, Relay Conference, 1967.

"A Photographic Miss Test Method," C. A. STEWART, Relay Conference, 1968.

"Electronic Life Test Monitoring System," J. W. KULAGA, Relay Conference, 1969.

"The Engineering Approach to Failure Analysis of Switching Devices," HARRY D. SANTER, Relay Conference, 1969.

56 Instrumentation

"Electronic Relay Tester," S. BAGNO, *Electronics,* Aug. 1940, p. 44.

"An Electrical Contact Testing Machine," A. M. SUGGS, ASTM Bulletin No. 119, Dec. 1942, No. 118, Oct. 1942.

"Dynamic Relay Analyzer," E. L. DEETER, *Electronics,* July 1948, vol. 21, pp. 87-89.

"Leaf Spring Vibration Machine," F. W. STUBNER, *Bell Laboratories Record,* Sept. 1951, vol. 29, pp. 410-413.

"Recording Fluxmeter of High Accuracy," P. P. CIOFFI, *Review of Scientific Instruments,* June 1952.

"Simple Millisecond Meter," R. C. WALKER, *Electronics,* Sept. 1952, vol. 25, p. 188.

"Relay Measuring Equipment," H. N. WAGAR, *Bell System Technical Journal,* Jan. 1954, vol. 33, pp. 3-22.

"Electronic Relay Tester," T. E. DANS and A. L. BLAHA, *Bell System Technical Journal,* July 1954, vol. 33, pp. 925-938.

"Contact Chatter Indicator," K. B. AUSTIN and R. FERRY, Relay Conference, 1957.

"Performance Analyzer for Relays," A. HIRATA and E. J. DUFF, Relay Conference, 1958.

"Photographic Analysis of Relays," J. H. WADDELL, Relay Conference, 1958.

"An Electromechanical Analyzer for Studying Relay Parameters," J. G. KUNSCH, Relay Conference, 1960.

"An Instrument for Plotting Relay Characteristics," J. S. JORDAN, Relay Conference, 1959.

"Relay Testing With Modern Techniques," B. D. TREMBLY, Relay Conference, 1964.

"Design and Performance of a Relay Tester," W. BODEN, Relay Conference, 1957.

"Measuring Instrument For Relay," H. YAMAZAKI and T. KANEKO, Relay Conference, 1962.

"Accurate Prediction of Relay Performance and Reliability with Force-Function Measurements," T. R. WELCH, Relay Conference, 1958.

"Design by Test and Analysis Spurs Relay Progress" (NARM Relay Symposium), A. E. RUDAHL, *Electrical Manufacturing,* June 1958, p. 134.

"Application of Slip-Sync Systems to Relay Design," W. F. COX, Relay Conference, 1961.

"Magnetic Timing and Delay Circuitry As Applied to Relay Test Facility," S. D. T. ROBERTSON, B. N. BASU, G. R. SLEMON, and P. P. BIRINGER, *Proceedings T-159,* IEEE International Conference on Nonlinear Magnetics, 1964.

"Automatic Relay Test Station," CHARLES A. WINICK, Relay Conference, 1968.

"Testing High Reliability Relays by Use of Automatic Equipment," C. C. BATES and J. R. GUTH, Relay Conference, 1968.

Miscellaneous Articles Relating to Relays

57 Articles

"The Relation of the Electronic Components Information Center to Relay Problems," H. B. THOMPSON, Relay Conference, 1953.

"Relay Terminal Connections," R. D. BEAN, Relay Conference, 1953.

"Using Those Surplus Relays," E. B. BLETT, May 1956, *QST,* pp. 40:28:30.

"Information — Please," A. M. HADLEY, Relay Conference, 1956.

"Relays Versus Semi-Conductors as Switching Devices," G. L. LA PORTE and R. A. MARCOTTE, Relay Conference, 1959.

"Today's Challenge to the Relay Industry," W. M. CRAWFORD, Relay Conference, 1963.

"Have Semiconductors Relegated Relays to a Second-Class Status?," W. A. MURRAY, *Electronic Design,* Nov. 29, 1965, pp. 14-17.

"Relay Manufacturers and Their Lines," *Electronic Design,* Nov. 29, 1965, pp. 64-67 (list of manufacturers classified as to type of relay).

"Electronic Sensitivity and Electromechanical Sturdiness = Microwatt Relays," H. C. ROBERTS, *ISA Journal,* May 1966.

"Relays — A Report on Progress," ROBERT E. KOEPER, Tech. Ed., *Electronic Design News,* Nov. 9, 1966.

"Twenty Ways to Wreck a Relay," ROBERT E. KOEPER, Tech. Ed., *Electronic Design News,* Nov. 9, 1966.

"Relay Reliablity and Life," R. R. FOWLER, Staff Engineer, Automatic Electric Company, *Electronic Design News,* Nov. 9, 1966.

"Auxiliary Relay Circuits," — a collection of circuits by ASEA Electric Inc., New York, N.Y., *Electromechanical Design,* Oct. 1967.

"A Host of Relays for Controls Jobs," BOND M. BLAKE, *Control Engineering,* Jan. 1967.

"The Logic of Relay Switching and Counting," J. D. ASHBY, Staff Engineer, Automatic Electric Company, *Machine Design,* Aug. 1967.

"Relay Roundup," MERRILL JACKSON, Assoc. Ed., *Electronic Engineer,* July 1967.

"Metallic Contacts vs Solid State Switches," WILLIAM ARNETT, Cohm Electronics, Inc. *Control Engineering,* March, 1967.

"Many Relays and Semiconductors," E. KEITH HOWELL, Mgr., Semiconductor Prod. Dept., General Electric Co., *Electronic Design,* March 1967.

"Relay Counting Chains," BJOURN ENGLEHARDT, *Electromechanical Design,* February 1967.

"Special Issue on Relays," *Electronics World,* April 1967.

"Forum on Relays," BILL SEGALLIS, Western Ed., *Electronic Products,* Oct. 1967.

"UJT Improves Timer Control," ANTHONY J. SOFIA, Avco Corp., *Electronic Design News,* Dec. 1967.

"Got the Relay Blues? — The Cure is to Write Proper Specifications," *Electronic Design News,* Dec. 1967.

"Joint Industry Council (JIC) Electrical Standards for General Purpose Machine Tools," WALTER B. DENNEN, Ed., *Electro-Technology,* May 1967.

"Magnet Wire," *Electro-Technology,* Nov. 1967.

"Electromechanical Choppers," *Electronic Engineer,* March 1968.

"The Making of a Good Contact," H. N. WAGAR, *Bell Laboratories Record,* July-August 1968.

"The Relay Problem," *Electronic Engineer,* July 1968.

"Standard Relays for Special Purposes," J. D. ASHBY, *Machine Design,* June 20, 1968.

"Suppressing Relay Transients," PHILIP W. KOETSCH, Consultants and Designers, Inc., *Electro-Technology,* Dec. 1968.

"Contact Resistance — Average of Several Test Sites," *Electronic Engineer,* March 1968.

"Why Go Solid State?" A. THATE, Square D Company, *Automation,* August 1968.

"Meter-Relays," W. R. HOWARD, *Machine Design*, July 18, 1968.

"Two Wires Transmit and Identify Remote Switch Closures," R. J. KRUSBERG, *Electronic Design*, March 1, 1969.

Reference Books
58 Applications and circuits

The Design of Switching Circuits, W. KEISTER and others, D. Van Nostrand Co., New York, 1951.

Relay Engineering, 3rd ed., Struthers-Dunn, Pitman, N. J. 1962.

Electric Control Systems, 3rd ed., R. W. JONES, John Wiley & Sons, New York.

How to Use Rotary Stepping Switches, ed. V. E. JAMES, Automatic Electric Co., Northlake, Ill., 1964.

Fundamentals of Relay Circuit Design, A. R. KNOOP, Reinhold Publishing Corp., New York, 1965.

59 Contacts and contact phenomena

Electrical Contacts, G. WINDRED, D. Van Nostrand Co., New York, 1940.

Fundamental Processes of Electrical Contact Phenomena, F. LLEWELLYN-JONES, H. M. Stationery Office, London, 1953.

"Engineering Seminar on Electrical Contacts," *Proceedings*, Penn State University, State College, Pa., 1954, 1956, 1959.

Physics of Electrical Contacts, F. LLEWELLYN-JONES, Oxford: Clarendon Press, England, 1957.

Electrical Contacts Handbook, 3rd ed., R. HOLM, Springer Verlag, Berlin, 1958.

"Electrical Contacts — 1963, — 1965" (Seminars on Electrical Contacts), Electrical Engineering Dept., University of Maine, Orono, Me.

"Bibliography on Electrical Contacts," published annually (supplements) by American Society for Testing and Materials, 1916 Race St., Philadelphia 3, Pa.

60 Device design

Electromagnetic Devices, H. C. ROTERS, John Wiley & Sons, New York, 1941.

Electro-Magnetics, J. D. KRAUS, McGraw-Hill Book Co., New York, 1953.

Switching Relay Design, R. L. PEEK, JR., and H. N. WAGAR, D. Van Nostrand Co., New York, 1955.

Permanent Magnets and Their Applications, PARKER and STUDERS, John Wiley & Sons, New York, 1962.

Special Relay Publications
61 Publications

Proceedings of Annual National Relay Conferences, sponsored by NARM and the School of Electrical Engineering, Oklahoma State U., 1953-66. Many years are out of print but all are on microfilm. Microfilm copies of complete yearly sessions (no individual papers) may be obtained for $25.00 (two rolls) from Executive Director, Nat. Assoc. of Relay Mfrs., P. O. Box 7765, Phoenix, Ariz. 85011.

"Reliability of Military Equipment," The AGREE Report. Office, Asst. Secy. of Defense (Research and Engineering), U. S. Govt. Printing Office, June 4, 1957.

Failure Rates for Relays and Switches: "Reliability Stress and Failure Rate Data for Electronic Equipment," *Military Standardization Handbook*, MIL-HDBK-217A, Dec., 1965.

"Reed Switching Devices," includes "Reed Relays," ROGER L. ROSENBERG; "Mercury Wetted Contact Relays," A. J. KODA; "Armature Relays," J. V. FOSTER; "Stepping Switches," D. A. DIBBERN and V. E. JAMES; "NEMA Control Relays" and "Circuit Breakers" *Machine Design* (Electric Controls Reference Issue), March 13, 1969.

"Parts Specification Management for Reliability," PSMR-1, vols., I and II (The Darnell Report[1]). Office, Director of Defense (Research and Engineering) and Office, Asst. Secy. of Defense (Supply and Logistics), U. S. Govt. Printing Office, May, 1960.

National Electrical Manufacturers Association (NEMA) — Approved Standards IC1-1956, NEMA Standards publication, Industrial Control.

United States of America Standards Institute (USASI) — C42 — American Standard Definitions for Electrical Terms. C83.16-1959 — Relay Definitions and Terminology. C83.25-1967 — Testing Procedures for Relays. Y32.2 — Symbols (Superseding MIL-STD-15-1). Y32.16 — Letter Designations (Superseding MIL-STD-16). Y.10-19 — Letter symbol for units used in electrical science and electrical engineering, and various other relay specifications. C37.1-1962 (Reaffirmed 1967) — Relays and Relay Systems Associated with Electric Power Apparatus. C37.2-1962 — Manual and Automatic Station Control, Supervisory, and Associated Telemetering Equipment.

---

[1]Ad hoc study group on Parts Specification Management for Reliability.

National Association of Relay Manufacturers (NARM) — Standard for Electro-Magnetic Relays for Industrial and/or Commercial Applications. (See Sect. 12.)

National Association of Relay Manufacturers/ Electronics Industries Association (NARM/ EIA) — Joint Industry P-5.7 Committee's Specification on Relays (to be given a "MIL-SPEC." number).

Various *Government Specifications,* some of which are: MIL-R-5757, General Specification for Relays, Electrical, for Electronic and Communication-Type Equipment. MIL-R-6106, General Specification for (ASG) Relays, Electric. MIL-R-19648, General Specification for (ES) Relays, Time Delay, Thermal. MIL-R-22527, Relays, Armature (BuWeps). MIL-R-39016, Relays, Electromagnetic, Established Reliability. MIL-S-24329, General Specification for Switches, Stepping, Rotary. NASA-MSFC-Spec.-339A, Relays, DC, Hermetically Sealed for Space Vehicles and Ground Support Equipment. NASA-GSFC-5 601.10D, General Specification for Relays, DC, Hermetically Sealed, Grid Header, For Space Flight Application. NASA, MSC, ST-R-001, General Specifications for Acceptance Testing of E-M Relays for Use in Manned Space Flight Applications (Houston, Texas). MIL-STD-454, Requirement 57-Relays ——— (MIL-SPEC. number to be assigned) Work of NARM/EIA P-5.7 Committee on Military Relays.

62 Other publications

Society of Automotive Engineers, Inc. (SAE) — Aerospace Information Report, AIR 875, a comparison of government relay specifications of A-2R subcommittee of committee A-2R on Aerospace Electrical Equipment. AIR 904, Polarized Relay Conventions. ARP 909, Relays, Electric Applications.

Naval Air Systems Command (NAVAIR) — Technical Manual "NAVAIR 01-1A-514, Design of Electric Systems for Naval Aircraft and Missiles."

Joint Industrial Council — EGP-1-1967, Electrical Standards for General Purpose Machine Tools.

The Association of American Railroads (AAR), Aircraft Industries Association (AIA), Joint Industrial Council (JIC), Electronic Industries Association (EIA), and *National Electrical Manufacturers Association (NEMA)* — all have various publications on relays. Others, as referred to in Sec. 9.

Addresses

63 Nongovernmental organizations having publications relating to relay terms, symbols, and specifications

AIA Aerospace Industries Association
1725 De Sales Street, N. W.
Washington, D. C. 20036

AAR Association of American Railroads
1920 L Street, N. W.
Washington, D. C. 20036

EIA Electronic Industries Association
2001 I Street, N. W.
Washington, D. C. 20006

IEEE Institute of Electrical and
Electronics Engineers
345 East 47th Street
New York, New York 10017

JIC Joint Industrial Council
2139 Wisconsin Avenue
Washington, D. C. 20007

NARM National Association of Relay
Manufacturers
P. O. Box 1649
Scottsdale, Arizona 85252

NEMA National Electric Manufacturers
Association
155 East 44th Street
New York, New York 10017

SAE Society of Automotive Engineers,
Inc.
2 Pennsylvania Plaza
New York, New York 10001

USASI United States of America Standards
Institute
1430 Broadway
New York, New York 10018

64 Governmental specifications relating to relays and relay equipment may be obtained from:

Commanding Officer
U. S. Naval Supply Depot
5801 Tabor Avenue
Philadelphia, Pennsylvania 19120
Tel. No. (215) 697-3321/3322/3323 or 3324

Index

Index